Readings in Anthropology

VOLUME I   PHYSICAL ANTHROPOLOGY, LINGUISTICS,
AND ARCHEOLOGY

Readings in
Anthropology

SECOND EDITION

Morton H. Fried

COLUMBIA UNIVERSITY

Volume I   *Physical Anthropology, Linguistics, and Archeology*

Thomas Y. Crowell Company, New York, ESTABLISHED 1834

Preface

In a preface, Mischa Titiev says that he wrote his text in order to instruct his students, not to impress his colleagues. I believe him because this book is edited in the same spirit. Besides, who would try to impress his colleagues with the contributions of others?

Actually, the idea of editing this book was not mine. One day John T. Hawes of the Thomas Y. Crowell Company walked into my office, introduced himself and asked me to assemble a book of readings in anthropology. My first inclination was to refuse the invitation and I have often wished that I had yielded to that impulse. On reflection it occurred to me that I could use such a book in my own teaching for I had various objections to the anthologies already available. It was at that time I decided to run the selections without cutting, though footnotes and bibliographic references had to be omitted. With but one or two exceptions, both of these rules have been followed throughout.

An editor, like a teacher, learns a great deal from his job—that is one of its rewards. As an anthropologist, the editor is proud to record his impression that the literature of his field is rich in fine and significant contributions; the supply far exceeded his demand.

In light of this bounty the professional reader may ask why certain familiar names are missing from the list of authors, and why certain names reappear. No simple answer can be given: choice was determined by commitment to pre-existing categories; by the mechanically limiting considerations of copyright; by the fact that certain topics have been handled by only one thinker; and by personal taste and familiarity. Paradoxically, some effort was made to present major concepts through little-known articles by well-known scholars. The student who reads the source credits will be introduced to most of the major anthropological journals as well as a number of minor ones.

If this book indulges a vice, its name is controversy. The reader will soon conclude that no one can simultaneously hold the diverse and clashing opinions which follow. If the editor has been successful, the reader will be uncertain as to the editor's position in these disagreements. Be assured. The editor does have a position.

Though the responsibility for this volume falls on the editor alone, he has had much friendly assistance. Dave Smith helped in a variety of ways, theoretical and practical. Philip Winsor, of the Thomas Y. Crowell Company, supplied much of the biographical data and considerable and friendly editorial assistance. Miss Sara Stalder typed the introductions, reading from copy that was a thicket of corrections. Martha Fried, my wife, read most of the introductions and rendered sound advice. Mr. Oscar Ogg allowed me to use the line drawings which decorate this book (except for the character which appears on page 94 of Volume II). These drawings were done by Mr. Ogg and appear in his book *The 26 Letters* (copyright 1948 by Thomas Y. Crowell Company). Hubbard Ballou, head of Photographic Services, Columbia University Libraries, sped my reproductions and Mrs. Eleanor Malloy rescued me at the very end by reproducing the piece I had forgotten. Thanks also to Mrs. Nan Pendrell for various corrective suggestions. Most of all, my gratitude goes to the scientists and authors whose thoughts and words are the value of this book.

Department of Anthropology
Columbia University

Preface to the Second Edition

In a bleak time of unjust war, it is pleasant to be able to regard some aspects of one's own chosen field with pleasure. One's colleagues continue to open new vistas and present such riches in the form of new books and articles, that the editor of a compendium is sometimes hard put to make his selections. Of course, this is not true uniformly of the different subdisciplines or special questions. In some areas there haven't been any significant new ideas or approaches in more than a generation. I hope that some readers will pause to compare this and the first edition, to garner some notion of the changes in information, theory, method and outlook that have occurred since 1959.

As anthropologists particularly well know, all achievements are essentially social rather than individual. To the extent that these *Readings,* in their second edition, may be classified under that heading, there are many to be thanked for contributions great or small, but all quite necessary. Since there are too many to name, let me mention only two, Miss Judith Brabham, who linked the authors with the editor, sometimes across the Pacific, and generally kept order in the face of a whirlwind, and Miss Susan Hall, who inherited that whirlwind.

Finally, and once again, I cannot refrain from thanking again the scientist scholars whose work *is* this book.

M.H.F.
September, 1967

Introductory Note

THIS VOLUME CONTAINS 43 articles devoted to three of the four main component fields of modern anthropology. They define the subject and present concrete examples of the work which is carried out, both descriptive and analytical, in the fields of physical anthropology, linguistics, and archeology.

The selections are uneven. They differ in degree of detail, in complexity of analysis, in the facility of their authors' pens. Some guide to the main point or points made in each article will be found in the editor's statement which precedes it. Those who read this book in conjunction with a course in anthropology will be guided by their instructor. A few technical remarks, however, may make the reading of this book easier and more enjoyable.

Though the articles proceed in an order sensible to the editor, many other alternative organizations are possible, and one does not have to examine the materials sequentially. Often more than one article is devoted to a single subject. For example, four pieces (Nos. I:33–36) discuss paleolithic archeology. In selecting these four articles, which may be discussed by way of illustrating the philosophy behind these *Readings*, the editor was guided by the desire to present something about the earliest known archeological appearances of culture (I:33), and the general sequence of subsequent development, emphasizing the growth of technological sophistication (I:34). It also seemed appropriate, since this book is intended primarily for an audience of American students, to include the essentials of what is known about the Paleolithic in the New World, and how populations and cultures came to this hemisphere in the first place (I:35, 36).

A certain amount of cross referencing has been done in the prefatory statements. References are, e.g., to I:32. This means selection No. 32 in this volume, which is the first of two. Articles in the second volume, *Cultural Anthropology*, are referred to, for example, as No. II: 1, etc.

A correlations table will be found at the end of this book showing the correspondence between the selections in these pages and the organization of presently available text books in anthropology. In the contest between the desire to include as many selections as possible and the obvious limitations of space, one important compromise was made: the extensive footnoting, particularly bibliographical, of most of these articles was deleted. Students who wish to pursue the subject further are urged to look up the original selection and examine its bibliography.

It may be noted that the glossaries found in the two volumes of the first edition of these *Readings* no longer appear. The decision to drop them was made easy when they grew to unmanageable proportions. A check made with two of the most popular "college"-type dictionaries proved that most of the words likely to be sought could be found with ease. Even the greatest portion of anatomical terms can be swiftly located in a good ordinary lexicon. Practically all of the remainder of obscure words and terms can be found in an unabridged dictionary. The editor recommends *Webster's Third New International Dictionary* for its fine coverage of the lexicon of social science. There remains a handful of words that cannot be found in any dictionary presently available. Mostly these words are the "newspeak" of science—for these *ask your teacher!*

Contents

The Scope
and Aims
of Anthropology

Anthropos, the Greek word for man, is combined with *logia,* the Greek word for study, to produce a word that did not exist in the time of Aristotle or Plato. Anthropology, the study or, preferably, the *science* of man is a new discipline. While its prescientific origins go back into the remote past, long before any people invented writing, the basis of the modern discipline of anthropology was laid in Europe in the period known as the Enlightenment. Scientific anthropology itself is even younger than this. Formulated in the nineteenth century, it is still in the process of defining itself, mapping the subjects with which it is primarily concerned, and establishing and testing methods of inquiring into these subjects.

The excitement that anthropology breeds in its professional students is by no means unique, but it is intense. In part this may be credited to the youth of the field but many other things contribute to the love affair between anthropologists and their discipline. The scope of anthropology is so broad that nothing which impinges upon man is, at least in theory, overlooked. Anthropology has vital roots in biology and psychology and studies man as an organism. But a major portion of anthropology is devoted not to man, the organism or life form, but to his activities and products both physical, such as tools, buildings and ikons, and conceptual, like ideals of craftsmanship, style, and ideas about the soul. The whole world and all history is the preserve of anthropology.

1

Naturally, no anthropologist can marshal the huge range of skills which comprise anthropology as a whole; specialization is the necessary result. The following pages reflect the division of labor which has developed, most of the selections representing the achievements of a particular group of experts who have been grappling with certain specific problems. The thoughtful reader, however, will also note with increasing awareness that each of the selections is related to others in a multitude of ways. Findings in one area of inquiry are applied to other problems which at first glance seem remote. Methods used in certain technical studies have analogues in other branches of study and some concepts crop up almost everywhere.

Anthropology, then, is a collection of disparate fields unified by a ubiquitous concern with man and his products. It is fitting that the selections begin with a group of statements which treat of the science as a whole.

1 The Subject Matter of Anthropology

Alfred L. Kroeber

DERIVED FROM GREEK ROOTS, THE WORD "ANTHROPOLOGY" ENTERED ENGLISH *from the French. By the sixteenth century it seems to have been used in the broad sense of "the science of man." For a long time thereafter, however, it was most often employed in more limited fashion to refer to studies of human thought and physiology. Since the middle of the nineteenth century the older usage has been the most common in English, although in some European contexts the word is intended to imply what these* Readings *cover under the rubric of physical anthropology.*

Anthropologists enjoy discussing what their discipline means in terms of its diverse contents. Alfred L. Kroeber turned his attention several times to this question but never more succinctly than in this selection.

If the profession is small, the subject matter of anthropology is enormous, as well as unusually varied. There was therefore every prospect of

SOURCE: Reprinted from "Introduction" to *Anthropology Today: An Encyclopedic Inventory* (Chicago: The University of Chicago Press, 1953), pp. xiii–xiv. Copyright 1953 by The University of Chicago. Reprinted with permission of the author and publisher.

A prolific contributor to anthropology in most of its major facets, Professor Kroeber (1876–1960) is particularly well known for his early endorsement of the "super-organic" approach to culture (see No. I:3), for his work in the difficult areas of "cultural configurations" and "style," and for his definitive work on the geographical analysis of the cultures of the Indians of North America. Among the many books from Kroeber's pen are *Cultural and Natural Areas of Native North America* (1939), *Configurations of Culture Growth* (1944), and *Style and Civilization* (1957). Some of Kroeber's major essays are collected in *The Nature of Culture* (1952).

advantage to be gained from a gathering that would envisage the field as a whole with the intent of pulling together what belongs together.

After all, the subject of anthropology is limited only by man. It is not restricted by time—it goes back into geology as far as man can be traced. It is not restricted by region but is worldwide in scope. It has specialized on the primitives because no other science would deal seriously with them, but it has never renounced its intent to understand the high civilizations also. Anthropology is interested in what is most exotic in mankind but equally in ourselves, here, now, at home. It concerns itself with men's physiques, with their societies, with the communications and products—the languages and cultures—of these societies. It wants to know about particular languages and particular cultures in order to appraise the range and variety of human speech and civilization. Still more does it want to understand speech and civilization in general, in the abstract: the nature and process of language and culture. Sociology, economics, government, and jurisprudence investigate social, economic, political, and legal functionings, particularly in our own or other advance civilizations. Anthropology tries to formulate the interactions of these more special activities within the total culture of which they form a part, and equally so, whether the culture be high or low, present or past.

It is evident that anthropology—however specific it may often be in dealing with data—aims at being ultimately a co-ordinating science, somewhat as a legitimate holding corporation co-ordinates constituent companies. We anthropologists will never know China as intensively as a Sinologist does, or prices, credit and banking as well as an economist, or heredity with the fulness of the genetic biologist. But we face what these more intensive scholars only glance at intermittently and tangentially, if at all: to try to understand in some measure how Chinese civilization and economics and human heredity, and some dozens of other highly developed special bodies of knowledge, do indeed interrelate in being all parts of "man"—flowing out of man, centered in him, products of him.

It may sound like a pipe dream—to forge together this vast array of knowledge, to hammer it into a set of coherent interpretations. Perhaps it is a dream; but some dreams come true. Leonardo da Vinci's sketched-out dreams of flying machines came true, when physics and engineering had developed sufficiently.

And there is one principle that anthropology already has in hand to serve toward a larger synthesis of understanding: the concept of culture.

This is the idea of culture—of human civilizations, whether rudimentary or advanced—as something entirely a part of nature, wholly an evolutionary development within nature, and therefore to be investigated by the methods of fundamental natural science, but an unprecedented, unique, and richly ramifying development of nature. It is culture that is at once the precondition of all human history and its abiding and growing precipitate. It is the hereditary faculty for culture that is the most distinctive feature of man as an animal. It is that part of the larger whole of culture which we ordinarily call "speech" that makes the accumulation of the remaining part of culture possible; and it is this remainder—culture in the more specific sense—that gives speech most of its content, gives us human beings something to talk about. Social behavior extends far back in the history of life on earth—certain insect families are much more effectively socialized than we are. But culture is a peculiarly human "invention"—or windfall; and in man culture, though secondary in origin, overshadows society, to the extent that human society is more affected and molded by culture than culture can be derived from society. Even the individual viewed as abstracted from his society is culturally influenced to a degree that makes it an unending task of the individualizing psychologist to hold his "cultural variable constant" before he can hope to make "pure" psychological findings. It is even possible to consider rat and other animal psychology an attempt to sidestep this perennial bothersome variable of culture. In spite of which, personality-in-culture, or culture-and-personality, has crept back into both psychology and anthropology as a frankly avowed and increasingly practiced field of study.

So the principle of culture already gives anthropology a viewpoint of enormous range, a center for co-ordination of most phenomena that relate to man. And we anthropologists feel that this is only a beginning.

2 The Fields of Anthropology

William C. Sturtevant

AS THE SCIENCE OF MAN, ANTHROPOLOGY CAN BE CONSTRUED TO INCLUDE *just about everything. It is incumbent on a science, however, that it take logical steps to narrow and define its subject matter and concomitantly to develop the methods and theory necessary to pursue the resulting studies. There has developed a conventional set of divisions of anthropology, within which finer distinctions are made. While there has been a little faddism in the development of these subdivisions, and while the extent of some fields has varied with changes in method and theory, by far the greater number have remained foci of interest and training for many years and continue to offer the major frameworks for current and fore-seeable research problems. It should scarcely need statement, but the boundaries of disciplines and subdisciplines should be of minor signifi-cance compared to the goal of attaining better answers to the questions we raise. Anthropologists, then, are not likely to ask if a certain question is an anthropological one. Instead they become interested in certain prob-lems and ask if their anthropological theory and methods can contribute to solutions.*

In addition to staking out the various divisions of anthropology, Dr. Sturtevant, in the following selection, manages quite independently to give the rationale behind the organization of Readings in Anthropology.

SOURCE: *Anthropology as a Career* (Washington, D.C.: Smithsonian Institution, Pub-lication 4343, 1958), pp. 1–8.

The author (b. 1926) is Staff Ethnologist, Bureau of American Ethnology, Smith-sonian Institution. An expert on the Seminole Indians, his interests focus on the South-eastern Indians and the Iroquois but extend to more general theoretical problems as well. He has published extensively on his Indian researches in various scholarly jour-nals.

Anthropology is the scientific study of man and his culture: the study of human physical form, social behavior, beliefs, languages, and ways of doing and making things.

There are two main divisions of the science: physical anthropology and cultural anthropology. The latter includes several rather distinct topical specializations, which are described below. Most anthropologists concentrate on one of these specialties in one or two large geographical areas. This narrowing of primary interest often begins in the early stages of academic training, and it should certainly influence the student's choice of a university at which to study for an advanced degree (M.A. or Ph.D.). However, the eventual specialization is not so important in undergraduate work. Furthermore, in order to receive an advanced degree the student must show competence in the anthropological subjects that lie outside his own specialization. A broad knowledge of the whole science is necessary for two reasons: new developments in methods and theory that are made in one topical or geographical specialty are often also applicable in others; and most anthropologists are employed as teachers or museum workers, who must be able to deal competently with subjects outside their own specializations.

A. *Physical anthropology* is concerned with the biology of human groups and is a part of both biology and anthropology. The subject matter falls into two large interrelated categories: human paleontology, which studies human fossils and their meaning in terms of long-range human evolution, and human population biology and human genetics, which study the adaptations to differing environments and the hereditary characteristics of living populations ranging in size from regional stocks and races to local inbreeding groups such as religious castes. The physical anthropologist, in contrast with other biologists who study man, is mainly concerned with human variation—in aging phenomena, sexual differences, growth patterns, and physical and physiological differences between human groups, current and past, and the geographical distributions of human physical characteristics.

This branch of anthropology is now in a period of rapid change. The earlier primary interest in the description and classification of human physical form by means of anthropometry (measurement of the outside of the body and of bones) is now being strongly supplemented by attention to processes and evolution—the meanings and causes of human physical differences, the complex interrelated effects of heredity and environment on human form. The older measuring and descriptive techniques are still the most useful in studies of skeletal remains, where the more genetically oriented techniques are less applicable, and in certain applications of physical anthropology such as the improvement of clothing sizes. The new approaches modify the interpretations of the results of older techniques, and open new possibilities of research on problems of human biology. Physical anthropology has close relations with other fields of biology, especially genetics, anatomy, physiology, taxonomy or classification, and paleontology. The student of physical anthropology needs training in these fields and sometimes takes at least part of a pre-medical and medical course. The field also has close connections with cultural anthropology, since man among all animals is preeminently a creature with a culture and can hardly be studied unless this fact is taken into account. Such factors as mating and interbreeding patterns, food resources and food habits, intentional modifications and mutilations of the body, and the history of migrations and pioneering settlements, since they are aspects of culture, are within the scope of cultural anthropology; yet, since they affect human physical form or racial history, they are also important for physical anthropology. On the other hand, the concern of physical anthropology with the history of human populations often yields results useful to other anthropologists who are interested in cultural history. For these reasons, physical anthropology is usually taught within anthropology departments, and the advanced degrees are in anthropology.

The work of the physical anthropologist depends upon his interests. He may study museum collections of human and primate skeletal remains from various parts of the world and different periods of time. He may be called on to describe skeletons from archeological excavations and to determine their racial and subracial setting by means of comparative analysis. Research on living populations (sometimes with contributory experiments on laboratory animals) may involve making body measurements, taking X-rays, collecting blood samples, or making other observations, in order to learn about inherited differences, growth and adaptations to climate, altitude, nutrition, and other aspects of the environment. Like other anthropologists, the physical anthropologist combines information previously published by others with the results of his own studies in the field, the museum, or the laboratory.

B. *Cultural anthropology* is the subdivision of the field that deals with culture. The word "culture" in the sense used by anthropologists means all the behavior and beliefs which people learn and share with others. It includes such topics as religion, social and political organization, economics, technology, arts, narrative forms, and language.

Traditionally, cultural anthropologists have studied the cultures of nonliterate peoples, including peoples who have acquired writing only as a result of European influence in recent centuries. Other fields outside anthropology have studied the cultures (or parts of the cultures) of literate peoples: the Asian civilizations with vast and complex written histories and literatures have been studied by sinologists and other orientalists; European and Europe-derived societies (sometimes also Asian civilizations) have been the concern of other social sciences and humanities—sociology, economics, political science, psychology, history, classical archeology, philology and linguistics, musicology, comparative literature, comparative religion, comparative law, and the history and criticism of art and literature.

The cultural anthropologist has usually studied smaller, less complicated, more "exotic" societies with little or no native written records. Such societies are those of the New World Indians and Eskimos, tribal groups in parts of Asia, and the aborigines of Oceania, Australia, and Africa south of the Sahara. Cultural anthropologists have studied all aspects of these simpler societies—topics which in literate societies are the concern of the various nonanthropological disciplines (sociology, economics, etc.) mentioned above.

However, the research techniques developed in studying such societies have lately been transferred and adapted to the study of literate societies. In recent years, cultural anthropologists have conducted research in peasant communities in China, Japan, India, Southeast Asia, Europe, and among non-Indian New World peoples; they have studied towns and cities in these areas; they have written on the characteristics of whole national states. There has also been an increasing interest in the characteristics of nonresidence social groups such as the personnel of factories, businesses, professions, units of the armed forces, and hospitals. Some cultural anthropologists are now studying major world religions and important literary traditions.

Interdisciplinary studies—both cooperative endeavors among representatives of several fields (anthropologists, psychologists, sociologists, etc.) and combined training and research in several fields by the same individual—have also lately tended to blur the divisions between the social sciences. Hence both the spread of areal interests and the borrowing of techniques and viewpoints from other fields make definition of the field of cultural anthropology difficult and increase the breadth of competence necessary for a professional anthropologist.

1. *Archeology* is the subdivision of cultural anthropology that deals with man's past. It includes both cultural history—the tracing of changes over time—and the reconstruction of the daily life and interests of prehistoric peoples.

Historians and classical archeologists study the literate periods of the major civilizations of the Near and Middle East, Europe, and the Far East. In contrast, the prehistorian or anthropological archeologist studies the tremendously long preliterate periods of these major civilizations, and all but the very recent past of nonliterate peoples. We owe to archeology our knowledge and understanding of human culture during all but a minute fraction of the period of human existence.

For his data, the archeologist is dependent on the surviving material remains of human activities. By means of his highly developed techniques for excavating and observing these remains, for recording the contexts in which they are found, and for preserving, identifying, classifying, and comparing them, the archeologist is able to recover information on many aspects of culture beyond the mere material remains. The aim is to reconstruct past cultures as completely as possible, and to study their changes, movements, contacts, and influences on each other. Cooperation with other specialists is necessary in this work. Ethnologists, historians, or classical archeologists provide information on the cultures which come after and develop out of the prehistoric ones, and their descriptions of whole cultures in the same and different geographical areas provide comparative information necessary for the interpretation of the meanings and uses of the material remains recovered by the archeologist. Geologists, paleobotanists, zoologists, and climatologists often aid in dating, identifying, and interpreting archeological remains. Laboratory studies and experimentation are sometimes used to discover significant characteristics of the materials and methods of construction of archeological specimens. Such research may involve detailed knowledge of chemistry, physics, and various technological skills. New methods of more accurate dating by radioactive carbon (C^{14}) require the help of physicists. Physical anthropologists cooperate by studying the skeletal remains frequently found associated with cultural remains.

In his field research, the archeologist concentrates on scientific excavation of the remains of human activities. His analyses and reports are based on the evidence thus obtained. He must thoroughly study the objects collected and the circumstances under which they were found and compare his own findings with those of others that are preserved in museum collections and reported in published accounts. In dealing with more recent periods of the past, historical research is often necessary in order to identify the peoples whose remains are found, and to interpret these remains. In recent years, some archeologists have made studies of European colonial and postcolonial remains in the New World, which bring them into closer relations with historians. American archeologists have long been interested in Indian sites of historic times, which yield European materials of great value in establishing dates.

2. *Ethnology*, another subdivision of cultural anthropology, is the study of the culture of living peoples and also of cultures no longer in existence but for which eyewitness written records survive. The ethnologist studies the whole culture of such societies—social and political organization; religion, traditions, folklore, and knowledge; technology and economics; music, dance, and the other arts. His interests are twofold. On the one hand, he is interested in accurate description and full understanding of individual societies—the details of customs and beliefs, and how these are interrelated and patterned in the larger structure of the whole culture of the given society. This interest, which is often termed "eth-

nography," is similar to that of some historians and sociologists who are concerned with the nature of European societies at given periods, past or present; but ethnography covers more aspects of culture than is generally the case with history or sociology. The other interest of ethnology is in comparison between cultures: both the search for valid general laws of human custom and human nature, and the classification of individual cultures in terms of cultural types or historical connections. Studies of continuing cultural change and of the effects of contact between peoples involve the cultural details and their patterning in a given society, and also the comparison of interacting societies and generalizations about processes of cultural change.

The term "cultural anthropology" is sometimes (illogically) restricted to what is here called ethnology. Other writers use "social anthropology" with this meaning. However, social anthropology is more often considered to be the branch of ethnology which studies less exotic societies or, more frequently, an approach which considers that the central task of ethnology, in studying both nonliterate and complex literate societies, is the analysis of social organization—the structure of the social relations between the members of a society. Social anthropologists are normally little concerned with those aspects of culture that are not directly related to social organization, and they are also usually uninterested in history. They are interested in the definition of types of social organization, and in the search for general laws of human social behavior.

Another special subdivision of ethnology, usually called "culture and personality," attempts to identify relationships between cultures and the personalities of individual participants in them. Workers in this field commonly assume that the personalities of members of a society are to some degree determined by the culture they share, and that this culture is in turn affected, especially in situations of cultural change, by the personalities of its bearers. The field combines the techniques, theories, and personnel of anthropology with those of psychology and psychiatry.

The work of the modern ethnologist is centered on field research. He lives among the group he is studying in order to gain his data at first hand with the special techniques and controls developed for this type of study. If he is forced to rely on eyewitness descriptions by others, he interprets these in terms of the experience which has been built up by ethnological fieldwork. Analysis of the data proceeds hand in hand with the fieldwork, to permit checking and controlled expansion of the information. The final analysis and the writing up of the results for publication are done after the return from fieldwork. Comparative studies are based wholly or in part on published descriptions by ethnologists and others, and on museum collections. In recent years, ethnologists have also been paying more attention to the same sort of materials with which historians work, including unpublished manuscript records in archives and elsewhere, which frequently contain data useful from an anthropological point of view. This approach, known as "ethnohistory," is likely to become increasingly important.

3. *Linguistics* is the scientific study of languages. Logically, it is a subdivision of cultural anthropology or even of ethnology, but in terms of training and university departments it is often an independent subject. This separation is the result of the relatively independent historical development of linguistics and anthropology, and is related to the fact that much of the structure of a language can be analyzed quite independently of the rest of the culture of which it forms a part. Furthermore, the methods and techniques of linguistics are equally applicable to all languages, so that the distinction between exotic and familiar societies is less important here than it has been in cultural anthropology. However, most anthropology departments require their students to gain some knowledge of linguistics, and many have linguists on their faculties. This is because language, as a part of culture, cannot be ignored by anthropologists.

Linguistics has two subdivisions. Descriptive linguistics is concerned with the analysis of languages at one point in time: their sound systems, grammar, and vocabulary. The linguist is concerned with spoken language and derives his material for analysis by listening to, and writing down with special symbols, the spoken words of people to whom the language is native. The same procedures are used whether or not there is a conventional system for writing the language; however, anthropological linguists usually study the languages of nonliterate peoples.

The other field of linguistics is historical or comparative linguistics, which deals with the historical relationships between languages. Techniques in this field were developed with languages whose history can be traced through written records; but these techniques have progressed to the point where they can be reliably used for establishing the relationships and reconstructing the history of unwritten languages.

Anthropological linguists have made important contributions to the theory and method of both subdivisions of linguistics. Their work on a multitude of independent language families has increased the range of possible comparisons and contributed importantly to the development of understanding of language in general.

For ethnologists, linguistic training is very useful. Some knowledge of the language of the people he studies is now essential for the ethnologist, and the techniques of descriptive linguistics afford the most effective basis for learning a language. Furthermore, the field ethnologist is increasingly felt to be obligated to provide at least a preliminary description and analysis of the previously unrecorded languages he encounters. Some concern with language is also necessary in the study of all other aspects of culture, and descriptive linguistics provides the accurate descriptions that are needed in the study of other aspects of culture. A field overlapping linguistics and ethnology, often called "ethnolinguistics," has as its aim the study of the connections between language and the rest of culture, in particular the relationship between the linguistic habits of the speakers of a language and their logical or philosophical preconceptions and psychological characteristics.

Descriptive linguists have been very successful in developing ways of analyzing the structure or patterns of languages. Their methods promise to be increasingly useful as they are applied, with modifications, to the analysis and description of the more complex cultural patterns studied by other cultural anthropologists. Recent work in social organization has demonstrated the usefulness of this approach.

Historical linguistics yields reliable data which are of much use for anthropologists concerned with historical relationships. Glottochronology, a new technique for establishing the dates of separation of the ancestors of related languages, is of particular interest to archeologists.

4. *Cultural theory.* Archeologists, ethnologists, and linguists all contribute to the growing knowledge of culture in general. Among the interest shared by different subdivisions of cultural anthropology are the nature of culture change and cultural evolution; the processes of cultural borrowing; the results of contact between different cultures (acculturation); the characteristics and causes of similar types of cultures or cultural patterns which occur independently in various places and times; and the relationship between cultures and the natural environments in which they occur.

Many of the findings and theories on such topics have been found to be applicable in the studies of more than one of the subdivisions of cultural anthropology, and anthropologists interested in these fields—as most are—must take into account the findings of specializations other than their own.

C. *Applied anthropology.* In recent years there have been increased efforts to apply anthropological knowledge directly to the solution of practical problems. Anthropology remains primarily a field of pure research, but with increasing knowledge and increasing personnel, attempts to get results of immediate practical value have been more frequent.

Physical anthropologists have applied their measuring and statistical techniques to the improvement of clothing sizing, and to the designing of machinery and equipment more efficiently adapted to the structure of the human body. They have cooperated with physiologists in the development of clothing suited to extreme environments such as deserts and the Arctic. Their findings on human osteology and growth and development have medical applications. Their knowledge of skeletal differences in sex, age, and race has often been called on for purposes of legal identification.

Ethnologists have been involved in a wide variety of attempts to apply their knowledge of social behavior and culture, particularly by efforts to predict the consequences of proposed programs, in such areas as public health, psychiatry, and medicine; social rehabilitation and resettlement; economic assistance programs; the administration of dependent peoples; personnel work in industry and business; advertising and mass communications; training and advising those engaged in foreign service, international relations, and missionizing; and attempts to lessen social and "racial" prejudice and discrimination. There are more ethnologists engaged in applied anthropology than there are physical anthropologists or linguists, and the name of the field is sometimes understood as referring only to applied ethnology.

Linguistics has been especially valuable in improving language teaching, in literacy programs, and in developing language-data processing by machines. Linguists have also contributed to communication work (codes, signal systems, etc.) and to Bible translation. There are at least potential applications of the field in psychiatry and medicine, in the correction of speech defects, and in the creation and intentional modification of national languages (such as Hebrew, Hindi, Indonesian, and Tagalog).

Direct applications such as these are relatively new and have not always been successful. Many anthropologists agree that the principal practical value of the field is its recognition that cultures differ for respectable reasons and that our own is only one among many. Knowledge of the many different ways of life which satisfy members of other societies gives one a new perspective on our own culture and increases one's tolerance and appreciation of foreign customs and attitudes. Kluckhohn has recently remarked that "in a world where educated people now recognize that the ways of other clans and nations cannot remain matters of indifference or contempt or antiquarian curiosity, anthropology suddenly finds itself fashionable." It is the one field that has wide experience with the differences between peoples, and an increasing body of systematized understanding of the reasons for these differences and the relationships between them.

3 The Expansion of the Scope of Science

Leslie A. White

THE TARDY EMERGENCE OF ANTHROPOLOGY AS A SCIENCE IS A PHENOMENON *in itself. Among those most interested in the causes of the delay are the Positivists, who inhabit many disciplines. Among the earliest was the sociologist, Auguste Comte, who related the development of sociology to the universal evolution of civilization. Reminiscent of Comte, but armed with the theory and conclusions of a century of progress in evolutionary science, is Leslie White who asserts that man has resisted knowledge longest where it threatens his self-image, particularly as that image is sanctified in theology. For White, the development of the science of culture is a scientific innovation as revolutionary as the Copernican theory, the theory of natural selection, and Freud's insistence on the role of the unconscious in individual behavior.*

When we survey the history of science we see at a glance that progress has not been equal and uniform on all fronts. Advance has been

SOURCE: *Journal of the Washington Academy of Sciences,* Vol. 37 (1947), pp. 181–210. Abridged and reprinted with the permission of the author and the publisher. Prof. White revised and expanded this article, and it appears as Chapter V of the author's *The Science of Culture* (New York: Farrar, Straus and Company, 1949; also in paperback edition, New York: Evergreen Books, Grove Press, n.d.).

The author (b. 1900) is Professor of Anthropology at the University of Michigan. A major defender of evolutionary theory in anthropology when most voices were raised in opposition, White has had the rare pleasure of seeing his once unpopular views taken up by many younger anthropologists. The author is a painstaking ethnographer and specialist on the Pueblo Indians of the American Southwest. In addition to *The Science of Culture* and several monographs on the Pueblos of San Felipe, Santo Domingo and Santa Ana, he has written on Lewis Henry Morgan, a founder of scientific anthropology. White's latest books are *The Evolution of Culture* (1959) and *The Social Organization of Ethnological Theory* (1966).

more rapid in some quarters than in others. Greater progress has been made in astronomy and physics than in biology; physiology is more advanced, as a science, than psychology; and psychology is older and more mature than sociology. The birth of each science can not be neatly marked with a precise date, of course; there has been overlapping, and growth has been simultaneous among many, if not all, of them. Nevertheless, it is clear that some sciences are older and more mature than others. Since there is a close correspondence between the age of a science and its degree of development, we may treat these two factors as one. We may thus arrange the sciences stratigraphically in the order of their respective ages and degrees of maturity:

"Social" sciences	Cultural anthropology Sociology Social psychology
Biological sciences	Psychology Physiology Anatomy
Physical sciences	Chemistry Physics Astronomy

Generalizing broadly, we may say that the physical sciences appeared earlier and have developed farther than the biological sciences; the biological sciences took form earlier and have developed farther than the social sciences. The question naturally arises, Why has this been so? Why do we find this order, both with regard to time and to degree of development, in the history of science?

Every living organism strives to evaluate the various items in its environment, to discover which are beneficial, which injurious, so that advantage may be derived from the one and injury from the latter avoided. In addition to the sensory means employed in this evaluating process by other animals, man employs verbal symbols. He not only translates the evaluations of his senses into words—"fire is hot," "thorns are sharp" —but he posits relational values between one thing and another. Thus he declares that the hoot of the owl presages death, a falling star means good luck, etc. In this manner, man creates a philosophy, a body of ideas and beliefs expressed in verbal form, which he employs as a means of adjustment to the world he lives in.

From our standpoint of analysis and classification, there have been, and logically can be, only two major types of philosophy: one in which the external world is interpreted in terms of the human ego; the other in which it is explained in terms of *itself*. In the first type, man uncon-

sciously projects himself into the external world, describing and interpreting it in terms of his own psychic processes. The whole world is thus
made alive and peopled with spirits who feel and behave as men do. They
have desires like men, show preferences for certain foods and drink; they
are susceptible to jealousy and flattery; they fight and make love. One
spirit makes the earth, another brings rain, a third sends game or brings
forth crops. The gods favor or oppose certain types of economic and political systems, and aid the armies of their chosen nations. Thus man creates the world in his own image. This is the philosophy of supernatural-
ism: of animism and anthropomorphism.

In the second type of philosophy, the phenomena of nature are explained in terms of themselves, in terms of the events of nature. Thus,
rain falls because other meteorologic phenomena precede and accompany
rainfall; a fossil is merely a link in a chain of paleontologic events. Explanation in this type of philosophy consists of a recitation of relevant
events; scientific explanation is thus condensed description. This is the
philosophy of naturalism.

Between these two major types, in the process of development of
philosophy, lies an intermediate, or transitional type, which Comte has
called "metaphysical." This may be illustrated by such statements as "fossils were produced by stone-making forces"; "opium puts one to sleep because of its dormative powers"; "cattle graze together because of a gregarious instinct." This kind of interpretation partakes of both of the
major types of philosophy. It eschews animism and points to the external
world for its explanations. Thus it says that fossils are produced by stone-
making forces—i.e., by natural phenomena that exist and function in the
realm of nature—not by gods with minds like ours. But, the explanatory
device, "stone-making forces," is merely a part of ourselves, a verbal formula created *ad hoc*, and projected into the external world. *Functionally*,
it is like the concept "spirit," and hence has affinity with the anthropomorphic philosophy of animism.

In the beginning of human history man's philosophies were wholly
animistic; he diffused his psyche throughout the cosmos; he confused the
self with the not-self at almost every point. As culture advanced philosophy grew and matured. Little by little the animistic philosophy was out-
grown and the naturalistic philosophy developed. But progress in philo-
sophic interpretation was not uniform in all fields of experience; it was
greater in some sectors than others. The distinction between the self and
the not-self—i.e., explanation of natural phenomena in terms of natural
events rather than in terms of the human ego disguised as gods and spirits
—was made first in the realm of celestial phenomena. This was followed
by the distinction in the field of terrestrial physical phenomena. Then it
was made in the biological field in anatomical, physiological, and psychological phenomena, and in that order. The distinction between the self

and the not-self was achieved in astronomy and physics before it was made in physiology and psychology because it was *easier* of accomplishment in the former than in the latter. And it was easier because *the phenomena of astronomy and physics are more remote and less significant as determinants of human behavior than are the processes of physiology and psychology.*

Man gradually learned, through ages of observation and experience, that all things do not affect his life equally. Some things are immediate and exert a powerful influence upon him; others are remote and effect his life but little. It is significant to note that systematic observation of the stars was begun under the belief that they exert a powerful influence upon man's daily life. Vestiges of this belief are still preserved in the names of the days of the week: Sun's day, Saturn's day, etc. And enough of this ancient belief still flourishes to make astrology a profitable business enterprise even today.

But as mankind accumulated experience and compared one thing with another, he discovered that stars exert less influence upon his life than such terrestrial phenomena as those of climate, topography, flora, and fauna. At the same time, systematic observation of planets and stars revealed regularities and an order that fostered description in terms of natural law rather than divine caprice. Thus astronomy was lost to animism, won for naturalism.

As observation was continued and experience accumulated, it was discovered that, intimate as man is with his habitat, and influential as it is upon his life, there is yet another class of determinants of behavior even more immediate and significant: the human body. The man, the ox, the snake, and the bird all dwell in the same environmental setting, but they behave very differently. The deer is swift, the squirrel climbs trees, the bird flies, because they have different kinds of bodily structure. An appreciation of this fact was the dawn of the science of anatomy.

Anatomy developed before physiology, not because the structure of the body is "simpler" than its functioning, but because it is easier to distinguish between one's self (one's ego) and one's arms and legs than between one's self and one's glandular processes. The body, unsophisticated man feels, is but a shell, the house in which the true self dwells. The ego and the body, he feels, are two different things. The self that he regards in "self-respect" is in no way affected by the amputation of a limb. One may lose both legs, his teeth, and even his eyes, but his "self" remains untouched and unscathed. But when glands flow hot in anger or in love, naïve man does not distinguish them from his ego; he identifies the process with himself.

Similarly, the science of physiology matured before psychology: it is easier to distinguish between the self and the not-self when dealing with physiological processes than with mental phenomena. We observe that a hungry man behaves one way, a well-filled man another. The effects of work and rest are obvious. Disposition is influenced by digestion. Profound changes in behavior can be effected by drugs and alcohol. But, unsophisticated man feels, there is a point beyond which outside forces can not go, boundaries which they can not cross. Deep within him, naïve man believes, is a citadel that is impregnable, a sanctuary inviolable. Here he lives—his real self, his essential character, his very soul. The "human spirit" or Will is free, he thinks, subject to no laws natural or physical. He sees himself as *subject* only; he is unable to regard the self as an *object*, as an event in the world of nature. The distinction between self and not-self at this point lies beyond his grasp and comprehension.

It was a great day for science when man became able to look upon mental processes as so many events in a world of nature, when, to use William James's fine phrase, minds could be studied "as *objects*, in a world of other objects." The distinction between subject and object was made. But the fight for naturalism has not been wholly won yet. Mental life is still called "the human spirit" in many circles, and the soul and mind still walk hand in hand in psychologies, sociologies, and anthropologies even today.

Thus we find the reason for the order in which the sciences have made their appearance and the extent to which they have matured to consist, not in varying degrees of universality or complexity, but in the varying ability of mankind to distinguish between the self and the not-self in various sectors of experience. This distinction is made most easily when one deals with phenomena which play an insignificant role as determinants of human behavior. Conversely, it is difficult to distinguish between the self and the not-self where phenomena are intimate and powerful determinants. The human race has discovered which are the powerful determinants and which the insignificant through experience; there was no *a priori* way of knowing.

The heavenly bodies being more remote and less significant as determinants of human behavior than the winds, rain, frost, and terrain, the science of astronomy appears earlier and matures faster than terrestrial physics, geology, and geography. Anatomical determinants being more remote and less influential than physiological processes, the science of anatomy precedes physiology. Physiology comes before psychology for the same reason. We may conclude our argument by formulating the following law of development: *Science emerges first and matures fastest in fields where the determinants of human behavior are weakest and most remote; conversely, science appears latest and matures slowest in those portions of our experience where the most intimate and powerful determinants of our behavior are found.*

We may illustrate the development and the sequence of the sciences in the accompanying diagram. In the center of the circle is man, surrounded by events which influence his behavior in varying degrees, some intimate, some remote. From this point of view, the advance of science has been more in the nature of expansion of scope than of growth or

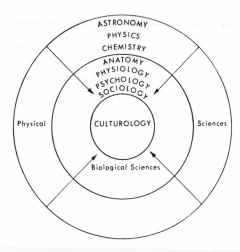

development. The cosmos lies everywhere about man. Science, a particular way of dealing with experience, appeared first in interpretations of a particular portion of our field of experience, namely, in astronomy, where phenomena are most remote and insignificant as determinants of human behavior. From there its techniques have spread and extended to other segments of experience. As science advances and expands, the anthropomorphic philosophy of animism recedes and contracts; as the concepts of natural law and determinism gain ground, the philosophy of free will retreats. The logical conclusion is, of course, to have the whole field of human experience embraced by the philosophy of science rather than that of animism.

According to Comte, Spencer, and others since their day, sociology is the last link in the logical chain of science, the final stage of its development. In terms of our theory, this would mean that when astronomical, geological, physical, chemical, anatomical, physiological, and psychological determinants of human behavior had been dealt with there would remain but one more class of determinants: the sociological. But are we willing to accept this conclusion? Is this classification adequate and final? We do not believe it is. On the contrary, we find it inadequate and immature. There is still another class of determinants of human behavior, which lie outside and beyond the scope of psychology and, for the most part, sociology. These are the traditional customs, institutions, tools, philosophies, languages, etc., which we call, collectively, *culture*. Cultural phenomena are super-, or supra-, psychological determinants of human behavior. They are super-psychological in the sense that it is beyond the scope of psychology to account for them. Psychology can not explain, e.g., why one people has clans (behaves "clanwise") while another does not; why one people eats with knives and forks, another with chopsticks; why a people prohibits marriage between parallel cousins but requires marriage between cross cousins; why a tribe practices polyandry, observes the mother-in-law taboo, forms plurals by affixation, uses money, etc. Culture *as culture* can be explained only in terms of culture.

Of course culture traits could do nothing were it not for human beings; they could not even exist. And who, we might ask, has ever thought otherwise? Certainly not Tylor, Durkheim, Kroeber, Lowie, Wissler, or any other culturologist that we know of. But it is a false realism to argue that culture traits do not react upon each other immediately and directly. A hoe is a culture trait. It acts directly upon and influences other culture traits such as division of labor between the sexes, customs of residence, food habits, religious beliefs and ceremonies, and so on. The introduction of the automobile in modern American culture directly affected many other culture traits: harness and carriage manufacture, the steel and rubber industries, road-building, urban development, roadhouses and tourist camps, consolidated schools, etc. To be sure, these cultural events could not have taken place had it not been for human organisms. But is our account of the influence of the automobile upon other culture traits made any more realistic by introducing these organisms into it? Not one whit. The development of the symphony or non-Euclidean geometry could not have taken place without the respiratory and digestive processes of composers and mathematicians. But to inject these physiologic processes into a scientific explanation of these cultural processes would not add a single thing to our understanding of them. On the contrary, it would only confuse because of their irrelevance. Thus we see that, although culture traits have no existence, and hence can do nothing, without the agency of human beings, we can treat them scientifically as if they had an independent existence. In fact, the problem of the direct and immediate influence of one trait upon another can be solved most effectively by eliminating the human organism from our consideration entirely. Far from being unrealistic . . . . it is a common procedure in science. The physicist may treat falling bodies *as if* they fell in a perfect vacuum; or imagine an airplane passing without friction through the atmosphere. But no physicist is so naive as to protest that such things simply don't occur; it goes without saying that they do not. Every physicist knows that the most effective—if not the only—way to arrive at the formulas and propositions necessary to explain physical phenomena is to substitute ideal situations for *real* ones. The only way, for example, to arrive at a law of falling bodies is to imagine them falling through a perfect vacuum—a situation that does not and can not exist on this earth.

Similarly the culturologist knows full well that culture traits do not go walking about like disembodied souls interacting with each other. But he realizes that he can explain cultural phenomena *as cultural phenomena* only when he treats them *as if* they had a life of their own, quite apart from the glands, nerves, muscles, etc., of human organisms. The remarkable thing about this argument is not that it is revolutionary, but that it should be necessary to defend it. It is neither revolutionary nor novel. As a matter of fact, scholars in many fields have been making culturological studies for decades. We have had studies of Indo-European and other languages on a purely linguistic, i.e., nonbiological, level. We have had studies of the evolution of currency; the effect of telescopes upon theological beliefs; the influence of the industrial revolution upon political institutions; the development of Greek tragedy, non-Euclidean geometry, Gothic architecture, and parliamentary government; the relationship between taxi dance halls and prostitution, delicatessens and the divorce rate: money spent on medical schools and death rates for contagious diseases, etc., etc. All these are culturological problems and their solutions are culturological. Need one insist that none of these situations could exist were it not for human organisms? It is obvious, of course, that they could not. But it is equally obvious that the introduction of human organisms into a consideration of these problems is not only not necessary, it is irrelevant and confusing. It is only the traditional habit of thinking anthropomorphically which still clings to "social science" that keeps one from seeing that in the man-culture *system*, it is the cultural, rather than the organic, factor that is the *determinant* of events within this system.

Summary

Man is an animal, and like all other living beings he strives to live: to adapt himself to his habitat, to exercise some control over his environment so that life can be made secure and his kind perpetuated. Man has the same means of adjustment and control that other animals have: neuro-sensory-muscular-glandular, etc. But in addition to these purely animal means, he has a technique that is peculiarly human: articulate speech. With language man constructs philosophies in which the whole cosmos is evaluated and interpreted. In terms of these philosophies, man effects his adjustment to and control over his environment. The function of philosophy is at bottom a biological one.

The first philosophies of mankind were animistic, supernaturalistic, and anthropomorphic. The external world was explained, not in terms of its own properties but in terms of human psychological forces, in terms of spiritual beings with minds like our own. This primitive type of philosophy although emotionally satisfying, was, of course, ineffective practically, as a means of understanding and controlling the external world.

Gradually, after hundreds of thousands of years, a new type of philosophy was developed. It interpreted the external world in terms of its own properties instead of terms of wish and will projected from the human mind. Free will and caprice gave way to determinism and natural law. But this transition in point of view was not effected throughout the whole range of philosophy at once. On the contrary it began in certain areas of experience and spread from there to others. It got a foothold first in the study of the heavens and spread from there to other physical phenomena. Then it invaded the realm of biological phenomena, conquering first the anatomical, next the physiological, and finally the psychological levels. From the psychology of the individual, the new interpretation was extended to the psychology of society. And always, as the new naturalistic philosophy of science advanced, it pushed out and displaced the old philosophy of free will.

The order in which the various realms of nature were invaded and subdued by the new philosophy was determined by the following law: *Scientific interpretation will appear first and grow fastest in those areas where the determinants of human behavior are the weakest and least significant.* Since the primitive philosophy rested upon a projection of the human psyche into the external world, upon a confusion of the self with the not-self, the new philosophy would begin first and flourish best where the identification of the self with the external world was weakest, namely, in relation to the heavenly bodies and other inanimate objects. Biological phenomena were next brought within the scope of the new interpretation, and eventually social behavior.

But sociology, the science of society, was not the end of the road of science as Comte and many others supposed. There was one more class of determinants of human behavior to be dealt with, the most intimate and powerful of all: culture. Just as psychologists found it difficult to envisage a collective psychology beyond an individualistic one, so have sociologists found it hard to envisage a science of culture beyond the horizon of "social interaction." But science can not and will not stop in its onward march, in its movement of expansion, until it has fulfilled its potentialities to the utmost, and this means until it has embraced and subdued the whole realm of human experience.

The science of culture is the next item of business on the agenda of science. Many of our "best minds" still talk as if the fate of civilization lay in the hands of man, to be wrecked or saved as he chooses of his own free will. Many are still prattling about how "we" are going to construct the postwar world, nursing, in Durkheim's phrase, the illusion of omnipotence. There is, as Tylor, Durkheim, Kroeber, and a few others have pointed out, a powerful and sometimes bitter antagonism to the view that it is not "we" who control our culture but that our culture controls us. And our culture grows and changes according to its own laws. As we outgrow our primitive and infantile notion of mastery and set about to learn the nature of the culture in which we live, we will have a less flattering conception of ourselves, perhaps, but a greater capacity for rational and effective living.

And so today, we witness one of the most critical and dramatic episodes in the long and exciting history of science. Advancing over the charred bones of hapless astronomers, put to death in a frantic attempt to stem the tide of the new philosophy, science has gone on to new conquests. After a bitter battle over Darwinism, science has securely held the field of biology. Psychology has at last made it possible to regard "minds" as objects, and Sociology has illuminated the laws of social interaction. It now remains to discover the principles of a million years of culture growth and to formulate the laws of this development. When this has been done, science will have captured the last remaining stronghold of the old philosophy; it will have reached its final boundary.

Physical Anthropology

MAN IS AN ANIMAL. Every criterion of the biological sciences establishes and confirms this fact. While only a few decades ago there was considerable resistance to the idea, the kinship of man and other animals and the broader theory of evolution which explains this kinship are now generally taken for granted.

Indeed, we begin by locating man in the zoological universe, identifying all living people (and all people who have lived for several tens of thousands of years) as members of a single animal species, *sapiens*, of the genus *Homo*, which belongs in turn to the larger category of the *Hominidae*. While man is the only living member of this family, there were, in the remote past, several others (see Nos. I:9, 10, 11, 12). The family *Hominidae*, along with monkeys and apes, contemporary species as well as those of the past, form a great suborder, the *Anthropoidea*. Here are our closest living non-human relatives and our ancestors. While people are not descended from any living variety of monkey or ape, the evidence is incontrovertible that if we go far enough back in time, perhaps 17,000,000 years, we can find creatures from whom both man and the great apes are descended. And if we go back even further, perhaps 40,000,000 years, we come upon creatures who seem to be ancestral to man, the apes, and the monkeys as well.

Tracing the ancestry of man is one of the most important tasks of physical anthropology, but there are many others. Pursuing the zoological classification of man further, we note that the primates, an order which includes man, are a subdivision of the class of *Mammalia*. Without going on, as the biologists do, to investigate larger and larger areas of relationship, identifying all creatures with backbones, with notochords, etc., we note that man's animal, specifically mammalian, nature spells out a great number of defining and limiting characteristics which must be taken into account when dealing with this creature we are. For example, we reproduce sexually and our offspring assume certain gross forms because of specific genetic processes. Modern physical anthropologists must be versed in genetics, as is apparent in several selections in this section.

One of the major and traditional activities of physical anthropologists is the classification, study and explanation of the varieties of types comprising the human species. This is a classical example of scientific application: the existence of patterned variations which distinguish certain human populations from others is a challenge to knowledge. But there is more here than academic curiosity. Physical anthropologists, no less than zoologists or marine biologists, are faced with the task of unravelling the mysteries of evolution. Racial variation is one result of evolutionary processes, and studies of race will contribute to our understanding of this colossal life tide.

While physical anthropologists concern themselves with race in terms of such physical things as morphology and physiology, the study of race can hardly, in the present climate of human relations, be divorced from the study of racism. Where the study of race pertains to the biological sciences, however, the study of racism pertains to the analysis of culture, for race, at best, has no necessary relationship with racism; each of these things can and does exist in the absence of the other. Of considerable bearing upon both, however, are the findings of psychologists which, to date, have established no significant causal relations between race and intelligence or race and personality or, to put it most sweepingly, between race and behavior.

GENETICS AND EVOLUTION

4 Genes, Culture and Man

George W. Beadle

IN THE SELECTION WHICH FOLLOWS THIS ONE, SIR GAVIN DE BEER WILL BE *found to remark that "it is neither variation nor mutation but* selection *that determines the course of evolution." To many scientists in the field this will seem an overly strong statement. Without reducing the significance of selection, it is clear that the* direction *of biological evolution is the resultant of the interaction of various things: mutation, selection, isolation and random drift serving to summarize them. In a sense, the latter three things are the effective determinants of the course of evolution, and all of them act on the basic genetic material which, as a consequence, may be regarded as the raw material of the evolutionary stream.*

It was 1866 when Gregor Mendel published the paper which set forth some of the basic ideas of genetics. But, although Mendel was an avid reader of Darwin, there is no indication that Darwin ever heard of Mendel or his work. Despite Mendel's contribution, biological scientists continued feverishly to investigate evolution, all the while lacking any but the vaguest idea of the mechanisms by which one generation passes its general physical character to the next. Then, in 1900, no fewer than three independent researchers in three separate countries each individually dis-

SOURCE: *Columbia University Forum*, Vol. 8, iii (Fall, 1965), pp. 12–16, copyright 1965 by Columbia University. Dr. Beadle's essay was adapted from his lecture that was the first in the 1965-6 Symposium on Biology and Physics. The Symposium was supported by the New York State Foundation for Science and Technology. Reprinted with the permission of author and publisher.

The author (b. 1903) has been Chancellor of the University of Chicago since 1961. He was a winner of the Nobel Prize for Medicine and Physiology in 1958 and has published extensively in the fields of cytology and genetics.

covered the principles about which Mendel had written more than a generation before.

Since then the science of genetics has made incredibly swift advances, penetrating the secrets of heredity to a degree that would have been unimaginable a century earlier. One of the most recent and thrilling of breakthroughs was the discovery of the biochemical nature of hereditary matter, a giant step beyond the proof that it is not "blood" that determines heredity, but sex cells which contain chromosomes. Now we know that within these chromosomes is a substance, deoxyribonucleic acid, whose molecular structure undergoing change in arrangement is responsible for the variations upon which selection operates.

In this selection a distinguished scientist, who in 1958 received a Nobel Prize for showing that genes regulate certain chemical processes, surveys the new view of genetics.

Man is the product of two kinds of interdependent evolution that for convenience and simplicity we call biological and cultural. The latter is of far greater significance in man than in any of his fellow creatures on earth. In biological inheritance and evolution, we are not basically different from other species, whether these be submicroscopic viruses, bacteria, protozoa or more complex plants and animals; in cultural characteristics there is an enormous gap between us.

Let us first consider biological inheritance. In all living beings, this depends in large degree on the generation-to-generation transmission of giant nucleic acid molecules of one or the other of two kinds: deoxyribonucleic acid, DNA, or ribonucleic acid, RNA. In addition, as John Moore and Ruth Sager of Columbia University, and others have shown, cytoplasm is also essential, directly or indirectly; even the simplest viruses cannot multiply outside of cellular hosts, all of which have specific cytoplasms that have continuity from one generation to the next.

Let me illustrate by describing what happens in man. Each of us develops from a tiny, almost microscopic, spherical cell, the fertilized egg. It is surrounded by membranes. Inside, there is a layer of jelly-like, viscous cytoplasm and in the center is a nucleus. In the nucleus are 46 chromosomes. In the chromosomes, there are genes. And the genes are made of DNA. Today we know an enormous amount about DNA. Our knowledge began to accumulate almost a century ago with the work of a biochemist named Miescher. Piece-by-piece we began to understand the structure of giant DNA molecules, which can be likened to a submicroscopic three-dimensional jigsaw puzzle. Finally, in 1953, the pieces fell into place in the skillful hands of James Dewey Watson and Francis H. C. Crick, working together at Cambridge University. Several of the key clues to the final solution were provided by Professor Erwin Chargaff at Columbia. The working out of the detailed structure of DNA is one of the great achievements of biology of the twentieth century, comparable in importance to those of Darwin and Mendel of the previous century. The Watson-Crick structure immediately suggested how DNA carries information, how it replicates or copies itself with each cell generation, how it is used in development and function, and how it undergoes the mutational changes that are the basis of organic evolution.

DNA is composed of units called nucleotides, molecules—sub-units of larger molecules—that are made of five kinds of atoms: carbon, hydrogen, oxygen, nitrogen and phosphorus. There are thirty-some atoms in each of these nucleotides and there are four kinds of nucleotides in DNA, arranged in long chain-like molecules, many hundreds or thousands strung together and paired in what is called an anti-parallel manner, that is, one chain runs up and paired with it is a chain that runs down. This pairing is accomplished through hydrogen bonding.

The sequence of the nucleotide units in the molecule is a kind of molecular code which spells out information. In the fertilized egg, there are approximately five billion nucleotides strung together in the nucleic acid of the genes that determine the final human organism. How much information does this represent? Encoded in letters of the alphabet, it would be sufficient to fill about a thousand volumes, 600 pages per volume, 500 words per page. If one were to take all the nucleic acid from all the cells that gave rise to all the people on earth today (three billion) it would make a cube about ⅛th of an inch on a side, and represent some three trillion volumes of information—about 60,000 times as much information as has been printed since Gutenberg invented the press. This molecular language is quite amazing. There are only three letters in the alphabet, all of the words turn out to be three-letter words, and there are only 64 words in the dictionary.

The DNA molecule replicates with each cell division as illustrated in Figure 1. Each half of the double molecule makes a new complement, resulting in two double molecules, each an exact copy of the original. This is the basis of all biological reproduction at the molecular level. Is it true? The fact is, it is true. And it has been demonstrated in many ways. Kornberg has been able to get DNA molecules to replicate in a test tube. Meselson and Stahl have shown by isotope labeling that the molecule does in fact do exactly what Watson and Crick predicted it should do. And more recently, Spiegleman has shown that a related nucleic acid, RNA, does exactly the same thing in a cell-free test tube system. So the Watson-Crick hypothesis is well substantiated.

How is this information used in making a human being out of a single egg cell? We do not know everything about it by any means, but it is quite clear now that the DNA of the nucleus transfers information to a related nucleic acid, RNA. RNA molecules which are called messenger

RNA move out into the cytoplasm of the cell, outside the nucleus, where, in association with submicroscopic particles called ribosomes they collect the amino acids that are to make protein molecules. The amino acids are collected in the right sequence to make a protein that corresponds in its amino acid sequence to the coding of the DNA of the nucleus and the messenger RNA. For a long time many physicists, chemists, biologists, and mathematicians worked on this coding problem. A few years ago, a young biochemist at the National Institutes of Health, Marshall Nirenberg, found the clue to breaking this code by using synthetic RNA. Practically all of the 64 code words have now been identified as to their meaning in terms of protein synthesis. There are words that specify the 20 kinds of amino acids. There are words that indicate the beginning of the message and others that indicate the end of the message.

The raw materials of evolution are mutations, and the Watson-Crick structure suggests how mutations occur in DNA. In this copying mechanism, occasionally there is a mistake—the equivalent of a typographical error. Indeed, we know now that all of the kinds of errors that can be made in typing a message in our alphabet can be made in DNA. There can be additions, deletions, transpositions, and substitutions of letters. And all of these are known genetically. These mutations may occur spontaneously, be induced by high energy radiation, or be produced by chemical means. Mutations in general tend to be unfavorable, and, in man, the unfavorable mutations lead to what we call genetic disease; there are hundreds of these known. However, I should like to point out that mutations, like typographical errors, are favorable or unfavorable not in an absolute sense, but in terms of the environmental context and also in terms of the genetic context.

For example, a bacterium which acquires a mutation that makes it resistant to penicillin is obviously favored in the presence of penicillin; but in the absence of penicillin, it has a lower reproductive rate and the mutation is unfavorable. In the same sense, if a unit of DNA is omitted at one point, then adding one nearby is a favorable mutation because it restores a reading frame and most of the message is read correctly. Either mutation is unfavorable if it occurs alone, but if it occurs as a second one, it may be favorable.

Mutations are the basis of evolution in the sense that those that are favorable are multiplied by Darwinian natural selection and those that are unfavorable are eliminated. To give an analogy, suppose you had a typist copying and recopying the Gettysburg Address without ever correcting or proofreading. If she averages one mistake in a thousand letters—there are about 1,100 letters in the Gettysburg Address—she will make somewhat more than one error per typing of the Gettysburg Address. In a thousand typings, she will have accumulated something over 1,000 typographical errors and the Gettysburg Address will be a mess. Now change

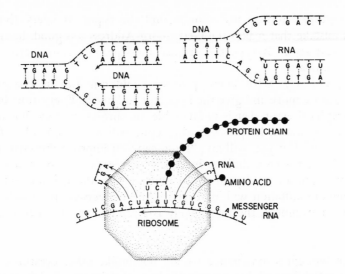

Figure 1 The Watson-Crick model of the DNA molecule consists of two complementary helical chains, the links of which are the four different nucleotides that contain the genetic information. A nucleotide is made up of one sugar molecule plus one phosphoric acid molecule plus one of the four bases that are the gene's code "letters": adenine (A), thymine (T), guanine (G) and cytosine (C); these also serve to bind the two chains together, A always bonding with T and G with C. The drawing at upper left shows the DNA molecule duplicating itself. In a way not yet entirely understood, the two chains part at one end of the molecule, and as the molecule unwinds and the chains continue to separate (from right to left in this schematic drawing), each chain serves as a template on which a new complementary chain is formed. In the same fashion, in the drawing at right, one chain of DNA serves as a template to form a molecule of RNA. Again each base determines its complement and hence the order of the code "letters" in the forming RNA molecule, with the exception that in RNA uracil (U) takes the place of T as the bond of A. The bottom drawing shows how messenger RNA determines the sequence of amino acids that form protein molecules. Each one of the 20 amino acids is specified by a three-letter RNA sequence, and thus the four-letter "language" of DNA is translated into the 20-letter language of proteins. Messenger RNA, having received its information from a DNA template in the nucleus of the cell, passes into the cytoplasm, where in association with a ribosome it can be matched with a different type of RNA that specifies a particular amino acid. The ribosome apparently acts as a sort of vise for positioning amino acids in the growing protein chain. In the drawing, the RNA molecule UGA, having matched with the ACU "word" of the messenger RNA molecule and added its amino acid to the protein chain, is just leaving the ribosome; UCA matches with AGU to add a different amino acid; GCA will match with CGU to add the next link to the protein chain. When another three-letter combination signifies that the "message" is over, the protein molecule will be complete.

the analogy and put an inspector behind the typist. If every time she makes a mistake that makes the Gettysburg Address less good, he throws it away and says, "Retype the original message," of course errors will never accumulate.

But, you say, what about positive evolution? Let us change the analogy a little more and give the inspector judgment. Every time he sees a typographical error that is unfavorable, he throws it away, but if it is neutral or favorable, he passes it; the typist will now accumulate favorable mutations. But you will say, "How can you improve the Gettysburg Address?" That is very difficult indeed, which leads to a conclusion. The better an organism is adapted to its environment, the less probable it is that a random mutation will improve it. And conversely, the less fitted it is to the environment, the more likely is a random mutation to improve it.

If in biological inheritance we are not unlike other creatures, how, then, are we different? Most significantly in the degree of elaboration of our nervous systems, especially the brain. The gap between our brain and that of the nearest nonhuman relatives is a very wide one indeed. Ours and his are both constructed in large part according to DNA instruction, in a manner that we are far from understanding. But ours, unlike his, has evolved in a highly special way through feedback of cultural inheritance.

Some two million or more years ago, Louis Leakey's *Homo habilis*, or whatever you prefer to call him, began to make and use simple tools, of which only crudely chipped stone choppers have survived, along with his bones. Tools certainly gave *Homo habilis* great selective advantage over his less cultured relatives. This cultural inheritance accelerated biological inheritance and man was off on a cultural evolutionary binge never experienced by any other species we know. At first it was slow—but probably continuous. Civilizations rose and fell—one after another—rising to great heights at times, and dropping back to the depths, much faster than can be accounted for by genetic change, I am convinced. All this because of the evolution of that DNA-directed brain, by which men could make bigger and better artifacts.

Our brains, like those of our ancestors and related species, contain what we may call built-in information that regulates many of our bodily functions, like breathing, circulating blood, instinctive behavior and so forth. But unlike them, it contains a vast amount of "put-in" information that is our cultural inheritance.

Our ability to put information into the brain, record it, remember it, rearrange it, and retrieve it, is what makes possible our awareness, our insight, our reason, our communication—all of which has led to language, art, religion, literature, technology, and science. This ability has brought us now to a knowledge of how we have evolved. It has given us the power to direct the evolution of plants and animals to our ends and the knowledge to control our own evolutionary future—both the biological and the cultural components of it. Are we prepared to use that knowledge intelligently and wisely? I have grave doubts.

First, consider biological evolution. We can reduce genetic disease by negative eugenic methods and we do—to some extent. Except for relatively rare dominant genetic diseases, the process is so discouragingly slow as to be almost ineffective. Each of us probably has recessive genes for half a dozen or more genetic diseases. Carried to the extreme, negative eugenic methods would mean that few of us would have children. On the other hand, we know that positive eugenics, that is, preferential multiplication of the fittest, can be accomplished in man. We do it regularly with plants we cultivate and with animals we domesticate. The unanswered questions are: what do we want in man? Who is to decide? And there is another question. What parts of a great many desirable traits are genetically and what parts are culturally determined? Few of us would have advocated preferential multiplication of Hitler's genes through germinal selection. Yet who can say that in a different cultural context Hitler might not have been one of the truly great leaders of men, or that an Einstein might not have been a diabolical villain. I prefer to believe that in the absence of much more understanding than we now have, we will do best to preserve maximum genetic diversity. That is, aside from those who are clearly and significantly genetically defective, let all segments of the species multiply equally rapidly—but at an over-all rate that our resources can sensibly support.

The circumvention of genetic disease by nongenetic methods is called euphenics. Phenylketonuria or PKU, galactosemia, cretinism, retina blastoma and many other diseases are diseases that through medical intervention or diet control can be circumvented in the sense that we make the individual normal but do not change the underlying genetic constitution. If such individuals are made completely normal, including reproductively, and if indeed they do reproduce normally, these diseases will increase in frequency. The increase will be slow because it is a function of the mutation rate, which is something like one in 100,000 per generation or one in a million per generation. This slow rate of increase is fortunate in one sense, for it means we have much time to think about the problem, and we need it. But it is unfortunate in another sense, for in no one generation will the increase be dramatic enough so that we will, in fact, think about it. There is one simple solution, to persuade people affected with genetic disease to adopt children rather than have them in the normal manner. According to popular press reports seen recently, another series of euphenic advances promises that worn-out organs will be replaced by artificially cultured counterparts before too long. Already we have artificial kidneys, artificial veins and arteries, partly artificial hearts.

We welcome such advances, but there is one difficulty, and I think it is a serious one. The rapidly increasing social cost of these endeavors is great indeed. How much further can it increase?

Let me turn to the possibility of what we might call cultural euphenics. Unlike biological inheritance, our cultural inheritance begins anew each generation. In the absence of cultural information put into the brain, none of us would speak or write or sing in any intelligent way, or build even the simplest tool. We would revert half a million years or more in the cultural sense. Still, in another generation it could all be restored. There is almost no inherent limit to the speed with which culture can be lost, improved, or otherwise modified. It can spread over the face of the earth, nowadays, in days or in months. One of its characteristics is that in each generation it is acquired beginning at birth, or even before.

We have only recently come to recognize how much culture goes in during the earliest years. Professor Benjamin Bloom of the University of Chicago has shown that about one half of general intelligence is acquired by the age of four, and about one half of normal school learning is acquired by about the age of nine. The implications for the culturally deprived, the culturally impoverished and changing nations is great indeed. The trick is to break or supplement early in life, in an acceptable way, the normal parent-to-child chain of cultural transmission.

In education, we are inclined to believe quite firmly, lies the road to a better life. But, as has been pointed out, there are cultures in which education is considered a hurdle to be overcome in order to get a job. Cultural euphenics has unlimited potential in changing such attitudes. It is safe, for it is easily reversed, unlike eugenic change.

What about genetic differences in ability to acquire specific cultural patterns? Obviously, differences in ability to acquire culture do occur among individuals. But do such differences occur in significant degree among large populations? That is quite a different question. If one were to take 1,000 healthy babies of Australian aborigines and put them in our cultural context at birth, with our tradition of parental affection and all the rest, would they be as successful in acquiring our cultural pattern as a similar sample of our children? Or, would the converse lead to an equal degree of change in a single generation of our children in their cultural context? We simply do not know the answer. No culture-free test of ability to acquire a given cultural pattern has ever been devised and the experimental approach that I mentioned has never been made.

It seems quite clear to me that we can and must do a far better job of up-grading our cultural environment. I see no need, while doing so, to be obsessed with a desire for cultural uniformity. Cultural diversity may be as important for man's future evolution as is genetic diversity.

5 Evolution by Natural Selection

Sir Gavin de Beer

IT IS MORE THAN A CENTURY SINCE DARWIN PUBLISHED *Origin of Species*. IN *all the cultures in which ideologies give a major role to science, the idea of biological evolution is a commonplace, a fundamental concept upon which much of the world-view is based. Despite the currency of evolutionary ideas and their penetration into the curriculum on almost all levels, there is a surprising amount of uncertainty and confusion about the exact contents of evolutionary doctrine and its modern formulation.*

While the pioneering contributions of Charles Darwin and his great contemporaries should not be forgotten, the study of evolution has proceeded far beyond the understanding they achieved. Current evolutionary theory is actually a synthesis of diverse knowledge and approaches, hence it is sometimes referred to as "the synthetic theory of evolution." Three major components can be distinguished. To the fundamental Darwinian contribution of the mechanism of natural selection has been added genetics and mathematical statistics.

The following selection was written to commemorate the Centennial of Darwin's (and Wallace's) great advance. It celebrates that event in the

SOURCE: "The Darwin-Wallace Centenary," *Endeavor*, Vol. 17, 66 (1958), pp. 61-76. Reprinted with permission of author and publisher.

The author (b. 1899) is currently Director, Thomas Nelson and Sons Ltd., Publishers. He is a former Director of the British Museum (Natural History section) and Professor of Embryology (University College, London) who has written widely on zoology, embryology, evolution, the history of science and Swiss mountaineering. Among his many publications are *Textbook of Vertebrate Zoology* (1928, 1956), *Embryos and Ancestors* (1930, 1958), *The Development of the Vertebrate Skull* (1938), and *Atlas of Evolution* (1964).

most optimistic scientific manner, by sketching the highlights of subsequent development and the broad outlines of evolutionary theory as they are presently construed. It should also be noted that some of the problems of genetics referred to by Sir Gavin as unsolved are now at least partially understood as the previous selection by George Beadle has shown.

From Special Creation to Transformism

Only one hundred years have gone by since the concept of evolution was brought to the attention of thinking men in a manner which has compelled its acceptance. The demonstration that the members of the plant and animal kingdoms are as they are because they have become what they are, and that change, not immutability, is the rule of living things, is one of the most important contributions ever made to knowledge, and its effects have been felt in every field of human thought.

That plants and animals constitute natural kinds, or species, had become clear by the end of the seventeenth century, when John Ray defined them as groups of individuals that breed among themselves. In general, species were accepted as being the result of special creation in each case, and there was little incentive to inquire further.

In the eighteenth century doubts began to arise concerning the immutability of species. Some philosophers arguing theoretically, and a small number of naturalists who encountered difficulty in distinguishing between varieties of cultivated plants, and of domestic animals, which were recognized as the diversified products of species, found difficulty in accepting the view that species were unchangeable. Some naturalists, including Linnaeus himself in his later years, adopted a compromise, allowing that species could have descended with modification from genera, but that genera were immutable.

With the increase in detailed knowledge of the flora and fauna of the world consequent upon the final stages of exploration, the problem of the distinction between varieties and species became acute. With boldness, and a breadth of vision amounting to genius, the French naturalist Lamarck cut the knot by proclaiming that there was no essential difference between species and varieties, that both species and varieties were subject to change, and that 'transformism', not immutability of species, was the basis of life. As it happened, there were two reasons why Lamarck's ideas were unacceptable. The first was that he undertook no analysis to provide evidence for his notion of evolution: it flashed across his mind, and he assumed its truth without taking the trouble to prove it. Secondly, he attempted to give an explanation of the causes of evolution which, unfortunately, raised opposition to the acceptance of the concept of evolution itself. He supposed that as a result of new needs experienced by the animal, its 'inner feelings' or subconscious activities produced new organs which satisfied those needs. Not only was such a supposition unacceptable for the solution of the problem of the origin of species of animals, but it was totally inapplicable to plants. On the other hand, Lamarck put forward a view which for a long time was accepted but which is now known to be without foundation, namely that the effects of use and disuse were transmitted by inheritance. There for a time the matter rested.

The Fact of Evolution

When Darwin started on the voyage of the *Beagle* in 1831, he had no reason to doubt the immutability of species. The speculations of his grandfather Erasmus counted for nothing with him, because they were not supported by evidence. Those of Lamarck on the causes of evolution had the additional demerit of bringing the subject into disrepute by their fanciful nature. It must be added that in Lyell's 'Principles of Geology', to which Darwin owed so much because of the general background of uniformitarianism in place of catastrophism that it advocated, the possibility of evolution was firmly rejected.

Three sets of observations started Darwin's revolt against the immutability of species. The first was occasioned by his studies of the fauna of the Galapagos Islands, where he found that species of finches differed slightly from island to island, while showing general resemblances not only to each other but to the finches on the adjacent mainland of South America. If these species had been separately created, why should there have been such a prodigal expenditure of 'creation' just there; why should geographical propinquity have caused these 'creations' to resemble each other so closely; why, in spite of the similarity in physical conditions between the islands of the Galapagos Archipelago and the Cape Verde Islands, are their faunas totally different, the former resembling that of South America while the fauna of the latter resembles that of Africa?

The second set of observations related to the fact that as he travelled over South America he noticed that the species occupying a particular niche in some regions were replaced in neighbouring regions by other species that were different, yet closely similar. Why are the rabbit-like animals on the savannahs of La Plata built on the plan of the peculiar South American type of rodent and not on that of North America or the Old World?

The third set of observations was concerned with the fact that in the pampas he found fossil remains of large mammals covered with armour like that of the armadillos now living on that continent. Why were these extinct animals built on the same plan as those now living?

On the view that species were immutable and had not changed since they were severally created, there was no rational answer to any of these questions, which would have had to remain as unfathomable mysteries. On the other hand, if species, like varieties, were subject to modification during descent and to divergence into different lines of descent, all these questions could be satisfactorily and simply answered. The finches of the Galapagos resemble each other and those of South America because they are descended from a common ancestor; they differ from one another because they are each adapted to modes of life restricted to their own particular island, one for instance feeding on seeds on the ground and another on insects in trees. The volcanic nature and physical conditions of the Galapagos Islands resemble those of the Cape Verde Islands, and yet the Galapagos birds all differ from the birds of the Cape Verde Islands: therefore it is not the physical conditions of the islands that determine their differences. These differences arose because the Cape Verde Island birds share a common ancestor with the birds of Africa, whereas the Galapagos birds share a common ancestor with those of South America. The hares of South America are built on the South American rodent plan because all South American rodents are descended from a common ancestor. The fossil *Glyptodon* resembles the living armadillos because they also share a common ancestor; this case is particularly important because, if living species show affinity with extinct species, there is no necessity to believe that extinct types of animals have left no living descendants. They may have representatives alive today, and this means that the whole wealth of the palaeontological record of fossils is available as material for the study of the problem of evolution.

In possession of a working hypothesis that species have undergone evolution and successive origination by descent, with modification, from ancestral species shared in common with other species, Darwin next proceeded to search the whole field of botanical and zoological knowledge for evidence bearing on his hypothesis. He realized that no general principle that explained the evolution of animals was acceptable unless it also applied to plants. The result was one of the most remarkable attacks on a problem ever made by the inductive method of searching for facts, whatever their import might be.

In the first place, in cultivated plants and domestic animals such as the dahlia, the potato, the pigeon, and the rabbit, a large number of varieties have in each case been produced from a single original stock. Descent with modification and divergence into several lines is therefore certainly possible within the species.

Comparative anatomy reveals the existence of similar plans of structure in large groups of organisms. Plants may have vegetative leaves, and in some cases these are modified into parts of flowers. Vertebrate animals have forelimbs that may be used for walking, running, swimming, or flying, but in which the various parts of the skeleton correspond, bone for bone, from the upper arm to the last joints of the fingers, whether the animal is a frog, a lizard, a turtle, a bird, a rabbit, a seal, a bat, or a man. This is what is meant by saying that such structures are homologous, and these correspondences are inexplicable unless the animals are descended from a common ancestor. Fundamental resemblance is therefore evidence of genetic affinity.

The study of comparative behaviour proves that related forms show gradations in their instincts, such as shamming death in insects and nest-building in birds. At the same time, related species inhabiting different parts of the earth under very different conditions retain similar instincts. Examples are the habit of thrushes in England and in South America of lining nests with mud, and that of wrens in England and North America of the males building 'cock-nests'. Why should this be, unless the different species of thrushes and wrens are descended from common ancestors in each case?

Embryology reveals remarkable similarity in structure between young embryos of animals which in the adult stage are as different as fish, lizard, fowl, and man. This similarity even extends to such details as the manner in which the blood-vessels run from the heart to the dorsal aorta, a plan which is of obvious significance in the case of the fish that breathes by means of gills, but not so obvious in that of lizard, chick, or man, where gill-pouches are formed in the embryo but soon become transformed into different structures, and breathing is carried out by other means. This similarity between embryos is explained by the affinity and descent from a common ancestor of the groups to which they belong.

Embryology also provides evidence of vestiges of structures which once performed important functions in the ancestors but now either perform different functions or none at all. Examples of such organs are the teeth of whalebone whales, the limbs of snakes, the wings of ostriches and penguins, and the flowers of the feather-hyacinth. Since Darwin's time countless other examples have been discovered. The most striking of these are the pineal gland which is a vestigial eye, and vestiges of the egg-tooth still found in marsupials, although it is 75 million years since their ancestors had to use an egg-tooth to crack the shell and hatch out of their eggs. Here again, descent from common ancestral forms explains all these cases.

Knowledge of the fossil record in Darwin's time was so imperfect that nothing was then available in the way of series illustrating the course of evolution. Nevertheless, he noticed that in Tertiary strata, the lower the horizon the fewer fossils there were belonging to species alive today. Palaeontology therefore showed that new species had appeared and old species become extinct, not all at the same time, but in succession and gradually. Why should this be so unless new species have come into existence from time to time by descent with modification from other species?

Plants and animals are classified according to their resemblance, and they are placed in one or other of a not very large number of groups, such as ferns, conifers, molluscs, or mammals. But within each of these groups there is subdivision into other smaller groups, mammals being so subdivided into rodents, carnivores, ungulates, and primates for example. Within these again there is further subdivision, and the important point to notice is that classification always places species in groups that are contained within other larger groups. This is such a commonplace that its significance is often overlooked. Why do organisms have to be classified like this? Why are they not strewn in single file up the ladder of the plant and animal kingdoms, or fortuitously like pebbles on a beach, or arbitrarily like the stars in imaginary constellations? The reason is that the arrangement of groups within groups is a natural classification reflecting the course of evolution. It is the result of descent from common ancestors and an indication of affinity; the differences between the groups are due to modification and divergence during such descent.

Darwin also investigated the problem of interspecific sterility and saw that it was by no means absolute, because numerous examples can be found of different species that produce hybrids, and in some cases these hybrids are themselves fertile. From the point of view of breeding, therefore, such species behave like varieties. Why, then, can species not have originated as varieties, by descent and modification from other species?

From the evidence provided by all these sources Darwin built up an irrefutable argument that species have changed and originated from other species and that evolution has occurred. That he should have been able to do so from such few data is a mark of genius, for at the time when he worked out his conclusions, none of the cases had been discovered which would now be used as the most striking examples with which to illustrate the fact and the course of evolution. Chief among these are the beautiful series of fossils which reveal the evolution of the ammonites or of the horses, step by step, and those which represent the precursors of the various classes and groups of vertebrates such as *Archaeopteryx* or *Pithecanthropus*.

The main steps in Darwin's proof of the fact of evolution were established by 1842, when he committed them to paper in the form of a Sketch which he expanded into an Essay in 1844, though neither was published by him. Soon after this, another naturalist, Alfred Russel Wallace, was led to explore similar lines of research. From some simple observations on the distribution of organisms, both geographically over the world and geologically in the fossil record, Wallace drew some equally simple conclusions that are of great importance in the history of thought that led to the realization of evolution. They show that, independently of Darwin and in complete ignorance of his work, Wallace had hit upon the same solution of the problem of the mutability of species.

Wallace's observations were based on the facts, firstly, that large systematic groups such as classes and orders are usually distributed over the whole of the earth, whereas groups of low systematic value such as families, genera, and species frequently have a very small localized distribution. Secondly, 'when a group is confined to one district, and is rich in species, it is almost invariably the case that the most closely allied species are found in the same locality or in closely adjoining localities, and that therefore the natural sequence of the species by affinity is also geographical.' Thirdly, in the fossil record large groups extend through several geological formations, and 'no group or species has come into existence twice.'

The conclusion which Wallace drew from these observations was that 'Every species has come into existence coincident both in space and time with a pre-existing closely allied species.' Thought out about 1845, written at Sarawak in 1855, and published in the same year, Wallace's theory already allowed him to say that 'the natural series of affinities will also represent the order in which the several species came into existence, each one having had for its immediate antitype a closely allied species existing at the time of its origin. It is evidently possible that two or three distinct species may have had a common antitype, and that each of these may again have become the antitype from which other closely allied species were created.'

With the help of this principle, in which it is only necessary to substitute 'ancestor' for 'antitype' for the formulation of evolution to be complete, Wallace showed that it was possible to give a simple explanation of natural classification, of the geographical distribution of plants and animals, including those of the Galapagos Islands, of the succession of forms in the fossil record, and of rudimentary organs which would be inexplicable 'if each species had been created independently, and without any necessary relations with preexisting species.'

So much of the credit for the establishment of the fact of evolution has, rightly, been accorded to Darwin that it is only just that Wallace's contribution to this problem should be recognized and honoured.

The evidence on which Darwin and Wallace based their demonstration that evolution was a fact is not only valid to this day, but has been confirmed in all the branches of science concerned as well as in many new fields. There was in their day not even an inkling of the possibilities of research opened up by comparative physiology and biochemistry, or of serology as a quantitative indicator of the amount of divergence that has taken place between related forms. Why should the chemical substance involved in the mechanism of muscular contraction in most invertebrates be arginine, whereas it is creatine in vertebrates and echinoderms, which on independent evidence are regarded as related? Why should serum immunized against man give precipitations of 64 per cent when mixed with blood of a gorilla, but 42 per cent with that of an orang-utan, 29 per cent with that of a baboon, and only 10 per cent with that of an ox? Why should syphilis attack the chimpanzee more seriously than the orang-utan, and the latter more seriously than the baboon? Why should the human ABO blood group system also be found in the apes? The answer to all these questions is that the organisms concerned have undergone evolution from common ancestors, as a result of which members of the various lines of descent share not only structural, mental, and genetical characters, but also physiological and biochemical mechanisms and immunological reactions.

The Mechanism of Natural Selection

Although Darwin already knew in 1837 that evolution was an inescapable conclusion to be drawn from the evidence, he did not allow himself to proceed any further with his discovery until he had found an explanation of the fact of adaptations. In a general way, all plants and animals are adapted to their environment, for otherwise they could not live. A man drowns in the sea; a fish dies out of water. But there are some structures which show a particularly intimate relationship between the organism and its conditions of life. Mistletoe is a parasite that requires a tree of certain species to live on, a particular insect to pollinate its flowers, and a thrush to eat its berries and deposit its seeds on branches of the same species of tree. A woodpecker has two of its toes turned backwards with which it grips the bark of a tree; it has stiff tail-feathers with which it props itself against the tree; it has a very stout beak with which it bores holes in the tree trunk; and it has an abnormally long tongue with which it takes the grubs at the bottom of the holes. Other plants than mistletoe and other birds than woodpeckers do not have all these adaptations, and therefore, if evolution has occurred, it is necessary to give an objective explanation of how these adaptations arose.

Darwin knew that all members of a species are not identical but show variation in size, strength, health, fertility, longevity, instincts, habits, mental attributes, and countless other characters. He soon perceived that such variation could be, and in fact was, turned to good account by man in the course of artificial selection, which he has practised in the production of cultivated plants and domestic animals since the New Stone Age. The key was selection, the practice of breeding only from those parents that possess the desired qualities. But how could selection have operated on wild plants and animals in nature since the beginning of life on earth without man or a conscious being to direct it? The solution of this puzzle occurred to Darwin accidentally when he read Malthus's 'Essay on Population' and realized that under the conditions of competition in which plants and animals live, any variations would be preserved which increased the organisms' ability to leave fertile offspring, while those variations which decreased it would be eliminated. In a state of nature, selection works automatically, which is why Darwin called it Natural Selection.

Darwin was then able to formulate a complete theory providing a rational explanation of the causes as well as of the fact of evolution in plants and animals. It is formally based on four propositions which he already knew to be true, and three deductions which are now also known to be true. They may be enumerated as follows.

1. Organisms produce a far greater number of reproductive cells than ever give rise to mature individuals.

2. The numbers of individuals in species remain more or less constant.

3. Therefore there must be a high rate of mortality.

4. The individuals in a species are not all identical, but show variation in all characters.

5. Therefore some variants will succeed better and others less well in the competition for survival, and the parents of the next generation will be naturally selected from among those members of the species that show variation in the direction of more effective adaptation to the conditions of their environment.

6. Hereditary resemblance between parent and offspring is a fact.

7. Therefore subsequent generations will by gradual change maintain and improve on the degree of adaptation realized by their parents.

This is the formal theory of evolution by natural selection, first announced jointly on 1st July 1858 by Darwin and Alfred Russel Wallace, who had, again independently, come to the identical conclusion. It represents a step in knowledge comparable to Newton's discovery of the law of gravitation.

The Integration of Mendelian Genetics with Selection

When Darwin wrote, nothing whatever was known about the laws of heredity, and all that he had to go upon was the vague notion that offspring tended to strike an average between the characters of their parents. This supposition went by the name of 'blending inheritance', and it occasioned for Darwin the greatest difficulty with which he had to contend in formulating his theory. In the first place, if blending inheritance were true, it would mean that any new variation which appeared, even if heritable, would be rapidly diluted by 'swamping', and in about ten generations would have been obliterated. To compensate for this it would be necessary to suppose that new variations were extremely frequent. Since whole brothers, sons of the same father and mother, share an identical heredity, any difference between them would have to be due to new variation that had arisen during their own early lives, and variation would have to affect practically all members of a species. This problem of the supply of variation was a difficulty which Darwin felt so acutely that it even led him to look for a source of this supply in the supposed hereditary effects of use and disuse.

This reliance on the effects of use and disuse as a source of variation, without any effect on his main argument, is the only part of Darwin's demonstration that has had to be abandoned, and he would have welcomed the reasons for it. If only Darwin had realized it, the solution to all these difficulties was at that very time being provided by Gregor Mendel, but his results remained unknown until 1900, eighteen years after Darwin's death.

The Mendelian theory of the gene was worked out by T. H. Morgan and his colleagues with an unprecedented wealth of experimental evidence from the breeding pen and from cytological studies on the structure of the cell and its chromosomes. It has established, as firmly as Newton's laws of motion or the atomic theory, that hereditary resemblances are determined by discrete particles, the genes, situated in the chromosomes of the cells, which are transmitted to offspring in accordance with the mechanism of germ-cell formation and fertilization, and conform to distributional patterns known as Mendelian inheritance. The researches of C. D. Darlington and others on the structure and behaviour of the chromosomes have reached such a degree of refinement and precision that each step in the mechanism of Mendelian inheritance can actually be seen under the microscope.

The genes preserve their separate identity; they collaborate in the production of the characters of the individual that possesses them, but they never contaminate each other; they remain constant for long periods, but from time to time they undergo a change, known as mutation, which involves a change in the characters which they control; after this they remain constant in their new condition until they mutate again. It has been conclusively proved that the theory of the gene applies to all plants and all animals investigated, and that the mutation of genes is the only known way in which heritable variation arises. The modifications resulting from good or bad food supply, or from the climatic conditions in which plants and animals live, are not inherited and are therefore without significance in evolution.

The history of the reception of Mendelian genetics after its discovery has been peculiar. The earliest mutations discovered, often called 'sports', were usually deleterious and showed marked and discontinuous steps instead of the gradual and continuous variation which Darwinian selectionists looked for as the raw material of evolution. Selectionists therefore rejected Mendelian genetics as the source of variation. On the other hand, the Mendelian geneticists, knowing that their mutations were the only source of heritable variation, thought that as they showed wide discontinuous steps and arose suddenly, ready-made and apparently without long-continued selection, selection was inoperative in evolution, and they rejected it.

With the progress of knowledge it gradually became obvious that each of these two schools of research objected to the other for reasons which were baseless. As more and more genes were identified and their effects studied, it became clear that the wide and discontinuous mutations first observed were the more easily detected extremes of a range in which the majority exert only slight effects. For the same reason, these mutations were deleterious because organisms are delicately adjusted systems, more likely to be upset by large and discontinuous changes than by small and gradual steps.

The Mendelian geneticists also had to learn two lessons. On the one hand they discovered that although individual genes are associated with particular characters, their control of those characters is also affected by all the other genes, which constitute an organized gene-complex. As a result of previous mutations, gene-complexes of plants and animals in nature contain many genes, and these are sorted out and recombined at fertilization in astronomically numerous possibilities of permutations. These recombinations have been shown to bring about gradual and continuous changes in the characters under the major control of individual genes. Sir Ronald Fisher demonstrated the significance of this by showing that a mutant gene that now exhibits the quality known as dominance has gradually become dominant from a previous intermediate condition. This is what has happened to those mutations that confer a benefit on their possessors, and in their case there has been a selection of gene-complexes in favour of those which accentuate the effects of a favourable mutant, so that these effects are manifested even if the mutant gene is inherited from only one parent, which is the definition of dominance. Conversely, with genes that place a handicap on their possessors, there has been a selection of gene-complexes in favour of those which suppress the effects of such genes so that they are manifested only when the mutant gene is inherited from both parents, which is the definition of recessiveness. They may be suppressed even further, as when the effects of such a gene are obliterated and the gene becomes what is known as a 'modifier', without major control over characters. It has even been demonstrated by E. B. Ford, under rigorous experimental conditions, that one and the same mutant gene can be made to become dominant in one strain and recessive in another, simply by selecting as parents those individuals whose gene-complexes accentuate or diminish the effects of the gene.

The second lesson that Mendelian geneticists had to learn was that although the effects of the mutations which they first observed appeared to be clear-cut, they were already the results of past gene-complexes. For these mutations have occurred before, and the gene-complexes have become adjusted to them. The fact that a single gene may now act as a switch controlling the production of one or other character-difference does not mean that this character-difference originally arose at one stroke by one mutation of such a witch-gene, because it has probably been built up gradually as a result of past selection in the gene-complex.

It is therefore clear that mutations and recombinations of genes provide the supply of variation on which selection acts to cause evolution exactly in the way Darwin's theory requires. Its requirements are exacting, for, as T. H. Huxley pointed out, some organisms have evolved slowly and others have evolved fast; he saw that natural selection was the only mechanism that could satisfy both those requirements. It is able to do so because Mendelian inheritance is capable of producing both diversity and stability. As Ford has said, an immense range of types must be available for natural selection to act upon, and this is provided by mutation and recombination of genes. Yet when a favourable gene-complex has been achieved it must not be dissipated and broken down, and this is provided against by the facts that the genes do not blend or contaminate one another, and that they mutate only rarely.

The Significance of Particulate Inheritance in Evolution

The particulate theory of inheritance which Mendelian genetics has established involves a number of consequences of fundamental importance for the problem of evolution. In the first place, the substitution of this quantitative and deterministic science for the vague and baseless notion of 'blending inheritance' completely disposes of the difficulty under which Darwin laboured to account for the necessary supply of variation on which natural selection could act. The most characteristic feature of the Mendelian gene is that it never blends, but retains its identity and properties intact for long periods of time until it mutates, after which it remains intact in its new condition until it eventually mutates again. This means that the amount of variation, or variance, present in a population resulting from previous mutations, is not only conserved through generation after generation, but is actually increased as a result of the recombinations of the gene-complexes in their innumerable possible permutations. This power of increase is one of the most important results of the bi-parental method of reproduction and is the reason why organisms possessed of this mechanism have evolved further than those that lack it.

This conservation of variance is to be considered in relation to the rate at which mutation normally occurs. It has been calculated that in organisms as diverse as a bacterium, a maize-plant, a fruitfly, and in man, any given gene mutates in one in about half a million individuals. It is also clear that this rate is itself the result of selection, and that although seemingly slow, it has been adequate to provide the requisite basic heritable variation which the mechanism of germ-cell formation and fertilization has multiplied, and on which selection has worked to produce whatever evolution has taken place. In other words, mutation not only need not, but must not be more rapid than a slow rate. This rate is ten thousand times slower than what it would have to be if 'blending inheritance' were a fact, and Darwin's difficulty in accounting for an adequate supply of variation is lightened by that amount.

As the originating mechanism for basic heritable variation, mutation has naturally been intensively studied. It has been found that certain physical and chemical agents, including radioactivity, can accelerate the rate at which mutation would naturally occur, but that these induced mutations are similar to those which occur and recur normally, and no correlation whatever exists between the mutagenic agents and the quality of 'direction' of the mutations. Mutations take place with 'blindness and molar indeterminacy', as H. J. Muller has expressed it. This is a finding of capital importance, for it shows that there is no basis for attempts to explain the origin of heritable variation by appealing to environmental factors to evoke appropriate responses, or to the internal factors to make such responses. Nor is there any basis for the view that the environment would evoke appropriate heritable responses if its actions were continued for a sufficient time, because, as J. B. S. Haldane showed, such responses as might be significant in evolution would be detected within the period of the experiment carried out.

In organisms that reproduce by simple division of the whole body, such as bacteria, special conditions apply because reproduction in them involves not only transmission of genetic material in the form of genes, but also transmission of bodily characters, since the latter are carried over wholesale from 'parent' to offspring. Adaptation to new environments can take place in bacteria. Furthermore, in bacteria, and perhaps also in higher organisms, it is possible for organic molecules such as bacteriophage particles to enter organisms and become incorporated in the genetic mechanisms so as to behave like genes. These results are full of promise as a field of research into the nature of genes, and perhaps of mutations, but they do not in any way invalidate the principles of Mendelian genetics and inheritance.

Mutations are chemical changes in the gene-molecule, and since chemical stability is not absolute, the puzzle about mutations is not so much that they occur as that they occur so infrequently. This ignorance of the causes which determine the directions in which mutations take place, if such causes indeed exist, is, strange to relate, no handicap to the understanding of the mechanism of evolution, because it is emphatically selection, not mutation, that determines the direction of evolution. This all-important conclusion is based not only on detailed experimental studies on the effects of selection in nature, but also on the demonstration by Sir Ronald Fisher of a general principle. The effects of selection in changing the frequency of genes in a population have been calculated for various percentage benefits in survival-value conferred by such genes. It has been found by calculation that at the observed natural average mutation-rate of one in half a million, no mutant gene has the slightest chance of maintaining itself against even the faintest degree of adverse selection. Furthermore, if the direction of evolution were determined by the direction of mutation, it would be necessary to suppose that such mutations must be predominantly favourable. In fact, the vast majority of mutations have been unfavourable, and natural selection has acted against them by converting the resulting mutant genes into recessives, or by suppressing them into the condition of mere modifiers, or by exacting the more drastic price of abolition consequent on the rapid death of the organisms containing them. It is natural selection, not mutation, that has governed the direction as well as the amount of evolution, and it has been estimated that if mutation were to stop now, there is already sufficient variation in the plant and animal kingdoms for evolution to continue for as long in the future as it has continued hitherto in the past.

The bearing of this demonstration on hypotheses that attempt to explain evolution by postulating the existence of agencies capable of directing mutation is plain. It means that all such theories as invoke the effects of use and disuse, 'inheritance of acquired characters', environmental stimuli, 'organic selection', 'inner feelings', 'inherited memory', momentum along particular directions, orthogenesis, nomogenesis, and others, which assume that mutation can be made to follow adaptively desirable directions, are not only devoid of any known mechanism by which the direction of mutation might be brought about, and devoid of evidence for the existence of such mechanisms, but they involve a cause 'which demonstrably would not work even if it were known to exist'. It is therefore not surprising that in spite of repeated attempts, many undertaken with impure and insufficiently standardized genetic material, and others in which the results were simply faked, no evidence has been provided that the effects of use and disuse or adaptive response to environmental conditions are inherited or induce appropriate mutations. From the evidence provided by genetics, natural selection is the only mechanism capable of explaining evolution.

Natural Selection, 'Improbability' and 'Chance'

An argument sometimes used against the efficacy of natural selection involves the claim that the initial stages in the evolution of complex structures or functions could not have been favoured by natural selection until such structures or functions had reached a certain level of perfection. Like all other arguments of the *non possumus* type, this one melts away before the progress of knowledge. A case in point is that of the electric organs of fish, developed out of muscles which are capable of discharges strong enough to catch prey and defend the fish against its enemies. These organs are clearly adaptive and confer survival-value on their possessors, but the question arises what functions they could perform in the initial stages of their evolution, when it must be supposed that their power was too weak to kill prey or to deter predators. Darwin himself was well aware of this problem, and he met the argument by pointing out that 'it would be extremely bold to maintain that no serviceable transitions are possible by which these organs might have been gradually developed'. He has been proved to be right, because of the discovery by H. W. Lissmann that weak electric discharges given off by certain fish function in a manner analogous to those of radar equipment, and serve to convey information of the proximity of objects in the water. Electric organs can therefore be adaptive even when they are too weak to kill prey or deter predators.

Another case may be cited because it illustrates the manner in which an adaptive result may be achieved without itself being a direct object of selection. Colour vision has been evolved independently in many groups of animals. Among the light-sensitive elements in the eye, some are specially sensitive in dim illumination; others confer acuteness of vision in bright light when they are individually innervated, with the result that light-stimuli are perceived separately by very small areas of the retina. In each of the two functions of seeing in relative darkness and seeing accurately in the light, increased efficiency confers survival-value from the very start of the improvement. But when both these functions have been achieved in the same eye a mechanism is produced, as E. N. Willmer has indicated, in which the visual elements are differently sensitive to light of different wavelengths, and this is the basis of colour vision. The emergence of colour vision as an unexpected 'bonus' resulting from the perfection of two other functions is a concrete example of the principle to which Lloyd Morgan applied the term 'emergent evolution'.

It has also been objected that natural selection is a difficult concept to apply to the evolution of very complex adaptations involving co-ordinated variations either in one and the same organism, or even in two different organisms. It is not necessary to go far afield to find examples of this, for in all animals with separate sexes and internal fertilization there has been a separate yet harmonious evolution of the reproductive organs in the two sexes. It has been supposed that such situations argued so high a degree of 'mathematical improbability' that they could not be explained as a result of natural selection, which was, very erroneously, called 'chance'. To this objection there are several answers.

In the first place, those who invoke mathematical improbability against natural selection can be refuted out of their own mouths. Muller has estimated that on the existing knowledge of the percentage of mutations that are beneficial, and a reasoned estimate of the number of mutations that would be necessary to convert an amoeba into a horse, based on the average magnitude of the effects of mutations, the number of mutations required on the basis of chance alone, if there were no natural selection, would be of the order of one thousand raised to the power of one million. This impossible and meaningless figure serves to illustrate the power of natural selection in collecting favourable mutations and minimizing waste of variation, for horses do exist and they have evolved.

It is worth while to study the question of improbability more closely. As Fisher has pointed out, improbability has a different aspect when considered from time before or time after the event. The probability that any man alive today will have sons, grandsons, and successive descendants in the male line uninterruptedly for one hundred generations is infinitesimally small. Yet every man today is the living proof that this contingency, so highly improbable as it may have seemed one hundred generations ago, has nevertheless occurred. Similarly, the effects of natural selection are the reverse of chance when considered *ex post facto;* they are rigorously determined, and what they have done is to channel random variation into adaptive directions and thereby simulate the appearance of purposive change. This is why natural selection has been paradoxically defined as 'a mechanism for generating an exceedingly high degree of improbability'.

Mention of purpose introduces the notion of teleology or fulfilment of design which has sometimes been invoked to explain the production of complex adaptations. Teleology and providential guidance are double-edged weapons with which to attack the problem of evolution, because it can be shown that the more detailed the adaptation, the more 'improbable' it may appear as a product of 'chance', the more likely its possessor is to be doomed to extinction through inability to become adapted to changed conditions.

Structures may be developed which at first benefit individuals in their competition to survive; but by continued selection such structures may become exaggerated and lead to the extinction of the species. This seems to have been what happened to the Huia-bird, where mated pairs constantly remained in company together, and the beaks of the male and female reached an extraordinary disparity of size in adaptation to their very special feeding, but failed to enable the birds to obtain ordinary food when their special diet was unavailable. Excess, even of adaptation, is harmful, and the fossil record shows that the vast majority of lines of evolution have led to extinction, which is a grim comment on the alleged powers of providential guidance and purpose.

From the undoubted fact that many of the products of the plant and animal kingdom convey to man the aesthetic quality of beauty, it has been supposed that beauty is an end in itself to which the criterion of usefulness and survival-value could not be applied, and therefore that it could not be imagined as a product of evolution. To this argument Wallace opposed the demonstration that if the quality of beauty were an exception to the principle of evolution by natural selection, it would be necessary to find an explanation for the existence of so much in plants and animals that is positively ugly.

Darwin showed it to be an invariable rule that 'When a flower is fertilised by the wind it never has a gaily-coloured corolla'. The beauty of flowers has been gradually achieved because of the survival-value of cross-fertilization (consequent upon the attraction of insects to such flowers) conferred on plants possessing them. The beautiful colours and structures of birds and some other animals have resulted from the survival-value conferred on successful competitors in sexual selection.

This demonstration of what may be called the natural nature of beauty has been developed still further by Ray Lankester in the course of a soliloquy on alpine flowers: 'All beauty of living things, it seems, is due to Nature's selection, and not only all beauty of colour and form, but that beauty of behaviour and excellence of inner quality which we call "goodness". The fittest, that which has survived and will survive in the struggle of organic growth, is, (we see it in these flowers) in man's estimation the beautiful. Is it possible to doubt that just as we approve and delightedly revel in the beauty created by "natural selection," so we give our admiration and reverence, without question, to "goodness," which also is the creation of Nature's great unfolding?'

In many of the higher animals, parental care and self-sacrifice, in the interest of other members of the family such as incubating or gravid females and young, have been favoured by natural selection and conferred benefit on the species. From earliest human times, the survival-value of altruistic behaviour has been enhanced because of the prolongation of childhood and the consolidation of the family that have characterized the evolution of man. The size of the unit within which altruistic behaviour conferred survival-value has grown progressively larger, but fitfully, as history and anthropology have shown, from the family to the clan, the tribe, and the nation. In this manner, ethical standards of conduct and morality have arisen which can be seen to develop in individuals and have been seen to evolve in societies. Between these units, competition on the subhuman level of natural selection has persisted. With the development of man's higher mental faculties, conscious choice and purposiveness became factors in evolution, and for this reason the subsequent evolution of man has been of a nature different from that of other organisms because it was no longer governed solely by natural selection.

Natural Selection in Action

Natural selection can be seen to be at work here and now in directing evolution. Modern techniques of study of genetics in populations in the field developed by T. Dobzhansky and E. B. Ford have shown that the relative longevities of variants in different environments can be directly measured, and that the effects of such differential mortality have been to produce evolutionary change. An example of this type of research is that of H. B. D. Kettlewell on 'industrial melanism' in moths. Up to 1850 the British peppered moth existed in its typical grey form known as *Biston betularia*, which is remarkably well adapted to resemble the lichens on the bark of trees. From that date a dark melanic variety appeared, known as *carbonaria*, which is extremely conspicuous against the natural bark of trees. The melanic variation is controlled by a single dominant Mendelian gene and is slightly more vigorous than the normal grey type. Nevertheless, because of its conspicuous colour the *carbonaria* variety was constantly eliminated, and this variety persisted in the populations of the peppered moth only because the same mutation kept on occurring again and again. The Industrial Revolution brought about a marked change in the environment, since the pollution of the air by increasing quantities of carbon dust killed the lichens on the trees and rendered their trunks and branches black. Under these conditions it is the *carbonaria* variety which is favoured and the *betularia* penalized. This has been proved by direct observation of the feeding of birds, and by measurement of the survival-rates of the different forms in the different environments. The dark *carbonaria* form survives 17 per cent less well in an unpolluted area and 10 per cent better in a polluted area. One hundred years ago the dark variety of the peppered moth formed less than 1 per cent of the population; today in industrial areas it forms 99 per cent, and selection has made it more intensively black than when it first appeared.

The case of melanism in the peppered moth also introduces a principle to which L. Cuénot drew attention and gave the name of 'preadaptation'. The melanic form of the peppered moth happened to be 'preadapted' to conditions which were only subsequently realized, or in other words, if the Industrial Revolution had not taken place, the melanic variety would never have become adaptive at all, and would have suffered the same fate as the countless other mutations resulting in variations which, whether 'pre-adapted' or not, have been eliminated because they fell short of the requirements imposed by natural selection.

The evolutionary change actually witnessed in the peppered moth is directly attributable to selection, and it is matched by similar studies on other forms. Experiments by A. J. Cain and P. M. Sheppard on the survival-rate of snails with shells of different colours and banding patterns, living on dark- or light-coloured backgrounds, have shown that selection does not act like an all-obliterating steam-roller going in one direction. As the seasons change, the adaptive value of the colour of a shell changes from disadvantageous to advantageous and back again. This proves that the effects of selection vary from place to place and from season to season, and that the balance between an organism and its environment is delicate, changing, and dynamic.

The phenomenon of Batesian mimicry has also been proved not only to be adaptive and to confer survival-value, but to have been achieved by selection. Ford has shown that the degree of perfection with which the mimics copy their models is a function of the prevalence of the models. The percentage of imperfect mimics in the populations of *Papilio dardanus* is only 4 at places like Entebbe, where models are numerous. At Nairobi, on the other hand, where the models are 70 times less numerous than at Entebbe, the imperfect mimics are 8 times more numerous and constitute 32 per cent of the population. Less survival-value is conferred by resemblance to a model when the latter is too infrequent to teach predators to shun it, and there is then less selection-pressure on the mimic to resemble it.

While the overriding importance of the effects of selection is now generally realized, it has been suggested that when populations are split up into very small isolated colonies, changes in the relative frequencies of different genes might result from the errors of random sampling in the formation of the germ-cells and their fertilization, without involving selection. This concept, advanced by Sewall Wright and known as 'random genetic drift', has been invoked as a possible cause of non-selective, non-adaptive evolution. It has, however, been invalidated by the results of experimental studies in the field such as those of Fisher and Ford on moths, which have shown that selective factors are much more important than casual non-adaptive factors in determining the relative frequency of genes and in bringing about close adaptation to local environmental conditions. Even in comparatively numerous populations, from one generation to the next there are fluctuations in gene-ratio larger than can be attributed to random sampling and which are controlled by selection. Such effects as may be due to random sampling in small populations can only be of negligible significance in evolution.

Selection frequently works on a basis of compromise. Among the natives of Africa there is a condition known as sickle-cell anaemia, in which the red blood-corpuscles are deformed and shaped like the blades of sickles. This is controlled by a Mendelian gene which, when inherited from both parents (homozygous), produces an extreme effect which frequently kills the subject by thrombosis. When inherited from only one parent (heterozygous), the danger from thrombosis is not so great. In areas where malaria is present, however, there is a positive advantage in possessing the sickle-cell gene, because the malaria parasite cannot enter the sickle-shaped red blood-corpuscles. In accordance with the prevalence of malaria in the environment, therefore, a balance is automatically struck in the population between the danger of dying from malaria if the individual has no sickle-cell gene, and the danger of dying of thrombosis if the individual has two sickle-cell genes. Survival-value and ability to leave more offspring therefore accrues to the possessors of one sickle-cell gene up to a certain frequency, and this example shows in what unexpected ways selection is able to make the best even of a bad gene-complex.

Natural Selection and Palaeontology

The palaeontological record provides the evidence of the course which evolution has followed in the past. The fossil material is in places now so rich that it can be used for quantitative studies in evolution. Firstly, the radioactive time-clocks enable various levels of evolutionary lineage to be dated and the time measured during which certain changes have occurred. This provides quantitative evidence of evolution rates. From such data estimates can be obtained of the duration-times of genera and species. Statistical study of large samples of fossil materials enables the variability of the different species to be assessed. By methods such as these, G. G. Simpson has worked out that the evolution from *Hyracotherium* to *Equus* occupied 60 million years. This involved passage through 8 genera, the duration of each being on the average 7.5 million years; 30 species of a duration-time of 2 million years each; and 15 million generations each reaching maturity in 4 years. These data can be compared with those obtained from other groups of animals, from which they differ considerably. The results show that evolution rate is not correlated with variability, nor with generation-time, and that it is selection that controls the direction and intensity of evolution.

These results are all the more important because in the past some palaeontologists, unequipped with knowledge of modern genetics, have imagined that from tracing the course of evolution in the lineage of fossils which they established they were in a position to draw conclusions about the cause of such evolution. Some have thought that they had found support for the inheritance of acquired characters, although they knew nothing about inheritance; others imagined that as the lineage of some fossils showed linear progression of certain characters, they were justified in concluding that evolution involved an innate directional component, an expression of 'momentum' leading to evolution in 'straight lines', which they called orthogenesis. They failed to realize that if selection in a particular direction benefits an organism, continued selection in the same direction will, up to a certain point, benefit it further. Others again have concluded from their materials that a distinction in principle could be made out between 'big' evolution leading to large evolutionary changes, and 'small' evolution producing trifling results. None of these speculations can stand up to the evidence that selection determines the course of evolution, its speed or its slowness, the greatness or smallness of the effects produced, and its direction, which if constant for any length of time simulates orthogenesis.

It is of interest to consider how far it is possible to extrapolate the results of modern genetics into the palaeontological past. C. R. Diver has shown that, in snails, the patterns of banding found today were already in existence in Pleistocene times. It is necessary, however, to beware of concluding that because characters are similar they must be controlled by the same genes. Even in one and the same species today, the gene-complex can undergo permutations which reproduce the same structures with different genes. An example is provided by the gene 'eyeless' in *Drosophila* which produces flies with very small or no eyes; this is, of course, extremely harmful. Eyeless flies can, however, be made to breed, and although the mortality is very high, progeny can be reared which after a few generations have eyes like normal flies. In such a stock the 'eyeless' gene is nevertheless present unaltered, as can be proved by mating these flies with normal flies, when the effects of the 'eyeless' gene manifest themsleves in all their force, though in the second generation, because 'eyeless' is recessive. This result is therefore in perfect accordance with the principle that Mendelian genes do not become contaminated. What has happened during the inbreeding of 'eyeless' flies is that the reshuffling of the other genes has produced a gene-complex in which the harmful effects of 'eyeless' have been suppressed.

The gene-complex is therefore a dynamic system, as S. C. Harland concluded from his researches on cotton. Genes compete, i.e. are selected in the gene-complex, old genes being dropped and new genes incorporated. During the course of evolution the effective membership of the gene-complex must have changed, and it is not legitimate to conclude that because a character or a structure like the eye of vertebrates was in existence 400 million years ago, it was then controlled by the same genes as control it now. The evidence is entirely opposed to such a static view. It is precisely because the gene-complexes change that characters, structures, and organisms have evolved.

The New Systematics and the Origin of Species

The researches on industrial melanism in the peppered moth, banding and colour of snails, mimicry in butterflies, local adaptation in moths, and sickle-cell in man, which have here been briefly described, are examples of new techniques of experimental study of evolution in the field. They have grown out of what Julian Huxley has aptly called 'The New Systematics', to which he has himself contributed so much. Systematics, the study of species and of the higher groups of classification, began by the recognition of differences between species, defined from type specimens preserved in museums. But with the realization that species now or in the past are or were populations of live plants and animals in nature, living under varying conditions of equilibrium with each other and with the inorganic factors of the environments—themselves showing geographical variation in space, and undergoing variation in time, subject to mutation and recombination of their genes, constantly under the influence of selection—species can no longer be considered as static milestones of evolution, for they are themselves the dynamic systems by which the roads of evolution are trodden. As genes mutate and are reshuffled, and geographical races invade new ecological niches, advance and retreat, it is already possible on a map to mark out lines of gene-flow, as R. C. Stebbins has suggested from his researches on Californian newts. It may become possible to plot the areas of gene-complex alteration, as can to a certain extent already be done for the origin of cultivated plants such as wheat; but such maps will be continually changing, like the species themselves.

Nobody would have welcomed these developments of biological science more than Darwin himself, as a glance at the last few pages of 'The Origin of Species' will show. It is therefore appropriate to return to the problem with which this article began. As is now certain, species are not immutable but have undergone change, and many examples have been given above. Evolution can take place up to a point without the production of new species, but if this process continues the time must come when new species originate, and it is legitimate to ask whether modern research has revealed any evidence of this. The answer is that new species can be seen originating in nature here and now, and new species have been artificially produced in the laboratory.

Speciation takes place when, for various reasons, populations cease to breed with neighbouring populations and, under different conditions of selection, accumulate heritable variations by mutation and recombination of genes in different directions. As E. Mayr has shown, some form of biological isolation between portions of populations is a necessary condition for divergence leading to the formation of new species and higher groups.

Among the kinds of isolation that are chiefly responsible for the origination of species, geographical isolation is the most important; it involves physical barriers such as oceans, mountain ranges, or deserts which separate whole populations. Geographical races are the chief raw materials from which new species are formed, and it was the different finches on the different Galapagos Islands which first suggested to Darwin that evolution had occurred. Here, to various extents, geographical isolation has assisted the origination of a number of species.

A case in which geographical isolation may be expected to produce its effects at almost any moment now is provided by the gulls. These birds occupy a zone shaped like a ring round the North Pole and form what B. Rensch has called a chain of races. Starting with the British lesser black-backed gull, with its dark mantle and yellow legs, this is found to grade into the Scandinavian lesser black-backed gull, and, continuing in an easterly direction round the chain, this in turn grades into the Siberian Vega gull with its lighter mantle and dull flesh-coloured legs. The Siberian gull grades into the American herring gull, which in turn grades into the British herring gull, with its light mantle and pinkish legs. Although the British lesser black-backed gull may be regarded as belonging to the same species as all the other gulls in the chain to the east of it, when it is compared with the other end of the chain represented by the British herring gull the two may almost be regarded as separate species. Already they differ not only in colour but in habits, for the latter nests on cliffs and is dispersive in winter, whereas the former breeds inland on moors and is migratory in winter. If at any time the chain becomes severed by the erection of a sterility barrier at any point, either through inability to breed or through a rupture of the chain by local extinction of the gull population, the two British gulls will effectively have originated new species.

Geographical isolation is important for the origin of species of plants as well as of animals, but there is another form of isolation which appears to be restricted to plants and involves the sudden erection of sterility barriers between individuals in the same population as a result of changes in the chromosome mechanism. This is known as genetic isolation. When *Primula verticillata* is crossed with *Primula floribunda*, hybrid offspring are produced, but they are sterile because the chromosomes of one parent species are incompatible with those of the other, and the intricate machinery involved in the formation of germ-cells is thrown out of gear. Occasionally, however, the hybrid plant undergoes doubling of its chromosomes, a condition known as polyploidy, and when that has occurred the hybrid is able to breed with hybrids similar to itself because all the chromosomes have compatible partners, but it is sterile in respect of both parent species. Furthermore, the hybrid is not only true-breeding but is different in structure and in habit from each of its parent species. It therefore fulfils all the criteria of a species and has been called *Primula kewensis*. Many other new species have originated by intentional hybridization and accidental polyploidy in this way. Some of these artificially produced species have been found to be identical with, and to breed with, wild species, and this is the proof that this method of species-formation occurs in nature.

The Centenary of Evolution by Natural Selection

In conclusion, it may be said that during the hundred years that have elapsed since Darwin and Wallace first published their theory, the fact of organic evolution is now universally accepted and its mechanism has been formally explained.

The alternative to evolution is so naïve that it comes as a shock to realize that as recently as one hundred years ago, ideas such as called for the following questions could still be current: 'Do they really believe that at innumerable periods in the earth's history certain elemental atoms have been commanded suddenly to flash into living tissues? Do they believe that at each supposed act of creation one individual or many were produced? Were all the infinitely numerous kinds of animals and plants created as eggs or seeds, or as full grown? And in the case of mammals, were they created bearing the false marks of nourishment from the mother's womb?' Darwin might well allow himself to ask these questions, for he and Wallace had found the answer to them.

So soundly was the theory of evolution by natural selection grounded that research does nothing but confirm the links in its chain of evidence and the inferences to be drawn from them. Its field has extended from the explanation of the production of plants and animals to every aspect of the intellectual life of man, and it would be imprudent to doubt that its greatest triumph may yet lie in the highest aspect of that life. Some persons have attempted to discredit natural selection, on the grounds that being a destructive agent it cannot produce anything new or make the fit fitter. Such persons have only demonstrated that they have neither understood the problem nor studied 'The Origin of Species', in which Darwin carefully pointed out that 'several writers have misapprehended or objected to the term Natural Selection. Some have even imagined that natural selection induces variability, whereas it implies only the preservation of such variations as arise and are beneficial to the being under its conditions of life.' Variation produces novelties at random, but selection determines which are preserved. Only a genius could have discovered a key of such simplicity to so great a problem. Only ignorance, neglect of truth, or prejudice could actuate those who, in the present state of knowledge, without discovering new facts in the laboratory or in the field, seek to impugn the scientific evidence for evolution.

With such new formulations as may be required, the concept of evolution by natural selection continues and will continue to provide what Darwin hoped when he wrote in 1837 in his Notebook: 'My theory would give zest to recent and fossil comparative anatomy; it would lead to the study of instincts, heredity and mind . . . to closest examination of hybridity—to what circumstances favour crossings and what prevents it—and generation, causes of change in order to know what we have come from and to what we tend. This and direct examination of direct passages of structure of species, might lead to laws of change, which would then be the main object of study, to guide our speculations.'

With the same confidence as it accepts Copernicus's demonstration of the movement of the Earth around the Sun and Newton's formulation of the laws of this movement, science can now celebrate the centenary of the first general principle to be discovered applicable to the entire realm of living beings.

6 The Meaning of Taxonomic Statements

George Gaylord Simpson

IN THE TEACHING OF WHAT IS KNOWN ABOUT HUMAN BIOLOGICAL EVOLUTION *few things are more irritating to most competent lecturers than treelike models. You know the kind; they usually have "man" stuck at the top and other forms arranged beneath. Man is invariably the highest fruit, and the diagram implies that evolution was a process existing in the past in order to produce* him. *Somewhat paradoxically, as the late Franz Weidenreich, a noted human paleontologist, remarked, man on one of these tree diagrams is always shown right on the trunk or main line of descent, but usually that main line is devoid of significant ancestors, since all relevant fossils have been placed to one side or the other, where they dangle on limbs that go nowhere.*

The present selection cuts to the heart of this important matter and offers a view of systematics and taxonomy that fits harmoniously with present knowledge and theory. While its author approaches the problem with a broad technical and theoretical viewpoint, he is noted, among other things, as a designer of the modern classification of the mammals. He also has deep interest in human evolution to which he devoted several

SOURCE: Sherwood L. Washburn (ed.), *Classification and Human Evolution*, pp. 1–16, 22–30. Copyright 1963 by the Wenner-Gren Foundation for Anthropological Research, Inc. First published in 1963 by Aldine Publishing Company, Chicago, Illinois. Published with permission of the author and publisher.

The author (b. 1902) is Agassiz Profesor of Vertebrate Paleontology at the Museum of Comparative Zoology, Harvard University. Besides his technical publications in vertebrate paleontology, Dr. Simpson has written on general problems of classification and on evolution. In addition to his widely read *The Meaning of Evolution* (1949, available in paperback), he is the author of many books. Among the most recent are *Principles of Animal Taxonomy* (1961) and *Quantitative Zoology* (1961).

additional sections in the original version of this article. Here, however, we are concentrating on Simpson's contribution to the clarification of problems of classification in understanding human evolution. The student will be specially interested, therefore, in the various junctures at which Simpson makes it clear that alternative systems can be proposed with equal rational basis. The important thing, then, is not the specific taxonomic suggestions, but the principles on which useful taxonomy rests.

Introduction

Everyone who deals with evolution has occasion to use and to understand statements in the special language of taxonomy and classification. Communication is impeded by the facts that not all who use that language speak it fluently and that those fluent in it do not all speak the same dialect. In our conference on classification in relationship to human evolution we were talking this language much of the time. The main function of this contribution was to discuss the grammar and semantics of a reasonably standard dialect of the language. Centering the discussion on hominoid classification brings up and may clarify certain crucial points. This chapter is not, however, concerned with expressing opinions about human classification and evolution, but with discussing how such opinions are or should be expressed. I have recently covered theoretical aspects of animal taxonomy in some detail, and mere repetition of parts of that book is here avoided.

Classification, Terminology, and Nomenclature

Taxonomic language involves not only a very large number of different designative words (names, terms) but also several different *kinds* of designations. The things or concepts designated by these words, technically their referents,[1] are also of different kinds, and the meanings or semantic implications are likewise diverse. It is therefore essential that they be clearly distinguished. One way to do this is to consider the main operations involved in classification and the points or levels where special designations are required, as shown schematically in Figure 1.

The process starts with observation of the specimens in hand, the objective materials. The specimens studied and believed to be related in some biologically relevant way are a *sample*. If they are believed to represent a definite taxon (as determined at another level of inference), they constitute a *hypodigm*. Unequivocal designations of the specimens must refer to them as concrete, discrete objects; they are not designated by any name of the population or taxon to which they are supposed to belong. The ideal designation, practically universal in zoology but unfortunately

[1] A psycholinguistic term also useful in zoological taxonomy.

not in anthropology, is by a collection or repository symbol and a catalogue number uniquely associated with each specimen. This is one kind of designation, one set of names (symbols of some sort, not necessarily or usually in words), and may be called the N_1 naming set.

Observations and specimens, no matter how numerous, have no scientific significance purely per se. They acquire significance only when they are considered as representative of a larger group, or population, of possible observations or of individuals united by some common principle or relationship. The population may be abstract, for instance as symbolized in the equation for gravitation, applicable to a potentially infinite number of events but derived from a finite series of experimental observations. In zoological taxonomy the population is finite and concrete: a set

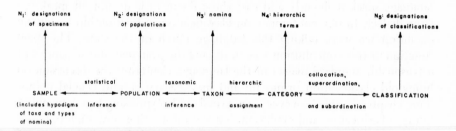

Figure 1 Schema of processes (arrows), name sets (N), and referents (capitals) in taxonomy. Vertical arrows all represent the process of designation or symbolization. The processes represented by horizontal arrows proceed logically from left to right, but in practice no one operation can be carried out without reference to the others. These arrows are therefore drawn pointing both ways.

of organisms existing (now or formerly) in nature. The existence and characteristics of that population are inferred from the sample drawn (we hope at random) from the population. The methods of inference are statistical by definition, which does not mean that any particular procedure of mathematical statistics is necessarily used although, of course, that is often appropriate and useful. A population is obviously not the same as the specimens actually studied, a sample drawn from the population.

At the next step in the process, all populations belong to taxa and all taxa are composed of populations. However, the two are not necessarily coextensive. It is often necessary to recognize and designate a local population that is a part of a taxon but does not in itself comprise a whole taxon. For some populations a different set of names or symbols, N_2, may therefore be required. Populations are in fact sometimes given distinct designations in zoological systematics, commonly by specification of their geographic location, but there is no established and uniform system. It may be sufficient to designate a population either as that from which a given sample was drawn (hence by extension of an N_1 designation) or as identical with that of a given taxon (hence by an N_3 designation).

A taxon is a group of real organisms recognized as a formal unit at any level of a hierarchic classification. A taxon is therefore a population, although the over-all population of one taxon may included many distinct populations of lesser scope. A taxon is created by inference that a population (itself statistically inferred from a sample which now becomes a hypodigm) meets a definition adopted for units in an author's classification. The set of designations for taxa, N_3 names, are those of formal, technical zoological nomenclature, e.g. *Homo,* the name of a taxon in primate classification. The word "name" is used in many different ways, both in the vernacular and in technical discussion, and this has engendered confusion. I propose that technical Neo-Linnaean names in the N_3 set be called *nomina* (singular, *nomen*). Vernacular names ("lion," "monkey," "Neanderthal man") are in the N_3 set if they designate taxa, but they are not nomina.

Each taxon is assigned to (considered as a member of) a category, which has a defined rank in hierarchic classification. A category is a set, the members of which are all the taxa placed at a given level in such a classification. Categories are distinct from taxa, do not have populations as members, and are not represented by samples. They have their own set of names, N_4, which are the relatively few terms applied to levels of the Neo-Linnaean system: basically phylum, class, order, family, genus, and species, with various combinations in super-, sub-, and infra-, and occasionally such additional terms as cohort or tribe.

Finally the various taxa of assigned categorical rank are collocated, superordinated, and subordinated among themselves and so form a hierarchic classification. This is done in terms of the N_3 (nomina) and N_4 (hierarchic terms) names. The added implications are conveyed less by nomenclatural than by topological means, primarily by arrangement and not consistently by verbal or related symbolization. Designations of classifications, N_5, are normally bibliographic references to their authors and places of publication.

What, now, are the meanings or implications of the various sets of designations? N_1 designations refer to particular objects. They imply only that a given specimen exists. They assure that when the same designation is used, the same object is meant. N_2 and N_3 designations both refer to groups that are considered to be populations related in some way. An author using such designations must make clear, explicitly or implicitly, the kind of relationship he has in mind. In modern zoology unless some other usage is definitely stated, it is generally understood that the relationship is genetic, that is, that it reflects evolutionary relationships. Concepts of what constitutes evolutionary relationships, how they are to be determined, and how reflected in classification become difficult and complex, but that is a different point.

Besides the implication that a population, usually genetic in relationship, is designated, nomina, N_3 names, further imply that the unit designated is given a definite rank in classification, that it is associated with an N_4 term. Under the International Code the forms of some nomina reflect the categorical rank of the corresponding taxa. For example, nomina ending in -idae (e.g. Hominidae) name families, and italicized, capitalized single words (e.g. *Homo*) name genera.

Most nomina, however, lack implications as to superordination, and *none have any implications beyond those mentioned*. For instance, nomina have no implications as to relationships among taxa at the same categorical level (e.g. *Homo* and *Tarsius*) or among taxa at any levels with etymologically distinct names (e.g. *Gorilla* and Pongidae). Further implications, which may be numerous and intricate as will be illustrated later, are inherent in the arrangement of nomina in a classification and not in the nomina themselves.

Discussion at the conference repeatedly illustrated the need for employing and distinguishing the different naming sets. The ambiguity and clumsiness of usual references to particular specimens and populations were especially evident. For example no clear and simple way was found for designating the various specimens from Olduvai Bed I that are believed not to belong to the taxon called *Zinjanthropus boisei* by Leakey. Presumably they will eventually be placed in taxa with distinct nomina (in the N_3 set), but that will not solve the problem of referring to the specimens themselves or to the populations inferred from them without ambiguity and without prejudice as to their taxonomic interpretation. As another example, no one maintains that *Telanthropus* is a valid taxon at the generic level, but no way has been found to refer to the specimens in question except as *Telanthropus,* an N_3 designation that necessarily implies a taxonomic conclusion agreed to be incorrect.

It must be emphasized that one of the greatest linguistic needs in this field is for clear, uniform, and distinct sets of N_1 and N_2 designations, applied to specimens and to local populations as distinct from taxa. Just what form such designations should take is a matter for proposal and agreement among those directly concerned with the specimens and their interpretation. It suffices here to stress that they *must not* have the form of Neo-Linnaean nomina. (The catalogue now being compiled by Oakley and Campbell may opportunely provide designations for specimens of fossil Hominidae.)

The Chaos of Anthropological Nomenclature

Men and all recent and fossil organisms pertinent to their affinities are animals, and the appropriate language for discussing their classification and relationships is that of animal taxonomy. When anthropologists have special purposes for which zoological taxonomic language is not appropriate, they should devise a separate language that does not duplicate any of the functions of this one and that does not permit confusion with its forms. There is, I believe, no reason for use of an additional language when what is being discussed is in fact the taxonomy of organisms. This language has been developed over a period of hundreds of years by cumulative experience and thought and has been thoroughly tested in nonanthropological use. It is admittedly imperfect, but for its purpose it is the best instrument available. Its imperfections call rather for improvement than for replacement. The most important needed improvement, with particular reference to anthropology, is that all those who use it should speak it well and in accordance with the best established current usages.

It is notorious that hominid nomenclature, particularly, has become chaotic. It is ironical that some of those who have most complained of the chaos have been leading contributors to it. A recent proposal that an international commission be formed to deal with the chaos refuses to recognize the appropriate code and the appropriate commission already set up. The author then proceeds to compound the confusion that he condemns.

Insofar as the chaos is merely formal or grammatical, it could be cleared up by knowledge of and adherence to the International Code of Zoological Nomenclature, supplemented, if necessary, by whatever action might be proposed to and endorsed by the International Commission for Zoological Nomenclature. Much of the complexity and lack of agreement in nomenclature in this field does not, however, stem from ignorance or flouting of formal procedures but from differences of opinion that cannot be settled by rule or fiat. For example, when Leakey inferred from an Olduvai specimen (which he made a hypodigm) the existence of a taxon that he called *Zinjanthropus boisei* he was using correct taxonomic grammar to express the opinion that the taxon was distinct at both specific and generic categorical levels from any previously named. In equally grammatical expression of other opinions many other nomina, such as *Paranthropus boisei, Australopithecus robustus boisei,* or *Homo africanus boisei,* might have been proposed and might now be used. Or the specimen might have been and might now be referred to (or added to the hypodigm of) some previously named taxon such as *Paranthropus crassidens.* Any of those alternatives accord equally with the Code and would have equal status before the Commission. Decision among them is a zoological, not a nomenclatural or linguistic question, and it will be made by an eventual consensus of zoologists qualified in this special field.

Insofar as the chaos is due to faulty linguistics rather than to zoological disagreements, it stems either from ignorance or from refusal to follow rules and usages. This must be almost the only field of science in which those who do not know and follow the established norms have so frequently had the termerity and opportunity to publish research that is, in this respect, incompetent.

An overt reason sometimes given for refusal to follow known nomenclatural norms is that some nomen is, in the opinion of a particular author, inappropriate. For example, some choose to rename *Australopithecus* as *Australanthropus*, thus adding another objective synonym to the chaos, on the grounds that the Greek *anthropos* more nearly expresses their opinion as to the affinities of the genus than does *pithekos*. The argument is completely irrelevant. *Australopithecus* does not mean "southern ape." Its meaning (defined by its referent) is simply the taxon to which the nomen was first attached and to which it was the first nomen attached. *Palaeolumbricus* or *Jitu* would have served just as well. The generic nomen does not, in itself, express any opinion as to the affinities of the taxon, and if nomina were changed in accord with every shade of opinion on affinites the chaos would be even worse than it is.[2]

Another reason for the chaos is the previously mentioned failure to develop and use consistently different designations for specimens, populations, and taxa, that is, distinct N_1, N_2, and N_3 name sets. A truly eminent anthropologist insisted on using the (N_3) nomen *Sinanthropus pekinensis* for specimens and a population although he concluded that this nomen does not designate a *taxon* specifically distinct from *Pithecanthropus erectus* or indeed from *Homo sapiens*. The example is far from unique.

Probably no one has ever admitted this, but it seems almost obvious that nomina (N_3) have sometimes been given to single specimens just to emphasize the importance of a discovery that could and should have been designated merely by a catalogue number (N_1). Of course no two specimens are alike, and it is always possible to fulfill the formal requirement that ostensible definition of a taxon must accompany proposal of a nomen. However, and again I would say obviously, the "definition" has often been only a description of an individual "type" with no regard for or even apparent consciousness of the fact that taxa are *populations*. This is not just a matter of exaggerating the taxonomic difference between specimens. It is a much more fundamental misunderstanding of what taxonomy is all about, of what nomina actually name. It is a relapse into pre-evolutionary typology, from which (I must confess) even the non-anthropological zoologists have not yet entirely freed themselves.

[2] It is true that when the system was being developed, from 200 to 250 years ago, the then relatively few nomina were usually intended to be etymologically descriptive. The experience of two centuries has, however, conclusively demonstrated that as a general principle this is absolutely unworkable. Except for the occasional mnemonic value, it is unfortunate that nomina do often have ostensible etymological meanings in addition to their real, taxonomic meanings.

Nomina have types, but not in the old typological sense. The types are not the referents of the N_3 nomina but are among the referents of N_1 designations. The referents of nomina are taxa—certain kinds of populations.

It is of course also true that the significance of differences between any two specimens has almost invariably come to be enormously exaggerated by one authority or another in this field. Here the fault is not so much lack of taxonomic grammar as lack of taxonomic common sense or experience. Many fossil hominids have been described and named by workers with no other experience in taxonomy. They have inevitably lacked the sense of balance and the interpretive skill of zoologists who have worked extensively on larger groups of animals. It must, however, be sadly noted that even broadly equipped zoologists often seem to lose their judgment if they work on hominids. Here factors of prestige, of personal involvement, of emotional investment rarely fail to affect the fully human scientist, although they hardly trouble the workers on, say, angleworms or dung beetles.

It is not really my intention to read an admonitory sermon to the anthropologists. You are all well aware of these shortcomings—in the work of others. I must pass on to matters more positive in value.

Species and Genera

The undue proliferation of specific and generic nomina is in part a semantic problem. The proposal of such nomina is rarely accompanied by an appropriate definition of the categories (as distinct from the taxa) involved, but ascribing specific or generic status to slightly variant specimens can be rationalized only on a typological basis. Whether consciously or not, taxa are evidently being defined as morphological types and statistical-taxonomic inferences from hypodigm to population to taxon (see Fig. 1) are being omitted. But in modern biology taxa are populations and the following two nonconflicting definitions of the species are widely accepted:

Species are groups of actually or potentially interbreeding populations, which are reproductively isolated from other such groups.

An evolutionary species is a lineage (an ancestral-descendant sequence of populations) evolving separately from others and with its own unitary evolutionary role and tendencies.

The naming of a species either should imply that the taxon is believed to correspond with one or both of those definitions or should be accompanied by the author's own equally clear alternative definition.

Evidence that the definition is met is largely morphological in most cases, especially for fossils. The most widely available and acceptable evidence is demonstration of a sufficient level of statistical confidence that a discontinuity exists *not* between specimens in hand but *between the populations inferred from those specimens.* The import of such evidence and the semantic implication of the word "species" are that populations placed in separate species are either

(1) in separate lineages (contemporaneous or not) between which significant interbreeding does not occur, or

(2) at successive stages in one lineage but with intervening evolutionary change of such magnitude that populations differ about as much as do contemporaneous species.

In dealing with the incomplete fossil record the information at hand commonly cannot establish the original presence or absence of a discontinuity. Allowance must be made for probabilities that further discovery will confirm or confute the existence of an ostensible discontinuity. Those probabilities depend on various circumstances. If populations are approximately contemporaneous, only moderately distinctive, and separated by a large geographic area from which no comparable specimens are known, there is considerable possibility that discovery of intervening populations would eliminate discontinuity. That is, for example, the situation regarding the original hypodigms of *Pithecanthropus erectus* and *Atlanthropus mauritanicus.* In my opinion the possibility that the Trinil population and the Ternifine population belong to the same species is such that different specific (a fortiori, generic) nomina are not justified at present.

If, on the other hand, populations being compared are of markedly different ages, decision to give them different specific nomina should depend on judgment whether such nomina would be justified if it turned out that they belong in successive segments of the same lineage. That would apply, for example, to the Mauer population as compared with the late Pleistocene European neanderthaloid population, and I should think would justify different specific nomina in this example.[3] Still a third situation arises when samples indicate populations that were approximately contemporaneous and living in the same region (synchronous and sympatric) as may be true, at least in part, for the Kromdrai, Swartkrans, Makapan, and Sterkfontein populations. In such cases allowance hardly has to be made for possible discoveries of populations living at other times and in different places. The degree of statistical confidence generated by the samples actually in hand may be taken as definitive of the probability of an original discontinuity, for instance between *Australopithecus africanus* and *A. robustus.*

The category genus is necessarily more arbitrary and less precise in definition than the species. A genus is a group of species believed to be

---

[3] I am not suggesting what those nomina should be. Among many other possibilities they might be *Homo heidelbergensis* and *Homo neanderthalensis,* or *Homo erectus* and *Homo sapiens.*

more closely related among themselves than to any species placed in other genera. Pertinent morphological evidence is provided when a species differs less from another in the same genus than from any in another genus. When in fact only one species of a genus is known, that criterion is not available, and judgment may be based on differences comparable to those between accepted genera in the same general zoological group. There is no absolute criterion for the degree of difference to be called generic, and it is particularly here that experience and common sense are required.

It must be kept in mind that a genus is a *different* category from a species and that it is in principle a *group* of species. Much of the chaos in anthropological nomenclature has arisen from giving a different generic nomen to every supposed species, even some clearly not meriting specific rank. In effect no semantic distinction has been made between genus and species, and indeed the number of proposed generic nomina for hominids is much greater than the number of validly definable species. Monotypic genera are justified when, and only when, a single, isolated known species is so distinctive that the probability is that it belongs to a generic group of otherwise unknown ancestral, collateral, or descendent species. No one can reasonably doubt that this is true, for example, of *Oreopithecus bambolii* and that in this case the (at present) monotypic genus is justified. It is, however, hard to see how the application of more than one generic name to the various presently known australopithecine populations can possibly be justified, whatever the specific status of those populations may be.

Phylogeny and Resemblance

As most biologists understand modern taxonomic language, its implications are primarily evolutionary, but there is some persisting confusion even among professional taxonomists. It is not possible for classification directly to *express*, in all detail, opinions either as to phylogenetic relationships or as to degrees of resemblance. As a rule with important exceptions, degrees of resemblance tend to be correlated with degrees of evolutionary affinity. Resemblance provides important, but *not the only*, evidence of affinity. Classification can be made consistent with, even though not directly or fully expressive of, evolutionary affinity, and its language then has appropriate and understandable genetic implications. Classification cannot, at least in some cases, be made fully consistent with resemblance, and any implications as to resemblance are secondary and not necessarily reliable. These relationships can be explored by consideration of several hypothetical models or examples, set up so as to be simplified parallels of real problems in the use of taxonomic language to discuss human origins and relationships.

Classification and taxonomic discussion of related but distinct contemporaneous groups, such as the living apes and living men, involves a pattern of evolutionary divergence. That will first be discussed by means of a model. Discovery of related fossils almost always complicates the picture by revealing other groups divergent from both of those primarily concerned. It may, however, also reveal forms that are ancestral or that are close enough to the ancestry to strengthen inferences about the common ancestor and the course of evolution in the diverging lineages. In general the characters of two contemporaneous groups as compared with their common ancestry will tend to fall into the following classes, exemplified by characters of recent Pongidae and Homidae:

A. Ancestral characters retained in both descendent groups. E.g. absence of external tail, pentadactylism, dental formula.
B. Ancestral characters retained in the first descendent group but divergently evolved in the second. E.g. quadrupedalism, grasping pes.
C. Ancestral characters retained in the second but divergent in the first group. E.g. undifferentiated lower premolars.
D. Characters divergently specialized in both. E.g. brachiation versus bipedalism.
E. Characters progressive but parallel in both. E.g. increase in average body size.
F. Convergent characters. I know of none between pongids and hominids, a fact which (if it is a fact) greatly simplifies judgment as to their affinities.

Different numbers of characters will fall into different categories. For instance in pongid-hominid comparison there are certainly many more A characters than any others and more B than C characters. (The given example of a C character is dubious.) Many characters do not simply and absolutely fall into one category or other. Retention of ancestral characters is usually relative and not absolute; some changes generally occur and "retained" usually means only "less changed." In constructing the simplest possible model on this basis, further simplifying postulates are that characters evolve at constant rates and that characters in the same group (e.g. D or E) evolve at the same rates. Those postulates are certainly never true in real phylogenies, and more realistic but also much more complicated models can be constructed by taking varying rates of evolution into account. The simplest possible limiting case, although unrealistic in detail, nevertheless more clearly illustrates valid and pertinent matters of principle. Such a model, analogous to pongid-hominid divergence, is illustrated in Fig. 2. Numbers preceding the category designations symbolize relative numbers of characters in the corresponding categories. Exponents symbolize progressive change: a-b-c, or in a different direction x-y-z. It is assumed that in this example there are no F (convergent) characters. Roman numerals represent taxa: IV and V the two contemporaneous groups being compared, and I their common ancestry, ancestral to IV through II and to V through III.

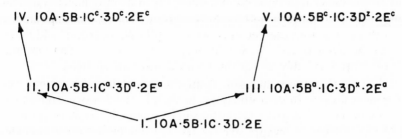

IV. $10A \cdot 5B \cdot 1C^c \cdot 3D^c \cdot 2E^c$ V. $10A \cdot 5B^c \cdot 1C \cdot 3D^z \cdot 2E^c$

II. $10A \cdot 5B \cdot 1C^a \cdot 3D^a \cdot 2E^a$ III. $10A \cdot 5B^a \cdot 1C \cdot 3D^x \cdot 2E^a$

I. $10A \cdot 5B \cdot 1C \cdot 3D \cdot 2E$

Figure 2 A model of simple evolutionary divergence. Symbols are explained in the text.

From such data a comparison matrix can be formed. For present purposes a simple and sufficient method is to tabulate step differences between taxa. Change from C to C^a, for instance, is one step and from C^a to C^c is two more. These are multiplied by the number of characters in the category, 1 for C characters. The matrix for the model in Fig. 2 is given in Table 1. In this form of comparison, the smaller the number the greater the similarity. In this model I and II are most and IV and V least alike.

Let us suppose now that classification were to be based *entirely* on degrees of resemblance, as has been proposed by some taxonomists, and that classificatory language was therefore understood to be directly and solely expressive of resemblance. In building up higher taxa one would of

Table 1 COMPARISON MATRIX FOR DATA OF THE MODEL IN FIG. 2

	I	*II*	*III*	*IV*	*V*
I	0	6	9	18	29
II	6	0	12	12	32
III	9	12	0	24	19
IV	18	12	24	0	36
V	29	32	19	36	0

course start by uniting I and II. If I and II are species, they would be placed in one genus; if genera, in one family. The maximum difference within the higher taxon would be 6. If no greater difference were allowed, all other lower taxa, III, IV, and V, would have to be placed in separate, monotypic higher taxa, an arrangement with nearly minimal significance, indicating no more than the close resemblance of I and II. If a difference of 12 were allowed in the higher taxon, II would be united with I and II, but IV should now also go with II, from which its difference is also 12. However, a taxon including IV and I would have to allow a difference of 18 and one including IV and III a difference of 24. But now V must also be added, for its difference from III is only 19.

Thus *all* the lower taxa must go in a single taxon of next higher rank, an arrangement that indicates nothing of resemblances or relationships among any of those taxa. Insertion, or in actual examples discovery, of additional taxa, say between II and IV, would only compound the difficulties and lead still more inevitably to equally unsatisfactory alternatives.

I believe that the conclusion from the model is quite general for analogous real cases. In such situations the use of classificatory language as direct expression of degrees of resemblance commonly tends to produce one of two extremely inexpressive results: (1) one higher taxon includes the two most similar lower taxa and all other higher taxa are monotypic; or (2) one higher taxon includes all the lower taxa, no matter how numerous.[4]

Now let us agree that classificatory language is to have primarily evolutionary significance. For the moment degrees of resemblance need not be considered at all. It is clear from consideration of characters in categories B, C, and D that II can be ancestral to IV but not to III or V, and that III can be ancestral to V but not to II or IV. In actual instances the conclusions are neither so simple nor so obvious, but probabilities are readily established by the same categories of evidence. On this basis, II and IV can be placed in one higher taxon and III and V in another of the same categorical rank. That arrangement expresses the opinion, postulated as true in the model, that II and IV are phylogenetically related to each other and that III and V are also related in more or less the same way and degree. The arrangement is also consistent with but does not express the opinion, also postulated as true, that II is ancestral to IV and III to V.

In completion of this arrangement there are two alternatives as regards I. It could be placed in a third higher taxon ancestral to both of the two already formed, or it could be placed in the same higher taxon as II and IV, because it is phylogenetically closer to II than to III. Degree of resemblance here enters in as evidence for the latter inference.

Those are not the only classifications that would be consistent with the postulated evolutionary history. It would also be consistent to put I, II, and III in one higher taxon and IV and V in two others, I, II, III, and IV in one and V in another. The implications on affinity would be somewhat different in each case but not conflicting: all are consistent with the postulates of the model. Choice would depend in part on what implications one wanted especially to bring out, since not all can be expressed in one classification. It would also depend on other considerations such as not changing previous classifications unnecessarily and

---

[4] Even extremists who would classify by resemblance *only*, usually admit that the biological significance of such classification may be confused by differential rates of evolution and by convergence. Note that in our simplified model both of those admitted sources of confusion have been eliminated by postulation, and that biologically significant classification from the numerical data alone still is impossible.

conveying as much significant information as possible. (The last alternative mentioned above is the least informative.)

The model also illustrates the tendency, which is open to exception, for degree of resemblance to correlate with nearness of common ancestry. II and III are nearer their common ancestry than are IV and V, and they resemble each other more closely. The same is true of III and IV or of II and V as against IV and V. Such relationships are not directly implicit in the classification, but they are important in arriving at the judgments of affinity that are implicit in it.

Another important point illustrated in the model is that II and III resemble each other much more closely than III resembles its descendent V. It is realistic to expect an early—say Miocene—ancestor of *Homo* to be more like an ancestral ape than like modern man. It is unrealistic to expect the Miocene ancestors of either (or both) groups *necessarily* to have any of the specialized features that are diagnostic between *recent* members of the two families.

Taxonomic Language: Hominidae as Example

The Hominidae may be taken as an example of different principles (e.g. typological versus evolutionary) of classification and of the classificatory implications of different interpretations of data. For purposes of exemplification the data are postulated to be as in Figure 3*A*. Postulated ranges of variation of known specimens are indicated by the stippled areas, and in order to simplify the subsequent diagrams parts of those ranges are labeled A-F. X is a postulated individual specimen to be classified; it does not represent a specimen actually known. This arrangement is not presented as a realistic summary of what is, in fact, known. It is greatly simplified in several respects. Some known fossils do not fit clearly into the stippled areas, and some parts of those areas are not clearly represented by known fossils. Structure does not, in fact, follow a linear, one-dimensional scale and could be realistically indicated only by a (quite impractical) *n*-dimensional scale. Nevertheless this is the general *kind* of pattern, however grossly oversimplified, that the data do present.

Typological interpretation, Figure 3*B*, takes into account morphology only. It ignores temporal sequence and makes no phylogenetic interpretations. It abstracts an arbitrary number of fixed, distinctive types in the morphogenetic field and exercises subjective judgment as to whether a given, concrete specimen belongs to one type or another. Types may be hierarchically divided into sub-types, but variation is then ignored in the sub-types, and genetical or evolutionary considerations do not enter in at any categorical level. As previously mentioned, this basis for classification has been largely abandoned in modern taxonomy. Nevertheless hominid classification started out on this basis, and even some of the

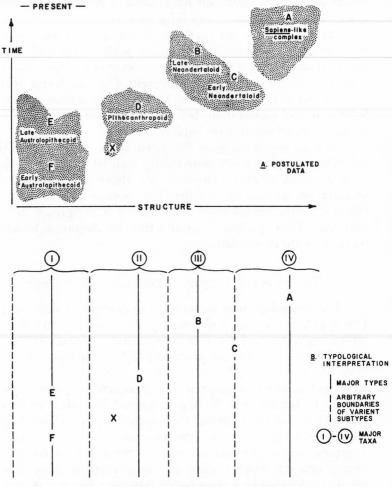

Figure 3 Postulated data (simplified and generalized) and three possible tax-

most recent work in that field is at least covertly typological. The classificatory and nomenclatural expression of the typological arrangement in the diagram could take several forms, depending on the categorical level assigned to differences between types, for example:

I	*Homo africanus*	*Australopithecus africanus*
II	*Homo erectus*	*Pithecanthropus erectus*
III	*Homo neanderthalensis*	*Homo neanderthalensis*
IV	*Homo sapiens*	*Homo sapiens*

Figures 3C and D represent two possible kinds of phylogenetic interpretations of the same postulated data. Here temporal and genetic relationships are taken into account, and classification is based in principle

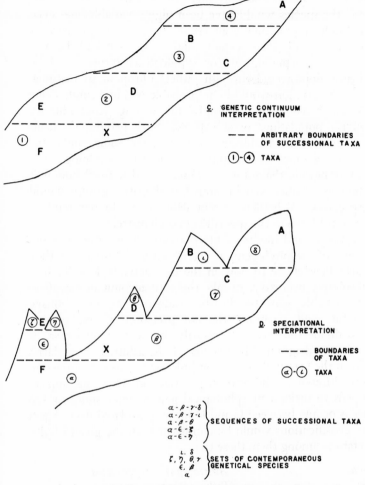

onomic interpretations of known hominidae. Further explanation in text.

on inferences as to evolutionary affinity. The differences between Figures 3C and D do not involve any difference in taxonomic principle but only in opinion as to probable evolutionary relationships. Both kinds of interpretation (with many differences in detail as to the particular placing of actual specimens) are currently supported by different students. Choice between them will depend on the accumulation of more data, and the ultimate arrangement will probably not be entirely of either kind in a clear-cut way but will involve elements of both. It will certainly be more complex than either of my diagrams.

Figure 3C diagrammatically represents the interpretation that hominids have been represented by only one interbreeding population since the early Pleistocene, at least. On this interpretation there is only one lineage or evolutionary species and only one genetical species at any one time. In that case, the species would have been highly variable, and even more so during much of past time than *Homo sapiens* is at present. At some time around the middle Pleistocene it might have varied all the way from what in purely morphological (or typological) terms could be called marginal australopithecoid through pithecanthropoid to marginal neanderthaloid. Such variation would be improbable within a single deme or local population. It would be less improbable among geographically separate (allopatric) populations or sub-species. Such geographic semi-isolates would of course be variable in themselves, but some might, for instance, vary about a more australopithecoid modal morphology and others about a more neanderthaloid mode. Discovery that fossil hominids fall into such modally distinct, synchronous but allopatric groups would favor this interpretation. Whether current data do or do not tend to follow such a pattern I leave to the specialists in such matters.

The over-all ranges and modes of morphology change greatly from earlier to later parts of the phylogeny as postulated in Figure 3C, as they also do from early Pleistocene to now in the data actually known. It is useful, if not absolutely necessary, to take this into account in classification. The only possible way to do this (adhering to evolutionary taxonomic principles and accepting the interpretation of one genetic continuum) is to divide the lineage arbitrarily into successional taxa, as also exemplified in the diagram. The placing of the arbitrary boundaries and the ranks given the taxa will depend on judgment as to categorization of morphological differences and also, in practice, on where incomplete knowledge happens to make a morphological gap coincide more or less with a time line, as occurs between C and D in my postulated data. Again several different classifications would be consistent with the given phylogenetic interpretation, among them these two:

1. *Homo africanus*   *Australopithecus africanus*
2. *Homo erectus*   *Pithecanthropus erectus*
3. *Homo neanderthalensis* *Homo neanderthalensis*
4. *Homo sapiens*   *Homo sapiens*

The same nomina are used here as in the typological interpretation, but the diagrams show that their meanings are different in the two. That is further shown by the fact that specimen X here falls into *africanus* but in Figure 3B into *erectus*.

Figure 3D represents an interpretation with speciation occurring within the Pleistocene hominid group so that there is not a single lineage but successive branching giving rise to two or more distinct, contemporaneous species, of which only one of the last to arise has survived. The sets of contemporaneous species are separated by natural gaps (noninterbreeding) are are not arbitrary. Successive species in a lineage like α-β-γ-δ are arbitrary as regards that lineage, alone, but in the whole pattern their boundaries are also fixed by the (hypothetically) nonarbitrary points of splitting of the lineage into two species. The probability of this kind of pattern would be supported by discovery of contemporaneous (synchronous) populations with overlapping geographic distribution (sympatric) that did not intergrade and hence were probably not interbreeding significantly. (The existence of two or more distinct species does not, however, depend on their being sympatric.) Again I leave to the appropriate specialists whether data actually in hand do support such an interpretation.

One of several possible nomenclatures consistent with this pattern would be:

ζ *Australopithecus robustus*
η *Australopithecus africanus*
θ *Pithecanthropus erectus*
ι *Homo neanderthalensis*
δ *Homo sapiens*

It is not clear what actual specimens might fall into the hypothetical species a, β, γ, and ϵ, and I therefore suggest no nomenclature for them. It is clear, in any event, that some, at least, of the same nomina as used under the interpretations in Figure 3B and C are also applicable in D but again have different significance and contents. Specimen X, for example, is now neither in *africanus* nor in *erectus* but in unnamed hypothetical species β.

If identical nomina in Figures 3C and D referred to the same populations, there would be no ambiguity. Unfortunately, however, this is not likely to be the case. Population C in Figure 3C would probably be placed in the same taxon and referred to by the same specific nomen as population B. In Figure 3D population C would probably be placed in a different taxon and given a different nomen from population B. The ambiguity resides not in the taxonomic system but in the imperfection of our data and lack of agreement in their zoological interpretation. When such ambiguity persists, clarity demands that an author specify the populations included in his taxa, for example by adequate designation of their hypodigms. In the present example a possible clarifying device (if it accorded with an accepted zoological interpretation) would be to place populations B and C in separate subspecies. The placing of those subspecies in species would then clearly show different placing of the corresponding populations by different students.

AFFINITIES AND CLASSIFICATION OF THE HOMINOIDEA

Within the last few years data for classification of the hominoids have been greatly enriched in breadth and depth: discovery of new pertinent fossils; continued anatomical investigation; studies of serology, hemoglobins, and chromosomes; more detailed behavioral observations of nonhuman hominoids, particularly under natural conditions. Since almost every conceivable view (along with some rather inconceivable ones) has been upheld at one time or another, this new information is useful not so much in giving us a new pattern of affinities as in enabling us to choose more surely among the many already proposed and to gain more confidence in various points of detail. Without reviewing evidence or arguments, in this note I shall briefly state how the probabilities look to me now. I shall also briefly sketch some of the main, different family-group (superfamily, family, subfamily) classifications that would be consistent with those probabilities and indicate my own preference among them.

Gibbons On fossil evidence, the gibbon ancestry was probably distinct from that of other apes when hominoids first appear in the fossil record, early Oligocene, and was certainly so in the Miocene. Recent karyological and serological evidence, presented by Klinger and by Goodman, respectively, also indicates strong divergence of living gibbons from all other living hominoids. No evidence suggests special affinities with orangs, on one hand, or with the chimpanzee-gorilla group on the other. Special affinity with *Homo* is out of the question. It is probable that these three groups did not diverge among themselves until after the gibbon ancestry had already split off. On the other hand, the gibbons have not diverged radically from other apes either morphologically or adaptively. What is distinctive in their facies is largely due to their having remained smaller than other hominoids and to their specialized locomotion, which in turn seems to require the first peculiarity. Miocene fossils (demonstrated to members of the 1962 conference by Professor Zapfe in Vienna) suggest that the locomotory specialization evolved comparatively late. Although gibbons, strictly speaking, and siamangs are usually placed in different genera, they are manifestly very closely related and I now prefer to place them all in *Hylobates*.

Orangs Morphologically and to some extent also adaptively *Pongo* is not markedly unlike the living chimpanzees and, to less extent, gorillas. This has long, although not quite unanimously, been considered evidence of rather close relationship. Schultz, whose knowledge of orangs is unexcelled, continued to uphold that view in the conference. On the other hand, karyological (Klinger) and serological (Goodman) evidence seems to separate *Pongo* from *Pan* (and *Gorilla*) as sharply as *Hylobates*. Fossil orangs have not been identified before the Pleistocene, but there is no evident reason why the ancestry of *Pongo* may not be found near that of *Pan* in the dryopithecine complex. On balance, it still seems *Pongo* is especially related to the African apes, but that the split was far enough back to permit considerable, more or less clandestine molecular and chromosomal divergence. Morphological divergence has been less, probably because of retention of somewhat similar adaptation.

Gigantopithecus When known only from isolated molars, this Chinese Pleistocene genus was claimed to be a hominid. Later finds of lower jaws and dentitions, not yet adequately described as far as I know, seem clearly to exclude it from the Hominidae. It seems to be a terminal specialization not very close to any living form. During the 1962 conference Leakey suggested special affinity with *Pongo*, and that is a possibility. On present very inadequate evidence I would, however, prefer to place it only as Pongidae *incertae sedis*, and I omit it from further consideration.

African Apes A consensus has always considered gorillas and chimpanzees as especially and rather closely related, and all the recent evidence, including that of serology and karyology, confirms that view. They are of course sharply distinct species, at a point of divergence where experienced taxonomists may well waver between giving only specific or also generic weight to that divergence. Merely listing characters that demonstrate the self-evident fact of their distinctness does not necessarily suffice to maintain the time-honored generic separation, and at present I prefer to consider both chimpanzees and gorillas as species of *Pan*. Whether *P. paniscus* is a valid third species, closer to *P. troglodytes* than to *P. gorilla*, is still moot. Placing all the African apes in *Pan* permits classification to express the clear fact that they are much more closely related to each other than to any species of other genera, and henceforth I shall use the nomen *Pan* in this sense.

It has long been the virtually universal opinion that *Pan* is anatomically and adaptively rather close first to *Pongo* and then to *Hylobates*. Recent studies, while also confirming that these are quite distinct groups well separated at a generic level, at least, agree with the old conclusion that the three genera belong together in a natural taxon at some higher level. Nevertheless, as noted above, newer subanatomical evidence suggests that separation of the ancestors of the three genera within that higher taxon is ancient. The situation is complicated only by comparisons with the Hominidae, summarized below.

No explicit and particular connection of *Pan* with a Tertiary ancestry has yet been found or, at least, clearly recognized. It is, however, probable that in a general sense the ancestry occurred somewhere in known or unknown members of what is here called the dryopithecine complex.

The Dryopithecine Complex The Miocene and Pliocene of Africa, Europe, and Asia have produced many specimens clearly apelike and distinct from contemporaneous closer relatives of *Hylobates* (notably *Pliopithecus* and the closely allied, perhaps not generically distinct, *Limnopithecus*). They are otherwise highly diverse and clearly represent a greater number of lineages than the four or perhaps five recent species that might possibly have arisen from this complex (*Pongo pygmaens, Pan troglodytes,* perhaps *Pan paniscus, Pan gorilla,* and *Homo sapiens*). Many or most of the dryopithecine-complex lineages have therefore become extinct, and it is the opposite of surprising to find that some of them (e.g. *Proconsul*) have combinations of characters not found in taxa as diagnosed primarily on the basis of living species.

With the sole exception of *Proconsul,* the members of this complex are known only from very incomplete remains, largely single teeth or unassociated upper and lower jaws with partial dentitions. Their classification and nomenclature are unsatisfactory and almost chaotic within the group. This situation could surely be improved by a revision even of the already known fragments, and I consider such revision plus a really systematic search for better specimens the greatest desideratum of primate paleontology at present. Some of these forms, such as *Dryopithecus* itself, may be rather near the ancestry of the living great apes, *Pan* and perhaps also *Pongo.* Others, such as *Ramapithecus,* and possibly *Kenyapithecus,* may belong near the ancestry of *Homo.* Still others, as already mentioned, are doubtless more or less terminal in lineages not close to any living forms. If or when more probable affinities with later groups are established, it should be possible to place some of the dryopithecine-complex species and genera in taxa, e.g. in subfamilies, currently based primarily on living species. It is, however, my opinion that the present unsatisfactory stage of study and incompleteness of sampling do not establish such connections at a sufficient level of probability.

Oreopithecus Elsewhere in this chapter I have sufficiently expressed the opinion that *Oreopithecus* probably represents a lineage separate from near the base of hominoid differentiation, with limited parallelism with the Hominidae, but culminating in an extinct terminal form adaptively very unlike either the great apes or any hominids.

Australopithecus Despite earlier polemics, it is now perfectly clear that among other sufficiently known genera *Australopithecus* (*sensu lato,* including *Paranthropus* and *Zinjanthropus*) is more closely allied to *Homo.* Late *Australopithecus,* at least, is almost certainly contemporaneous with early *Homo* (including *Pithecanthropus,* etc.) and hence not ancestral to it. Present evidence does not exclude, and may be taken to favor, the possibility that early *Australopithecus,* or an unknown genus close to it, was such a direct ancestor. Although *Australopithecus* greatly strengthens the opinion that *Homo* had an apelike ancestor in common with the living great apes, it does not at present seem to me to give additional clear evidence as to precisely which apes, among living forms or the dryopithecine complex, are most nearly related to *Homo.*

Homo Since the 19th century it has been the usual, although by no means the universal, opinion that among living mammals *Homo* is most closely allied to *Pan*. That conclusion, based originally on classical anatomical grounds, is strongly supported by all the new evidence, anatomical, karyological, biochemical, and behavioral, presented at recent conferences. It now seems to me so probable that other alternatives need no longer be seriously considered. It should, however, be strongly emphasized that *Homo* represents an anatomical and adaptive complex very radically different from that of any other known animal and (with the partial exception of *Homo's* close ally *Australopithecus*) differing far more from other living or adequately known fossil hominoids than they differ among themselves. Seemingly contradictory evidence (e.g. that of the haemoglobins as reported by Zuckerkandl) indicates merely that in *certain* characters *Homo* and its allies retain ancestral resemblances and that *these* are not the characters involved in their otherwise radical divergence—a common and indeed universal phenomenon of evolution.

Affinities, Adaptive Radiation, and Phylogeny Figure 4 shows, by combination of a dendrogram and an adaptive grid, my present views as to the affinities and the adaptive or structural-functional relationships of the living hominoids. Interpretation of probable closeness of genetic connection is indicated by depth of branching, although it is to be emphasized that such a diagram is not a phylogenetic tree and has no time dimension. Adaptive or ecological (and corresponding structural-functional-behavioral) resemblances and differences are approximated by horizontal distances between the terminal points.

Figure 5 shows in schematic form the combined phylogenetic inferences reviewed above for various groups of hominoids.

Classification Evolutionary classification takes into account: degrees of homologous resemblance in *all* available respects; the most probable phylogenetic inferences from all data (including the foregoing resemblances plus evolutionary analysis and weighting of the various characteristics); and also the practical needs of discussion and communication.

It now seems perfectly clear and is all but universally recognized that the animals here called hominoids (in anticipation of a conclusion) form a natural evolutionary unit that should be recognized and named as a taxon. When the whole order Primates is taken into account, the categorical level of this taxon should clearly be no higher than infraorder and no lower than family. A case could be made out for either extreme of those rankings, but in my opinion the intermediate ranking, that of superfamily, is best in balance and convenience. It also accords with the recent consensus, and thus with the principle that communication is best served if nomenclature is not changed unnecessarily. The current and nomenclaturally correct nomen for this superfamily is Hominoidea.

At the next lower level, I have already expressed the opinion that the apparent lineage *Apidium-Oreopithecus* is at present best ranked as a

ADAPTIVE AND STRUCTURAL-FUNCTIONAL ZONES

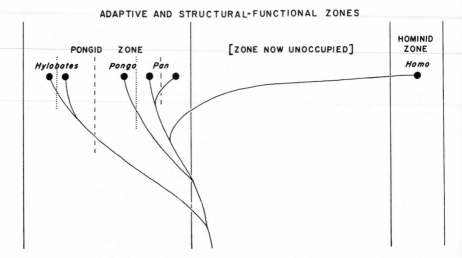

Figure 4 Dendrogram of probable affinities of recent hominoids in relationship to their radiation into adaptive-structural-functional zones. The two major adaptive zones are bordered by solid lines. Pongid radiation into sub- and sub-sub-zones is schematically suggested by broken and dotted lines. A dendrogram of this sort has no time dimension and does not indicate lineages, but it is probable that divergences of lines showing affinities are topologically similar to the phylogenetic lineage pattern.

family, because of its ancient separation plus its marked divergence from any other group now usually given family rank. In view especially of Straus's analysis, the only reasonable alternative is to rank this lineage as a subfamily of Hominidae on balance of anatomical resemblance alone. That is not wholly excluded by present evidence, but its phylogenetic implications seem to me extremely improbable. (Unless *Pongo, Pan,* and all the dryopithecine complex were also placed in the Hominidae it would be definitely inconsistent with the phylogeny of Figure 5.)

Because of the clear and ancient separation of *Hylobates* and its fossil allies from other hominoids, those forms are now frequently, probably usually, given family status. On the other hand, *Hylobates* almost certainly had a common hominoid ancestry with *Pongo* and *Pan,* and its evolutionary divergence from those genera and their fossil allies is decidedly less than that of either *Homo* or *Oreopithecus.* That would justify placing the *Hylobates* group as a subfamily of a family also containing *Pongo, Pan,* and some, at least, of the dryopithecine complex. Both arrangements are consistent with reasonable interpretations of the available data, and choice becomes a matter of personal judgment and convenience. I continue to prefer the second alternative, partly as a matter of linguistic convenience. One frequently wants to distinguish humans and apes (plus or including gibbons) and this is most conveniently done at the family level. The secondary distinction between gibbons and (other) apes is convenient at the subfamily level.

If the gibbons are given family rank, an analogous argument can be made for also giving *Pongo* separate family rank, since it cannot be *demonstrated* to have split off more recently from the *Pan* ancestry and since it now proves to be serologically about equally distinct. This is nevertheless still largely an argument from ignorance, and the most extensive positive evidence we have, that of anatomy, still suggests closer

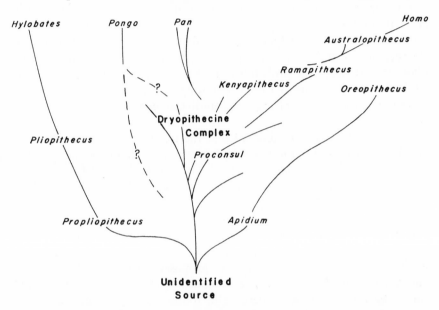

Figure 5 Tentative and schematic phylogeny of the Hominoidea. Most of the individual fossil genera are omitted, and lineages as drawn are meant to be impressionistic and diagrammatic (especially in and around the dryopithecine complex) rather than representing all or particular generic or specific lines.

affinities between *Pongo* and *Pan*. Certainly if *Hylobates* and *Pan* are in one family, *Pongo* belongs in the same family and the alternatives involve subfamilies. Of the five possible subfamily arrangements of the three genera (and their fossil allies), only placing *Hylobates* in one subfamily and *Pongo* and *Pan* in another or placing each in a separate subfamily seem worthy of consideration on present knowledge. Both can be defended, but I continue tentatively to favor the former, because I believe that *Pongo* and *Pan* probably are more closely related than *Hylobates* and *Pongo* and because I think monotypic subfamilies should be as few as possible.

For the dryopithecine complex, there are three possibilities: (1) all could be put in the same subfamily as *Pongo* and *Pan;* (2) they could all be placed in a subfamily or family of their own; (3) those clearly related to *Pongo, Pan,* or *Homo* could be put in family-group taxa with those genera and the others in one or more separate subfamilies or families. The first could be justified on grounds of general resemblance and of probability that *part* of this complex is near the ancestry of *Pan,* perhaps also of *Pongo.* The second arrangement makes a horizontal grouping that is phyletically complex and to some extent artificial, but is justifiable *faute de mieux* in our present lack of almost any good knowledge of detailed relationships in this group, and pending withdrawal of particular genera if their affinities with other established taxa are later demonstrated. The third arrangement is definitely preferable and should ultimately be adopted, but as indicated above present knowledge seems inadequate to follow it with sufficient probability. I now waver between (1) and (2), but hesitantly continue to follow (2) simply because there seem to be insufficient grounds for changing it until this complex is better understood.

It is now virtually established that the affinities of *Homo* with *Pan* are closer than with *Pongo* or *Hylobates.* That suggests the possible desirability of placing *Pan* in the Hominidae and *Pongo* and *Hylobates* in one or two other families, an arrangement supported by Goodman and by Klinger at the conference. In fact, as noted above, this view as to affinities is an old one and has been held for two or three generations by students who nevertheless all excluded *Pan* from the Hominidae. The new data increase confidence in the conclusion as to affinities but do not, in my opinion, either require or justify the proposed change in classification. The question involves the whole complex of taxonomic principles and cannot be argued in detail here. The following, in briefest form, are among the principal reasons for continuing to exclude *Pan* from the Hominidae:

1. *Pan* is the terminus of a conservative lineage, retaining in a general way an anatomical and adaptive facies common to all recent hominoids *except Homo* (and probably to all adequately known fossil ones except *Australopithecus* and the very different *Oreopithecus*). *Homo* is both anatomically and adaptively the most radically distinctive of all hominoids, divergent to a degree considered familial by all primatologists.

2. *Pan* is obviously not ancestral to *Homo.* The common ancestor was almost certainly more *Pan*-like than *Homo*-like, which suggests not that *Pan* should go in the Hominidae but that the common ancestor should be in a separate family with *Pan* (or in still another ancestral family).

3. When a younger family arises from an older, the situation is

frequently or usually similar to that of the *Pan* and *Homo* lineages: one of several lineages of the older family splits into two or more, *one* of which diverges (and/or diversifies) until its descendents warrant family status. If the lineages that did *not* diverge are also placed in the later family on the basis of more recent common ancestry, carrying this process on down will eventually require inclusion of all descendents of earlier splittings also in the latest family—eventually the whole animal kingdom would be in the Hominidae on this principle. An arbitrary division must be made in practical classification, and the obvious place to make it is where the lineage *later* reaching family status split off—in this instance where the ancestors of *Homo* split from those of *Pan* and other pongids. Classification cannot be based on recency of common ancestry *alone*.

4. Both arrangements are equally consistent with our present understanding of hominid phylogeny, but the proposed new arrangement is less consistent with other evolutionary considerations, notably that of adaptive divergence. Therefore the change is neither required nor warranted. The radical change of nomenclatural usage would also create great confusion in discussion of hominoid relationships.

Subfamily separation of *Australopithecus* and *Homo* became usual at the time when placing of *Australopithecus* in the Pongidae (as here used) or Hominidae (also of present usage) was disputed and the australopithecines were claimed to include several genera. Now that there is essential agreement that *Australopithecus* belongs in the Hominidae, I see no sufficient reason for having two subfamilies, especially as each has only one known genus as I and, I believe, most others now define the genera. "Australopithecine" and "hominine" may still be used as strictly vernacular terms of structural levels, although there is little need for such terms as long as we know only one genus at each level.

Finally, Leakey suggested at the conference a possible alternative classification that requires comment. (I do not know whether he himself considers the alternative preferable and proposes to use it.) He pointed out that the Hominoidea of my classification could be reduced to family rank and that my families and subfamilies, with some reassignment of genera, could be considered subfamilies (plus other subfamily for *Proconsul,* which I give only generic rank). The supporting phylogeny looked rather different from mine, but was topologically almost identical. Aside from minor points, either classification was consistent with either phylogeny. Without going into detail, I here only say that at the very best I do not think his classification an improvement justifying so many departures from current usage. The reasons are mostly implicit or explicit in the preceding comments.

The following is the outline classification that I now favor, with all accepted recent genera included but a number of fossil genera omitted:

Superfamily Hominoidea
  Family Pongidae
    Subfamily Hylobatinae
      Pliopithecus
      Hylobates
    Subfamily Dryopithecinae
      Dryopithecus and other genera of the dryopithecine complex, *tentatively*
        including *Proconsul, Ramapithecus,* and *Kenyapithecus.*
    Subfamily Ponginae
      Pongo
      Pan
  Family Hominidae
      Australopithecus
      Homo
  Family Oreopithecidae
      Apidium
      Oreopithecus

(Placing Oreopithecidae at the end and next to Hominidae has no special significance; as Darwin noted over a century ago, you cannot put organisms in one linear evolutionary sequence or show their true affinities on a sheet of paper. Putting *Australopithecus* in the Hominidae and adding the Oreopithecidae are the only essential changes from my 1945 classification, which I believe *in general* to be consistent with the mass of more recent information. Unfortunately that is less true of some of the nonhominoid primates.)

7 On Understanding Geochronological Time

Terah L. Smiley

THE POET'S "WORLD ENOUGH AND TIME," IT HAS BEEN NOTED, IS VIRTUALLY *the theme of evolution. When Bishop Usher's figure for the age of the earth (5,568 years in 1654, when his work was published) was accepted, there was simply no time for evolution. Then early geologists, like James Hutton, began at the end of the eighteenth century to prepare the way for dropping the bottom out of calculations of the age of the world. Now we frolic in a colossal span of years; Dr. Smiley in this paper offers 5 billion, but others have suggested 6 billion and more years as the age of the planet. Whatever the geologists may now settle on as its duration, the period of existence of the world is fully adequate for the evolutionary changes it has seen.*

Within this vast time span the nearer ancestors of man have been evolving for some 70 million years; and man himself, depending on how you identify him, is discernible for one, two or more million years. How we know this, and how we attempt to offer more specific dates for the fossils we find is described in this selection.

SOURCE: *Arizona Geological Society Digest*, Vol. VII (1964), pp. 1–11. Reprinted with the permission of author and publisher.

The author (b. 1914) is Professor and Director of the Geochronology Laboratories at the University of Arizona. Among his articles on dating are "A Foundation for the Dating of Some Late Archaeological Sites in the Rio Grande Area, New Mexico," with Stanley A. Stubbs and Bryant Bannister, *Laboratory of Tree-Ring Research*, Bulletin No. 6 (1953); "General Aspects of Dating in the Field of Archaeology," *Asian Perspectives*, Vol. V, ii (1962), pp. 181–187. He has also served as editor of *Geochronology*.

Introduction

Until recently, estimates on the age of the Earth and the length of geochronological time making up the history of this planet have fluctuated between periods of time ranging from thousands of years to those amounting to billions of years. The present-day estimates are given as being in the general magnitude of 5×10^9 (5 billion) years. One can well question how these estimates have been derived, what is their total meaning, and exactly how valid we believe them to be. Also, one may question the value of knowing or the need of having accurate answers to this age problem. These questions, simple in wording and intent, require careful analysis before attempts to give answers can be made.

The topic of *geochronological time,* or geological time as it is sometimes called, under discussion here is in itself something of an enigma. In 1941, Adolph Knoph remarked in a James Arthur Foundation lecture at New York University that if he were ever asked, as a geologist, ". . . . what is the single greatest contribution of the science of geology to modern civilized thought?" the answer could be "the realization of the immense length of time. So vast is the span of time recorded in the history of the Earth, that it is generally distinguished from the more modest kinds of time by being called 'geologic time.' "

Geologic processes have been operating through this 5-billion year history, and biological processes have been in operation at least 3 billion years. Mountains have been pushed high above the surrounding plains only to be worn back to their base levels through erosion and the eroded materials carried away to be deposited in basins where later mountain-building processes thrust these rocks high above their base levels to form new mountains. Certain ocean bottom levels have been thrust upward until they emerged from the sea and became continental areas, and certain continental areas have sunk beneath the oceans where they were covered with marine sediments only to later be raised once again. Ore bodies have been formed, eroded, or carried away in solution form and these materials used in the reconstitution of new ore bodies. Volcanoes have time and again raised their bombastic voices and coughed up materials from deep inside the earth. When plant and animal life did appear, the biological forms lived and died, and the material from their bodies enriched the ocean bottom ooze and the continental soils from which later forms of life could thrive. The crust of the earth has never been completely quiescent, nor is it today; rather in places it has constantly been raised, lowered, and shifted. If we had had a time-lapse rate camera focused on the Earth since its beginning, we would be able to see and study these processes in dynamic operation, similar to the way cloud formations are now photographed.

Before we can understand such a history, we must examine the basis on which our premises are built, one of the most basic of which is time itself. There is probably no English word as commonly used and as little understood as the word *time*. Interpretations of the word are as varied as the countless people who use it. To a large extent this is probably because it has never been satisfactorily defined for many fields of science and remains mainly as a concept for most of us in spite of all that has been said and written on it. If each of us were to take pencil and paper to write a personal concept of time, the probability would be small that any two of these concepts would be exactly the same. For some reason we generally refuse to come to grips with the problem of a definition and slough off any concern with it by the feeling that the concept is "too immense" or "too complex" to hold our attention in more than a cursory way.

In the theoretical and philosophical books and articles on time—such as Schlegel's "Time and the physical world," Blum's "Time's arrow and evolution," Reichenbach's "The direction of time," Whitrow's "The natural philosophy of time," and Grunbaum's "Time and entropy"—the major problem involved centers around *entropy* and how the direction of time is affected by "reversible time" when working with isolated particles on the subatomic level.

The trend of modern science dictates that we must set up some common working definition of time. We must have some basis for understanding it at least to a point where we can work with results achieved by research in our own laboratories and by colleagues in other fields who are also concerned with temporal problems. We cannot advance far without this type of cooperative and understanding effort.

I believe that to be effective a definition of time should encompass biological and radioactive matter if it is to be used in such fields as geochronology, geology, and archaeology. The definition I use ignores, having little bearing on our particular problem, the Lorentz transformation equation as illustrated by the clock paradox problem and the time-invariant Clausius process. Also, it assumes that there is some "loss" of usable energy in the universe, and I'll put the word loss in parenthesis, because unless we look upon it as a perfect perpetual-motion machine, the universe has to be moving toward some increased degree of entropy. With these exceptions in mind, I would define time as *the direction and continuance taken by all matter in the universe as it moves toward higher entropy.*

This definition includes all matter ranging in size from submolecular particles to megascopic plant and animal life. The original source of this matter, or particles making up this matter, is a complex study and not our concern in this discussion. Our interest centers around the particles from the moment they became part of this planet. We must not, however, attempt to treat these particles as isolated matter else we come back to the problems bothering the theorists working with the reversible direction of time and with entropy. Using this definition of time, we should have no great difficulty fitting into the total time continuum the life history of the Earth, including the minutia making up this history, such as the dating of rocks formed during certain periods or when certain events occurred.

The geochronological time scale as we know it today is, in brief, the geologic column containing interpreted "dates" on the various divisions of the column that have been derived by applying radioactivity dating and other techniques to particular rock types, and it represents the composite work of many people through the last two centuries.

The geologic column is a descriptive outline of time-rock units, which enables students of the earth sciences to properly categorize and order historical materials in their proper position on a relative time basis. These time-rock units are practical divisions representing sediments deposited in a given area somewhere within the total corresponding time unit. In almost all cases, as will be explained later, identifications of these units are based on the remains of plants and animals that lived in that general area at that time.

In the column, for example, the *Paleozoic Era* refers to "early" life forms, the *Mesozoic Era* refers to "middle" life forms, and the *Cenozoic Era* refers to "recent or late" life forms. So few fossils have been found in pre-Paleozoic or *Precambrian* rocks that, coupled with the external similarities of the rocks, it has been virtually impossible to set up worldwide time-rock units for this vast span of time comprising approximately 85 to 90 percent of the Earth's history. Some fossils have been found, however, in these ancient rock types, such as those studied and described by Tyler and Barghoorn for the Gunflint Formation in southern Ontario that are dated at approximately 2 billion years of age and those described by Glaessener stratigraphically located deep in Precambrian rocks in southern Australia.

Cambrian rocks are distinguished, or characterized, by the first abundant records of fossil life of which trilobites are the most famous. In general, the Cambrian Period rocks contain such a diversity of types that we can be certain of a long period of Precambrian development that has not been reflected in the fossil record; most of the major phyla at least of the invertebrates were already in existence by this time. One might say that perhaps in the life forms the major development in the Cambrian was that of "hard parts" or "bony" material that could be more easily fossilized. The Ordovician Period contains abundant remains of fishlike vertebates and more highly developed trilobites. The Silurian Period is based on the presence of reef-corals and abundant brachiopods. The Devonian contains numerous remains of fish and primitive land plants. And so the story goes, each *Era, Period,* and *Epoch* having its own characteristic forms. It must be kept in mind that, although each subdivision has its own characteristic forms, these do not represent sudden changes in life forms; rather, as the fossil record is studied, described, and as additional material makes it more complete, we can see a continuous sequence of life evolving and diversifying, and finally we subdivide the total history, as based on faunal succession, on a more or less arbitrary basis.

The first written record on fossils, to my knowledge, is that reported by the Greek philosopher Anaximander in the sixth century B.C., who wrote that the peculiar forms of rocklike materials within the rocks in the Nile Valley were actually remains of fish; therefore, at one time these rocks had to have been on the bottom of the sea. Aside from rather sporadic and scanty references written during intervening centuries, it was not until the time of Nicolaus Steno in the A.D. 1600's and Linnaeus in the 1700's that serious consideration was given to fossil remains.

These "early-day" people, such as the Englishman William (Strata) Smith, studied fossil remains primarily in England and France. They learned to recognize particular groups or assemblages of fossils, and they began correlating these fossil assemblages over wider and wider areas. They found that the best material for correlation was the "guide" types, which had a limited time span but were of widespread distribution. In this correlation work, they were aided by generalizations, such as the one first formally presented by Steno in approximately 1669 and called the "Law of Superposition" in which it is stated that in an undisturbed sequence of sedimentary rocks, the youngest strata are on the top.

After considerable study, Conybeare and Phillips described in 1822 the rocks of the Carboniferous Period. They were followed in the 1830's by Sedgwick, Murchison, Lyell, and Alberti who described still other periods.

Prior to the development and use of radioactivity dating methods, numerous theories were advanced by various individuals concerning the age of the Earth and the total span of time for the geologic column. Certain people concerned themselves with measuring the increasing salt content of the oceans, and, extrapolating that data back in time to a period when the oceans were free of salt, they calculated figures on the minimum age of the Earth. Other people worked with the rates of sedimentation of various deposits, then, compiling all the data they could locate on the thickness of *all* deposits, they came forth with minimum ages on the Earth. Still other techniques were applied with so-so results.

No matter what techniques were employed to determine the time span in actual years, the "elastic" geologic column could be stretched or shrunk according to the latest estimates. This was made possible because the major division of the column was and still is, as previously stated, based on fossil life forms found imbedded in the sediments. Paleontologists paid little attention to time in finite years, and it was only when some theorist shrunk the scale to such a ridiculously low figure that even the fossils squirmed did they come forth with personal ideas on "rates" of evolution and other paleontological processes that sometimes needed to be taken with almost as much salt as the salinity of the oceans theories demanded.

Nevertheless, it was the paleontologists who developed the first sound approaches to the problem of finite years for the geologic column, although they did this by a round-about means while studying the origin and development of faunal life forms. These characteristic forms were used to correlate "time" units within the limits set by crustal disturbances and unconformities of varying importance that mark the boundaries of the *Eras*. With more refined taxonomic classification and procedures, they have learned to identify types marking the divisions of lesser importance, such as the *Periods*, the *Epochs*, the *Ages*, and the *Stages*.

Such divisions were, and are, easy to recognize where unconformities and (or) other rock "breaks" occur. In areas where no lithologic breaks are discernible, deep-seated problems arose, and still arise, on whether or not the particular rocks belong to this or that time period. Only a few of these problems have as yet been solved to everyone's satisfaction. The more minutely the uplift of mountains and crustal movements are studied and dated by radioactivity techniques, the more drawn out and complex the tectonic processes become, until at present it seems that these processes are always in operation in some degree in some locality, although certain major events may have occurred in a comparatively short span of years. Thus, crustal movements and unconformities are losing some of their importance as universal boundary markers.

The stratigraphic paleontologist has had to concern himself with problems such as those encountered in working out the biostratigraphy of an area where a particular rock unit is based on the assemblage of fossils. In this usage, time is relative because the major problems center around the relationship of one unit to another.

In February 1896, I believe it was, Henri Bacquerel, while waiting for the skies to clear in order to conduct an X-ray experiment on fluorescing substances in sunlight, left a photographic plate and a piece of uranium salt in a desk drawer. Several days later the sun was shining, and when he went to remove the plate to continue his study, he found it had been exposed to some unknown radiation. This rather fortuitous incident led to new investigations and ultimately into radioactive disintegration, nuclear fusion and fission, and to other such studies. Shortly after this incident, the Curies began their search for sources of radioactivity.

In 1909, John Holy, in his book "Radioactivity in Geology," discussed radioactivity in rocks and the energy needed for the mountain-building processes. Thus, for the first time the "radioactive" clock gave us our very first technique for measuring in actual years the long expanses of time involved in the Earth's history. Discovery after discovery followed, and by 1931 "The Age of the Earth" was published by the National Research Council. This work was based on the lead-ratio techniques and traced an orderly succession of geologic events back over 2 billion years. With the development of mass spectrometry in the late 1930's still other and more accurate methods were made available. All these depend, however, on the concept of the statistically derived invariant rate of radioactive disintegration. Investigations into better instrumentation and new methods continue to the present time, and refinements are constantly being made in the framework of the history of the Earth.

Methods

There are today many techniques being used to study the Earth's history and processes that have operated during this history. These various techniques and methods being used give results we can classify into three broad categories. These are:

1. Relative placement methods or those that are concerned with relating particular materials or events to other materials or events to the extent that one is previous to, contemporaneous with, or follows the other. Time cannot be considered here in terms of years or even as a theoretical unit of measurement. In this category are such methods as:

> Paleontology (invertebrate and vertebrate)
> Stratigraphy
> Geomorphology
> Palynology
> Thermoluminescence
> Thephrochronology
> Fluorine analysis
> Etc.

2. Time placement methods that include those that attempt to place definite dates in terms of calendar years on events or items, but because these methods incorporate within that temporal placement a certain statistical error, the results are given in intervals (or globs) of time rather than in points in time. All the actual age determinations used in the geochronological time scale have been derived by these methods with the exception of that covering the last several thousand years in which tree-ring "dating" can be employed. In this group are such methods as:

> Radiocarbon
> Potassium-argon

Lead ratio techniques
Rubidium-strontium
Laminations, including glacial and nonglacial varves
Ionium
Etc.

3. Absolute placement methods. In this category are those methods that attempt to place in terms of a single year various materials or events. The only entry in this group is:

Dendrochronology (tree-ring dating)

There is no method known that yields "dates," rather they yield such information as ratios between parent and daughter materials, or they tell us when a certain annual lamination was deposited, or when a particular ring was formed on a particular tree.

Without going into the details on how radioactive techniques such as potassium-argon are carried out, let me say that all these involve laboratory analyses of materials composed of small particles that were part of still older materials during the first part of their stay on this planet, excluding, of course, recently arrived extraterrestrial material such as meteorites and cosmic dust. We do not "date" the particles, rather we derive the elapsed time since their assemblage into a particular type of matter or the elapsed time since they were metamorphosed into their present form. The better our techniques can pinpoint the elapsed time of this assemblage or metamorphosis, the smaller will be the "glob" of time concerning this transformation. This glob represents the period of time during which these materials *could have been* assembled.

It is not possible to walk into the field and simply remove a chunk of rock from an outcrop and take it into the laboratory for dating. In the first place, we cannot take a piece of innocuous material, place it in a magical black box, close the door, twist a few dials, make a few adjustments, then turn on the power and, after lights have flashed, bells have rung, and puffs of white smoke have cleared, read off the age of the object on a dial attached to the box. As magical as some of the laboratory apparatus might seem to be, it can only do tasks which it was designed, constructed, and programmed to do. The results yielded in these analyses are so much analytical gibberish until the data are translated into understandable terms.

Our laboratory methods or techniques are designed to give to us information we can use for age determinations. What do we mean by the term *aging* of rocks and how is this aging accomplished? If you can pardon my loose usage of common expressions and terms, I might say that *aging* is the result of the wear and tear on materials caused by the operation of life processes with the passage of *time*. When the term *aging* is voiced, most of us immediately think of it in terms of "life" and "biological" life" at that. Without going into the philosophy of life and the causes that brought it about, or bring it about, let me simplify this by stating that in an analogous way, "life" exists on a submolecular or submicroscopic level as well as on the megascopic one. By submolecular or submicroscopic level, I mean the levels on which are the molecules, the atoms, and the subatomic particles that make up the material we see when looking through an optical microscope. These materials constitute all matter in the Universe, and this matter has "life." To be certain, it is not the same life on the biological microscopic or megascopic level, and it is called *molecular* or *atomic* life to differentiate it from the biological type.

As this matter "ages" through time, it undergoes changes in its structure as energy and matter are assimilated and dispensed. Those we normally consider as biological aging processes, similar to our life processes, are on a different level from those processes on subatomic or submolecular levels. Rocks and minerals are comprised of the same type of minute particles as those in our bodies and from which our bodies derive their building materials and their energies. If we could look deeply enough into our own or other biological life, we would see that the same aging processes are in operation within the minute particles making up these biological forms. I should say perhaps, for the sake of accuracy, that our bodies are simultaneously aging on several levels, which are the submolecular, the molecular, and the megascopic levels of assemblages of matter.

Rocks are *born*, that is the particles are assembled into a particular matter, or they are metamorphosed from one type into a new type of matter through external pressures, temperatures, and the disintegration process common to radioactive isotopes. Rocks *age*, because with the passing of time, there are changes brought about in their internal structures because of various "life" processes; and rocks *die*, either through disintegration by mechanical and chemical weathering or metamorphosis into different materials.

Thus, the passage of time brings on changes in the inanimate as well as the animate material. Such common expressions as "the eternal hills" or the "everlasting rocks" may give a connotation of no change, but the various processes in operation do, with the passage of enough time, cause mountains to be worn down; even the particles making up the rocks and mountains are subject to aging and change. Our laboratory methods simply measure some of these changes, mainly radioactive decay, and from these age-determination studies we can go on to calculate *dates* in the Earth's history.

Providing the total time span of the Earth is anywhere near the estimates now being given, we have very little if any definite knowledge of the matter making up this planet during the first half of its stay. Earth scientists now consider this age to be in the general magnitude of 5 billion years; some astronomers are thinking of the age of the Universe as being in the magnitude of 8 to 10 billion years.

Most of our knowledge extends back only through the Cambrian Era, but the aging of materials taken from the oldest rocks thus far located and studied takes us back to a period approximately 3 billion years ago. These materials are undoubtedly reconstituted from earlier materials; thus, all we can say is that this age represents the beginning of the present life cycle of this particular material. As more and more studies are done, there is some possibility that still older rocks will be located, and eventually we may learn something of this earlier part of the Earth's history.

Problems

The second major division of this portion of the discussion is concerned with *problems* in age determinations, and of these I will only touch on what I consider to be a few highlights. In the Geochronology Laboratories, for example, only a small percentage of the staff's time is devoted to the so-called age determinations. Approximately 75 to 80 percent of our time is concerned with understanding the material being analyzed and interpreting the results yielded by such analyses.

All *dating* is a matter of interpretation no matter whether it is a *date* on a structure in an archaeological site, or the *date* of a glacial recession, or the *date* of a particular rock formation. In my own experience, I believe that interpretation can be strengthened and made more accurate by following three steps, which need not necessarily be undertaken in the order given here. These are: (1) to determine exactly *what is the material* being analyzed for its age, (2) the determination of the complete "life history" of the material being studied, and (3) learn the precise association between the material studied and the phenomenon being "dated."

The physical properties of the material being analyzed must be minutely examined if we are to know what we are studying. The inside rings of a thousand-year old tree will, for example, give a radiocarbon age of 1,000 years, although the tree was a live growing entity when cut for our study.

Not all materials can be so analyzed that we can obtain their age even if they seem to be of the proper type. Of these so-called "datable" materials, some yield such data and some do not. I can best compare this to what would happen if I were to walk out on the University campus and, considering all coeds to be "datable," ask the precise age of each one I met. The answers would fall into three general categories, I believe.

Most of them would tell me it was none of my business how old they are. A smaller number would give me some sort of vague reply, such as that they are over 16 (and obviously under 75). Only a very few would give me a straightforward answer. Our "datable" materials are much like this; most of them ignore all that we can do to obtain clear-cut *aging* data, a few specimens give us evasive or vague information, and only a very few yield definite quantitative data.

We need to study the materials to the extent that we rather fully understand what they tell us when we make an analysis. To illustrate this point, let me again use radiocarbon work as an example. Every radiocarbon analysis coming out of the laboratory is as accurate as can be determined by modern science. In other words, every radiocarbon age determination has an extremely high degree of probability of being correct. This does not mean, however, that the application of that age determination in terms of calendar years to an archaeological or geological event can be done with any high degree of accuracy. All that any radiocarbon analysis does is to simply determine the ratio in a given amount of material between the existing nonradioactive carbon 12 and 13, and the radioactive carbon 14 isotopes, and plugging this ratio information into an equation based on the disintegration processes, we calculate the time when the material was a live substance. This ratio may have subsequently been altered or disturbed through either a natural or an artificial cause, and this cannot be determined on the basis of the laboratory analysis alone. We cannot simply assume that all such analyses are valid for the dating of a prehistoric event.

The second major problem is the determination of the complete "life history" of the material being studied. Aside from dendrochronology, all our dating techniques are based on the disintegration of radioactive materials. The analyses of these materials yield results based on the ratio between the amount of parent material still remaining in our sample and the amount of daughter products given off during disintegration. Any disturbance in this ratio leads to an "erroneous" figure as far as the true age relationship is concerned. Recognition of this problem causes us to carefully study field and laboratory conditions to determine whether or not exogenic or endogenic processes may have disturbed the natural ratio. Samples are discarded if there is much doubt that we must have contamination that cannot be overcome or for which we cannot correct.

In radiocarbon work many samples submitted for study are comprised of small bits of charcoal because there is no single piece large enough to analyze by itself. The small bits may represent many individual shrubs, trees, or other types of organic matter that may have had a long life or a short one. What are we dating? It is not *a* piece of homogeneous material, but rather we are obtaining *an average age of all the material making up the total sample.* Some of these materials may be reliable and some may not; we have no way to know exactly how much contamination may be in the sample, thus, the "date" can be erroneous.

We have found in potassium-argon work that we need to study the source locality in detail to determine the field conditions that controlled the geologic structure of the area and the exogenic and endogenic processes that may have had some effect on the sample. These latter would include nearby volcanic activity, long exposure to the atmosphere, hydrothermal conditions, and other such phenomena. We must know, as an added example, if the sample studied is an indigenous part of the parent rock or if it is a bit of residue from an older rock that was carried in during sedimentation. If we understand the complete life history of the sample, this problem will not be of extreme importance when proper steps are taken to counteract such conditions, or it will tell us that we cannot expect reliable results from the laboratory analyses.

In tree-ring dating we know that the tree was a live growing botanical entity at the time when the last seasonal growth was formed. It stands to reason that the use of the tree in the construction of a house or some other architectural or functional feature could not have occurred until after the tree died. The investigator must determine the length of time after such a terminal date before the tree was used in construction. This means that he needs to reconstruct the story of that particular specimen from the time it was a living tree until it was found in the site in question. To do this, he must determine how the tree was used, under what conditions it was used, when it was used, and, unless it is an integral part of a wall or some other architectural feature, how did the specimen come to be where it was found.

The third major problem concerns the precise association between the material studied and the event or item we want dated. Solutions to this problem are based in part on answers derived from the preceding problem concerning the life history of the sample.

We cannot assume that simply because an object or a bit of material has been found in a certain stratum that its history is exactly the same as that for the stratum. We know that certain minerals migrate from the country rock into the particular samples we are studying and that there is cross migration from the sample materials into the country rocks. The entire processes of erosion and sedimentation are concerned with the tearing down of rocks and the transportation of that material into another environment where it is used to create new types of rocks. Under these conditions, we can have older materials being incorporated into younger sediments.

We must also realize that to "date" material from a lava does not, necessarily, date the eruption of a particular volcano. We have to determine the association between the lava, in this case, and the particular volcano—they may or may not be related. In such problems there must be close coordination between the laboratory and fieldwork. Further, the researcher should test several different types of material from the same horizon to learn what has happened in the field in regard to the material being studied. Such analyses may indicate that two seemingly contemporaneous materials were actually not contemporaneous or that two apparently unrelated events might actually be the result of a common event and so on.

Each particle of material studied has its own history, but each particle has never been completely isolated from all other matter. In this same sense, no event in the Earth's history was ever a complete entity in itself; thus, we must study the total chain of related events if we are to understand the one with which we are working. The investigator must assume responsibility for these field observations, and to do this he must be cognizant of the total conditions of the particular temporal problem and its relationship to other events in the history of that specific area. "Sloppy" fieldwork is no more excusable than "sloppy" laboratory work.

The literature on earth sciences contains numerous "dates" on rocks and events. What is meant when such a "date" reads, for example, 2.3×10^9 years? Geochronologists or geologists do not have the same definition for the word date as do physicists, historians, or other scientists. The common dictionary definition of the word date is that it is a point in space-time. We must modify this definition because we cannot be nearly precise enough to pick out *a point* in space-time. As stated earlier, what comes from the various aging methods are "globs" of time during which the material we are studying could have been "born." When geologists speak of an "absolute" date they mean that this is a "date" in terms of calendar years, whereas they had been using dates based on guesswork and estimations or on the relative time relationship of one rock type to another or of one event to another. While they strive for accuracy and precision, they are not using the term "absolute" in its normal dictionary definition.

The "date" of 2.3×10^9 years, then, simply means that the material was assembled into its present form somewhere around 2 billion 300 million years ago. There is the strong tendency to forget the standard deviation that is a part of this "age." Thus, although this is a statistical calculation, we feel that this date is very precise, as far as our present-day instruments go, and its accuracy is somewhere in the proper magnitude.

In tree-ring studies, when the term *date* is used it refers to *the year* in which a particular ring was formed on a particular specimen. When this tree was cut and used to help construct a house, or put to some other use, is a different matter. All we *know* is that it could not have been so used until after the year in which the last ring was formed.

Our love for pigeonholes and our consuming desire to place each piece of data in a labeled box has led us into some false assumptions regarding the use of the units making up the divisions or the column. In probably no single locality can we be absolutely certain that the deposit represents the total time span of a single division of the time scale. All we can do is work with one segment and extrapolate from that segment into the others.

Although few believe, I hope, in the catastrophic theory on the periodic extinction of whole groups of animals and plants, as first advanced by the early-day French paleontologist Cuvier, I fear that we try to read into the column such breaks as these even though none exist. Unless we have unconformities marking the boundaries, we become confused in relating materials to one time unit or another.

I want to close here by stating that in discussing these problems I am always reminded of an analogy that has been used many times but is still pertinent. You perhaps recall the scene in Carroll's story of Alice in Wonderland where she is talking to the Mad Hatter about many things, and they finally come around to the topic of time. The Mad Hatter remarked, "I dare say you never even spoke to Time." "Perhaps not," Alice cautiously replied, "but I know I have to beat time when I learn music." "Ah, that accounts for it," said the Mad Hatter, "He won't stand beating. Now if you only kept on good terms with him, he'd do almost anything you like with the clock."

Any investigator working with temporal problems also has to keep on good terms with time because it is capricious and undependable unless mastered to a point where it can serve the purpose that we need for these problems. I am afraid, however, that many of us only think in terms of beating time rather than understanding it and putting it to its proper usage.

8 Flourine and the Relative Dating of Bones

Kenneth P. Oakley

THE FLUORINE TECHNIQUE FOR THE RELATIVE DATING OF FOSSIL BONES IS
*still used but has yielded place to a variety of "harder" methods whose
results are more absolute, or at least pertain to more closely bounded
"globs" of time, as described in the previous selection. Dr. Oakley's
essay is retained from the earlier edition of the* Readings, *however,
largely for the light it throws on the matter of scientific self-scrutiny.
Written before the whole truth was known about the notorious Piltdown
hoax, it represents an important point in the scientific process by which
the fraud was gradually penetrated and exposed. Science has no* a priori
*immunity to false data and conclusions but is built about techniques and a
general ideology which in time will correct error and improve reliability.
This is by no means an inevitable process; scientists must continue in each
generation to be skeptical and crusty about accepted truth.*

The interest of anthropologists in dating the past is ultimately
focused on the dating of the remains of early man. Various geochronological methods have been applied to dating the *deposits* which yield the
remains, but methods for the relative dating of bones within a particular
deposit would serve a none the less useful purpose from the anthropological point of view.

SOURCE: *The Advancement of Science,* Vol. IV, No. 16 (1948), pp. 336–337, and "Analytical Methods of Dating Bones," *Ibid.,* Vol. XII, No. 45 (1955), pp. 3–8. Reprinted
with the permission of the author and the British Association for the Advancement
of Science.

The author (b. 1911) is Principal Scientific Officer, British Museum (Natural
History). He is both a geologist and physical anthropologist. Among his works is a
paperback edition, *Man the Toolmaker* (1949), and the recent *Framework for Dating Fossil Man* (1964; second edition 1966).

Many of the most famous finds of fossil man have been marred by doubt as to the genuineness of bones. Boule and others have questioned the association of the Piltdown mandible with the cranial fragments; Marston has gone so far as to suggest that they may be of different ages. Again, fragments of human skulls of *sapiens*-type were found in apparent association with a Kamasian ('Middle' Pleistocene) fauna at Kanjera in the Kavirondo region of Victoria Nyanza; but it has been suggested that the 'association' was due to disturbance of the beds.

If there were a reliable time-keeping mineral in bones such problems might be solved. Carnot, a French mineralogist, analysed a large number of bones from different geological horizons, and showed that their average fluorine-content increased with geological age. The reason for this is now known to be that bone is partly composed of hydroxy-apatite, a form of calcium phosphate which acts as a trap for wandering fluorine ions, present at least in small numbers in most ground waters. The hydroxy-apatite crystal-units become converted one by one into fluor-apatite, which is a stable mineral, resistant to weathering. For this reason fluorine is not readily leached out after it has been fixed in bone; and on balance the F-content increases with passage of time. Owing to the porosity of bone the alteration presumably proceeds not zonally but uniformly throughout the body of the material.

Taking the proportion of fluorine to phosphate of lime in fluor-apatite as unity, Carnot showed that the average proportion in bones of increasing age was as follows:

Recent	0.058
Pleistocene	0.360
Late Tertiary	0.595
Early Tertiary	0.645
Mesozoic	0.907
Palaeozoic	0.993

It must be emphasized that these figures are only averages, and that one cannot date a bone by estimating its F-content; because in one locality fluorine may be abundant in the ground-waters, in another rare. Thus, a Pleistocene bone from a F-rich region may have acquired as much fluorine as a Tertiary bone from a F-poor environment. Nevertheless, if one is dealing with two bones from a particular site, or more reliably two series of bones from a particular region, it should be possible to determine whether they are of the same geological age, or whether one is significantly younger than the other.

The only bones tested from this point of view so far are from a F-rich environment and as might have been predicted from theory, the results are negative but none the less interesting and worthy of record. Dr. L. S. B. Leakey, hearing from me during the Pan-African Congress on

Prehistory (1947) about the possibility of such tests, provided for analysis a small parietal fragment belonging to one of the controversial skulls from Kanjera, together with comparative material from the same site, namely: (i) animal bones of undoubted Kamasian age, (ii) a fragment of human parietal of late prehistoric (Wilton)) date from a surface deposit. By permission of the Director of the Home Office S. W. Forensic Science Laboratory, Dr. H. J. Walls of that laboratory kindly undertook to test the F-content of these samples. Before proceeding to make accurate determinations, he submitted the samples to preliminary spectographic tests and these indicated that the F-content of all the bones was approximately of the same order, with the atomic ratio F : Ca in the region of 1 : 5. *This is theoretically the maximum F-content of bone.*

The Kanjera beds contain quantities of volcanic ash and are therefore exceptionally rich in fluorine. The conversion of bone into fluorapatite evidently proceeds so rapidly in such an environment that no separation of early prehistoric from late prehistoric bones is going to be possible in the case of Kavirondo sites (Kanam and Kanjera). Carnot's results, however, were based on the analysis of bones obtained in Europe mainly from fluorine-deficient environments. Thus there is a fair prospect that the relative ages of bones from sites where the F-content of ground-waters is low, as in most of the river terraces of southern England, will be determinable by analysis.

It should be possible to determine for example, whether the Galley Hill skeleton was contemporary with the gravels of the 100 ft.-terrace (Thames) in which it was found, or whether, on the other hand, it was a later burial, by comparing its average F-content with that of undoubted fossil bones from those gravels, including the Swanscombe skull. To obtain conclusive proof an elaborate series of carefully controlled and accurate micro-determinations of fluorine would be required; but preliminary spectrographic tests would suffice to show the relative abundance of this element in the two sets of bones and would indicate whether a thorough investigation was warranted.

The Piltdown remains might be investigated on the same lines. It has been suggested by Mr. A. T. Marston that the Piltdown mandible (and canine) may not be stratigraphically contemporary with the cranial fragments; that the former is simian and from undisturbed basal gravel, and that the latter belong to *Homo sapiens* and came from an overlaying layer of disturbed gravel of Upper Pleistocene age. Geologists and palaeontologists equally conversant with the evidence do not accept this interpretation of the finds; but Mr. Marston has made a stimulating challenge which might be put to the test by application of the fluorine technique. It is undoubtedly true that the Piltdown gravels contain two groups of animal bones: derived (Red Crag) and contemporary ('Middle' Pleistocene) and it would in any case be instructive to know, through preliminary spectrographic tests at least, whether the F-contents of the bones, animal and human, corresponded in any way to this grouping.

The solving of the Piltdown Problem began in 1949 with the application of the fluorine-dating method to all the specimens from the Piltdown gravel. In addition to the jaw-bone, canine or eye-tooth and fragments of human braincase, eighteen fossil mammalian specimens had been recorded from the pit. These appeared to be of two ages: an older group originally called Pliocene, including pieces of the grinding teeth of a rare type of elephant (*Elephas* cf. *planifrons*) which died out near the beginning of the Pleistocene period, that is more than 500,000 years ago according to geological estimates of an indirect kind; and a much later group including remains of beaver, red deer and perhaps hippopotamus, dating from just before the last glaciation of about 50,000 years ago. It appeared that fossils of two formations had been washed together, through some strange chance. Those authorities who could not believe that the jawbone belonged to the skull held the view that the jaw belonged to the 'pliocene' group, and the skull to the later. Small samples of all these supposedly precious specimens were drilled out in the geological laboratory of the British Museum (Natural History) and submitted to the Government Chemist's Department, where they were analyzed by Dr. C. R. Hoskins. The fossils of the older group proved to contain a great deal of fluorine, 2–3% (3.8 is the theoretical maximum). In striking contrast, the amount of fluorine in small samples of the famous skull, jawbone and canine tooth proved to be only 0.2% ± 0.2 (that is to say < 0.1 to 0.4%). It was not immediately obvious that these remains were bogus, because there did not appear to be any significant difference in fluorine content between the jawbone and skull, or between the skull and an associated molar tooth of hippopotamus (extinct in Britain since before the last glaciation).

In 1953, to test Dr. J. S. Weiner's hypothesis that the jawbone and canine tooth were modern specimens faked to match fossilized human skull bones, larger samples were removed and submitted to the Government Chemist's Department, where they were analyzed by Mr. C. F. M. Fryd, using a more refined technique than that available in 1949. The jawbone and canine proved to contain no more fluorine than fresh bones and teeth, whereas the human skull bones contained just enough to indicate that they were ancient. The organic (nitrogen) content of the jawbone and teeth was also determined, and proved the modernity of the jawbone conclusively without the cross-check provided by fluorine. A woolly rhinoceros bone from clay below the Lloyd's building in Leadenhall Street, London, has the same nitrogen content as the Piltdown jawbone, yet it is undoubtedly fossil. The reason for its remarkable preservation is that it was embedded in clay which has provided an anacrobic and sterile environment since the latter part of the Pleistocene

Ice Age. A fragment of mammoth bone from the same site, but from a layer of *sand*, contains almost no nitrogen. Fortunately the fluorine content of buried bones increases at almost the same rate in sand (or gravel) and in clay. Thus the rhino and mammoth bones both contain about 1.0% fluorine, as expected in alluvial deposits of Upper Pleistocene age in Southern England. If for the sake of argument, it were supposed that the Piltdown jawbone had been encased in clay since Pleistocene times, and this had prevented its organic content from being degraded, its fluorine content should nevertheless be higher than in modern bone. In fact its matrix was said to be gravel.

The fluorine content of the Piltdown skull bones is lower than that of any fossil bones from Pleistocene gravels in Britain. But so long as the hippopotamus tooth with the same low fluorine content was accepted as a local fossil it could be argued that the ground-water at Piltdown had been exceptionally deficient in fluorine since the Ice Age. (The exposed dentine of a tooth and compact bone adsorb fluorine at about the same rate.) When evidence came to light that the hippopotamus tooth and, indeed, almost all the Piltdown fossils had been artificially stained, and therefore were fraudulent introductions, the provisional dating of the skull as late Pleistocene lost its foundation. Eventually it was proved that the skull bones had been transplanted and therefore were of uncertain origin.

9 Some Fallacies in the Study of Hominid Phylogeny

Elwyn L. Simons

THE "STAR" SYSTEM OPERATES IN THE THEATER, UNIVERSITY AND IN HUMAN *evolution. Almost every student comes into class knowing something about Australopithecus, Pithecanthropus, or Neanderthal (though what he knows is often incorrect). He is likely to be much less familiar with our probable ancestors of the Pliocene and earlier geological periods. Yet the biological events which led up to the appearance of recognizable manlike forms in the Pleistocene are equally important to our understanding of our own evolution.*

In this selection Professor Elwyn Simons, who also co-authors the next selection relating taxonomy and primate evolution, concentrates on problems in our understanding of hominid phylogeny during the past 30 million years. In pursuing his argument, Simons introduces by means of broad generalizations many of the key Miocene and Pliocene fossils. His main concern, however, is less with the individual fossils than with great principles of biology and evolution, and he comes to grips with a number of previous concepts which he feels have clouded our understanding and led us astray. As in many other selections, the reader is offered substantive data in the context of critical scientific thought.

SOURCE: *Science*, Vol. 141, 6 (1963), pp. 879–888. Copyright 1963 by American Association for the Advancement of Science. Reprinted with the permission of author and publisher.

The author (b. 1930) is now Associate Professor of Geology and Director of the Division of Vertebrate Paleontology of the Peabody Museum of Natural History, Yale University. He is the author of a monograph on an archaic ungulate order, *The Paleocene Pantodonta*, and of numerous articles on Tertiary primates.

The century-long search for documentation of the fossil record of man's ancestry, which was particularly stimulated by publication of Darwin's *Origin of Species* in 1859, has by now brought in relatively abundant evidence concerning the major stages of man's lineage during the Pleistocene epoch. Accelerated discovery during the past few years confirms the view that the mainstream of human evolution in Pleistocene times evidently passed through a species of *Australopithecus* and then through *Homo erectus* and men of Neanderthaloid type to the modern varieties of *Homo sapiens*. These comparatively new findings have shifted fundamental research somewhat away from the *Australopithecus-Homo sapiens* lineage, which most students consider a plausible sequence, toward the problem of the nature and distribution of pre-*Australopithecus* hominids and hominoids.[1] It is in this area that all new discoveries of the major stages in human phylogeny will come. Generally speaking, study of the Pleistocene section of human phylogeny has been carried out by anatomists and anthropologists, while the Miocene-Pliocene portion of the story has been investigated mainly by paleontologists. There have been, and perhaps there will continue to be, good reasons for this dichotomy. The study of Tertiary Mammalia (including nonhuman Primates) requires a more extensive background in stratigraphy, in field methods, and particularly in comparative osteology and mammalian taxonomy than is often possessed by students of man. Another factor has slowed progress in this area—the idea, expressed by some vertebrate paleontologists, that the evolution of higher Primates, and of man in particular, is too controversial and confused a subject to be worth much serious attention. If this view remains common among those best equipped to interpret fossil species, such lack of interest will only prolong the controversy.

In spite of the fact that there are almost no members of the Dryopithecinae of Miocene-Pliocene age for which reasonably comprehensive osteological remains are known, the actual number of specimens of this period that have been discovered is considerable (about 550), and the geographic range of the specimens is extensive. Moreover, advances in geochronometric dating techniques (potassium-argon analysis in particular) now, or shortly, will enable us to make a far more accurate temporal arrangement of man's pre-Pleistocene relatives than we have had. Many of these relatives fall taxonomically within the pongid subfamily Dryopi-

[1] A few taxonomic terms used in this article may require definition for the general reader: Dryopithecinae, a subfamily of pongids which includes several species of Miocene-Pliocene "apes"; Hominidae, the family of man and his immediate forerunners; Hominoidea (hominoids), a superfamily which includes the great apes and man, living and fossil, but excludes monkeys; Pongidae, the family of the fossil and living great apes. The term "Primates" is capitalized when the order Primates, as a major mammalian subdivision, is intended; "primates" (not capitalized) means some, but not all, members of this order.

thecinae. Although the fossil record for most dryopithecines is scanty, restudy of this osteologically limited material has now become imperative, because it is adequate to clarify the evolutionary succession of pongids and hominids.

I wish to state initially that I have carefully examined the view that *Proconsul*, from the East African Miocene, should be placed in a different subfamily from Eurasian dryopithecines and have found it unconvincing. Actually, there is hardly any morphological basis for separating Dryopithecinae (*Dryopithecus, Proconsul, Sivapithecus*, and related genera) from Ponginae (*Pongo, Pan, Gorilla*). Through the proper application of modern taxonomic principles, even without recovery of specimens more complete than those we now have, much more can be said about evolutionary relationships among the so-called dryopithecines than has been said to date. Dobzhansky recently summed up the pertinence of good taxonomy as it applies to fossil man. His point is equally relevant to the taxonomy of earlier hominoids.

"Does it really matter what Latin name one bestows on a fossil? Unfortunately it does. It flatters the discoverer's ego to have found a new hominid genus, or at least a new species, rather than a mere new race. But generic and specific names are not just arbitrary labels; they imply a biological status. Living men constitute a single species: *Homo sapiens*. Now, *Homo sapiens* can be descended from only one ancestral species living at any given time in the past. To be sure, some plant species arise from the hybridization of two ancestral species, followed by a doubling of the complement of chromosomes, but it is most unlikely that mankind could have arisen by such a process. It follows, then, that if two or several hominid species lived at a given time in the past, only one of them can possibly be our ancestor. All other species must be assumed to have died out without leaving descendants."

Undoubtedly a much more lucid picture of the Tertiary antecedents of man could be drawn on the basis of existing evidence were it not for the questionable nomenclatural practices of past years. Clearly, and regrettably, the taxonomic significance of the new systematics has been slower in gaining wide acceptance among anthropologists and paleontologists than among most biologists studying modern taxa. Of course, paleontologists have recognized for many years that the type individual of a fossil species is merely a specimen acquired through chance circumstances of fossilization and discovery from a population of variable organisms of which it may not even be a typical member. Types of fossil origin are thus chosen primarily as name-bearers for postulated species groups. Apparently it was less generally understood, until comparatively recently, that when one makes a specimen the type of a new species, or of a new genus and species, there is an obligation laid on the proposer of the new taxon to present a good deal of morphological or other evidence of probable genetic separation from any previously described species. This point applies particularly to Hominoidea, in which there is greater variability in dental pattern and relative tooth size than there is in many other mammal groups. Distinctions in dentition in a hominid specimen, sufficient to warrant designation of the specimen as the type for a new species, must be at least as great as the distinctions that occur between species of the closest living relatives of the fossil form.

Speciation

In order to understand what fossil species were and are, it is necessary to comprehend the processes of speciation and to be familiar with modern methods of species discrimination among living animals. Thus, in the case of the dryopithecines, in order to distinguish two fossil species of a given genus, one should be able to demonstrate that forms which are roughly contemporaneous show characters that fall outside the extreme range of morphological variability to be noted in comparable parts of all subspecies of present-day pongids, such as *Pan troglodytes* or *Gorilla gorilla*. High physical and dental variability in given species of man and apes has long been known, but it is clear that this has not been taken into account by the majority of past and recent describers of fossil hominoids. Beginning with Mayr in 1950, or slightly earlier, several experienced taxonomists have drawn attention to the extreme oversplitting of the known varieties of Pleistocene hominids. Since the late 19th century this erroneous approach to taxonomy has produced approximately 30 genera and almost countless species. At the other extreme from this taxonomic prolixity stand such workers as Mayr and Dobzhansky, who, drawing on their knowledge of modern speciation, have adduced evidence for a single line of but a few species, successive through time, in this particular lineage. To alter their view it would only be necessary to demonstrate the occurrence of two distinguishable species of hominids in a single zone of one site, but, despite much discussion of possible contemporaneity, in my opinion such contemporaneity has not been satisfactorily established. There is fair morphological evidence that there were two species of *Australopithecus* (*A. africanus* and *A. robustus*), but their synchronous existence has not been confirmed by finds of both at the same level in one site. Although the concept of monophyletic hominid evolution during the Pleistocene is now widely accepted, certain fallacies continue to affect thinking on probable pre-Pleistocene forms in this subfamily.

In the discussion that follows I attempt to outline and to clarify some of these fallacies. Changes in the taxonomy of fossil hominoids are suggested, on the basis of my direct observation of relevant original materials in America, Europe, East Africa, and India during the past 10 years. Among those acquainted with the traditional atmosphere of controversy that has surrounded the question of hominid origins there is often some reluctance to set forth an up-to-date survey of the implications of recent research on the subject. Clearly, all the points made here cannot be extensively supported by documentary evidence in this brief review. Nevertheless, it seems advisable to set some of the newer conclusions before the public at this stage.

Oversplitting of Fossil Species

Apart from the widespread temptation to be the author of a new species or genus, there are three primary causes of the oversubdivision of many extinct taxa (in the case under consideration, fossil Pongidae and Hominidae). These are, (i) uncertainties resulting from incompleteness of the available fossils; (ii) doubts concerning the identity and relative age of species (whether two or more given "types" are time-successive or contemporaneous); and (iii) questions relative to the possible, or probable, existence in the past of ecologic barriers that could perhaps have brought about speciation between populations widely separated geographically.

In view of these and other sources of uncertainty, taxonomists of fossil Primates have generally sidestepped the question of reference of new finds to previously established species, maintaining that it is unwise to assign later discoveries to species named earlier when finds are not strictly comparable or when they consist only of fragments of the whole skeleton; they frequently describe as separate species specimens which appear to come from clearly different time horizons; and they usually draw specific or generic distinctions when materials are recovered from sites that are widely separated geographically, particularly if these sites are on different continents. With continued advances in the dating of past faunas by geochemical means, and with advances in paleogeography, it becomes increasingly possible to improve procedures and practices in the taxonomy of extinct Primates, and to resolve many of the above-mentioned problems.

Generic and Specific Distinctions of Imperfectly Known Forms In the past it has sometimes happened that a taxonomist proposing a new species or genus of fossil vertebrate has maintained that, although no characteristics that would, of themselves, warrant separation of the new fossil specimen (B) from a previously known type (A) could be observed, the recovery of more complete osteological data would show the forms concerned to be different. This sort of anticipation is poor scientific practice, and such an argument should never be used in an effort to distinguish a new taxon unless (i) there is clear evidence of a marked separation in time between the previously described species A and the putative "new" form B, or (ii) there is definite geological evidence of geographic or ecologic separation—for example, evidence of a seaway or a desert—which would greatly reduce or eliminate the possibility of morphologically similar specimens A and B being members of one widespread, variable, but interbreeding, population. Some students would not grant even these two exceptions but believe that morphological distinctions must be demonstrated. Generally, some small distinction occurs as a result of individual variation and can be misused as evidence of species difference. Therefore it is best to rely mainly on differences which can be shown to be probable indicators of distinctly adapted, and consequently different, species.

Abundant data on Recent and late Tertiary mammals show that many of the larger species were, and are, distributed in more than one continent, particularly throughout Holarctica. Moreover, the belief that there were fairly close faunal ties between Africa and Eurasia during Miocene-Recent times has been confirmed by the recovery and description, during the past 3 years, of new samples of continental vertebrates of this period from Kenya, Tanganyika, and the Congo. Several of the mammals in these localities show close morphological similarity to Eurasian forms, and while many African species of the period do not show extra-African ties, the types which the two land masses have in common do show that increased intercommunication was possible. The fact that some stocks did not range outside Africa cannot offset the clear evidence that many of the same genera and even of the same species occurred in both Eurasia and Africa at this time.

Taxonomic Uncertainty Deriving from Temporal Differences Many hominoid species were proposed in the past mainly on the strength of a posited time separation from a nearly identical but presumably earlier (or later) "species." Most of the "species" designated on this basis should be reinvestigated in an effort to determine their true temporal position and taxonomic affinities. A "new look" is needed because of recent improvements in the potassium-argon method of dating, and in other geochemical dating methods which should ultimately enable students of past species to discuss them in terms of an absolute time scale. Like other kinds of scientific evidence, dates obtained by the potassium-argon method can of course be misapplied. For instance, it must be demonstrated that dated sediments come from (or bracket) the same zones as the faunas they are supposed to date. There are other well-known sources of error in geochemical dating, but in my experience the strongest criticisms of this method come from persons relatively unacquainted with the analytical techniques involved.

One example of the application of geochemical dating techniques to the study of fossil hominoids will suffice to show what wide application such information may have. Simons has proposed that, on morphological grounds, the primitive gibbon-like genera *Pliopithecus* and *Limnopi-*

thecus can no longer be considered distinguishable. Newly recovered materials of *Pliopithecus* [subgenus *Epipliopithecus*] from Miocene Vindobonian deposits of Europe are closely similar, both in dentition and in postcranial structure, to *"Limnopithecus"* from the Rusinga Island beds of Kenya, East Africa. The fauna associated with this East African primate was regarded, at the time of Hopwood's proposal that a genus *"Limnopithecus"* be established, as being of earliest Miocene age and, therefore, older than the European *Pliopithecus* materials. In his fullest discussion of the generic characteristics of *"Limnopithecus,"* Hopwood was able to list only a few slight features of distinction between the tooth rows, then known, of *Pliopithecus* and of *"Limnopithecus."* These are dental variations of a degree which have repeatedly been shown to occur even within members of one small population of such living pongids as *Pongo pygmaeus* and *Gorilla gorilla.* Hopwood further bolstered establishment of his new genus by remarking that additional bases for distinguishing the genera concerned "are the various ages of the deposits in which they are found and their widely separated localities." But he did comment, "apart from convenience neither reason [for placing the African species in a new genus] is particularly sound. . . ." The point I stress here is that taxonomic separations such as Hopwood proposed are not "convenient," for they create complexity where it does not exist.

Recently, Evernden and his associates have reported a date of 14.9± 1.5 million years obtained by the potassium-argon technique from biotite samples of tufaceous sediments in the Rusinga Island series. Admittedly this is only a single datum, but if this sample is truly satisfactory for dating by the potassium-argon method, and if it does come from the same horizons as the *"Proconsul* fauna," it shows that the fauna which contains *"Limnopithecus"* legetet and *"L."* macinnesi could be contemporary with the European Vindobonian materials. Nevertheless, more dating of this fauna will be necessary before we have proof that it is as young as this. If this younger age becomes established, species of *"Limnopithecus"* may well fall entirely within the known temporal distribution of European members of *Pliopithecus.* Evernden and his coworkers also state that the evidences from relative faunal dating suggest a middle or late, rather than an early, Miocene age for the Rusinga fossils. In my opinion this view is supported by close similarities between three other Rusinga primate species (which I discuss later) and forms which occur in the Siwalik deposits of India, of probable middle or late Miocene age.

Finally, it should be stressed that Hopwood did exhibit considerable foresight in recognizing the basic unsoundness of attempting to reinforce a taxonomic separation by the argument of possible (but not proved) temporal difference. The foregoing example, and others which could be noted, show the danger of using the temporal argument when separating closely similar fossil specimens taxonomically. Moreover, it has been demonstrated that many extant mammalian genera have time ranges greater than the entire Miocene epoch, as estimated at present. Numerous instances of genera with long time ranges could be adduced. For instance, the perissodactyl genera *Tapirus* and *Dicerorhinus* in all probability extend back to the early Miocene or late Oligocene, about 25×10^6 years ago; members of some genera of carnivores (*Ursus, Bassariscus, Lutra, Felis,* and others) have all been described from deposits of late Miocene or early Pliocene age (10 to 15×10^6 years ago). Of course, we do not know that any hominoid genera survived as long as the genera in these categories, but most hominoid genera probably endured for at least 3 to 7 million years without much change of form. Consequently, even if it were known that European and East African *Pliopithecus* differed in absolute age by 4 or 5 million years, taxonomic separation at the generic level could not safely be based on this fact alone.

Migration, Paleogeography, and Past Restrictions of Species Ranges One of the most widespread assumptions in the study of the antecedents of man is that at some early period (Miocene, Pliocene, or "Villafranchian," depending on the author concerned) the species ancestral to *Homo sapiens* was restricted to a comparatively small geographic area. This restriction is taken by many scientists to account for the supposed "failure" to find pre-Pleistocene human forerunners. Such an assumption may be referred to as the "Garden of Eden illusion." Insofar as this widespread view is held as a scientific theory by some persons interested in the evolutionary history of man, it appears to be based on analogy with the restricted ranges of various recent mammal species, particularly, in this case, of higher Primates with limited distributions, such as orangutan (*Pongo pygmaeus*) or mountain gorilla (*Gorilla g. beringei*).

Place of Man's Origin

Some people believe that the place of hominid or human origin has not been discovered; conjectures, by others, as to its location have followed shifting vogues. Thus, when the first materials of *"Megan-thropus"* were recovered in Java from levels lower stratigraphically than those at which *"Pithecanthropus"* remains were recovered, many students favored the view that differentiation of the ancestral stock of mankind occurred in Southeast Asia. Later, with the realization that *Australopithecus* finds from the Transvaal were hominid remains, a case was made for initial hominid differentiation in South Africa. Now, new additions to our knowledge of early Hominidae, made in East Africa by Leakey and his associates, have shifted attention northward to that quadrant of the African continent.

It should be obvious that the oldest *known* localities of occurrence of human tools, or of given species of higher Primates, are probably not the first places where these technical developments or species arose. In order to report with confidence the exact regions of origin of the human species and of earliest cultural items, we would need 100 times the archeological and paleontological evidence that we now have, with absolute dates for all sites.

There are a number of possible reasons for the persistence of the "Garden of Eden" concept among scientists, but here I mention only a few of the misconceptions through which this point of view appears to have been initiated and sustained. Students who believe that ancestral species occurred in restricted areas may have in mind four well-known kinds of diffusion from local centers: (i) spreading of cultural items from specific places of invention; (ii) wandering of tribes, both historic and prehistoric, over great distances; (iii) spreading of advantageous gene mutations from individuals or local populations outward throughout an entire species population; and (iv) intercontinental faunal migrations across land bridges at various times in the past.

All these, and other, similar concepts, while pertinent in their own right, do not in my opinion validate the illusion that, through time, each species, as a unit, wanders widely from one region to another. Such a picture is particularly inaccurate in the case of Late Tertiary land-mammal species, such as species among the dryopithecines, whose main area of distribution was the tropical and warm-temperate portion of the Old World. Of course, given sufficient time, species ranges, particularly among the large Mammalia, do expand and contract, and do occasionally shift from one continent to another in response to environmental change. Nevertheless, movement of subpopulations is much greater than the range shifts of an entire species. Even within an evolving species lineage, time-successive species apparently do not appear from one of several populations of the antecedent species; in general, all populations of a single species tend to evolve together, the species changing as a whole because, as the environment changes, newly advantageous genes originating in various sections of the group spread through the species. Of course, if these streams of gene flow are broken for sufficiently long periods, speciation will ultimately occur. A single species, however, *is* a single species just because gene flow throughout all its members is (or recently has been) taking place.

Range of Large Mammal Species

Now, in applying these ideas to the evolution of large mammals in the Miocene-Recent period, primarily to mammals of the tropical and warm-temperate regions of Palearctica, certain points extremely relevant to the interpretation of dryopithecine evolution emerge. The first of these is illustrated in Fig. 1, which shows a hypothetical model of the range of a large mammal species-series at three periods in the earth's history. The diagram is given as an abstraction because limitations in the distribution of sites yielding fossil land mammals (limitations that result from erosion of sediments or from nondeposition) are such that exact species ranges for past forms cannot now be drawn (and probably never can be). Nevertheless, this is the sort of distribution which recovered fossils indicate was characteristic, during the period with which we are concerned, of certain species of groups such as elephants, hyenas, the big cats, and ruminants. In this context it should be pointed out that the early supposition that many surviving species of large mammals have diminished ranges owing primarily to climatic fluctuations during the Pleistocene and to the activity of human hunters has, by now, been abundantly confirmed. Two examples, taken from dozens, illustrate this point. The lion, *Felis leo,* is now extinct in Eurasia except for a few small surviving populations in India. However, 15,000 to 20,000 years ago, *Felis leo* occurred widely in Europe and the Near East and was, presumably, then abundant in the Indian subcontinent and perhaps even further east. Ewer has reported fossil remains closely resembling *Felis tigris* (but from a mammal slightly larger than the largest of modern tigers) from Olduvai Gorge in Tanganyika. Today, of course, the tiger exists only in Asia.

In the sort of species succession through time that is diagramed in Fig. 1, is it not possible to say where the paleontological "species" came from—the population during, for example, the late Pliocene did not come *from* any one place and, strictly speaking, does not have a known place of origin. As nearly as can at present be determined, from the literature and from direct study of the relevant fossils in East Africa and in India in Miocene-Pliocene times, Eurasia and Africa had over 35 genera of land mammals in common. These included insectivores, anthracotheres, rodents, ruminants, monkeys, apes, hyracoids, hyenas, felids, mastodonts, deinotheres, and several other groups of mammals. Members of over 15 additional mammalian genera that now occur in Africa but have not yet been found in fossil sites on that continent have been found in Pliocene deposits of the Indian Siwalik Hills. This total figure of half-a-hundred genera stands in spite of the early tendency to separate, at the generic level, African mammals from allied forms found elsewhere, just because they are of African provenance. Nevertheless, there are some distinct differences in African and Eurasian faunas of Miocene and Pliocene times.

Although numerous groups do appear to have been prevented from crossing between the two areas, there is now evidence that certain mammal species had no difficulty in getting across whatever partial ecological barriers may have existed between the two regions in Pliocene times. One of these is the proboscidean species *Trilophodon angustidens,* which has been found as far east as Baluchistan, occurs in the Kenya Miocene, and has recently been reported by Hooijer from the Congo. There are enough such occurrences to indicate to me that there was reasonably free faunal interchange between these two major regions of the Old World at some time in the Miocene. I see no reason why certain species of dryopithecines or early hominids, or both, could not have participated in this interchange.

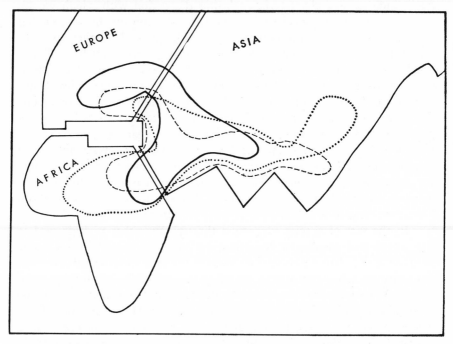

Figure 1 Three species ranges, successive through time, of a hypothetical lineage of a large mammal, as they might have appeared in (dashed lines) the late Miocene, (dotted lines) the early Pliocene, and (solid lines) the late Pliocene.

Nevertheless, one may ask whether higher Primates ever had range distributions as extensive as those of such later Tertiary Mammalia as I have mentioned. Clearly, the range distribution of most present-day great apes is a restricted or relict distribution, but the fossil record of the pongids for the Miocene through the Villafranchian, as it now stands, is ample indication that certain varieties of these animals had much wider range distributions formerly than they have now. This also appears to be true for many animals of the later Pleistocene. For instance, *Pongo pygmaeus*, now restricted to the islands of Borneo and Sumatra, was then present in South China, and if the Siwalik Pliocene fossils reported by Pilgrim are truly ancestors of this species, it probably had, at an earlier date, an extended range through the Malay Peninsula and Burma into India. Probable antecedents of the gibbons (*Pliopithecus*) are known from several scattered localities throughout Europe and northern and eastern Africa; at one time they must have been distributed (in suitable habitats) between these areas and the present range of members of this genus, in Southeast Asia. Evidently the ranges of modern species of great apes have dwindled greatly as a result of environmental changes in the relatively recent past. Among such changes was shrinking of the type of forest cover that was necessary for their existence. In certain populations, such as those of *Pongo* in South Asia, extermination or restriction of isolated enclaves on offshore islands surely came about as a result of hunting by human beings.

One of the varieties of primates least affected by these types of constriction are the present-day species of the genus *Macaca*. Distribution of members of this genus (Fig. 2) illustrates the extremes of geographic range which members of a single stock of a prehominoid grade of partly arboreal primates have been able to achieve. It need not be assumed that man's ancestors had limited species range until they became terrestrial bipeds. In late-Pliocene and Villafranchian times, *Macaca* was nearly twice as widespread geographically as it is today. An acceptable evolutionary interpretation of this distribution would be that the ancestors of present-day *Macaca* reached the present extremes of their range (Japan, Gibraltar, and so on) when continental shelves were exposed during one of the Pleistocene glaciations, and that the far-flung present-day populations are descendants of perhaps no more than one widespread species that existed 1 to 3 million years ago. Of course, this species could have been already differentiating into genetically diverse populations (subspecies), with only moderate gene exchange between them, before and while the total range of the species was approaching its greatest extent. But it seems more probable that such species distinctions as exist in *Macaca* came about through relatively recent cessation of gene flow between various populations within the entire genus range.[2] This would be particularly the case for populations isolated on islands since the last glaciation, or separated by late disappearance of suitable habitat, as between the western population of North Africa and its eastern allies. Members of *Macaca* appear to have been able to achieve such broad distribution mainly because its species have been ecologically plastic. Some varieties, such as the Japanese monkey, have remained relatively arboreal, while others, like the Barbary ape of Gibraltar, are almost entirely terrestrial.

[2] Although several present-day species of *Macaca* surely must be valid—that is, genetically isolated—it is of some interest to observe that most of these living "species" of the genus *Macaca* have not been shown by cross-breeding experiments to be distinct species.

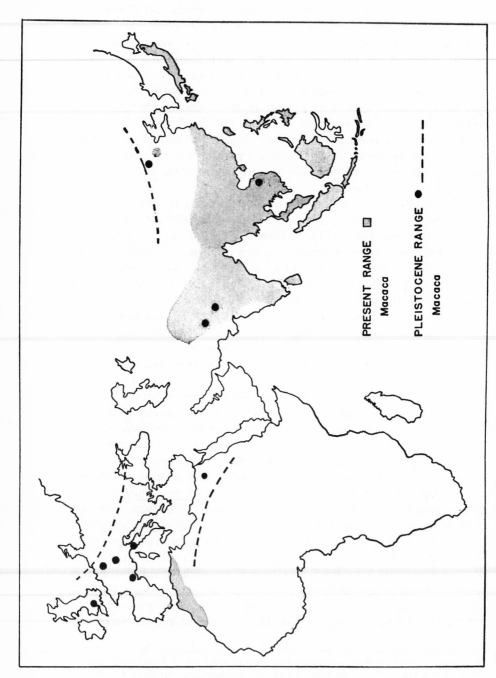

PRESENT RANGE ▨
Macaca

PLEISTOCENE RANGE ●
Macaca

Figure 2   Recent and fossil distribution of the species of *Macaca*.

Conceivably, from the late Miocene on, the earliest hominids were at least as capable of extending their range as the species of *Macaca* evidently were at a somewhat later date.

Thus, it can no longer be argued with confidence that the reason no pre-Pleistocene forerunners of man have been discovered is that these pre-hominids lived only in a limited geographical area of the Old World, and in a region (perhaps of tropical forests) which has yielded no fossil remains. It is now quite clear that the early hominoids as we know them from fossil remains ranged widely in the Old World in Miocene and Pliocene times. In Fig. 3 the scattered occurrences of the hominoid genera are connected by straight lines, forming rough approximations to range diagrams. Particulars of the sites and species upon which Fig. 3 is based can be found in Piveteau. In spite of three contrary factors—the rarity of fossil Primates, the enthusiasm of certain taxonomists for subdividing at the generic level, and failure to discover fossil-bearing localities in relevant areas—each of several "generic" units among Anthropoidea of this period have now been reported from at least two Old World continents, and some have been discovered in all three. That ancestors of man are not included among these extensive materials is, in my opinion, no longer an easily defended viewpoint. Moreover, the idea is equally controverted on morphological grounds. Some dryopithecines do show hominid features. The argument that human antecedents lived during pre-Pleistocene times in a restricted area which remains undiscovered has another rather unlikely consequence. This assumption implies that apes and even some monkeys (*Dryopithecus, Pliopithecus, Macaca*), although largely or partly arboreal, were able to spread their range widely, while the forerunners of man were somehow unable to do this. We are here concerned with a stock which, by the early Pliocene, was probably experimenting with terrestrial living and bipedal locomotion. If, at this time, man's predecessors were not able to distribute themselves as readily as their contemporaries among the monkeys and apes could, then it becomes necessary to conclude that man's evolutionary emergence from his pre-human past was truly explosive. This conclusion becomes all the more necessary if we assume that our supposedly poorly distributed antecedents suddenly outdistanced their more "primitive" contemporaries in the matter of species-range extension.

Species Distinctions

It should be noted that, although the particular specimens assigned by one or more competent authorities to the genera indicated in Fig. 3 are adequately known for purposes of generic placement, students cannot tell definitely whether the specimens assigned to a genus were members of the same or of different species. The common practice has been to regard

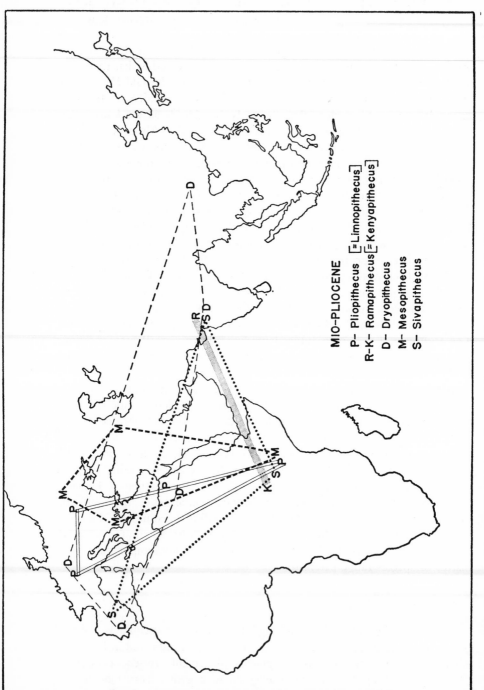

Figure 3 Occurrence and range distribution of some Miocene-Pliocene Hominoidea.

European, Asian, and African finds of later Tertiary fossil Mammalia as belonging to different species, presumably in part because of the tacit assumption that ecologic barriers would, in nearly all cases, have prevented members of a species from reaching all three areas. Nevertheless, since these fossil forms are known primarily from fragmentary dentitions, it remains as difficult to prove that members of populations discovered in different continents represent distinct species as to demonstrate that they are members of the same species. Consequently, it will not be possible to test the validity of species distinctions among many such extinct mammals until much greater numbers of fossils of particular groups are known. In the case of these fossil "apes," for instance, when enough material has been recovered, statistical methods may be used in making species distinctions.

In connection with Fig. 3, it should also be pointed out that leading taxonomists of fossils differ as to the generic assignment of some of the species represented. For instance, after initial assignment of certain Spanish dryopithecine remains to the genus *Sivapithecus* (an assignment followed here), this material was later referred elsewhere. On the other hand, Lewis believes that materials currently assigned to *Dryopithecus* from the Miocene of Czechoslovakia should be placed in the genus *Sivapithecus*.

Consequently, I doubt that it has been established that *Sivapithecus* does not occur in Europe. Conversely, Fig. 3 does not indicate a range extension of *Pliopithecus* into Southeast Asia, but it seems entirely possible that the very fragmentary type of "*Hylopithecus*" from the Siwalik "series" may represent a primitive gibbon, perhaps assignable to *Pliopithecus*. With reference to this specimen, it seems instructive to quote what must be one of the most amazing passages in the history of bad taxonomic practice. This remark occurs as a conclusion to the description of the type species of "*Hylopithecus*": "In preference to leaving the tooth now described without a generic name and so increasing the difficulty of reference I am giving it the name of *Hylopithecus*, although I am conscious that my material is quite insufficient for diagnosis."

Origin of the Hominidae

In 1910 Pilgrim was ready to state that Hominidae are descended from *Sivapithecus*. Later, in 1922, W. K. Gregory observed "that man is a late Tertiary offshoot of the *Dryopithecus-Sivapithecus* group. . . ." Discoveries of hominoids during the half century which has elapsed since Pilgrim's writing have reinforced his viewpoint. Entirely apart from morphological considerations, such conclusions gain strength in the light of the taxonomic procedures and zoogeographic examples that I have discussed. It is curious that, in spite of numerous suitably cautious demonstrations in paleontological papers that the origins of man lay among the dryopithecines, it is still widely held by experts that next to nothing of definite value is known about the pre-Pleistocene forerunners of man. One is reminded of a possibly apocryphal comment said to have been made in 1860 by the wife of the Bishop of Worcester. On learning from her husband that T. H. Huxley had then recently argued that man had apelike ancestors, she observed: "Descended from apes! My dear, let us hope that it is not true, but if it is let us pray that it will not become generally known." Although the fact of human evolution is no longer doubted, the phyletic sequence before the Pleistocene has never been elucidated during the more than 100 years which separate us from the pronouncements of T. H. Huxley.

Briefly, the following relevant facts as to the origin of the family of man are known. Fossil "apes" of the *Dryopithecus-Sivapithecus* type have now been recovered from deposits distributed throughout a vast area of warm-climate regions of the Old World, including sites in Spain, France, central Europe, Turkey, Georgia, the U.S.S.R., Egypt, Kenya, Uganda, Pakistan, India, and China. Without undertaking a taxonomic revision of these forms at this juncture, but assuming for the moment that all these occurrences do in fact pertain to dryopithecines, I must point out that far too many genera have been proposed for them. Some of the genera which have been named are *Ankarapithecus, Austriacopithecus, Bramapithecus, Griphopithecus, Dryopithecus, Hylopithecus, Indopithecus, Kenyapithecus, Neopithecus, Paidopithex, Proconsul, Paleosimia, Ramapithecus, Rhenopithecus, Sivapithecus, Sugrivapithecus,* and *Udabnopithecus.*

Such a large number of distinct genera implies an extensive adaptive radiation of sudden appearance in the early or middle Miocene, but in the case of the dryopithecines this diversification probably occurred more on paper than in reality. Direct study of nearly all of the original specimens of these Primates suggests to me that the dryopithecines should probably be assigned to only three or four distinct genera, perhaps even fewer.

Species of four of these "genera" (*Dryopithecus, Sivapithecus, Proconsul,* and *Ramapithecus*) are now fairly well known. To date, however, no student has adequately dealt with the possibility that not even all of these genera may be separable from each other. This is an important issue, for it now appears that the direct hominid lineage passed through members of at least two of these taxa.

Starting with the more *Australopithecus*-like of these forms and working backward through time, we can now draw some fairly clear inferences about the evolutionary appearance of Hominidae. *Ramapithecus brevirostris*, of probable early Pliocene (Pontian) age, from the Nagri zone of the Siwalik Hills of India, has long been known to possess several characters in the upper dentition and maxilla which significantly approach the dental conformation of Pleistocene species of tool-making man. Briefly, these characters, which distinguish the forms from typical pongids and suggest hominid ties, are a parabolic (not U-shaped) dental arcade, an arched palate, a canine fossa, low-crowned cheek teeth, small incisors and canines, a low degree of prognathism, and a short face. Separately, almost all of these features can be found among pongids, but their occurrence in combination in *R. brevirostris* is a strong indication of hominid ties. Recently, Leakey has described a new East African primate specimen, "*Kenyapithecus wickeri*," probably from about the same period or a little earlier, which is exactly like *R. brevirostris* in these and other features. In fact, in my opinion, not one *significant* character of difference exists between the two specimens (both are maxillae). This being so, the new form from Kenya should be assigned tentatively to *R. brevirostris*, at least until such a time as further material provides a basis for demonstrating that the two are different species. The conclusion that these two specimens are at least of the same genus has recently been supported by Frisch, who has also studied them directly. Perhaps the most extraordinary thing about Leakey's Fort Ternan, Kenya, specimen is its extreme similarity to the type specimen of *R. brevirostris*—an important and very significant fact that "generic" splitting only obscures. Greater differences than are to be noted here typically occur among members of a single-family social group within nearly all species of present-day hominoids. These two specimens indicate to me a considerable probability that in early Pliocene or latest Miocene times, or both, a single species of progressive (?)dryopithecine ranged all the way from northern India to East Africa, and perhaps farther. Personal examination of the specimens concerned also indicates that a third individual of this species, from the Nagri zone of the Siwalik Hills, in the Haritalyangar area, is represented by Pilgrim's specimen No. D185—the right maxilla of "*Dryopithecus punjabicus*"—in the Indian Museum, Calcutta. This specimen agrees with the other two in significant details of dental morphology, and in the possession of a much-reduced rostrum and an extremely short canine root (alveolus). These three specimens of *Ramapithecus* strongly reinforce each other in indicating a valid species group. Moreover, all three specimens come from a stratigraphic level higher than that at which most of the more generalized dryopithecine remains are found.

The transitional nature of these specimens itself raises the question of arbitrariness in separating the families Pongidae and Hominidae—a problem which has also been posed recently in connection with another event, the discovery of close biochemical similarities between man and the apes, in particular the African apes. Nevertheless, there do seem to be

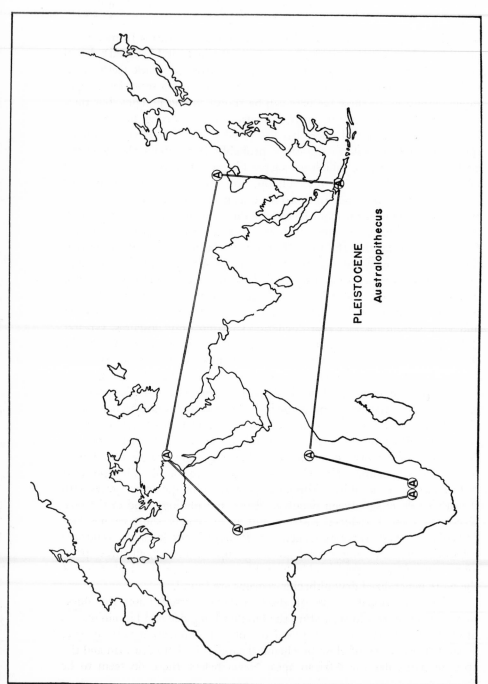

Figure 4 Reported range of *Australopithecus* species.

fairly good reasons for continuing to view the Pongidae and the Hominidae as distinct enough to be considered separate families. What I want to stress is the fact that the transitional nature of the *Ramapithecus* materials is such that they cannot be placed with finality in either group. Personally I do not see that it very much matters whether members of this genus be regarded as advanced pongids or as primitive hominids, but perhaps considerations of morphology slightly favor placement among the hominids. There is certainly no need to produce a new, higher category for such links—an alternative which has sometimes been resorted to in the past when a fossil taxon was determined to be roughly intermediate between two others.

Two Series of Dryopithecines

To date, the most extensive series of dryopithecines come from two main areas, the Rusinga Island and Fort Ternan beds of Kenya and the Siwalik Hills of India and Pakistan. A primary difficulty in understanding the actual significance of these two series of Primates arises from the fact that the Indian dryopithecines were studied and described primarily in the period between 1910 and 1937, while the dryopithecines of Kenya have been dealt with mainly since 1951. No one has ever published the results of extensive comparative study of the two sets of materials. Lewis, in the most recent taxonomic treatment of the Siwalik "apes," in 1937, reduced the number of genera to four (*Bramapithecus, Ramapithecus, Sivapithecus, Sugrivapithecus*), with ten contained species. Members of the first two of these genera he regarded as more manlike than members of the other two; *Sivapithecus* and *Sugrivapithecus* he regarded as being closer to the present-day great apes. Unfortunately, there was a lack of associations between upper and lower dentitions in the Siwalik material, and knowledge of some of these genera—such as *Bramapithecus*, known only from jaw fragments containing the last two molars—was very limited. There were no whole or nearly complete dentitions in which to study the range of variability. This situation has now changed, because of the recovery in Africa (1948–1962) of relatively complete portions of skulls, maxillae, and mandibles of several individual dryopithecines, together with postcranial bones and, in some cases, associated upper and lower jaws. Comparison of these two series of data indicate the following problems.

1) In both the Kenyan and the Indian sites (in the lower part of the section, in particular) is found a large form with large snout, protruding incisors, slicing anterior premolars, and rather high-crowned teeth. In the East African material the lingual molar cingula are more pronounced, but otherwise, characters of dentition, snout, and jaw do not differ significantly. Mainly, these Miocene varieties have been called *Sivapithecus in-*

dicus (Siwaliks), and *Proconsul major* (Rusinga). May it not be that these two sets of fossils represent a single species that ranged fairly widely, and perhaps over a long period, but which in known populations (even from far-flung portions of its range) is not particularly variable? This large-snouted type of ape is temporally distributed from early or middle Miocene (Rusinga; Chinji, in the Siwaliks) to latest Miocene or early Pliocene (Fort Ternan; Nagri, in the Siwaliks), as is evidenced by a very large upper canine recovered at Fort Ternan, at the same level as "*Kenyapithecus*," reported by Leakey; perhaps by other teeth found at Fort Ternan, that have not been described; and by several discoveries in the Nagri Zone. Differences in the molar-crown patterns of the two populations are about as great within each area as between the two groups. A few successive species may be indicated by this material, or only a single species may be involved. This species could well be ancestral to the gorilla and chimpanzee. Ancestors of the African apes certainly need not always have been restricted to that continent.

2) A second primate form common to the Kenya and Indian areas in the Miocene is represented by the *Sivapithecus africanus* material (Kenya) and the "species" *Sivapithecus sivalensis* (India). In this group the teeth, particularly the canines, are relatively smaller than in "*S.*" *indicus*, and lingual cingula on upper molars apparently occur less frequently. The possibility remains high that other East African and Siwalik species, of the 15 accepted as valid in the more recent literature, will fall into synonymy with these two species as new data are recovered, or as a result of a fuller comparative study now in progress. The main distinction in dentition (and almost the only difference in known parts) between some *Sivapithecus* and modern *Pongo* is the higher degree of crenulation of the crowns of cheek teeth in *Pongo*. Several specimens of Indian *Sivapithecus* show rather crenulate molar crowns, and this may be assumed to indicate something about the origin of the orangutan. Such crenulations are particularly developed in the upper molar described by Pilgrim as "*Paleosimia*," which may be a valid genus. In view of these crenulate teeth, it appears probable that a species that differentiated toward the Bornean great ape is represented in the Siwalik material, but this form has not been fully distinguished in taxonomic work to date. The probability that *Proconsul* cannot be separated generically from *Dryopithecus* is worth mentioning here. Both these genera, if indeed they are two rather than one, appear to be restricted to the Miocene. *Sivapithecus* apparently crosses the Mio-Pliocene boundary but is not easily separated from *Ramapithecus*, a conclusion indicated by Leakey's report on the East African materials and by my own studies on the Indian dryopithecines.

Conclusion

In concluding it seems advisable to make several observations as to the current state of knowledge of the origins of advanced hominoids.

The fossil hominoids of the Miocene of Kenya do not now appear to belong to the early part of that epoch, as had been previously believed, but may be of middle or, less probably, late Miocene age. Similarities between hominoids of the Miocene in India and Kenya, together with resemblances in other members of the two faunas, suggest that the Chinji Zone of the Siwaliks may be middle or late Miocene, as originally suggested by several early workers. At this time the "radiation" which produced the great apes of today and man seems barely to have begun. The possible occurrence of *Dryopithecus* in early Miocene equivalents of Egypt requires further investigation. There is now nearly universal agreement among those most competent to judge that *Oreopithecus* does not stand in the ancestral line of later pongids and hominids, although it is related to them. In view of these conclusions, the origins of man and of the great apes of Africa and Borneo are seen to lie directly among the dryopithecines. This conclusion supports the extensive discussions of Gregory as to the significance for human phylogeny of the *Dryopithecus* molar pattern and LeGros Clark's analysis of the morphological evidences favoring the occurrence of secondary canine reduction in the ancestry of Hominidae.

There is now adequate fossil evidence to indicate, (i) that, from about middle Miocene times, a few widely distributed species of the larger hominoids were present in both Eurasia and Africa and that successive differentiation of these species, through time, has occurred, with little branching or radiation; (ii) that the primary center of speciation among these animals was outside of Europe; (iii) that some dryopithecines in known parts entirely close the slight morphological gap between Hominidae and Pongidae; and (iv) that, if reports as to localities of *Australopithecus* [3] by several serious students be accepted, the data now show that this earliest generally accepted antecedent of man was widely distributed in tropical regions of the Old World in the early Pleistocene (Fig. 4). Present archeological evidence does suggest that the use of tools may have occurred first in Africa, but this is not the same as to suppose

---

[3] In addition to major finds in Olduvai Gorge, Tanganyika, and the Transvaal, South Africa, the reported assignments of fossils to the Australopithecinae and specifically to *Australopithecus* (subgenera *Australopithecus* and *Paranthropus*) are as follows. (i) Teeth found in association with a Villafranchian fauna at Tell Ubeidiya, Jordan Valley, Israel; (ii) *Australopithecus* cranial fragment found near Largeau, Lake Chad, North Africa; (iii) transfer of Javan *"Meganthropus"* to *Australopithecus* (subgenus *Paranthropus*); (iv) description of *Australopithecus* (= *Hemianthropus*) *peii*, from China.

that the initial species of man differentiated there, unless man be defined solely as a tool-manufacturing primate. To date, the latter supposition is an inference primarily supported by negative evidence—namely, the scanty recovery of australopithecines and of pebble tools in Southeast Asia and China. It must be remembered that one creditable occurrence is all that is needed to demonstrate the early presence of *Australopithecus* in the East. Such an occurrence apparently has now been confirmed by von Koenigswald, through his description of about a dozen teeth, assigned by him to a new genus, *"Hemianthropus,"* in materials recovered from Chinese drugstores. In my opinion these teeth are from members of the Australopithecinae assignable to the subgenus *Paranthropus*, but Woo suggests that some of these teeth could belong to *Gigantopithecus*.

10 Some Problems of Hominid Classification

David R. Pilbeam and
Elwyn L. Simons

GEORGE GAYLORD SIMPSON'S EFFORTS TO IMPROVE THE RIGOR AND RATIONALITY *of taxonomic statements have not yet achieved the success of universal conversions among scientists, but favorable results have already begun to flow in and the future looks brighter.*

While it will be the relevant sciences which will benefit most by re-organization of taxonomy and nomenclature, the reform will certainly benefit the beleaguered student who still frequently has to learn that Sinanthropus pekinensis *is really* Pithecanthropus erectus (pekinensis) *but really, really* Homo erectus (pekinensis). *And this in addition to a thundering variety of primate fossils who lived at different times during a 70-million-year period and whose precise relationships to each other and to ourselves is the subject of endless squabbling among the professors.*

As an act of charity towards the students, then, we offer a brilliant attempt to synthesize a coherent picture of what is known of hominid evolution from pre-Pliocene through Pleistocene times. That it culminates in an attempt to represent Pleistocene hominids as a single continuum evolving through time and does so through the medium of a diagram adapted from Simpson is, you may be sure, no accident.

The early 1950's were years of controversy in human paleontology; argument, discussion, and sometimes polemic were focused on the relationship to other primates of the genus *Australopithecus*, primates some-

SOURCE: *American Scientist*, Vol. 53 (1965), pp. 237–257. Reprinted with the permission of the authors and publisher.

David R. Pilbeam (b. 1940) is University Demonstrator in Physical Anthropology, University of Cambridge. For biographical data on Elwyn L. Simons, see I:9.

times called near-men or man-apes. These were known mainly, at that time, from finds made in the Transvaal, South Africa. Although the species of *Australopithecus* are now considered hominid, many students were reluctant at first to accept such a status, believing that small brain volume and "imperfect" adaptation to upright posture prevented their assignment to the Hominidae, the taxonomic family which includes living man. Instead, these creatures were regarded as aberrant apes.

Subsequently, it was realized that it is not possible to exclude species from the Hominidae on account of small brain size; the ancestors of modern man must obviously, at some stage, have had smaller brains. The "imperfections" of the *Australopithecus* pelvis were also overstressed; there is good reason to believe that the species of *Australopithecus* were now habitual and efficient bipeds. The concept that different functional systems may evolve independently and at varying rates (mosaic evolution), has also been assimilated by most anthropologists, and, in addition, it is no longer considered reasonable to discriminate taxa on the basis of a few characters alone.

Another sort of misunderstanding derives from one's reference point in studying hominid evolution. Perhaps we have been looking down the wrong end of the telescope, so to speak, trying to understand the evolution of man by looking backward through time "from the vantage point of the Recent." If *Homo* species evolved from the species *Australopithecus africanus*, as many believe, we should expect that these species would have many features in common. Those characters in which they differ, however, should be regarded as specializations of *Homo*, not as peculiarities of *Australopithecus*. One must not ask "How *Homo*-like is *Australopithecus*?" but rather the opposite.

Origin of the Hominidae

Washburn has stated recently that "most of the characters of *Homo* seem to have evolved well within the Pleistocene, and there is no need to postulate an early separation of man and ape." But the fossil record, although limited, instead seems to indicate a pre-Pliocene separation. Our Pliocene ancestors evidently were socially and adaptively more like man than great apes. By the early Pleistocene, except in the matter of brain-size, man's relatives (men or near-men) were almost as different morphologically from both living and extinct great apes as are men today. *Australopithecus* in fact resembles *Homo* far more than either resembles the African apes, man's closest living relatives.

Ever since the nineteenth-century inception of human paleontology, the comparison of early man with living apes, the only other well-known hominoids, has been overemphasized. This tendency has led, on the one hand, to stressing supposedly ape-like features in late forms of fossil man

(Boule's classic studies of European Neanderthals, for example). On the other hand, this has led to surprise whenever "advanced" characteristics are found in early forms (for example, the modern looking hominid foot from Bed I at Olduvai Gorge, Tanganyika).

Ramapithecus punjabicus (Fig. 1) is known from the Siwalik Hills of North India, from Fort Ternan, Kenya, and possibly from the Swabian Alps in Europe, appearing first in the latest Miocene. This species also occurs in sediments of uncertain age in Keiyuan, Yunnan, China. It is sufficient here to point out that the incisors, canines, and premolars are reduced relative to those of known species of dryopithecines and of present-day apes. In *Ramapithecus*, as in man, internal cingula are absent and molar crowns simple. *Ramapithecus* could have evolved with almost equal probability from a dryopithecine, sometime between early and middle Miocene, or from species more like the Egyptian Oligocene primate *Propliopithecus haeckeli*. Hominoid species evolving respectively in the direction of *Homo* and of *Pan* need not have shared a common ancestor later than early or middle Miocene times.

In our opinion, assignment to Hominidae can reasonably be made for all those species that show evolutionary trends toward modern *Homo*, whenever these trends appear. The evolutionary shift in a major adaptive zone indicated in the case of *Ramapithecus* by its reduced snout and anterior teeth (premolars, canines, and incisors) may well correlate with an increased use of the hands and the incipient development of bipedality, although direct fossil evidence for both these developments is presently lacking. Even if *Ramapithecus* and *Pan* had a more recent common ancestor than either did with the orangutan, the Hominidae are presumably definable in terms of this adaptive shift, as is indicated in Figure 2. Moreover, *Ramapithecus* is presently best regarded as a hominid, not a hominid-like pongid, because it already exhibits the basic dental adaptations of *Homo* and *Australopithecus*. If the other parts of the skeleton, subsequently found, should all be ape-like, this position could require alteration. But why should this be so? Of course, it is quite possible that, if and when cranial and post-cranial remains of *Ramapithecus* are discovered, they will prove to be rather more *Dryopithecus*-like than are those of *Australopithecus*, because *Ramapithecus* lies several million years closer in time to the common ancestor of apes and men. However, the known parts are not ape-like; *Ramapithecus* cannot logically be lumped any longer with the apes.

Fossil ancestors of the living orangutan of Asia are either unknown or unrecognized. Biochemical and serological research underlines the close relationship of modern man to the great apes of Africa. This supports other, mainly paleontological, evidence suggesting that chimpanzee, gorilla, and men are more closely related cladistically, that is, in recency of a common ancestor for all, than all three are to the orangutan and the

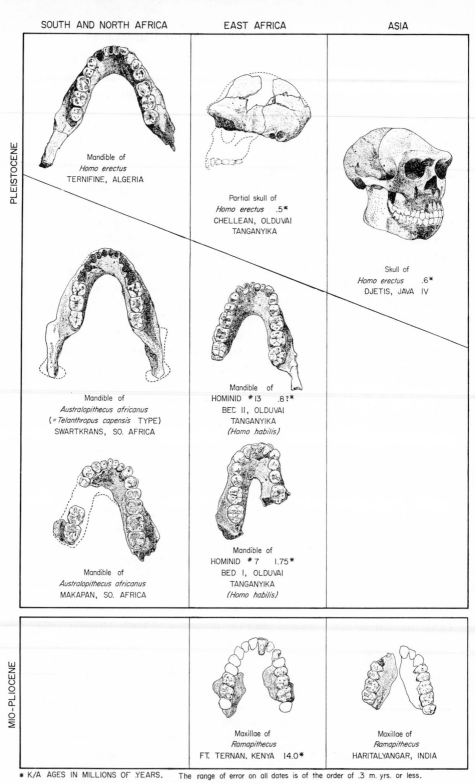

PLEISTOCENE

Mandible of
Homo erectus
TERNIFINE, ALGERIA

Partial skull of
Homo erectus   .5*
CHELLEAN, OLDUVAI
TANGANYIKA

Skull of
Homo erectus   .6*
DJETIS, JAVA IV

Mandible of
Australopithecus africanus
(=*Telanthropus capensis* TYPE)
SWARTKRANS, SO. AFRICA

Mandible of
HOMINID #13   .8?*
BED II, OLDUVAI
TANGANYIKA
(*Homo habilis*)

Mandible of
Australopithecus africanus
MAKAPAN, SO. AFRICA

Mandible of
HOMINID #7   1.75*
BED I, OLDUVAI
TANGANYIKA
(*Homo habilis*)

MIO-PLIOCENE

Maxillae of
Ramapithecus
FT. TERNAN, KENYA   14.0*

Maxillae of
Ramapithecus
HARITALYANGAR, INDIA

* K/A AGES IN MILLIONS OF YEARS.   The range of error on all dates is of the order of .3 m. yrs. or less.

Figure 1   Mio-Pliocene and Pleistocene hominids from Asia and Africa with potassium/argon dates. Specimens on the left and right are matched with morphologically similar forms from the K/A-dated East African sequence.

Asiatic gibbon. Even if the orangutan and the African apes are patristically related, that is, if all are more similar in outward (phenotypic or phenetic) morphology than any one of them is to *Homo,* they still could be less similar genetically. However, although the ancestral line leading to the orangutan probably differentiated from an early unknown member of the dryopithecine complex before the hominids did so, the hominids have differentiated more rapidly and now occupy an adaptive niche quite different from that presently filled by the African and Asian apes.

Classification of Hominoidea

In comparison with most other superfamilies, too many distinctions of higher taxa have been drawn among hominoids. This is presumably because much of the taxonomic work on these categories has been done by persons unacquainted with the manner in which higher categories have been, or should be, proposed in the light of the new systematics. Most mammalogists would probably now prefer to use three basic principles in justifying the erection or retention of families and subfamilies. Briefly, these principles are: (1) the group which is thought to deserve such status should have had a considerable time duration as a separate stock, (2) the proposed taxon (a formal unit grouping organisms) should show considerable diversity in terms of contained species and genera, (3) the category should be characterized by a reasonably thorough-going structural distinctiveness shared by its members and not like that of related families or subfamilies. Admittedly, criteria of morphological distinctiveness are subjective, but material on which to base such judgments can be derived from comparative anatomy. For instance, one can make an approximate answer to the question: Do members of the families of man and apes differ *more,* or *less,* in total skeletal and dental morphology than do species of other related families within one order, such as Canidae and Felidae?

Because classification should also reflect both the past evolution of given taxa and the morphology and adaptation of the present members of such taxa, a compromise must be reached which reflects both cladistic and patristic relationships (Fig. 1). Consequently, it is preferable in a classification of the superfamily Hominoidea to retain a separate family for the genera *Ramapithecus, Australopithecus,* and *Homo,* a family sustained primarily by the morphological features which indicate the adaptive shift to hominid feeding patterns and habitual bipedalism.

Species of orangutan, chimpanzee, and gorilla, together with those of *Dryopithecus* and *Gigantopithecus,* should be retained in the Pongidae. Dryopithecinae can be justified as a separate subfamily. Although two further subfamilies, Ponginae and Paninae, could be used, these would contain at the most only one or two genera and species, and the distinction would not, in our opinion, be particularly meaningful. It is even more difficult to justify the division of Hominidae into such subfamilies as Australopithecinae, Homininae, Praehomininae, and the like.

Ecology and Adaptation of Early Hominoids

Modern pongids and hominids are characterized by relative trunk erectness, a feature shared with more "primitive" primate species. For example, many prosimians are vertical tree-clingers, like *Indri*, *Propithecus*, and *Tarsius*, while the New World monkeys *Ateles*, *Lagothrix*, and *Brachyteles* are partial brachiators. Even the more terrestrial Old World monkeys sit erect while feeding, grooming, and resting. Avis has suggested that the hominoid superfamily differentiated from other primates by becoming arm-swingers confined to a small-branch niche in a forest habitat; in her opinion this differentiation occurred as early as the Eocene. This matter of arm-swinging raises the largely academic question of what is or is not formal "brachiation." (This form of locomotion requires suspension from alternate hands, forward movement being produced by pronation of the arm and trunk around the fixed hand; propulsive force in such locomotion comes entirely from the upper limbs.) *Proconsul africanus*, for instance, is said to have been a "probrachiator," and thus in some ways similar morphologically to modern colobine monkeys. *P. africanus* does not exhibit the extreme forelimb elongation characteristic of modern apes. Does this mean that *P. africanus* could not have "brachiated" in the formal sense? Perhaps so; perhaps not. Several genera of New World monkeys move through the trees in this manner without showing all the anatomical "brachiating" specializations of the Old World pongids.

Whether "brachiators" or "probrachiators," Miocene apes and their Oligocene ancestors probably showed a high degree of trunk erectness and doubtless spent much time walking and running bipedally, either in the trees or on the ground. As Gregory suggested, some brachiation would probably have been essential for the hominids before they could become habitual bipeds. The structure of the human arm, thorax, and abdomen all suggest that, at some stage, our early Tertiary forerunners may have, on occasion, moved by armswinging in the trees.

The idea of the "emancipated forelimb" has been greatly overstressed in discussions of hominid tool-using. Hands have been important throughout all of primate evolution; the higher primates, in particular, use their hands in a wide range of activities such as feeding and grooming. The habit of sitting erect, widespread in primates, insures that the hands are free for these activities. However, in nonhominid primates the hands are typically used in locomotion as well; it is in this respect that hominid forelimb "emancipation" becomes important. As Kortlandt and Schultz have suggested, stone- and branch-throwing in defense were probably important in early hominid behavior before tool-using became widespread. It is also clear from the dentition of *Ramapithecus* that the early hominids could not have fed by stripping vegetable material with the canines and incisors as do the African apes; such feeding behavior requires relatively large front teeth for nipping, tearing, and shredding. It is possible, as a consequence of both these factors, that hominids were *ad hoc* tool-users at least by the early Pliocene. Once hominids became committed to a terrestrial way of life and some degree of habitual bipedal locomotion, the freeing of their forelimbs would have greatly facilitated tool use.

The earliest hominids may, of course, have functioned fairly well bipedally long before noticeable skeletal alterations increasing the efficiency of this manner of locomotion had become genetically fixed. Such an hypothesis gains strength from observation of the crude walking of the living spider monkey (*Ateles*), gibbon (*Hylobates*), and even some lemurs (*Propithecus*). While it can be debated whether this type of progression should formally be called bipedal, it certainly cannot be written off as quadrupedal movement; none of these primates use the hands habitually to support the forebody during locomotion on the ground. Despite such tendencies toward bipedal walking, however, none of these primates show any man-like skeletal adjustments that make upright walking more efficient.

Selection pressures were doubtless strongly in favor of such trends when the hominids were evolving, but the nature of the ecological readjustments involved in the origin of the hominid line is likely to remain a matter of conjecture. A change in diet also occurred during the course of hominid evolution, but, as Schultz has pointed out, this shift has been overstressed. The modern great apes are often described as vegetarians, but Schultz suggests that, among the primates, perhaps only the colobine monkeys can be termed truly vegetarian. Most of the other primates tend to supplement their diets with animal protein. However, Miocene apes probably ate mostly vegetable material just as modern baboons, chimpanzees and gorillas do, and the earliest hominids presumably had a similar diet. During the Pliocene, the amount of animal protein in the hominid diet surely would have increased as scavenging and hunting, feeding habits evidently well established by the early Pleistocene, became more widespread in hominid populations. As this dietary shift brought with it increased calorific values, less time would have been required for feeding, and the habit of food-sharing could develop.

Bartholomew and Birdsell have discussed theoretical concepts of early hominid ecology and believe that the early hominids were wide-ranging, food-sharing, weapon-using omnivores. It has been said that "tool-using and tool-making were very probably associated with the tendency for early members of the phyletic line leading to man to take to a certain amount of meat-eating." The reduced canines and incisors of *Ramapithecus punjabicus* suggest that tool-using may have been established by the late Miocene, because smaller front teeth require the use of other means to prepare food, either animal or vegetable.[1] Noback and Moskowitz have emphasized that the increasing dexterity of the hand seems to have played a major role in the evolution of the central nervous system among higher primates, particularly in the case of the Hominidae, and this influence may well have been acting in *Ramapithecus* populations.

Robinson has discussed at length the alterations in pelvic anatomy and muscle function consequent to erect bipedalism. Unfortunately, no pelves of Miocene or Pliocene dryopithecines are yet known. It is generally assumed that the pelves of mid-Tertiary higher primates will prove to be similar to those of modern pongids. In this view, the human pelvis is considered to have been derived from an ancestral morphology similar to that of modern apes. It seems more likely, however, that some morphological differentiation has occurred in the pongid as well as the hominid line. Indeed, such pieces of evidence as the hominid-like pelvis of *Oreopithecus* and the broad ilia of New World brachiators, taken together with the considerable probability that early pongids were arboreal arm-swingers with erect trunks, suggest that the immediate ancestors of the hominids were actually pre-adapted as brachiators in terms of behavior, and perhaps to bipedal running and walking in terms of anatomy.

Chimpanzees and gorillas have prognathous, that is, projecting faces; their mid-Tertiary ancestors were evidently more orthognathous (straight-faced), and it seems that facial lengthening occurred, at least in part, as a response to demands of ground living, defensive display and vegetarian diet. Baboons and macaques have prognathous faces also. Large teeth and powerful muscles are required in order to chew tough plant food. Considerable sexual dimorphism in canine size is shown among various species of apes and Old World monkeys and, consequently, it is probable that (among other factors) elongated canines are associated with defensive display behavior. Increased stress on olfaction among mainly ground-feeding species such as baboons probably was important in the development of the snout. In contrast, colobine monkeys, New World monkeys, and the erect-postured tree-clinging prosimians such as *Indri*, *Propithecus*, and *Tarsius* all have relatively short faces and show less sexual dimorphism. Among fossil forms the small Miocene species *Proconsul africanus* was also relatively orthognathous as was *Oreopithecus*.

---

[1] It may be argued that all three *Ramapithecus* maxillary specimens are those of small-canined females. This is not too likely, but, even if true, it would not alter the fact that the premolars and incisors are also smaller relative to molar size than is the case in any pongid.

New evidence secured by the recent Yale expeditions indicates that several of the Egyptian Oligocene hominoids were short-faced too.

Trunk erectness and orthognathism are apparently closely linked. Erect posture is associated with changes in orientation of the cranial base, typically exemplified by downward rotation of the facial axis on the basicranial axis. Mills has suggested that the assumption of habitual erect posture would cause further flattening of the face. He points out that, in primates with large canines, the lower canines pass behind the upper incisors during chewing. With facial shortening, the canines no longer pass behind, but rather in the plane of, the maxillary incisors. As this happens, selection favors reduction of canine crowns. If tool use (and possible changes in male display behavior as well) had removed the selective advantage of large canines, canine reduction inevitably would have taken place.

Thus, it appears that several anatomical, behavioral, and "cultural" elements—erect posture, orthognathism, changes in diet and display behavior, an increasing use of tools and reduction of the anterior dentition—are here closely linked one to another. Members of the genus *Ramapithecus* have small front teeth and were apparently wide-ranging even in the late Miocene; the dental evidence implies that profound behavioral, dietary, and locomotor changes had already occurred among species of *Ramapithecus* by this time. The commitment to a hominid way of life could conceivably have been made by the late Miocene, and our earliest known probable ancestors, with brains perhaps comparable in size to those of chimpanzees, might have already adopted a way of life distinct from that of their ape contemporaries.

Appearance and Speciation of Man

Near the beginning of the Pleistocene, hominids are represented in the fossil record by two or more species of *Australopithecus*, a small-brained, large-jawed form similar dentally to *Homo*. Post-cranially, *Australopithecus* is similar to, although not identical with, later men and evidently was an habitual biped. Early Pleistocene sites at Olduvai in Tanganyika have yielded hominid remains, together with crude stone tools; stone tools of similar type are known from North Africa and the Jordan valley, and it seems likely that, at about the same time, bone tools were being made in South Africa. Regular tool-making, utilizing bone, stone, wood, and perhaps other material too, possibly began more than two million years ago.

It has been suggested by many authors that the transition from tool-using to regular tool-making was a step of crucial importance in the evolution of man. This may well be true but, like many generalizations in anthropology, this one has been oversimplified. As Napier has pointed out, tool-making may often have been invented and forgotten in the late Tertiary. During Villafranchian time (that is, during earliest Pleistocene time), some hominids were doubtless tool-makers while others were still only tool-users. Differing environmental demands would produce different behavioral responses. However, the advantages of regular tool-making are clear and, once invented, the spread of this skill would probably have been fairly rapid.

Speciation in the Hominidae

Simpson remarks:

Supposedly intergeneric hybridization, usually with sterile offspring, is possible among animals, for instance, in mammals, the artificial crosses *Bos* × *Bison*, *Equus* × *Asinus*, and *Ursus* × *Thalarctos*. In my opinion, however, this might better be taken as basis for uniting the nominal genera. I would not now give generic rank to *Bison*, *Asinus*, or *Thalarctos*.

There is considerable evidence that the African and Arabian baboons, previously thought to belong to several separate genera, can produce viable hybrids, and may, instead, be classified in perhaps as few as two or three species of a single genus. Hybrid studies, by the Russians and others, suggest that species of *Macaca* (the rhesus monkey) and perhaps of *Cercocebus* (the mangabey), too, should be classified as belonging instead to the baboon genus *Papio*. *Papio*, in this sense, can be regarded as a wide-ranging genus with local species populations which show variations in morphology, coloring, and behavior. Freedman's metrical work on cranial variation in *Papio* "species" lends support to this view. Some of the populations may be sibling species, others may warrant only subspecific rank; only interfertility studies can determine their validity as genetical species. Among members of *Papio*, greater morphological variability is to be seen among samples of adult males than among samples of adult females, particularly in cranial features. This, together with pronounced sexual dimorphism, suggests that differences in mating and display patterns have selected for a great deal of the specific and subspecific morphological differences. The small amount of speciation within the genus is also significant when compared with *Cercopithecus* (guenons) or colobine monkeys, and this is almost certainly a direct reflection of *Papio*'s wide-ranging terrestrial way of life. Among these primates, there is apparently a rough correlation between species range size and the degree of speciation within a genus. Highly arboreal primates, such as species of langurs and gibbons, tend to have more restricted ranges and tend to be less mobile as groups; isolation and speciation become more likely under these circumstances.

The earliest hominids probably were at least as wide-ranging and mobile as the baboons, and presumably would have been much more so by middle and late Pliocene time. As noted already, fossil evidence suggests that *Ramapithecus punjabicus* was already present in East Africa, India, China, and possibly Europe, by the early Pliocene; there is no reason to suppose that hominids have not been widely dispersed since then. Man has capitalized on plasticity rather than becoming restricted to narrow morphological and behavioral adaptations. His mobility, his ability to occupy a highly diversified ecological niche, and his apparently slow development of isolating mechanisms all tend to reduce speciation. It is a reasonable working hypothesis, therefore, that not more than one genus, and perhaps no more than one or two species of hominid, has existed at any particular time. Like most other mammals, man is polytypic; that is, a number of races are found within the species. We should expect fossil hominid species populations to be polytypic too.

Taxonomy of Australopithecus

Before the student can erect new fossil genera and species he must demonstrate that the new proposed taxon differs significantly from previously described taxa in a number of particular characters. Thus, any diagnosis should take full account of known variability in living related species and genera. Different specific and generic names also imply certain other differences. If two individual fossils or fossil populations have different specific names, this implies that they could not have been members of a single freely interbreeding population; this, in turn, requires a period of reproductive and probably geographic isolation. Different generic names, in their turn, generally imply that the taxa concerned were completely incompatible genetically; to develop such incompatibility would require a long period of isolation. As we have already noted, however, such isolation would probably have been an unusual event during the course of hominid evolution.

Early Pleistocene hominids are known from a number of African localities. The first to be described and discussed was *Australopithecus africanus* from South Africa. It is now fairly generally agreed that two species of this genus are known: *A. africanus* (Fig. 1) from Villafranchian deposits at Taung, Sterkfontein, and Makapansgat, and *A. robustus*, from possibly latest early Pleistocene and middle Pleistocene deposits at Kromdraai and Swartkrans. Another form, "*Telanthropus capensis*" (Fig. 1) has been recovered from Swartkrans; its status is equivocal and will be discussed later.[2] Robinson discussed these australopithecine forms at length, pointing out that *A. africanus* is, in his opinion, closer to the ancestry of later men than is *A. robustus*.

[2] Invalid or doubtful taxonomic terms are indicated here in quotes on initial citation only.

Definite or probable australopithecines have been reported also from Java, North Africa, Israel, and East Africa. *Meganthropus palaeojavanicus*—represented by finds from the Djetis beds of Java—is said by Robinson to be closely similar to the African form *A. robustus*. Although LeGros Clark considers the Java specimen's generic separation from another hominid form, *Homo erectus* (Fig. 1), unjustified in view of the fragmentary nature of the material, the fact is that these jaw fragments do not provide enough information to allow students to draw species distinctions between the Javan and African material.

Coppens has reported the recovery of an australopithecine skull from Koro-Toro, near Lake Chad south of the Sahara. The associated fauna suggests an early Villafranchian age. Arambourg states that this fossil is intermediate in morphology between *A. africanus* and *A. robustus* but with perhaps a greater cranial capacity. Robinson considers it closer to *A. robustus*. No pebble tools are associated, although they are present in later Villafranchian deposits of North Africa. "*Meganthropus africanus*" from the Laetolil beds of early Pleistocene age near Lake Eyassi in East Africa has been referred to *Australopithecus* by Robinson. In addition Stekelis has discovered fragmentary hominid remains of early or middle Pleistocene age associated with a pebble tool culture at Ubeidiya in the Central Jordan valley.

Finally, Leakey has recently described a number of hominid finds in deposits of early and middle Pleistocene age at Olduvai Gorge, Tanganyika. Two distinct species have been recognized and described, *Australopithecus* (=*Zinjanthropus*) "*boisei*" from Bed I at Olduvai and from possibly middle Pleistocene deposits near Lake Natron, Tanganyika, and "*Homo habilis*" (type, hominid #7) from Bed I and other specimens from Bed II at Olduvai. *A. boisei* is bigger and more robust than *H. habilis* (see Fig. 1) and has larger molars and premolars; we believe that it cannot be distinguished at the specific level from *A. robustus*.

The hominid sites from Bed I have been dated by the potassium-argon method, the three sites FLK I, FLKNN I, and MK falling between 1.57 and 1.89 million years. The Bed II hominids from FLK II, VEK IV, and MNK II are younger than 1.02 million years, the youngest date for the top of Bed I, and older than 0.49 million years, the date of a post-Chellean II tuff in Bed II. The *Homo habilis* material therefore falls into two groups, separated by perhaps as much as one million years. Once again, during the period of deposition of the lower parts of Bed II, two distinct taxa appear to have been present, *H. habilis* at Olduvai and *A. boisei* at Lake Natron.

Altogether, then, some half dozen supposedly distinct taxa (both genera and species) have been proposed for early and early Middle Pleistocene hominids; several of these are based on the most fragmentary and limited material. Schultz has repeatedly stressed the very high level of morphological variability among species of the Hominoidea. Nevertheless, small and taxonomically trivial differences in dental, cranial, and postcranial anatomy have still been used to establish or justify specific or generic distinctions among the earlier Pleistocene hominids. What follows is an attempt to bring some taxonomic order to this situation.

At present, *A. robustus* is known from South Africa (Swartkrans, Kromdraai), Olduvai Bed I, Lake Natron, and possibly Java. The other African forms of roughly equivalent age have been referred to three taxa, *A. africanus*, *Telanthropus capensis*, and *Homo habilis*. The relative dating of the North, East, and South African sites presents a number of problems. Faunally, there are few mammal species as they are presently defined common to all three sites, and those which are common are often unsuitable for purposes of correlation. Cooke has discussed this problem at length. He believes that the South African sites which have yielded *A. africanus* are broadly contemporaneous with the later Bed I levels at Olduvai. However, he points out that:

Although ecological differences prevent too close a comparison, the faunas suggest strongly that the sequence in East Africa from the Kaiso and the Kanam levels through Omo and Laetolil to Bed I corresponds fairly closely in time to the sequence Sterkfontein and Makapansgat to Swartkrans and Kromdraai. Although the evidence is extremely tenuous, the Villafranchian (equivalent) fauna of North Africa could well be contemporary with these East African deposits and the ape-man breccias. The occurrence of pebble tools in similar relationships in all three areas may be significant and if the North African beds are truly pre-Cromerian as has been suggested by several authorities this would provide additional grounds for keeping at least the major part of the ape-man deposits within the Villafranchian.

Biberson considers the Koro-Toro site at Lake Chad contemporary with Kaiso and Kanam in East Africa, and, if this is so, the Chad hominid could well be the oldest *Australopithecus* known. *Telanthropus capensis* from Swartkrans is probably the same age as *Homo habilis* from Olduvai Bed II, while *A. africanus* from Taung, Sterkfontein and Makapansgat and Bed I *H. habilis* are possibly of approximately equivalent age.

The New East African Hominids and the South African Australopithecines

Known *Homo habilis* material, as already noted, falls into two main groups separated by perhaps as much as a million years. The type specimen of *H. habilis* consists of a juvenile mandible, two parietal fragments, a hand and an upper molar. A foot and clavicle belonging to an older individual (or individuals—associations of all Olduvai individuals are certainly not clear) have been recovered from the same site (FLKNN I). Two other sites in Bed I have yielded teeth, mandibular and skull fragments, and a tibia and fibula belonging either to *H. habilis* or to *Australopithecus* (*Zinjanthropus*) *boisei*. Among remains from Bed II are: a complete mandible (with associated maxillae) together with the occipitals and broken parietals and temporals of possibly the same individual, cranial fragments, isolated teeth, and a damaged palate. Although there is insufficient material from which firm inferences can be drawn, the sequence through Bed I to Bed II suggests that teeth and mandibles became progressively reduced during this time, while there was little alteration in cranial capacity. (This seemingly unchanging brain size may correlate with the presence throughout the section of similar crude pebble tools, or the two faunas may be closer in time than K-dated horizons appear to indicate.) The juvenile mandible and teeth from FLKNN I in Bed I are some 10 per cent greater in all measurements than the mandible from MNK II in Bed II. Such a small number of mandibles cannot, of course, be regarded as necessarily typical of the populations from which they come, but it is possible that, during this period, jaws and teeth became reduced while cranial capacity remained fairly constant.

A large number of *A. africanus* specimens have been described. Because this taxon is known so well, some have tended to think typologically in terms of an "australopithecine stage" of human evolution during which all hominids would have been morphologically similar to these South African forms. However, if the hominids evolved in the main as a single, widespread, polytypic species, the Transvaal *A. africanus* more likely represents a sample, drawn from a time segment of unknown length, of a peripheral and perhaps aberrant race of this species. We should not expect contemporaneous or near contemporaneous races within this same species to be morphologically identical with, or even quite similar to, the South African *A. africanus*. A large number of fossil specimens, say, from a restricted geographic area and from a relatively small segment of time, may well resemble each other more than any one of them resembles a small sample of the same species from a different part of the geographic range and from an earlier or later time. In such a case, however, we must be careful not to regard the large sample as morphologically "typical" of the species. By so doing, we would prevent correct assignment of other specimens of the same taxon. Morphological differences between specimens due to age and sex differences and to geographic and temporal separation, as well as racial variation, must be carefully considered. In erecting new taxa, it is necessary for the discoverer to demonstrate that the new finds are *significantly* different from previously defined taxa.

Thus, when we consider the hominids from Lake Chad and Olduvai Bed I we must ask ourselves, could these represent taxa which are already known? *A. africanus* and *H. habilis* were both habitual bipeds. Unfortunately, we have pelves of the former but not of the latter, whereas we know the foot of the latter but not of the former. It is possible that the *H. habilis* foot from Olduvai Bed I is no more nor less *Homo*-like than is the pelvis of *A. africanus* from S. Africa.

The parietal bones from Olduvai FLKNN I have been reconstructed by Tobias to indicate a cranial capacity of between 642–724 cc. This volume estimate must be regarded with great caution because of the fragmentary nature of the specimen.[3] Tobias gives the australopithecine

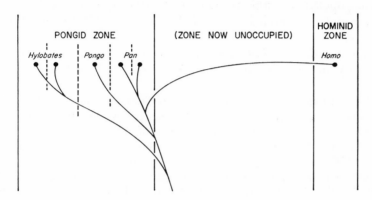

ADAPTIVE AND STRUCTURAL-FUNCTIONAL ZONES

Figure 2 Diagram showing relative closeness of phylogenetic relationships of living hominoids and their radiation into adaptive-structural-functional zones, from Simpson.

range of cranial capacity as 435–600 cc., this being lower than his estimates for this skull of *Homo habilis*. However, there seems to be no good reason for separating early species of the genera *Australopithecus* and *Homo* on grounds of differences in cranial volume. None of the crania from the Transvaal breccias or from Olduvai Beds I and II indicate volumes outside the range now known among the single species of living gorilla, and all these crania are distinctly smaller than those of *Homo erectus*.

The teeth and mandible of *H. habilis* from Olduvai Bed I FLKNN I do not differ greatly from specimens of *A. africanus* (Fig. 2) in shape or morphology. The molars are similar in size and shape to those of *A. africanus* from Sterkfontein. The premolars of *H. habilis* are somewhat narrower than those of the South African forms; but shape, as well as size, of teeth is known to vary greatly in all modern primates, including man, and this seems to be a relatively unimportant character on which to base generic and specific separation of the two forms. Unfortunately,

[3] The slightest mis-setting of the two bones at the midline, for instance if flared too much laterally, would markedly increase the brain volume estimate for this individual.

some of the Olduvai specimens are crushed and broken and this limits our ability to make comparisons. Collection of further hominids from the Olduvai beds is thus of the greatest importance; recovery of a more adequate sample should enable students to assess the range of variability within the local population represented at Olduvai, and would allow comparisons of this population with others of approximately equivalent age. *H. habilis* and *A. africanus* may represent nothing more than two variant populations within the same widespread species, but this hypothesis can only be verified or rejected when more information becomes available.

The validity of *Homo habilis*, as any new fossil taxon, depends on the reality and the plausibility of its diagnosis. As B. G. Campbell states:

It is here that the hypothesis of the new species must stand or fall; . . . The diagnosis must support the hypothesis for the species to stand, not in law, but in reality. . . . (Many examples of this state of affairs could be quoted. The most topical, and one of the most important, concerns the creation of the taxon *Homo habilis*. In their original publication the authors stated that *Telanthropus capensis* "may well prove, on closer comparative investigation, to belong to *Homo habilis*"; thus the effective demonstration of a novel taxon was negated. The name is valid, but the species has not been effectively shown to have existed, as a distinct taxon.)

Telanthropus capensis from Swartkrans is probably broadly contemporaneous with Bed II *Homo habilis*. In spite of its fragmentary nature, some general remarks can be made about *Telanthropus*. The teeth are smaller than those of *A. africanus*, although cusp patterns are similar. The mandible is smaller, too, and is said by Robinson to be reminiscent of other African and Asian hominids of Middle Pleistocene date. This is to be expected for a form transitional in time between the early Pleistocene hominids and middle Pleistocene *Homo erectus*. It is probable that Bed II *H. habilis* and *Telanthropus capensis* represent two populations of a single species or subspecies, but, once again, further material will be required before firm conclusions can be drawn. Both are similar to the mandible of *H. erectus* from the Djetis beds in Java (so-called *"Pithecanthropus B"*).

The primitive stone tools associated with *Homo habilis* throughout Bed I and the lower part of Bed II are evidently of uniform type for what may be a very long period of time; this is perhaps correlated with the equally protracted apparent stability of cranial capacity. Tools of similar type are found in Morocco and at Ubeidiya. It should be noted that the early Pleistocene hominid from Chad, found unassociated with tools, has a cranial capacity of the order of that of both *H. habilis* and *A. africanus*. Regular tool-making, as we noted earlier, seems to have been invented during the early Pleistocene, perhaps in Africa, at a time when hominids had already become efficient bipeds. Dates from Olduvai suggest the possibility that a full million years passed after the invention and spread to tool-making during which cranial capacity—and presumably manual dexterity, "intelligence," and hunting skill—remained fairly constant. Some time roughly between one million and five hundred thousand years ago, human brain size increased by more than 50 per cent. Also, during this period, the change from simple pebble chopping tools to hand-axes of Chellean type apparently took place. Elaboration of tool types and expansion in brain size were probably interrelated, and both, perhaps, were associated with the final anatomical perfection of hand structure. Napier

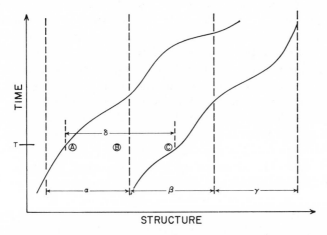

Figure 3 An attempt to represent Pleistocene hominids as a single genetic continuum evolving through time. Modified from Simpson.

has suggested that the hand of *Homo habilis* was not as refined structurally and functionally as that of later men. Undoubtedly, limits of both mental ability and hand anatomy affected the form of tools.

The earliest Pleistocene appearance of tool-making, then, seems to have heralded no immediate anatomical changes in the hominid line. Cranial capacity, in particular, remained constant. Jaws, teeth, and faces became reduced during the era of crude pebble tools, but exactly why this was so remains conjectural. Anthropologists have frequently suggested that the appearance of tool-making was causally related to the expansion of the brain. There was never any fossil evidence to support this view, and now we have some evidence to the contrary. Increase in brain size evidently lagged behind the regular making of tools. This skill had altered the lives of early Pleistocene hominids; apparently it did not immediately alter their morphology.

Taxonomy of Early African Hominids

We have concluded that *A. africanus* and Bed I *Homo habilis* may not be specifically distinct and also that the bulk of Bed II materials and *Telanthropus* may be specifically identical. *Telanthropus* itself is regarded by many students as an invalid genus which should be referred either to *Homo* or to *Australopithecus*. If referred to *Homo* the trivial name *capensis* can no longer be used, since this has already been applied to a Late Paleolithic skull from Boskop. If the Olduvai Bed I and Bed II *Homo habilis* material is regarded as belonging to a single taxon, it is not unreasonable also to include therein *A. africanus* and the *Telanthropus* material from South Africa. This taxon would extend over a very considerable time period; in fact it would be more than twice as long as the time covered by *H. erectus* and *H. sapiens* combined. Some hominid evolutionary change, particularly trends towards orthognathism and reduced dentition, occurred during this considerable span of time, although the amount of variation within the taxon is probably not greater than that observed in modern mammal species (including man).

If all early Pleistocene hominids ancestral to later men are regarded as members of the genus *Homo*, as the proposal of *H. habilis* by Leakey, Tobias, and Napier suggests, the prior binomial for this taxon would be *Homo africanus*. The evolution of early Pleistocene hominids, first to *Homo erectus*, and finally to *Homo sapiens*, can be shown diagrammatically in Fig. 3, which shows a single hominid species evolving through time. A, B, and C are hypothetical contemporaneous individuals, C being more "modern" than B, B more so than A. Simpson suggests as a possibility that:

. . . there is only one lineage or evolutionary species and only one genetical species at any one time. In that case, the species would have been highly variable, and even more so during much of past time than *Homo sapiens* is at present. At some time around the middle Pleistocene it might have varied all the way from what in purely morphological (or typological) terms could be called marginal australopithecoid through pithecanthropoid to marginal neanderthaloid. Such variation would be improbable within a single deme or local population. It would be less improbable among geographically separate "allopatric" populations or subspecies. Such geographic semi-isolates would of course be variable in themselves, but some might, for instance, vary about a more australopithecoid modal morphology and others about a more neanderthaloid mode. Discovery that fossil hominids fall into such modally distinct, synchronous but allopatric groups would favor this interpretation. Whether current data do or do not tend to follow such a pattern I leave to the specialists in such matters.

We prefer to accept Simpson's model for the moment.

A, B, and C of Figure 3 are contemporaneous at time *T* and are members of a single species. However, typologically A and B might be placed in one species α while C is referred to species β. The paradox is imagined rather than real, because the taxa α and β, and the taxon δ are of different types. If the hominids have evolved as a single unitary species, δ will represent a sample of the genetical species which existed at time *T*. α, β, and γ are morphospecies, species "established by morphological similarity regardless of other considerations." The problem here is largely one of definition and should not be overstressed. Nevertheless, this model will be useful in dealing with problems which will appear should "undoubted" (morphological) *Homo* be found contemporaneous with "undoubted" (morphological) *Australopithecus*.

Both *Australopithecus africanus* and *A. robustus* are bipeds, both have greatly reduced canines and incisors, both almost certainly would have been tool-users, and both probably made tools. If tool-making spread by copying within one species of small-brained hominids, it would presumably have been copied by any other species of equally small-brained hominids living in the same area.

Australopithecus robustus is said by Robinson to have been a vegetarian because of its massive premolars and molars. *A. robustus* specimens from Olduvai and Natron exhibit pronounced wear patterns on both upper and lower molars. Such wear patterns are found in certain Australian aboriginal tribes that eat roots and other vegetable material together with large quantities of sand and grit. In contrast, *Homo habilis* has wear patterns similar to those of meat-eating African tribes such as the Masai. *A. robustus* is said to have been a vegetarian and *A. africanus* and *H. habilis* more exclusively meat-eaters. Although the *A. robustus* wear patterns suggest that gritty vegetable material constituted a large part of the diet, they do not, however, enable us to state categorically that *A. robustus* did *not* eat meat. Nor are we entitled to assume that *A. robustus* and *A. africanus* were at all times vegetarians or omnivores respectively; diet can vary greatly (within contemporary *Homo sapiens* groups for example), and presumably changes with time too. Hominids were successful because they were behaviorally plastic and adaptable; we must take great care before we place ecological limitations on fossil hominids known only in relatively poor detail.

In summary, *Australopithecus robustus*, like *Ramapithecus punjabicus*, *Homo habilis* and *A. africanus*, has small canines and incisors. This implies that *A. robustus* prepared its food, presumably with tools, and there is no reason to suppose that it could not have eaten prepared animal as well as prepared vegetable food. The diet of modern "primitive" men is varied; could not earlier hominids have been similarly omnivorous? *A. robustus* and *H. habilis* were evidently co-existent in the same general areas for perhaps a million years, if the new dates and stratigraphic-faunal data of Leakey are right. They were, therefore, sympatric species, that is, species occupying the same geographic area. Both were bipeds, both were presumably tool-users and probably tool-makers; their diets might well have been similar at times. As mentioned earlier, there are theoretical difficulties involved in preparing a model of hominid speciation. If we are to distinguish these taxa at a specific level, we need to know far more about geographical barriers during the Pliocene and Pleistocene. Comparative study of closely related pairs of animal species indicates that they must have separate origins in different geographic areas, that is, they must originally be allopatric. Perhaps one species of hominid evolved in Africa and one in Asia only to mingle at the beginning of the Pleistocene when land connections between Eurasia and Africa presumably became re-established. The picture as to the number of *Australopithecus* species really indicated by known material is still obscure and the available evidence can be interpreted in a number of ways.

Post-Villafranchian Morphological Changes

The Pliocene was probably a time of great morphological change in hominid evolution. Locomotor adaptations were being improved and, by middle Pleistocene time at least, the skeletons of hominids were essentially like those of modern man even though the skulls were not. Throughout this time, hominids were getting larger; this size increase was probably associated with increased speed and efficiency in running and walking. Brain size increased in consequence. Some relative increase in brain size also occurred during the early Pleistocene, although the time and extent of this expansion is difficult to assess. The changes in cerebrum and cerebellum which must have taken place are still not satisfactorily documented, nor are the selection pressures that produced them fully understood. These problems are discussed by Garn who says that:

human brain size did increase, either because brainier *individuals* were at an adaptive advantage, or because *groups* with larger brains survived and groups with smaller brains did not. It gratifies our ego to believe that selection favored intelligence, that our own ancestral lines came to genetic fulfillment because they were so very smart. But it may be that our vaunted intelligence is merely an indirect product of the kind of brain that can discern meaningful signals in a complex social content generating a heavy static of informational or, rather, misinformational noise.

Ryle has discussed "intelligence" and "intellect" from the philosopher's viewpoint. He states that:

. . . both philosophers and laymen tend to treat intellectual operations as the core of mental conduct; that is to say, they tend to define all other mental-conduct concepts in terms of concepts of cognition. They suppose that the primary exercise of minds consists in finding the answer to questions and that their other occupations are merely applications of considered truths or even regrettable distractions from their consideration. . . (However) there are many activities which directly display qualities of mind, yet are neither themselves intellectual operations nor yet effects of intellectual operations.

Brains expanded as the cultural environment became more and more complex, and larger brains enabled more complex cultures to develop. The actions which we choose, arbitrarily, to term "intelligent," that is those involving theorizing and the manipulation of true propositions or facts, form merely one aspect of our responses to a complex environment.

An increase in adult brain size involves a larger fetal and infantile brain and a prolonged growth period, two of the important trends in higher primate evolution noted by Schultz. Bigger fetal brains require larger maternal pelves, and it is possible that the structural refinements in the hominid pelvis which have evolved since the Villafranchian are, to a large extent, due to the problems posed by the birth of large-brained offspring. During middle Pleistocene times, the brain increased in size with consequent remodeling of the cranial vault. The facial skeleton and the teeth became reduced, presumably because of further refinements in food preparation and tool-making. Changes in relative size of the braincase and the jaws and related muscles produced changes in shape and size of the cranium, and in size and form of the supra-orbital ridges. By the late middle Pleistocene, the brain had probably reached approximately its present-day volume, and the morphological evolution of the Hominidae was almost complete.

Conclusions

Earliest hominids known to date are recognizable, in the form of *Ramapithecus punjabicus*, in the late Miocene. This sets back the differentiation of hominids from pongids to the early Miocene or earlier. Circumstantial rather than direct evidence suggests that *R. punjabicus* could have been a tool-using animal and, at least, a partial biped. It was widespread throughout the Old World apparently because of the great mobility in range extension afforded by ground dwelling and/or bipedalism. These factors would have reduced tendencies towards speciation among early Hominidae. Known geographic distribution of *Ramapithecus* (East Africa, India, China) shows that hominids have been wide-ranging, as they are now, at least since late Miocene time.

The early Pleistocene hominids can be classified in *no more than* two species; one of these, *Australopithecus* (or perhaps *Homo*) *africanus*, found in South, East and North Africa, probably inhabited other regions too. The evolution of this species saw the final perfection of the foot and pelvis for habitual bipedal walking, the invention and spread of tool-making and the development of associated refinements in the hand, and finally, late in its history, the rapid expansion of the brain. *Homo erectus*, found throughout the Old World during much of the middle Pleistocene (from 500,000 or 600,000 years ago on), is barely distinguishable taxonomically from *Homo sapiens*.

11 Ecology and the Protohominids

George A. Bartholemew
and Joseph B. Birdsell

"ECOLOGY" IS THE WORD THAT WAS INVENTED BY THE BIOLOGIST ERNST *Haeckel at the end of the nineteenth century to refer to the active and mutual relationship between living organisms and their environment. The concept, if not the word, is fundamental to all Darwinian and post-Darwinian evolutionary thought, and the word itself is now used, with somewhat altered meaning, in sociology and, again with some further modification, in archeology (see Nos. I:40, 42, 43), and in cultural anthropology (see No. II:10).*

The concept is particularly useful in dealing with problems of human evolution. The ancestors of man at all times were flesh and blood creatures with problems of making a living under certain fairly well-defined conditions of temperature and climate, landscape, food supply and physical mobility. Evolution is not a struggle to produce a certain life form, be it man or amoeba; rather, it is a description and explanation of the process by which life under certain conditions develops in certain directions, leaving behind as milestones the fossil forms we salvage from the past—and ourselves as well.

Although the word ecology is used in both the biological and the so-

SOURCE: *American Anthropologist*, Vol. 55 (1953), pp. 481–498. Reprinted with the permission of the authors and the publisher.

George A. Bartholemew (b. 1919) is Professor of Zoology at the University of California, Los Angeles. He is a specialist on the ecology and physiology of vertebrates and author of a monograph on the elephant seal.

Joseph B. Birdsell (b. 1908) is Professor of Anthropology at the University of California, Los Angeles. A specialist in genetics and serology, he has done extensive fieldwork among the Australian aborigines. He is co-author, with Coon & Garn, of *Races* (1950).

cial sciences, attempts to bring the biologist and students of human society together by analogical reasoning are beset with traps for the unwary. The biological world lies primarily within genetic and physiological limits while that of the social sciences lies within cultural limits. However, whatever else man is, he is first an animal and hence subject, although usually indirectly, to environmental and biological factors.

It is generally agreed that the ecological generalizations and points of view which have proved helpful in interpreting the natural history of most mammals can be applied virtually intact to all primates except man. It should, therefore, be possible to extrapolate upward from ecological data on other mammals and suggest the biological attributes of the protohominids and to extrapolate downward from ethnological data on hunting and collecting peoples and suggest the minimal cultural attributes of the protohominids.

We propose first to discuss in general terms some aspects of mammalian ecology which appear to be applicable to the protohominids; second, to apply these ideas to the available data on the australopithecines; and third, to discuss the application of a few ecological ideas to pre-agricultural humans. A history of the development of ecology and suggestions for its applications to anthropology which has recently been published by Marston Bates provides basic historical orientation and perspective for such an effort.

Protohominids and Tools   In retrospect, the vast sweep of evolution appears to lead inevitably to the appearance of man, but a rational interpretation of the evidence refutes this. During the Cenozoic there have been three separate mammalian evolutionary complexes, one in Australia, one in South America, and one in Eurasia, Africa, and North America. Of these complexes, only the last has produced organisms of the hominid level. Further, since the major orders of mammals were already distinct in the Eocene, each has had a separate genetic history for approximately 70,000,000 years, and only one, primates, has produced an organism at the hominid level of organization.

Since a number of mammalian orders have shown a strong independent evolutionary trend toward a large brain size, this trend is by no means peculiar to the order primates. This striking parallelism is presumably related to the fact that large brain size favors varied behavior and learning as supplements to genetically fixed responses. Why then did not the primates, like the other mammals, reach an apparent evolutionary dead end in the Pliocene? The familiar and reasonable ideas concerning the importance of arboreal life in setting the stage for the appearance of man, i.e., dependence on vision, grasping hands, and the lack of restrictive skeletal adaptations, need not be labored here, but the importance of bipedalism can profitably be re-examined.

The primates comprise the only major order of mammals which is characteristically arboreal. There can be no doubt that this arboreal heritage has been of vital importance in human evolution, but the critical stage in the transition from ape to protohominid involves the assumption of a unique terrestrial mode of life. A number of cercopithecids have successfully invaded the terrestrial habitat, but these all show quadrupedal adaptations. This level of adaptation, while obviously effective if one may judge by the fossil record and by present abundance, appears to represent a stable, long-surviving, adaptive equilibrium.

The terrestrial adaptations of the hominid line represent a step into a new and previously unexploited mode of life in which the critical feature was bipedalism. Among mammals changes of this magnitude have occurred only rarely since the middle Cenozoic. Aside from the saltatorial rodents such as the jerboas and kangaroo rats, all placental terrestrial mammals other than man use both hind and front legs for locomotion. The extreme rarity of bipedalism among mammals suggests that it is inefficient except under very special circumstances. Even modern man's unique vertical bipedal locomotion, when compared to that of quadrupedal mammals, is relatively ineffective, and this implies that a significant nonlocomotor advantage must have resulted from even the partial freeing of the forelimbs. This advantage was the use of the hands for efficient manipulation of adventitious tools such as rocks, sticks, or bones. Of course, the terrestrial or semi-terrestrial living primates have their hands free when they are not moving, but only man has his locomotion essentially unimpeded while carrying or using a tool. Man has been characterized as the "tool-using animal," but this implies a degree of uniqueness to man's use of tools which is unrealistic. Not only do other primates use tools—the use of sticks and rocks by chimpanzees and baboons is generally familiar—but such unlikely animals as the sea otter and one of the Galapagos finches routinely use rocks or sticks to obtain food. Indeed, the natural history literature is replete with instances of the use of tools by animals, and there really is no clear-cut boundary between web-spinning, nest-building, and stick-wielding on the one hand, and tool use at the simplest human level on the other. However, in contrast to all other mammals, the larger arboreal primates are, in a sense, tool users in their locomotion. As they move through the maze of the tree tops, their use of branches anticipates the use of tools in that they routinely employ levers and angular momentum. The grasping hands on which the locomotion and feeding of primates depends, are of course obviously preadapted for tool use.

Rather than to say that man is unique in being the "tool-using" animal, it is more accurate to say that man is the only mammal which is continuously dependent on tools for survival. This dependence on the learned use of tools indicates a movement into a previously unexploited dimension of behavior, and this movement accompanied the advent of bipedalism. With the assumption of erect posture regular use of tools became obligatory; the ability occasionally to use tools must have preceded this in time.

Protohominids and Body Size The conditions of terrestrial life for a bipedal tool-using mammal virtually demanded that the protohominids be big mammals, i.e., at least in the 50 to 100 pound range, for large size of itself offers important biological advantages. In the case of the protohominids two such advantages at once suggest themselves: First, large size would remove them from the category of potential prey for all carnivorous birds, reptiles, and all mammals except the big cats and the pack-hunting dogs; second, it would allow them to utilize without restrictive anatomical specialization and with simple instrumentation, virtually the entire range of food size utilized by all other terrestrial mammals.

Sociality Social behavior is inextricably interwoven with ecology, and although it is not possible to review the subject in detail here, certain aspects of it are basic to the development of later ideas.

The transitional protohominids must have been social to the extent of forming relatively stable family groups. Even in the absence of direct evidence, such a statement can be made with complete confidence from knowledge of the other members of the suborder Anthropoidea. First, there is the absence of seasonal sexual periodism in man and the great apes. Thus sexual ties form a bond of sustained and continuing attraction which provides a biological basis for the long-surviving family unit. As has frequently been pointed out this is a central element in human sociability. Second, there is a long period of growth and maturation. The long childhood of man and the great apes is not a mere function of size—the blue whale, the largest mammal that has ever lived, grows to sexual maturity and to a length of 70 or more feet in two years—but it is related to the unique dependence for survival on learning in the higher primates. The acquisition of competence for independent life demands several years of parental care in the chimpanzee and a decade or more in man. Hence, survival requires a mother-offspring relation which is sustained through many years and, like sexual attraction, is not just a seasonal interlude as in other social mammals. Since these factors shape the social behavior of both the great apes and man, they must have shaped the social life of the protohominids.

Other cohesive forces, by analogy with living primates, must have supplied integration to the social organization of the protohominids. Important among these must have been dominance-subordinance relationships. The concept of social dominance has proved to be a touchstone to the understanding of the social behavior of vertebrates. It is a key factor in the social behavior of mammals as diverse as deer, seals, and primates.

In every case in which it has been studied in mammals, dominance is established at least in part on the basis of aggressive behavior, of which a large component is either directly or indirectly dependent on reproductive physiology. In mammals the male sex hormones stimulate aggressive behavior and contribute to greater body size, while the female sex hormones inhibit the former and do not contribute to the latter. Consequently, males tend to be dominant over females in most situations. In the higher primates, as in many other social mammals, sexual dimorphism in size reinforces the greater aggressiveness of the male and insures his superior social status in situations where force is involved. In most social mammals, gregariousness overcomes the disruptive effect of dominance-subordinance relations and maintains the social unit. In primates dominance is not an exclusively disruptive force, since the dominant animal may protect the subordinate animal which looks to it for protection as well as leadership.

In nonprimate social mammals, the resolution of the forces produced by dominance and gregariousness typically produces a seasonal breeding unit which consists of a dominant male and a harem of females and which usually excludes the young of previous years.

The social unit in nonhuman primates is variable, and too few detailed field studies have been published to allow extrapolation from living anthropoids to the protohominids. In modern hunting and collecting groups of man the smallest unit is the biological family including immature offspring, and in many cultures the most important functional group is the extended family, or band. In the case of man, even at the simplest level, social dominance is not based exclusively on successful aggressive behavior. The distance between nonprimate mammals and man is too broad to be spanned by the bracketing technique previously used, but the semi-permanent biological family, including offspring, must have been a basic unit among the protohominids. Integration on any more extensive scale must have depended upon the degree of cultural attainment. It should be observed however, that fairly large groups have been reported for living nonhominid anthropoids.

Territoriality   No aspect of the social behavior of wild vertebrates has attracted more attention than territoriality, a concept which includes the entire complex pattern of behavior associated with the defense of an area. The display of ownership of places and objects is very highly developed among human beings, but this behavior pattern is not peculiar to modern man. It is almost universally present in terrestrial vertebrates, either on a permanent or seasonal basis. The large literature on the subject with regard to birds has been reviewed by Margaret M. Nice. Its status in mammals has been discussed by W. H. Burt, and its relation to vertebrate populations has been examined by P. A. Errington.

Territoriality springs from the necessity for finding and maintaining environmental conditions suitable for survival and reproduction. The techniques of territory maintenance, the precise factors immediately responsible for it, and the immediate significance of it vary from species to species.

The maintenance of territories either by individuals or by social groups has profound effects on distribution. Birds and mammals tend to be neither continuously distributed nor irregularly grouped, but to be spaced at more or less regular intervals through ecologically suitable habitat. This spacing is determined by conflicts between pairs of individuals or between interacting groups of animals. Thus, territorial boundaries are learned and vary in time and space. If anthropologists were willing, this might almost be considered protocultural behavior at a subhuman level; in any event, it emphasizes the continuity of human behavior with that of other vertebrates.

As a result of the centrifugal effects of aggressive behavior, territory maintenance forces animals to disperse into adjacent areas. It distributes the individual organisms or social units of a species throughout the entire accessible area of suitable habitat. Should the population increase, local population density does not continue to build up indefinitely. Instead territorial defense forces individuals out into marginal situations, and thus the resources of the optimal habitat are not exhausted. Most of the displaced individuals do not survive, but some may find unexploited areas of suitable habitat and thus extend the range of the species. The result is that a population tends to be maintained at or below the optimum density in the preferred habitat, and the excess individuals are forced to marginal areas to which they must adapt or die.

Thus territoriality is one of the primary factors which determine the density of population. It organizes a local population into a well-spaced array that allows adequate living conditions for all successful individuals. It limits the breeding population which can exist in suitable habitats and thus helps to prevent increase beyond the long-term carrying capacity of the range. This dispersive effect of territoriality can hardly help but be an important causal factor both in migration and in the spread of genes through a population. Hence, it must contribute importantly to rate of evolutionary change.

The question of the importance of territoriality to the biology of protohominids at once presents itself. Clarence R. Carpenter has demonstrated that howler monkeys and gibbons maintain territory by group action. It is clear that territoriality exists in all complex human societies, and it is clearly established that group territoriality is also important at the simplest levels of human culture. It is, therefore, reasonable to assume that protohominids similarly possessed a well-developed territoriality, presumably on the basis of the family or extended family.

Population Equilibrium One of the most critical ecological factors which can be determined about an animal is the density of its population. The number of variables which contribute to the determination of population density is enormous; a complete analysis for even the best known of living wild mammals is difficult, perhaps impossible. Nevertheless, the framework within which such an analysis can be made is known, for the factors involved in population dynamics have been studied intensively in recent years.

Since organisms are transient biochemical systems which require continuous expenditure of energy for their maintenance, the struggle for existence becomes, in one sense at least, a struggle for the free energy available for doing physiological work. This fact offers a point of view from which to approach the problem of estimating the population of protohominids, or any other mammal.

There exists a series of nutrient or trophic levels that expresses the energy relations which tie together the various organisms of the terrestrial environment. The primary trophic level is that of the green plants, for only they can use radiant energy to synthesize significant quantities of organic material. The trophic level of the herbivores includes all animals directly dependent on plants for food. The next higher trophic level, that of the meat-eaters which may be primary carnivores (eaters of herbivores), secondary carnivores (eaters of other carnivores), and so on. The final trophic level, the eaters of dead organic material, eventually returns materials to the inorganic state depleted of biologically available energy.

Materials which are used as building blocks and sources of energy by organisms cycle continuously through these trophic levels, and at each level there is an endless competition for them. There are a number of obvious corollaries which follow from these relationships. An important one is that nutrition plays a primary role in determining the major functional adaptations of animals. Life demands a continuous expenditure of energy, and this energy is available only through nutrition. These energy relations involve a sustained long-term pressure sufficiently constant to maintain and give direction to the major evolutionary trends apparent in the adaptive changes of the sort shown by hoofed mammals and the carnivorous mammals. As George Gaylord Simpson and others have pointed out, these nutritive adaptations have for the most part led not only to greater efficiency but also to more and more specialization, with a consequent reduction in potentiality for new major nutritive adaptations. Thus adaptations toward increased efficiency in food getting, or toward avoidance of becoming food for other organisms, are largely restrictive from the standpoint of future evolutionary change.

The total weight of biological materials produced by one trophic level must necessarily be less than that of the level below it on which it depends, and greater than that of the level above, which it supports. Each nutritive level must in the long run live on the interest, not the capital, of the trophic level below it. From this there follows a maxim which allows of no exception. On a long-term basis the mean population of a species is in equilibrium with the trophic levels both above it and below it, as well as with the total limiting effects of the inorganic environment. This means that the birth rate must be great enough to balance the death rate from disease (a nutritive phenomenon from the standpoint of the disease-causing organism), predation, and accident. Consequently, birth rate is a factor subject to natural selection, and all natural populations represent approximate equilibria between biotic potentials and total resistance of the biological and physical environments. Short-lived mammals of high fecundity, such as rabbits and mice, are sometimes characterized by drastic short-term fluctuations in population size, the causes for which are still subject to active controversy. However, in this paper we shall ignore the problem of population cycles, for drastic cyclic fluctuations have rarely been observed in large tropical mammals with low reproductive potentials.

It has been generally appreciated since the time of Darwin that animals, despite their capacity to increase in numbers, tend to maintain a population which fluctuates around some equilibrium figure. This idea is of such a basic nature that it forms a foundation for the concept of natural selection which now appears to be an omnipresent evolutionary force. The factors involved in the maintenance of these equilibria are complex and variable. Since, as pointed out above, an animal population cannot possibly permanently exceed its food resources, these fix an upper limit. The determination of the actual equilibrium figure is a subtle problem which must be solved independently for each population. A thoughtful analysis of the factors limiting population in a non-hominid primate under natural conditions is presented by N. E. Collias and C. Southwick in their study of howling monkeys. For a population to maintain itself above that lower critical level which means inevitable extinction, many factors (which may vary independently) must be simultaneously satisfied. Such things as a suitable habitat which will include adequate food resources, water, and home sites, and climatic conditions that do not exceed the tolerance of the group must be present.

Since biological factors vary with time, values for population equilibria are not to be measured at a given point in time. They fluctuate about a balance which is determined, not by the mean condition, but by the extremes. Indeed, one of the most firmly established ecological generalizations is Liebig's law of the minimum, which states that a biological reaction at any level is controlled not by the factors which are present in excess, but by that essential factor which is present in minimal quantity. Since, as was previously pointed out, population density is the most critical single ecological datum, anthropologists studying the simpler cultures characterized by few storage techniques would do well to search for those critical limiting factors which do determine density. Such limiting factors are not necessarily either obvious or conspicuous at all points in time, and even when they occur their expression may be subtle or apparently indirect. A semi-arid area may have many fruitful years in succession, but a single drought year occurring once in a human generation may restrict the population to an otherwise inexplicably low density. For example, the Papago Indians of the lower Colorado River were forced in drought years to revert to a desert hunting and collecting economy for survival. Thus, their population density appears in part to have been strongly affected by the preagricultural carrying capacity of this area. In some cases the size of a population will be determined not by the availability of an abundance of food during ten months of the year but by a regular seasonal scarcity in the remaining two months.

The reproductive potential of animals is such that under favorable conditions, such as having available a previously unexploited habitat, the size of a population can increase at an essentially logarithmic rate. This capacity for rapid increase makes possible the recovery of populations following drastic population reduction. In a stable population, on the other hand, the reproductive potential is expressed only as a one-to-one replacement of adult individuals.

Anthropologists are properly impressed with the complexity of learned behavior in human groups, but may fail to appreciate its significance among other mammals. Each on the nonhuman level, population density may be controlled by behavioral factors, either genetic or learned. Territoriality and dominance relations, which are dependent on learned behavior, contribute to the determination of group relations and population density. Under certain circumstances behavioral factors may be more important than nutritive factors in determining population density. For example, recent work has shown that the Norway rat under controlled experimental conditions, in which food is present in excess at all times, reaches a population equilibrium that is determined by strictly behavioral factors related to territoriality and competition for suitable homesites. Thus, experimental work confirms extensive field observations on a variety of vertebrates. Since learned behavior operates as an important factor determining density in all terrestrial mammals which have been studied, and in modern man, it must have been an important factor in determining the population density of the protohominids. The importance of learned behavior increases directly with its complexity, and in man at cultural levels above the hunting and collecting stage of economy it becomes increasingly difficult to identify the ecological factors affecting population size.

Ecology and the Australopithecines

The dating of the australopithecines has proved troublesome, and final decision is not now possible. Raymond Dart and Robert Broom have suggested that these protohominids lived during a period extending from the Villafranchian into the middle Pleistocene. This time span overlaps the datings of early man in other parts of the world, and implies a collateral relationship with more evolved hominids. Another view has recently been given by Teilhard de Chardin, who places the australopithecines in Villafranchian time, and thus removes them from contemporaneity with known African hominids. Abbé Breuil seems to reflect a similar point of view. In the former case the australopithecines would have been competing in their closing phase with more advanced forms of man, and hence would have been decreasing in numbers and range. In the latter instance the australopithecines would apparently have been the sole occupants of the protohominid niche over wide areas in South Africa, with the resultant possibility of having an expanding population and range. For purposes of an ecological discussion it is necessary to assume one dating or the other; it is not important to decide whether or not the australopithecines were in fact ancestral to more advanced hominid types, but it is important to determine whether or not they were the sole occupants of the hominid niche in South Africa.

As Teilhard de Chardin points out, the australopithecine-bearing breccias and the human industry-bearing deposits have never been found conformably associated in the same site. This assumes, as did de Chardin, that *Telanthropus* is but a variant of the australopithecine type. Therefore, for purposes of discussion we shall assume that the australopithecines are Villafranchian in date and hence earlier than the makers of the pebble-cultures of South Africa. By analogy with the ecology of other animals it would be surprising if man and the australopithecines had remained contemporaries in the same area over very long periods of time, for closely-related forms with similar requirements rarely occupy the same area simultaneously.

Use of Tools Neither the archeological nor morphological evidence concerning australopithecines suggests an alternative to the assumption, which we made earlier, that protohominids were dependent on the use of tools for survival. It is generally agreed that the australopithecines were bipedal. Referring to our previous discussion, this strongly implies that the australopithecines routinely utilized adventitious or perhaps even slightly modified tools. Dart's evidence for the use of ungulate humeri as clubs offers empirical support for this theoretical position. Unmodified rocks used as tools can rarely be identified except by context. Familiar evidence from both archeology and ethnology shows that at the simplest level, rough tools commonly are discarded after initial use. Hence, a lack of recognizable stone tools in the breccias does not indicate that these were not used. Time alone precludes the survival of wooden implements such as clubs and digging sticks, although their use by australopithecines is certainly to be expected, for even the living great apes use sticks spontaneously.

The dentition of the partly carnivorous australopithecines (see section on food size) is uniformly characterized by reduced canines and incisors, and by nonsectorial premolars and molars. These dental characteristics are unique to them among all the large carnivorous mammals. The absence of teeth adapted for stabbing or shearing clearly implies the killing of game by weapons and butchering by simple tools. This observation would hold true even if the assignment of carnivorous habits to australopithecines were based only upon the abundant evidence that baboons were an important item in their diet. It is not dependent on the controversial question of their killing large hoofed mammals.

The dentition of australopithecines offers further evidence concerning their dependence on tools. As pointed out previously, intrasexual combat is characteristic of the males of virtually all strongly dimorphic mammals. Australopithecines are dimorphic, but they do not have the large piercing canines so characteristic of most of the larger living primates. This striking reduction of canines strongly implies that even in intrasexual (and intraspecific) combat, the australopithecines placed primary dependence on tools.

Scale of Food Size It should be possible on theoretical grounds to fix the approximate upper and lower size limits of the food which could economically be handled by the australopithecines with nothing more elaborate than a crude stick for digging and a limb bone for a club. Their capabilities would allow the utilization of the following animal foods: virtually all terrestrial reptiles and the smaller aquatic ones; eggs and nesting birds; some fish; fresh-water mollusks and crustaceans; insects; all of the smaller mammals including some burrowing forms, and larger mammals up to and including baboons. It is difficult, perhaps impossible, to determine whether or not the remains of the large giraffids and bovids reported from the bone breccias, represent kills by australopithecines or their scavenging from the kills of the larger cats. Since few meat eaters are loath to scavenge, and the implementation which would allow the australopithecines to kill such large animals is not apparent, we suggest that scavenging from the kills of the larger carnivores may have been systematically carried out.

Like most present-day hunting and collecting peoples, the australopithecines probably used plants as their major source of food. Without imputing to the australopithecines any cultural capabilities beyond the use of a simple stick for digging, at least the following types of vegetable food would be available to them: berries, fruits, nuts, buds and shoots, shallow-growing roots and tubers, and fruiting bodies of fungi. Some of the very small vegetable foods exploited by modern human groups were probably not extensively used. Effective utilization of grass seeds and other hard-shelled small seeds require specialized gathering implements and containers, and processing by grinding or cooking.

Such activities imply technologies which cannot be assigned *a priori* to the australopithecines, and for which there is no archeological indication until much later times. In this connection it may be noted that the evidence for the use of fire by *Australopithecus prometheus*, though impressive, is still regarded by some as controversial. In summary, it seems reasonable to treat the australopithecines as generalized carnivorous animals for which the freeing of hands and the use of simple implements enormously broadened the scale of food size to include a surprisingly large proportion of the total food resources of the terrestrial environment.

Social Behavior The biological bases for the family and social organization at the protohominid level which have already been discussed should apply to the australopithecines. Group organization beyond the family level is not indicated by the archeological context of the finds, because the rather large number of individuals recorded from Swartkrans and Sterkfontein might result from sampling of family-sized groups over many generations. However, there is at least one line of archeological evidence which suggests social organization beyond the simple family level. Since baboons travel in large aggregations and were a significant item of australopithecine diet, it would seem likely that the latter hunted in bands. A single australopithecine, even armed with a club, would not be a serious threat to a band of baboons. Such group hunting does not necessarily imply a high level of communication, such as speech, or permanence of organization, for it is characteristic of a number of nonprimate carnivorous vertebrates—many canids, some fish-eating birds, and killer-whales. Broom has shown that the australopithecines were characterized by sexual dimorphism, a widespread trait in the primates, including man. In social mammals, sexual dimorphism is almost invariably a product of the sexual selection associated with competition between males for females. Characteristically this sexual selection produces males which are larger, and more aggressive than females, and which have specialized structures for offense and defense. Although these dimorphic characters are a product of competition between males they usually result in the males assuming the role of group defender. We propose that the sexual dimorphism of the australopithecine males may have favored a secondarily derived function related to aggressive behavior, namely the hunting of large prey, including perhaps other australopithecines. Thus it may be that a sexual division of labor such as is present in all known hunting peoples was foreshadowed at this early level of hominid evolution.

The primates which first began to exploit a bipedal tool-using mode of life were establishing a level of adaptedness of enormous potentiality which had previously been inaccessible. They were entering a period of rapid change leading to a new kind of adaptedness. In the terminology of Simpson they were a group undergoing quantum evolution. It is to be expected that, like other similarly rapid evolving groups, they would be represented in the fossil record not by a uniform long-persistent type, but by a variable group of related forms. The australopithecines, which probably occupy a stage near the end of a step in quantum evolution, fit this theoretical prescription nicely. The various australopithecine forms which have been named can be considered representatives of a highly polymorphic assemblage. Their polymorphism is consistent with the idea of a rapidly evolving and radiating group and thus favors the probability of the Villafranchian dating.

It is reasonable to assume that most of the recovered australopithecine fossils date from a period prior to the time they faced competition from more highly evolved hominid types. When, as they inevitably must have, the australopithecines came in contact with culturally advanced hominids, they must have been subject to rapid replacement in terms of geological time.

Discussion

A paper such as this necessarily can be of only temporary utility. We feel that its principal contribution lies in raising questions, the answering of which may require orientation toward new points of view, the collection of new kinds of data, and perhaps the use of new techniques.

Students of animal ecology have developed a number of points of view which could be profitably applied to the study of preagricultural man. Two are particularly attractive. The first of these is that the basic problem of human behavior, like the behavior of other animals, is the obtaining of food, for the human body requires a continuous input of energy both for maintenance and for propagation. The second point of view involves the idea that population density normally is a complexly maintained equilibrium, dependent upon environmental as well as behavioral (and in the case of man, cultural) forces.

Anthropologists and archeologists to date have shown great ingenuity in utilizing the meager data for paleolithic and mesolithic man to establish tentative chronologies and outline cultural relationships. However, at the simplest level, the significance of material culture lies neither in the establishment of chronology nor as a measure of relationships, but as an indicator of efficiency in obtaining food. The lack of data concerning the food-getting effectiveness of the various items of material culture primarily results from preoccupation with typology rather than function. Even the best of typological labels tend to restrict functional interpretations and to ignore the role of varied behavior and human ingenuity in extending an implement's utility. Furthermore, functional interpretations can be determined only by studies of living peoples, and the ethnologist has not yet generally been stimulated to the realization of the basic importance of such data.

It is of interest that some food-getting devices which we presume to have been available to the australopithecines remain important today in the economy of hunting and gathering peoples. But there is little systematic quantitative information concerning the proportion of food obtained through the use of the hands alone, or that added by the use of the simple digging stick, club, or wooden spear. Nor at a more culturally sophisticated level is there quantitative data available to measure the increase in efficiency made possible by the invention of such devices as the spear-thrower and the bow and arrow. In making such analyses it would be useful to distinguish between the contributions of the relatively limited variety of primary tools and the more varied secondary tools. For example, the ecological significance of the fist-axes of the lower and middle Pleistocene varies enormously depending upon whether they are to be interpreted as primary tools used to make wooden implements such as clubs, digging sticks and spears, or whether they are regarded in the unlikely light of hand-held striking implements.

As pointed out previously, all animal populations, including human populations, depend on radiant energy stored chemically by photosynthesis. Animals compete endlessly between themselves for the one per cent of incident solar energy which plants are able to capture. The competitive success of an individual animal can be determined from its metabolism and the success of a population can be expressed quantitatively as the product of population density times individual metabolism.

If one can obtain even approximate figures for (1) the production of organic material by plants, (2) population densities and, (3) metabolism, one can evaluate from one point of view the biological success of different organisms. One can compare lions and elephants, earthworms and mice, humans and all other organisms, or more pertinent to anthropologists, one can compare simple cultures existing in either similar or different environmental situations. Since human beings comprise a single species, inter-group comparisons can be made on the basis of weight per unit area. An instructive analysis of this sort for small North American mammals has been made by C. O. Mohr.

To our knowledge this quantitative approach to human ecology has not been exploited by anthropologists; indeed, few attempts have been made by zoologists. O. P. Pearson has gathered figures which allow a comparison of Indians of northeastern United States with other animals common in the same area. Indians had less metabolic impact than deer, about the same impact as long-tailed shrews. E. S. Deevey, Jr. presents calculations which show the amazing trophic impact of the present human population of the world. Both these efforts are frankly exploratory and depend on approximations, but they point up an approach which merits consideration by anthropologists. If one could obtain for given areas even crude figures for human population density and for the production of organic material by the flora, he could compare the nutritive efficiencies of rainforest and grassland cultures, or the efficiency of Great Basin Indians and Australian Aborigines even though the two peoples live in arid regions of a very different character. Similarly one could obtain quantitative estimates for the effects of rivers, lakes, sea shore, and particularly vegetation types (i.e., oak woodland) on the capacity of an area to support human populations at a simple cultural level.

As discussed earlier, natural populations tend to fluctuate about some equilibrium figure. This fact has long been recognized by biologists, but to date, despite the perspectives which it supplies, it has not significantly influenced the approach of most anthropologists. From a short-term point of view, populations are in only approximate equilibrium, but viewed from the time scale of the Pleistocene, slowly expanding populations of man can be considered as being essentially in equilibrium. It appears to us that the idea that the populations of early man were in approximate equilibrium with the environment can supply a point of view from which to interpret the dynamics of technologically simple human populations. It should greatly facilitate qualitative exploration of such considerations as spatial variation of population density; growth or decline in numbers; rates of movement as influenced by migration and gene flow; and, shifts of populations into new climatic situations which demand new modes of life and may involve biological as well as cultural changes in adaptedness. As such qualitative interpretations are refined it may be possible to develop models which depict these processes semi-quantitatively and thus allow crude predictions.

Population density is a key to these dynamic processes, for either directly or indirectly it controls all of the others. As discussed in the sections on territoriality and population equilibrium, the density of early human populations, while immediately determined by a complex of variables in which behavior plays a central role, was ultimately controlled by the environment. Even in the most favorable environments the equilibrium density attained by natural populations is somewhat below the maximum which the environment can support. The factors restricting density are behavioral in an immediate sense and involve such things as aggressive behavior and territoriality. These behavioral factors must have brought dispersive forces to bear on Pleistocene man just as they do on other mammals. The existence of such dispersive forces suggests that the evolving australopithecines must have spread with great rapidity (i.e., almost instantaneously in terms of geological time) throughout the continental tropics and subtropics of the old world. Such an expansion would leave no suitable and accessible areas unoccupied. Consequently all subsequently evolved hominids in these regions must have expanded at the expense of already established populations. The replacement of the australopithecines by somewhat more advanced but related hominids may have followed the usual mammalian pattern of the gradual expansion of the more efficient form, and the slow reduction of the numbers of the less efficient. In many instances, however, population change must have resulted from gradual genetic penetration, and much of human evolution in the Pleistocene could easily have been powerfully affected by introgressive hybridization. In this regard it should be remembered that anatomical differences do not necessarily indicate genetic incompatability between groups, and that there is no evidence of reluctance to hybridize even between groups, and that there is no evidence of reluctance to hybridize even between widely different human types. If rapid and dramatic group replacement did occur it must have been a rare event occurring in special circumstances.

Although mammals are less affected by climate in a direct physical sense than are most organisms, physiological differences among mammals adapted to different climatic conditions have been clearly demonstrated. Distributionally the primates are an order characteristic of the tropics or subtropics. Modern man himself appears to be unable to invade the higher latitudes without fairly elaborate cultural accoutrements. It may therefore be concluded that during the Pliocene, the evolving protohominids occupied only the tropics, subtropics and perhaps the fringes of the temperate zones. The only place in which human populations could have expanded into a vacuum was at the margins of the then habitable areas. Thus changing cultural, and possibly changing biological, adaptedness would have allowed hominid expansion from the tropics into the temperate regions and ultimately into the arctic regions of the Old World. Aside from the initial continental expansion of the Old World protohominids, man expanded into major vacuums in populating Australasia, the New World, and much later, Micronesia and Polynesia. Once entered, these areas must have become filled rapidly, so that subsequent immigrants were faced for the most part with the problem of replacing established populations. Migrations, although spectacular, were probably of less importance in the Pleistocene than the processes discussed previously, which proceed normally without local catastrophic environmental change.

The anthropologists' lack of concern with the idea of population equilibrium in the simpler and more static human cultures is explicable in historical terms. Anthropologists, reacting to the claim by some anthropogeographers that extreme environmental determinism was operative on man, soon demonstrated that details of culture were not controlled directly by the environment. This broad denial overlooked man's nutritive dependence upon the environment, and long inhibited quantitative investigation of the relationship between man's population density and environmental factors.

The present interpretation of the mechanism of evolution is based upon natural selection which demands that populations be in a state of approximate equilibrium at a given time. To unravel the evolution of Pleistocene man, inevitably hampered as one is with inadequate data, one must necessarily use the idea of a population in equilibrium with the carrying capacity of the environment.

Most ecologists agree that no data are more crucial than those bearing upon population size, structure and density. Anthropologists, even though generally unconcerned with population equilibria, in some instances have been aware of the concept, but in general the importance of an ecological approach has not been appreciated. Some archeologists have hoped to reconstruct preagricultural population figures from studying the temporal and spatial distribution of sites, but the inescapable sampling errors in this approach render it unreliable. We suggest that an analysis of the energy relationships and the efficiency of the techniques for obtaining food offer a promising approach.

For several years it has been apparent that an ecological approach is imperative for all studies in population genetics, including those pertaining to man. It also offers a potentially useful point of view to the physical anthropologist, the ethnologist, and the archeologist, and it should provide an important integrative bridge between the various fields of anthropology.

12　Homo erectus

Sir Wilfred E. LeGros Clark

HOMO ERECTUS WAS DISCOVERED FIRST IN SIMPLER TIMES, WHEN IT WAS *assumed as a matter of course that the origins of man would be traced to Asia and when it was thought that there must have been a missing link— something between an ape and man that might answer to the name of apeman,* Pithecanthropus. *This apeman was discovered in Java—a real 1890's character—and for some time stood alone and almost unchallenged as our antediluvian ancestor. Then, at about the time that the australopithecine fossils were uncovered, which were to send the concept of a missing link into oblivion, scientists also began to discover other fossils that ultimately would show that* Pithecanthropus *was a remarkably well-distributed forerunner of* Homo sapiens. *Accordingly, it has since been necessary to get a new and more useful name for this species of fossil man. In this selection, a distinguished anthropologist summarizes what is known of this major category of our ancestors.*

1. The Discovery of Homo erectus *in Java*

In the last chapter we briefly reviewed the evidence for the existence in Europe during the last interglacial period of pre-Mousterian hominids not clearly distinguishable as a separate species from *Homo sapiens.* We saw that the few skulls so far available from deposits of this date are mostly characterized by a rather heavy development of the supra-orbital ridges (closely comparable with those not uncommonly found in Australian aboriginals today); to this extent they certainly present a some-

SOURCE: *The Fossil Evidence for Human Evolution,* 2d ed. (Chicago: The University of Chicago Press, 1964), Chap. III. Copyright © 1964 by The University of Chicago. Reprinted with the permission of the author and publisher.

The author (b. 1895) is Professor of Anatomy at Oxford University. A specialist on problems of primate evolution, he is the author of *A History of the Primates* (1949) and *The Fossil Evidence for Human Evolution* (1955; second edition, 1964). Among his most recent books is *Man-apes or Ape-men? The Story of Discoveries in Africa* (1967).

what primitive appearance. We have also noted the evidence of the Swanscombe skull bones that the species *H. sapiens* may already have been in existence during the second interglacial period. We now have to consider a group of extinct hominids of much more primitive appearance, known from skulls, teeth, and limb bones found in the Far East and North Africa which have been for many years commonly regarded as representing a separate genus of the Hominidae, *Pithecanthropus*. Today there is a general consensus of opinion that they are more properly to be included in the genus *Homo*, but specifically distinct from *H. sapiens* and *H. neanderthalensis*. The generic term *Pithecanthropus* has thus now to be replaced by the specific demonomination *Homo erectus*. The term *Pithecanthropus* has been time-honoured for almost seventy years, and it may be disconcerting to those familiar with it to accustom themselves to its replacement by the specific name *H. erectus*. But the morphological arguments for this change of nomenclature seem to be well-founded, and we shall now conform to it even though it may at first lead to some confusion for anthropologists long accustomed to "*Pithecanthropus*." We propose to ease this transitional period of nomenclatural change by using the colloquial term "pithecanthropines" here and there, and also by occasionally inserting the term *Pithecanthropus* in parentheses after the term *H. erectus*.

Homo erectus (*Pithecanthropus*) was for many years known only from two regions, Java (central and eastern) and China (Choukoutien, near Pekin). The Chinese fossils were at one time assigned to a distinct genus, *Sinanthropus*, but there is now general agreement that they are conspecific with the Javanese fossils. However, they present certain minor contrasts in skeletal and dental characters, which may be taken to indicate at least a subspecific difference.

The first outstanding discovery of *H. erectus* (*Pithecanthropus*) was made by Dubois at Trinil in central Java in 1891. The remains were recovered from alluvial deposits on the bank of the Solo River, at a stratigraphic level from which has also been derived a faunal assemblage including *Stegodon trigonocephalus*, *Hippopotamus antiquus*, a small axis deer (*Cervus lydekkeri*), and a small antelope (*Duboisia kroesenii*). It is now generally agreed that the Trinil fauna is post-Villafranchian, that the Trinil beds are of Middle Pleistocene age, and that they were probably laid down at a time corresponding to the second glaciaton of the Ice Age in other parts of the world. On the basis of potassium-argon datings it has been estimated that Java was occupied by *H. erectus* over a considerable period from about 450,000 to 500,000 years ago.

The most important item of Dubois's original discovery was a calvaria of *H. erectus*, which, in the very flattened frontal region, the powerfully developed supra-orbital ridges, the extreme platycephaly, and the low cranial capacity (estimated at about 900 cc.), presents a remarkably simian appearance. So much so, indeed, that some anatomists at first refused to recognize it as a hominid calvaria at all and supposed it to be the remains of a giant gibbon. In the same deposits and at the same stratigraphic level (but 15 meters upstream from the calvaria) Dubois found a complete femur, which, in its size and general confirmation, is quite similar to the femur of *H. sapiens*. Some doubt was naturally expressed (mainly because of their apparent incongruity) whether the femur and calvaria belonged to the same individual and whether the femur was really indigenous to the Trinil deposits. However, the accumulation of evidence speaks so strongly for their natural association that this is now generally accepted. In the first place, there seems little doubt that the femur was actually found *in situ* in the Trinil beds (and, according to Hooijer, the field notes kept by Dubois show that his excavations were carried out systematically and accurately). Second, it has been reported by Bergman and Karston that the fluorine content of the femur is equivalent to that of the calvaria and also of other representatives of the Trinil fauna, an observation which is in conformity with the geologic evidence that they were contemporaneous. Third, remains of five other femora of similar type in the Leiden Museum have been found among fossils collected from Trinil deposits (three of them were described by Dubois, in 1932), and these also show a fluorine content which is compatible with a Middle Pleistocene date. Thus they confirm that at this early time there existed in Java hominids with a type of femur indistinguishable from that of *H. sapiens,* though all the cranial remains so far found emphasize the extraordinarily primitive characters of the skull and dentition. Finally, portions of seven femora of the pithecanthropines from Choukoutien show that in the Chinese representatives of this population a femur of modern human type was also associated with the same primitive features of the skull and dentition. The combination in *H. erectus* of limb bones of modern type with cranial and dental characters of a primitive type is worth emphasizing, for it illustrates an important principle of vertebrate evolution—that the progressive modification of the several somatic systems may (and frequently does) proceed at different rates. This principle is well recognized by paleontologists but appears occasionally to have misled anthropologists. Such differential rates of somatic evolution may lead to structural contrasts which give an appearance of incongruity, and they are liable to be regarded as "disharmonies" because they do not conform with the sort of correlations which studies confined to living species may lead one unconsciously to expect. The true affinities of such fossil forms may thus be overlooked and misinterpreted, simply because they do not exhibit the particular combination or assemblage of characters of which we have created a rather rigid mental image from our preoccupation with the comparative anatomy of living forms (the latter, in many cases, being but the relics of a much greater diversity in the past). Differential rates of somatic evolution obviously need to be taken into account in regard to the taxonomic relevance of characters which are selected for assessing the phylogenetic status of fossil types.

For many years after Dubois's original discoveries in Java over half a century ago, no further remains of *H. erectus* (*Pithecanthropus*) were found, in spite of the efforts of the Selenka expedition of 1907-8. Then, during the few years preceding World War II, further important discoveries were made by von Koenigswald. With the exception of an immature skull found at Modjokerto in eastern Java, these new specimens come from Sangiran in central Java, about 50 km. from Trinil. They were derived from two horizons, one corresponding to the Trinil deposits and consisting of sandstones and conglomerates, and the other an underlying stratum of black clay, termed the "Djetis layer." The latter contains a faunal assemblage defintely older than that of the Trinil layer, characterized by *Epimachairodus zwierzyckii*, *Leptobos cosijni*, *Nestoritherium*, *Megacyon*, and *Cryptomastodon*; and by some authorities this has been taken to indicate an Early Pleistocene date. Beneath the Djetis horizon in Java is a still older formation, which contains remains of one of the first true elephants, *Archidiskodon planifrons*; and on the basis of faunal correlations this deposit is regarded as Villafranchian in age—that is, at the base of the Pleistocene. If this interpretation is correct, the Djetis horizon clearly does not represent the *earliest* Pleistocene.[1] Hooijer has pointed out that there is some doubt regarding the provenance of certain of the *H. erectus* remains discovered by von Koenigswald, i.e., whether their stratigraphic position is referable to the Trinil or Djetis horizons, because not all were found *in situ*. However, it appears to be reasonably certain that at least some of them came from the Djetis beds and therefore that the antiquity of *H. erectus* in Java may have extended back to the Early Pleistocene.

The fossil relics of *H. erectus* (*Pithecanthropus*) so far available are listed below. Those derived from the Trinil horizon are as follows:

1. *H. erectus* I, calvaria and femur discovered by Dubois in 1891.

2. *H. erectus* II, found in 1937. A calvaria, more complete than the type specimen and including part of the basis cranii.

3. *H. erectus* III, found in 1938. The parietal portion of a calvaria of a young adult individual (with the sutures completely patent).

The specimens known, or assumed on indirect evidence, to have been derived from the Djetis horizon are the following:

4. *H. erectus* IV, found in 1939. This consists of the posterior half of

---

[1] There appears still to be some disagreement regarding the stratigraphic level of the Plio-Pleistocene boundary in the Far East. Von Koenigswald regards the deposits underlying the Djetis layer as Pliocene, since they also contain a molluscan fauna which has been accepted as indicative of Pliocene age.

a calvaria, including part of the basis cranii, and a maxilla and palate with an excellently preserved dentition (except the incisors). It should be noted that there are, in addition, two small maxillary fragments with canines (mentioned, but not yet described in detail, by von Koenigswald).

5. *H. erectus* B, found in 1936. A mandibular fragment (somewhat eroded) including the symphysial region and containing P_2 to M_3.

6. The Modjokerto immature skull, found in 1936.

7. The Sangiran mandibular fragment, found in 1939 with M_1 M_2 in position.

8. The Sangiran mandibular fragment, found in 1941, with P_2 to M_1.

Besides the new specimens recorded in this list, which have been described by von Koenigswald and Weidenreich, there is a large number of isolated teeth from the Djetis layers of Sangiran which still await description. Mention should also be made of the tiny mandibular fragment found in 1890 by Dubois at Kedoeng Broeboes near Trinil (an interesting specimen, but not highly informative), and three teeth also found by him at Trinil. These three teeth were assumed at one time to belong to *H. erectus* I, but this allocation is now regarded as quite uncertain. Two of them, upper molars, are in a poor state of preservation and are likely to be the teeth of an orang (this ape survived in Java up to the Middle Pleistocene), while the third tooth, a premolar, is certainly hominid (but its stratigraphic position is questionable).

The whole problem of *H. erectus* in Java has unfortunately been much confused by the multiplicity of the taxonomic terms which have been applied to the various remains. The immature skull found at Modjokerto in 1936 was originally named *H. modjokertensis*, though there was no reason to suppose that it was other than that of a young individual of *H. erectus*. Von Koenigswald was also led to apply the specific term *modjokertensis* to other remains of *H. erectus* found in the Djetis layers at Sangiran "for morphological and stratigraphical reasons." However, he did not define any morphological differences which might justify a formal diagnosis of this new species, and, by themselves, the stratigraphic reasons do not appear to be valid. For, while the stratigraphic evidence certainly demonstrates that the pithecanthropines existed in Java during long periods of the Early and Middle Pleistocene, it does not preclude the possibility (or even the probability) that during this time it was represented by a single species, *H. erectus*. It may be noted that *H. erectus* IV was given the specific name *robustus* by Weidenreich, again with no morphological justification. As already mentioned, only the back part of the skull and the maxilla of this specimen were found. The back part of the skull shows no distinctive features whereby it can be separated specifically from *H. erectus*, and there is no other material available with which the maxilla can be compared. Of the two mandibular fragments found at Sangiran in 1939 and 1941, the latter has been referred, because of its large size, to another genus altogether, *Meganthropus palaeojavanicus*. The former, though quite similar in its general size and proportions, was given a specific distinction partly because of the wrinkled character of the enamel on the molar teeth (which may, however, be no more than the expression of an individual variation) and partly, it seems, because the specimen is rather poorly preserved, so that certain details of the dental morphology are

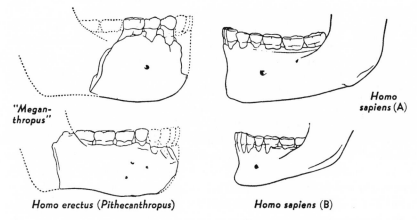

Figure 1 The mandibles (reconstructed) of *"Meganthropus palaeojavanicus"* and *H. erectus* B, compared with two mandibles of *Homo sapiens* (an Australian aboriginal and a European), to indicate that the range of variation in the size of the Javanese fossils does not exceed that of a single species of *Homo*. Approximately one-half natural size.

indeterminate. The generic separation of *"Meganthropus"* from *H. erectus* (*Pithecanthropus*) can hardly be justified on the basis of dental morphology; the two premolars and the first molar which have been preserved in the 1941 specimen conform in their total morphological pattern to a hominid dentition of the type found in the 1936 mandibular fragment (*H. erectus* B). The large size of the teeth and the preserved portion of the body of the mandible is certainly striking; but, as compared with the *H. erectus* B mandible, it does not indicate a range of variation exceeding that found (for example) in the single species *H. sapiens* (Fig. 1). It may readily be admitted that the available fossil material from Java is not yet adequate to decide finally whether there was more than one genus, or more than one species, of hominid living in Java during the Early Pleistocene. But from general considerations the probabilities seem to be against such a conclusion, and (it must be emphasized again) there is at present no really convincing morphological basis for the recognition of more than one species, *H. erectus*. In order to avoid further confusion, we shall here refer to all the specimens simply by the specific term *H. erectus*, while recognizing that there may well have been more than one subspecies or "race." [2]

2. The Morphological Characters of the Javanese Representatives of Homo erectus [3]

It has already been mentioned that the calvaria of the pithecanthropines in Java is known from four adult specimens and also one immature skull. Of the adult specimens, two are sufficiently complete to permit fairly close estimations of the cranial capacity by making endocranial casts and restoring the missing parts in porportion. According to Weidenreich, the cranial capacity of *H. erectus* I was probably not much greater than 900 cc., and that of *H. erectus* II is estimated at 775 cc. The capacity of *H. erectus* IV can be estimated only within rather broad limits, for, while the approximate breadth and height of the skull are directly ascertainable from the specimen itself, the total endocranial length has to be inferred indirectly from a reconstruction based on the other skulls. With these data, Weidenreich has calculated an endocranial volume of 880 cc. (or, say, approximately 900 cc.). Thus the mean cranial capacity of these three specimens is 860 cc.—a remarkably low figure when compared with the mean volume of 1,350 cc. for modern *H. sapiens*. The cranial capacity of the Modjokerto infant skull is estimated to be no more than 700 cc.; and, by reference to data concerning the brain growth of modern man and anthropoid apes, it may be inferred that this would not have expanded beyond about 1,000 cc. in the adult. So far as the meager fossil evidence goes, then, it may be surmised that the mean cranial capacity of the Javanese representatives of *H. erectus* was probably less than 1,000 cc.

As might be expected, a number of authorities have examined in detail the surface features of the endocranial casts of *H. erectus* in an attempt to find therefrom some clue to the intellectual status of these primitive hominids. Let it be said at once, however, that these studies have led to very disappointing results, for the information to be obtained

[2] It also remains possible, of course, that future discoveries will demonstrate that the owner of the "*Meganthropus*" mandible was so different from *H. erectus* in the morphological characters of skull, dentition, and limb bones as to justify a generic distinction. But the point is that, although I have a high regard for the judgment of my friend Professor von Koenigswald (which is, of course, based on quite considerable experience), I am not persuaded that such a distinction is valid on the fragmentary material so far available.

[3] I wish to express my indebtedness to Professor von Koenigswald for his courtesy in permitting me to examine the hominid fossils from Java at his laboratory in Utrecht.

from endocranial casts regarding brain functions is strictly limited. From time to time, indeed, dubious conclusions of this sort have been expressed, but they have mostly been based on a serious misconception of functional localization in the cerebral cortex and also on the false assumptions that certain of the structural areas of the cortex (as defined microscopically) have rather constant relationships to sulci and convolutions. In the past, many inferences have been made regarding the acquisition of articulate speech, the degree of manual skill, the ability to learn from experience, and other mental faculties in fossil hominids; these must now be discounted. This applies equally to the assumption that right- or left-handedness can be inferred from a consideration of the asymmetry of the cerebral hemispheres. There is no doubt, also, that some previous authorities have seriously exaggerated the extent to which the fissural pattern of the brain can be delineated from endocranial casts. In lower mammals the convolutions of the brain are often outlined with great precision on such casts; but, unfortunately, in hominids and the large anthropoid apes the sulci usually do not impress themselves clearly on the endocranial aspect of the skull except near the frontal and occipital poles of the brain and in the lower temporal region (for a useful critique on the interpretation of endocranial casts, see Hirschler). The most careful and critical studies which have been made of the endocranial casts of *H. erectus* are those of Ariëns Kappers and Bouman, and a reference to their papers will show how cautious are their conclusions. In *H. erectus* I it is noted that the frontal operculum is not defined by secondary sulci, as it is in the majority of brains of *H. sapiens*, and the region of the frontal lobe below the middle frontal sulcus is relatively small. The sulcal pattern of the frontal lobe, in general, also shows rather interesting resemblances to that of the chimpanzee brain. So far as its general shape is concerned, Kappers finds that the endocranial cast compares most closely with *Hylobates* among the anthropoid apes (but, of course, it is very much larger and shows a much more complicated sulcal pattern). In the endocranial cast of *H. erectus* II, Kappers and Bouman found the sulcal pattern of the frontal lobe to correspond very closely with that of the other skull, and the conclusion is again stated that this pattern "shows far more affinities with that of chimpanzees than ever observed in man." It will be noted that the results of these studies are expressed entirely in morphological terms—and rightly so, for even the study of the gross anatomy of the normal human brain itself has so far not demonstrated any feature by which the intellectual abilities of the individual during life can be deduced. All that can be said of the brain of *H. erectus* is that the low average size is presumably related to a rather low level of general intelligence (cf. Fig. 4, p. 184). By relating cranial capacity to femur size, Brummelkamp has tried to assess the degree of "cephalization" of fossil hominids. While the cephalization stage of less ancient fossil specimens of

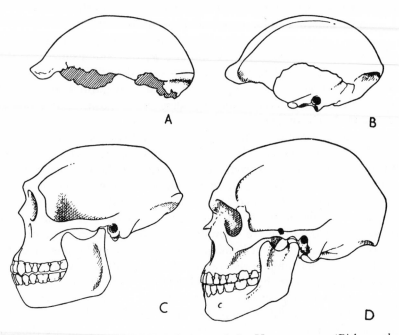

Figure 2 Comparison of the lateral views of the *Homo erectus* (*Pithecanthropus*) skulls found in Java with that of an Australian aboriginal. *A, H. erectus* I; *B, H. erectus* II; *C*, reconstruction of *H. erectus* IV (modified from Weidenreich); *D*, Australian aboriginal. Approximately one-quarter natural size.

Homo (e.g., those found at La Chapelle-aux-Saints, Combe Capelle, Spy, Grimaldi, and Chancelade) is found not to differ from that of Recent *H. sapiens*, in the case of *H. erectus* (from both Java and China) it is lower by a factor of $1/\sqrt{2}$.

The main characteristics of the skull of the Javanese representatives of *H. erectus* (Fig. 2) may be stated briefly as follows. The calvaria shows a very marked degee of platycephaly, with the maximum breadth low down in the temporal region. From this level the lateral walls of the cranium slope upward and medially to the position of the parietal eminence and then medially with a slight upward inclination to a median sagittal ridge. The supra-orbital torus is developed to an exaggerated degree and is bounded behind by a receding frontal contour and a very marked post-orbital constriction. The latter is associated with an inward curvature of the anterior part of the temporal squama, which accentuates the apelike appearance of the skull as a whole. The occipital torus is massive (particularly in *H. erectus* IV), and in all cases projects backward well beyond the level of the supra-occipital squama. The nuchal area of the occipital bone is relatively extensive (evidently for the attachment of a very powerful nuchal musculature) and slopes backward and upward to the occipital torus. The tympanic region and mandibular fossa are hominid in their general characters, but the rather weak development of the articular eminence in *H. erectus* IV and the rounded contour of the external auditory meatus in *H. erectus* II may be regarded as primitive characters of a somewhat simian type. The mastoid process is variably developed, and in *H. erectus* IV, where it is large, the apex is strongly deflected medially. The petrous bone, as seen from the endocranial aspect, is rather massive, and the cranial wall is everywhere of unusual thickness.[4] The foramen magnum (as far as can be judged from the crushed skull base in *H. erectus* IV) is situated as far forward in relation to the total cranial length as it is in *H. sapiens*.

The infant skull from Modjokerto shows features of particular interest. In age it may correspond to a modern child of about two years, for the specimen provides some evidence that the bregmatic fontanelle was just completing its closure, and the cranial walls are very thin (in the parietal region up to 3 mm., and elsewhere even less). The degree of ossification of the tympanic region, on the other hand, suggests an age corresponding to five or six in *H. sapiens*. But the precise age of this infant pithecanthropine is perhaps not a matter of great importance, for the primitive characters of the skull are in any case very obtrusive. The supra-orbital ridges are already assuming a marked prominence, with the incipient development of a post-orbital constriction; the forehead already has a retreating contour; and the occipital region shows the development of the angulation characteristic of the adult pithecanthropine skull. If the individual were as old as six years, the small cranial capacity assumes a greater significance; it it were as young as two years, the strong development of the supra-orbital eminences, the retreating character of the forehead, and the advanced degree of ossification of the tympanic region become all the more remarkable.

The palate and part of the facial skeleton of *H. erectus* are known from specimen IV. The size of the palate is relatively enormous, the maximum maxillo-alveolar width, according to Weidenreich, being 94 mm. The maximum width, it should be noted, is at the level of the last molar teeth and may be compared with the maximum width, 80 mm., of the palate of the Rhodesian skull, which is at the level of the second molars. The facial aspect of this specimen shows a pronounced alveolar prognathism, a great breadth of the anterior nares (which is near the uppermost limit so far recorded for *H. sapiens*), and an extensive maxillary sinus. The lower margin of the nasal aperture is bounded by a simple margin, with no sulcus or fossa prenasalis. The 1936 Sangiran mandible, *H. erectus* B, is heavily constructed, with a very thick and sloping symphysial region, and there is no indication of a mental

---

[4] Even in the young adult, *H. erectus* III, the parietal bone reaches a thickness of 10 mm.

eminence. It shows three mental foramina—a very unusual feature in *Homo sapiens* but quite common in anthropoid apes. In its general build the mandible conforms quite well with the maxilla of *H. erectus* IV. The mandibular fragments found at Sangiran in 1939 and 1941 provide evidence of a lower jaw even more massive; but (as already noted) there seems no sound morphological reason for not including them in the species *H. erectus*. In both specimens the mental foramen is single and is situated about midway between the alveolar and lower margins of the mandible—a hominid feature which contrasts rather strongly with the low position of the foramen in the large anthropoid apes. In the 1941 mandibular fragment the symphysial region is exceedingly thick, but in its general contour in sagittal section it resembles the Heidelberg mandible quite closely, and in the high position of the foramen spinosum it also shows a hominid, rather than a pongid, feature. In none of these mandibular specimens found in Java is there any indication of a "simian shelf." [5]

That in its total morphological pattern the dentition of the *H. erectus* group of fossils from Java is characteristically hominid in type has not been a matter for dispute. The contours of the dental arcade, the shape, size, and morphological details of the canines and premolars, and the morphological details and mode of wear of the molars, taken together, provide a marked contrast with the pongid type of dentition. On the other hand, the few specimens available show certain primitive features, in which some approach is made to a simian level of evolutionary development. For example, in the specimen *H. erectus* IV, the upper canine, though not very large relative to the adjacent teeth, and spatulate rather than conical in general shape, projects well beyond the level of the premolars and shows a well-marked attrition facet on its anterior margin, which indicates that it overlapped the lower canine to a slight degree. Moreover, it is separated from the socket for the lateral incisor by a distinct diastemic interval. Von Koenigswald noted that, of the two other maxillary fragments from the Djetis layers of Sangiran, one also shows evidence of a similar diastema, while in the other there is a contact facet on the canine which makes it clear that there was no diastema in this specimen. The primitive trait of a diastema in the upper dentition was thus not a consistent feature of the Javanese representatives of *H. erectus*. From isolated teeth (not hitherto described in detail), von Koenigswald concluded that the central upper incisors are "extremely shovel-shaped, by far surpassing the condition observed in *Sinanthropus*." The upper molars, premolars, and canine form converging rows on either side of the palate, with only a slight degree of curvature. The first upper premolars

[5] This term is applied to the thin ledge of bone which, in the Recent large anthropoid apes, commonly extends back from the lower border of the symphysis across the anterior end of the interramal space of the mandible.

(two specimens) are provided with three roots, as is normally the case in the Pongidae but uncommonly in *H. sapiens*. The upper molars are large, the second molar being larger than the first.[6]

Of the lower dentition, the mandibular fragment *H. erectus* B shows in a fairly well-preserved state the second premolar and the three molar teeth. The latter are noteworthy for their large size and for the fact that their length increases progressively from front to back. This is a primitive feature only very rarely found in *H. sapiens* (four examples were found by De Terra, in a series of 1,000 skulls). The alveolar socket for the first premolar is simple and indicates the single root construction characteristic of the Hominidae. The socket for the canine tooth is quite small (particularly when considered in relation to the massiveness of the jaw) and is placed medially to the anterior margin of the first premolar socket. Von Koenigswald has commented on the weak development of the incisors and canines when compared with the large size of the postcanine teeth, a character which is even more marked in the australopithecine material from South Africa. No isolated lower canines or incisors from Java have so far been described in detail. In the large mandibular fragment (1941) from Sangiran (*"Meganthropus"*), the two premolars and the first molar are well preserved but are in a somewhat worn condition. The first premolar is of the hominid type, bicuspid with well-marked anterior and posterior foveae, and shows no tendency toward the sectorialization which is in general characteristic of Pongidae (fossil and Recent). There is a surface indication of a subdivision of the root, but no separation of the component elements. The socket for the canine shows that this tooth was surprisingly small, the total length of the root being certainly not more than 20 mm. Von Koenigswald mentioned an isolated lower canine from Java, which he also referred to *"Meganthropus,"* but gave no details of this specimen except to say that it is small (presumably relative to the other teeth) and "in no way different from the canine of modern man except for the size." It should be noted that the preserved teeth in the large 1941 Sangiran mandible are quite similar to those of the *H. erectus* B mandible, except for their over-all dimensions. Weidenreich has also emphasized their strong resemblance to the corresponding teeth of the Pekin representatives of *H. erectus*, particularly in the arrangement of the cusps, the distinctness of the anterior and posterior foveae, and the development of the cingulum of the first premolar tooth. Some authorities have interpreted the large mandibular fragments from Sangiran as evidence for the existence in Java during the Pleistocene of "giant" hominids. This seems to be a misapplication of the term "giant," which is commonly taken to refer to stature. But a large hominid jaw does not

[6] It is of particular interest to note that the over-all dimensions of the first premolar and the first molar of the australopithecine maxilla found at Sterkfontein in 1936 differ from those of *H. erectus* IV by less than 0.5 mm.

imply a giant individual. On the contrary, so far as other paleontological evidence goes, there is some reason for assuming a negative correlation between the size of the mandible and the total stature. Certainly, in the case of the Javanese fossils, the femora, which can be assigned with reasonable certainty to the Trinil horizon, provide no evidence of great height—estimates based on these specimens indicate a stature of about 5 feet 8 inches or less, and in no case more than 5 feet 10 inches. It has already been noted that all these thigh bones (including the complete femur originally found by Dubois in 1891 and the incomplete shafts later discovered among other fossil material from Java) are quite similar to those of *H. sapiens;* if there is any minor difference of a biometric character, this has yet to be demonstrated.

If the calvariae of *H. erectus (Pithecanthropus)* are considered critically by themselves, it is perhaps not surprising that, at first sight, the original discovery gave rise to some doubt in the minds of anatomists whether it represented a primitive hominid or a giant gibbon. But the latter interpretation was clearly based on the assumption that the skull of a giant gibbon would be only an enlarged replica of the skull of the known gibbon, reproducing, that is to say, the same relative proportions and the same shape. In fact, however, our present knowledge of processes of allometric growth of the skull and brain in closely related species or genera would lead us to suppose that if a giant gibbon ever did exist, the proportions of the skull and cranial cavity would have differed even more markedly from the known gibbon than a large chimpanzee does from a pygmy chimpanzee. Indeed, the *H. erectus* calvaria provides an excellent illustration of the fallacies involved in the direct comparison of shape and relative dimensions (whether by visual comparison or biometric methods) without taking into account the factor of absolute size. It was, no doubt, the superficial impression of "gibbonoid" affinities in the calvaria which led some authorities to persuade themselves that similar evidence could be detected in certain morphological details of the femur. In fact, however, as already mentioned, it has not been demonstrated that the femur shows any significant difference from *H. sapiens.*

3. The Morphological Characters of the Chinese Representatives of Homo erectus

It was entirely due to the care and foresight of Professor von Koenigswald that the important discoveries of *H. erectus (Pithecanthropus)* which he made in Java shortly before the last war were preserved intact. On the eve of the Japanese invasion of Java, he distributed the valuable specimens among his friends of the local population, and when he himself was liberated from captivity with the final defeat of the Japanese, he was able to retrieve them intact. In the case of the remains of

H. erectus found at Choukoutien near Pekin, the story was, unhappily, very different. At the end of the war no trace of the fossils could be found. It is generally supposed that they had been crated for dispatch to a safe area and that the ship on which they had been loaded was sunk in the early stages of the war. Fortunately, however, detailed and comprehensive descriptions had been published by Davidson Black and Weidenreich, richly and accurately illustrated by drawings, photographs, and radiographs, and casts of the earlier fossils described by Davidson Black are available for study.

There is no need to recount here in detail the history of the first discovery of *H. erectus* (*Pithecanthropus*) in Pekin, for the story has been well told elsewhere. A single lower molar tooth found in 1927 at Choukoutien led Davidson Black—at that time professor of anatomy at Pekin University Medical College—to create a new genus and species of the Hominidae, *Sinanthropus pekinensis*. This decision, based as it was on one tooth only, was met with some skepticism; but Black's inference that the tooth provided evidence for the existence in China during the Pleistocene of a primitive type of hominid showing certain simian characters displayed in a remarkable way his perspicacity as a comparative anatomist. For, two years later, in 1929, an uncrushed and almost complete calvaria of a very primitive type was found at the same site. Its similarity to *H. erectus* I of Java was very obvious from the first, and subsequent studies and further discoveries finally made it clear that the Javanese and Chinese fossils were not generically, or even specifically, distinct. The generic term *Sinanthropus* has therefore now been discarded. There are certain minor differences, however, and, as already mentioned, these are held by some authorities to justify a subspecific distinction.

The Chinese variety of *H. erectus* is known from fourteen calvariae (or fragments of calvariae), as well as portions of facial bones, many teeth, and a few limb bones.[7] The main features of the skull are as follows (Fig. 3). The cranial capacity (based on Weidenreich's estimates from four calvariae) ranges from 850 to 1,300 cc., with a mean of 1,075 cc. So far as this limited material goes, therefore, it appears to indicate that the mean cranial capacity may have been about 100 cc. greater than that of the Java specimens, and at its upper levels the brain volume actually comes well within the normal range of variation of *H. sapiens*. All the calvarial specimens show a marked platycephaly, with heavily constructed supra-orbital and occipital tori and a rather well-marked sagittal ridge. They are relatively homogeneous in their general shape but differ considerably in size (possibly an expression of sexual variation). Viewed from behind, they are broader at the base, the width of the skull diminish-

[7] A complete list of all these remains (together with the sites of their discovery and the publications where they have been described) is to be found in Weidenreich's monographs.

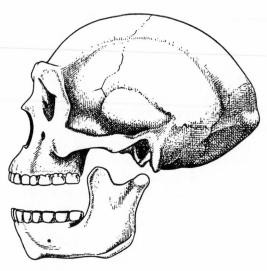

Figure 3 Skull and mandible of the Chinese variety of *Homo erectus* (formerly known as *Pithecanthropus pekinensis*), drawn from the cast of a reconstruction by Weidenreich. One-third natural size.

ing from the level of the interauricular plane upward. Compared with *H. erectus* of Java, the platycephaly is a little less extreme (though it should be emphasized that the cranial height can be only approximately estimated in the Javanese fossils), and there is a distinct, but slight, convexity of the frontal squama. The frontal sinus is unusually small in some of the specimens (in the Javanese types it is very large), though the other accessory air sinuses, e.g., in the maxilla and the mastoid process, are well developed. The bones of the skull wall are of massive thickness, the latter (according to Weidenreich) being due mainly to a thickening of the outer and inner tables. All the bones of the facial skeleton are likewise heavily constructed. The mandibular fossa is unusually deep, bounded in front by a conspicuous articular eminence. The tympanic plate is very thick and is disposed more horizontally than in *H. sapiens* (resembling in this respect *H. erectus* of Java, as well as the large anthropoid apes). The auditory aperture is wide; it varies in its shape but commonly has a transversely elliptical form. The mastoid process is relatively small. The nasal bones are said to exceed in width those of *H. sapiens,* and the nasal aperture (which is not bounded by a prenasal groove) is conspicuously broad. The palate shows the typical hominid contour and is not exceptionally large in its surface area. The cranial sutures appear to close earlier than they do in modern man. The mandible is robust, with a bicondylar width which reaches the upper limit of that of modern races such as the Eskimo (and perhaps exceeds it). The angle of inclination of the symphysial axis, according to Weidenreich, is about 60° and in this character corresponds with the Heidelberg mandible. There is no mental eminence. The digastric fossae (for the attachment of the digastric muscles to the back of the symphysial region of the jaw) are elongated and narrow and do not extend to the vertical inner surface of the mandible as in *H. sapiens.* The mental foramen is multiple in all the specimens found; indeed, there may be as many as five foramina—a remarkably simian feature. The ascending ramus is broad, and the muscular markings for the masseter and pterygoid muscles are strongly developed. The articular surface of the condyloid process shows no feature which differentiates from that of other species of *Homo.* The coronoid process is broad and thick and presumably served to attach a rather powerful temporal muscle.

The endocranial cast has been studied by Davidson Black and also by Shellshear and Elliot Smith. From the accounts of these authors it is very closely similar to that of the Javanese specimens of *H. erectus* and shows no real distinguishing features (Fig. 4).

The dentition has been studied in the greatest detail by Weidenreich on the basis of 147 teeth found at Choukoutien, representing probably 32 individuals. Of these specimens, 13 belong to the deciduous dentition. The teeth are large by modern standards, the enamel surface is frequently complicated by rather elaborate wrinkling, and the basal cingulum (i.e., the thickening of enamel at the base of the crown of the tooth) is particularly well developed. The canines show considerable variation in size, shape, and robustness, but those of the upper dentition are frequently large and conical. However, it is important to recognize that, in spite of these primitive features, there is no evidence that they projected to any marked degree beyond the level of the adjacent teeth,[8] and in the early stages of attrition they quickly became worn down to an even flat surface, in conformity with the occlusal plane of the dentition as a whole. Thus the upper and lower canines did not overlap, as appears to have been the case in some of the Javanese representatives of *H. erectus.* The first upper premolar may have two roots, with a surface indication of a third. The first lower premolar is a nonsectorial tooth of bicuspid shape, with a strong development of the lingual cusp. The two cusps, in fact, merit the term "subequal"; and herein the tooth contrasts strongly not only with that of the anthropoid apes but also with modern *H. sapiens.* For in the latter the lingual cusp seems to have secondarily undergone quite a considerable retrogression, being usually much smaller than the buccal cusp. The root is single but shows evidence of the fusion of two

[8] Weidenreich's statement to the contrary seems to have been based on the comparison of *isolated* teeth and on the assumption that the base line of the enamel of the canine tooth is level with that of the adjacent teeth. This, however, is by no means the case.

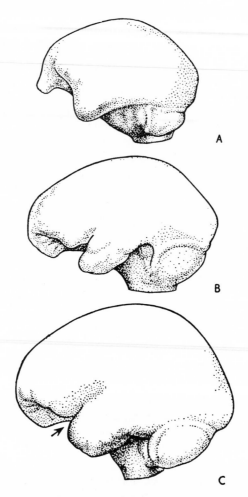

Figure 4 Lateral view of the endocranial casts of *A*, a male gorilla; *B*, *Homo erectus* (from Pekin); and *C*, *Homo sapiens* (the Sylvian notch is indicated by an arrow). One-third natural size.

separate roots. The molar teeth show no special features, apart from their size and the strong development of their main cusps and some secondary cuspules. They show a flat wear with even a moderate degree of attrition; in this feature they contrast quite definitely with the anthropoid apes. The second lower molar is slightly larger than the first, and the third molar is usually the smallest of the three. The dental arcade shows the even curvature characteristic of the Hominidae, and in none of the specimens is there a diastema. There is some evidence from immature jaws that in the eruption of the permanent dentition the second molar appeared before the canine, a sequence which is characteristic of the anthropoid apes, but also of *H. neanderthalensis* and of certain modern races of man (e.g., Bantu). The deciduous dentition is distinguished by the fact that the first milk molar is rather strongly compressed from side to side and by the sharply pointed shape of the canine, which also has a well-developed cingulum. In both these features the deciduous dentition may be said to show a slight degree of morphological approximation to that of the Pongidae.

The limb bones found at Choukoutien comprise portions of seven femora, two humeri, a clavicle, and one of the carpal bones (os lunatum). It may be said at once that in no characters has it been satisfactorily demonstrated that any of these limb bones are distinguishable from those of *H. sapiens*. Indeed, it has even been suggested that they actually are the remains of representatives of *H. sapiens*, who, on this view, were living at Choukoutien contemporaneously with *H. erectus*. But this argument is based entirely on the a priori (and invalid) assumption that hominids with primitive characters of the skull and dentition should also show equally primitive characters in the limb skeleton; and it takes no account of the improbabilities of finding in the same deposits the skulls and teeth of one genus of hominids (and no limb bones), and the limb bones of another genus of hominids (with no skulls or teeth). Moreover, as we have already noted, the femora from the Trinil deposits of Java, which on a strong presumption must be assigned to *H. erectus*, are also of modern type.

Of the seven femoral remains found at Choukoutien, one consists of almost the entire diaphysis, one of the proximal half of the diaphysis, and the others are still more fragmentary. They show a marked degree of platymeria (though not more so than may occur in *H. sapiens*), and the wall of the shaft is unusually thick. Weidenreich expressed the opinion that in certain features of the curvature of the shaft the bones differ from those of modern man; but if such a difference does exist, it must be a very minor one, and it has not so far been demonstrated by metrical analysis. In any case, it could hardly be held to constitute by itself a very significant difference. On the other hand, the femoral shafts certainly lack the robustness and curvature characteristic of *H. neanderthalensis*. From the most complete shaft (femur IV), the total length of this bone has been estimated by Weidenreich to have been 407 mm.; and from this the total standing height of the individual is computed to have been 5 feet 1½ inches. If this were to be taken as representative of the local population as a whole (obviously, an unsafe assumption!), it would suggest that the Chinese population of *H. erectus* was shorter in stature than the Javanese population of the same species. The humeral fragments found at Choukoutien consist of a diaphysis of one bone and a small portion of the distal end of another one. Apart from the thickness of the shaft walls, they show no distinguishing features at all. The clavicle and the os lunatum are also quite similar to those of *H. sapiens*.

So far as the scanty fossil material permits a comparison of the Javanese and Chinese representatives of *H. erectus*, it is probably true to say that the former were more primitive in their smaller cranial capacity, more marked platycephaly, greater flattening of the frontal region of the skull, more heavily constructed mandible, less pronounced curvature of the dental arcade, larger palate, a tendency to slight overlapping of the canines with the occasional presence of a diastema in the upper dentition, and the relative length of the last lower molar. There is also evidence that in Java *H. erectus* extended back to a greater antiquity than in China, for while (as already noted) the faunal correlations of the Djetis deposits have been taken to indicate an Early Pleistocene horizon, the Choukoutien deposits are certainly no earlier than the Middle Pleistocene (corresponding, according to some authorities, to the second interglacial period and by others estimated on indirect evidence to be about 350,000 years old). On purely morphological criteria, however, the two groups appear to be quite closely related, the distinction being certainly no more than a subspecific one.

It is not known certainly what degree of cultural development had been attained by *H. erectus* in Java, for the evidence is entirely negative. No implements were found in direct association with the skeletal remains. However, chopping tools, hand axes, and primitive flake tools of the Patjitanian industry have been recovered from deposits of a slightly later age, and it is not improbable that such tools were actually made and used during the Middle Pleistocene by hominids of the *H. erectus* type in Java. At Choukoutien, in the same deposits yielding remains of *H. erectus*, crude cores and trimmed flakes of quartz and silicified rocks were found, forming a local industry of an archaic, but fairly uniform, character. Animal bones were also found, broken and chipped, apparently by design for use as tools. Finally, the remains of hearths throughout the deposits, as well as charred animal bones, provide evidence that these early hominids were familiar with the art of making and using fire for domestic purposes, while the nature of their diet is indicated by collections of deer bones and hackberry seeds. It appears, therefore, that, in spite of the crudity of their stone and bone industry, the Middle Pleistocene population of *H. erectus* in China had already developed a communal life of a very active kind; and it is of particular interest that at this early time they had already acquired the intelligence and skill to use fire for culinary purposes. Some authorities have, indeed, expressed doubt whether the Choukoutien culture actually was developed by *H. erectus*, suggesting that it was the product of a more advanced type of hominid assumed to have been living contemporaneously in the same neighborhood. But this suggestion has no factual evidence to support it, being entirely based on the false supposition that hominids of such a primitive morphological status as *H. erectus* would not be capable of developing the Choukoutien culture. In fact, as far as the archeological evidence can be assessed from the careful and detailed reports issued by those who excavated the sites at Choukoutien, the conclusion that the cultural and skeletal remains were found in true association seems reasonably secure. It may also be emphasized (as noted above) that, in spite of the low average cranial capacity in some individuals, it came well within the normal range of variation for modern *H. sapiens*. So far as the volume of the brain is concerned, therefore, there is no anatomical reason for supposing that *H. erectus* in Pekin was not capable of establishing a primitive culture.

HOMO ERECTUS IN AFRICA AND EUROPE

For fifty years or more it has been tacitly assumed that the primitive type of man now called *Homo erectus* (but, as we have already noted, until recently regarded as a separate genus of the Hominidae, *Pithecanthropus*) was confined in geographical distribution to the Far East. More lately, evidence has accrued to make it reasonably certain that the same type also existed at about the same time in Africa during the Chellean and Early Acheulian phases of Paleolithic culture, and probably in Europe also.

In 1954 there were discovered by Arambourg at Ternifine in Algeria three mandibles and a parietal bone in deposits dating from early Paleolithic times—probably near the beginning of the second interglacial period. The jaws are remarkably robust and lack a chin eminence, the molar teeth are quite similar to those of *H. erectus* of Pekin, the canine teeth (as inferred from their sockets) were exceptionally strong, and the parietal bone conforms in size and curvature with known specimens of *H. erectus*. Indeed, there can be little doubt, so far as morphological evidence goes, that these remains do belong to the same species. It is unfortunate, therefore, that the group which they represent was at first designated *Atlanthropus mauritanicus*, with the implication that it was not only specifically but even generically distinct. This is but another example of the terminological confusion in paleoanthropology resulting from the misapplication of taxonomic principles. Other possible remains of *H. erectus* in North Africa are fragments of mandibles with the three molar teeth and one premolar tooth found in 1955 at Sidi Abd-er-Rahman in Morocco, but while the dimensions of the cheek teeth closely parallel those from Ternifine, the canine appears to have been more reduced. The antiquity of these jaw fragments is uncertain; by some authorities they are referred to the third glacial period and to the Acheulian phase of Paleolithic culture. The parts of a mandible and maxilla, together with a number of very small pieces of a cranial vault, discovered as long ago as

1933 at Rabat in Morocco, have also been compared with *H. erectus*. But in this case the remains are too scanty to permit firm conclusions, and their allocation in time to the last (Würm) glaciation suggests that affinities with Neanderthal man are more likely.

Farther south in Africa, at Olduvai Gorge in Tanganyika, Leakey has more recently reported the discovery of a calvaria from a stratigraphic horizon containing Chellean tools, and with an antiquity (based on potassium-argon dating) of 490,000 years. Thus it appears to have been more or less contemporaneous with the Javanese representatives of *H. erectus*. So far as can be inferred from a brief inspection of this important specimen and from published photographs (for it has yet to be described in full detail), the calvaria is so closely similar to some of the skulls of *H. erectus* from China that it would be difficult to justify a specific distinction. It is to be hoped that further and more complete remains of these ancient hominids in Africa will be found, for on the evidence so far available it certainly seems that *H. erectus* extended its distribution from the Far East to this continent almost half a million years ago.

The inference that *H. erectus* also occupied Europe depends (apart from the very indirect archeological evidence of stone cultures) on the interpretation of the mandible found at Mauer, near Heidelberg, and estimated on stratigraphical data to be about 400,000 years old. As already noted, the taxonomic reference of this specimen must remain dubious until more complete remains come to light. Although the dentition shows certain differences, notably in their smaller size relative to that of the mandible, the massive construction of the latter, together with the conformation of the symphysial region and the vertical ramus of the jaw, recalls very closely some of the known specimens of *H. erectus*. The antiquity of the jaw, and its association with animal bones broken as if by design (like those found in deposits containing the remains of Pekin man), provide some further argument for allocating it to the species *Homo erectus*, but it still has to be admitted that such an allocation rests on very slender evidence.

A brief reference should be made here to some isolated teeth found several years ago among a collection of fossil bones and teeth from Chinese drug-stores (where such material was commonly sold for medicinal purposes). They were described by von Koenigswald and referred by him to a new genus of fossil apes, *Gigantopithecus*. He regarded this extinct giant ape as probably the latest survivor of an Asiatic stock which more or less parallels the human line, while Weidenreich took the view that it represents a giant hominid. Since then, three mandibles of the creature have been recovered from the Kwangsi province of China in deposits stated to be of Early Pleistocene date. The opinion is still expressed by some authorities that *Gigantopithecus* may be the product of a very early aberrant branch of the Hominidae. But, while recognizing that the molar teeth show certain morphological characters suggestive of affinities with the Hominidae, an inspection of photographs of the specimens (including a cast of one of them) inclines the present writer to the opinion that it was a giant pongid in which the dental specializations of the modern large apes were less strongly developed.

4. The Species Homo erectus *and its Relationship to* Homo sapiens *and* Homo neanderthalensis

The recognition of the species *H. erectus* has been based mainly on the skeletal remains of a number of individuals from Java and China, which, as we have seen, show a moderate degree of individual and geographic variation. But they comprise a group whose morphological characters are held by most anthropologists to be sufficiently consistent and distinctive to justify their separation as a distinct species of the genus *Homo*. If this is so, it is a matter of some importance (particularly for future reference in paleoanthropology) to provide at least a provisional diagnosis of the species, and the following formal definition is suggested.

Homo Erectus A species of the Hominidae characterized by a cranial capacity with a mean value of about 1,000 cc.; marked platycephaly, with little frontal convexity; massive supra-orbital tori; pronounced post-orbital constriction; opisthocranian coincident with the inion; vertex of skull marked by sagittal ridge; mastoid process variable, but usually small; thick cranial wall; tympanic plate thickened and tending toward a horizontal disposition; broad, flat nasal bones; heavily constructed mandible lacking a mental eminence; teeth large, with well-developed basal cingulum; canines sometimes projecting and slightly interlocking, with small diastema in upper dentition; first lower premolar bicuspid with subequal cusps; molars with well-differentiated cusps complicated by secondary wrinkling of the enamel; second upper molar may be larger than the first, and the third lower molar may exceed the second in length; limb bones not distinguishable from those of *H. sapiens*.

It will be noted from this definition that the distinction between *H. erectus* and *H. sapiens* is pronounced. Indeed, the cranial and dental differences (as well as the even more significant contrast in cranial capacity) appear to be almost as well marked as those which are commonly accepted as justifying a generic distinction between the gorilla and chimpanzee. The distinction between *H. erectus* and *H. neanderthalensis* is at first sight less obtrusive; but that it is a real distinction is made evident by the still greater difference in cranial capacity, the differences in the limb skeleton, and the more primitive features of the dentition in *H. erectus* (at least in the Javanese forms). It is made all the more evident by a consideration of the evolutionary history of *H. neanderthalensis*, which has led to the conclusion that the latter species was secondarily derived from a type of hominid more closely akin to *H. sapiens* and that its evolutionary development was associated with certain retrogressive changes in the skull. These cranial modifications show some resemblance to *H. erectus* (e.g., in the platycephaly and the strong development of the supra-orbital torus); but, in so far as they are retrogressive features, the resemblance is clearly not indicative of close phylogenetic relationship.

The relationships of *H. erectus* are obviously a matter of the greatest interest for the problem of the origin of our own species. There is, indeed, a general consensus of opinion that *H. erectus* stands in an ancestral relationship to *H. sapiens* (and also *H. neanderthalensis*). This does not mean (as we have already emphasized) that the Far Eastern population of this species was itself the actual ancestral group—it means, at the most, that the species as a whole was probably ancestral to the later species; if so, of course, the transition from one to the other may have occurred in some other part of the world. The evidence for such a hypothesis is dependent in the following line of reasoning: (1) The morphological characters of *H. erectus* conform very well with theoretical postulates for an intermediate stage in the evolution of later species of *Homo* from still more archaic types approximating to the presumed common ancestral stock of the Pongidae and Hominidae. These theoretical postulates are based on comparative anatomical studies of the modern representatives of these two subdivisions of the Hominoidea and by analogy with the known evolutionary history of other mammalian groups. (2) The existence of *H. erectus* in the early part of the Pleistocene, antedating any of the well-authenticated fossil remains of *H. sapiens*, provides it with an antiquity which conforms well with the suggested ancestral relationship. (3) *H. erectus*, pre-Mousterian hominids such as that represented by the Steinheim skull, and modern types of *H. sapiens* of the late Paleolithic provide a temporal sequence which appears to illustrate a satisfactorily graded series of morphological changes leading from one type to the other. These arguments are precisely similar to those which have, for example, led to the conclusion that the genera *Merychippus* and *Pliohippus* were ancestral to *Equus*. But, whereas the fossil record of the Equidae has now accumulated in such detail that this phylogenetic sequence is as well demonstrated as any is ever likely to be on the evidence of paleontology, fossil hominid material is still scanty. Thus the inference that the species *H. erectus* was ancestral to *H. sapiens* must be accepted for the present as not very much more than a working hypothesis. But it is a working hypothesis which has the perfectly reasonable basis that it is consistent with the evidence so far available.

If the thesis is correct that the Hominidae and the Pongidae are divergent radiations from a common ancestral stock—the result, that is to say, of a phylogenetic dichotomy—the evolutionary precursors of *H. erectus* must presumably have shown morphological characters approximating much more nearly to a simian level of evolution. To some extent these characters might be tentatively predicated by a consideration of comparative anatomical data, by extrapolation backward of the *H. erectus–H. sapiens* sequence, and by analogy with the sort of morphological gradations which are known (from more complete fossil records) to have occurred in the evolution of other mammalian groups. For example, it is evident enough that one of the main features of hominid evolution (at least in its later stages) has been the progressive development of the brain; and there is some evidence that in the Early and Middle Pleistocene it proceeded with unusual rapidity in comparison with evolution rates in general. It may be presumed, therefore, that in the immediate ancestor of the genus *Homo* the cranial capacity would certainly have been still smaller—perhaps, indeed, not very much greater than that of the largest anthropoid ape of today, the gorilla. With this would probably have been associated massive jaws and large teeth similar to those of *H. erectus*, but of somewhat more impressive proportions, and, in further correlation, powerful temporal and masseter muscles with extensive areas of bony attachment to the skull. Since the essential characteristic features of the hominid dentition (by which it is so strongly contrasted with the pongid type of dentition) were already well established in *H. erectus*, it might be expected that in the immediately ancestral genus these hominid features would also be clearly evident (in spite of the size of the teeth), though no doubt more primitive in certain details. Lastly, the fact that in *H. erectus* the limb bones had already fully achieved the morphology and proportions of *H. sapiens* strongly suggests that the evolutionary modifications of the limbs related to erect bipedalism had been acquired very early in the line of hominid development and would thus already be apparent in the ancestral genus. These inferences are, of course, based on indirect evidence and are capable of verification only by the discovery of actual fossil remains. The remarkable fact is that they actually have been verified to a large extent by the discovery of the australopithecine fossils in Africa.

A point of some importance emerges from the supposition that the precursors of the genus *Homo* in the hominid line of evolution may have possessed a cranial capacity not much larger than that of an anthropoid ape and were therefore, *in this particular character*, not clearly distinguishable from an anthropoid ape. As we have already noted, the combined evidence of comparative anatomy and paleontology makes it fairly evident that the pongid and hominid radiations had become definitely segregated for several millions of years before the expansion of the brain in the Hominidae had become at all obtrusive. If this is so, the taxonomic interpretation of the fossil remains of an early hominoid with small cranial capacity—whether it is to be allocated to the Hominidae or whether it is to be grouped with the Pongidae—will have to depend on the analysis of other morphological characters which may be accepted as diagnostic of the evolutionary radiations to which the terms "Hominidae" and "Pongidae" are properly applied. It is here, obviously, that some attempt must be made to define the Hominidae, the more so because different meanings attached to the terms "Hominidae" and "hominid" by different authorities have quite evidently led to much of the confusion of thought that is so commonly to be found in discussions on human origins. Such a definition must be based primarily on a consideration of the dominant evolutionary trends [9] which have characterized this taxonomic group (and which thereby serve to differentiate it from the evolutionary trends in opposite and contrasting directions which have characterized the Pongidae); and the formulation of these trends, again, must be based objectively on a consideration of the end-products of hominid evolution, as well as on the paleontological evidence so far available. For the paleontologist, also, the definition must be limited to those characters which are available for study in fossilized remains, i.e., the skull, skeleton, and dentition. The following definition of the Hominidae is suggested.

Family Hominidae A subsidiary radiation of the Hominoidea distinguished from the Pongidae by the following evolutionary trends; progressive skeletal modifications in adaptation to erect bipedalism, shown particularly in a proportionate lengthening of the lower extremity, and changes in the proportions and morphological details of the pelvis, femur, and pedal skeleton related to mechanical requirements of erect posture and gait and to the muscular development associated therewith; preservation of well-developed pollex; ultimate loss of opposability of hallux; increasing flexion of basicranial axis associated with increasing cranial

[9] It should perhaps be emphasized that the phrase "evolutionary trends" is not meant to refer here to the *inherent* trends of evolution which have been postulated by orthogeneticists. It refers to the graduated sequence of morphological changes which must obviously have occurred in phylogenetic history to produce the known end-products of evolution and which in some cases has been demonstrated (or at least partly confirmed) by paleontological evidence. Identical evolutionary trends in related groups imply a community of origin, since they must depend on the possession of similar genetic constitutions associated with similar potentialities for producing the same mutational variations, and on these, again, depends the ability to achieve the same adaptations. In other words, identical evolutionary trends imply phylogenetic relationship and are to be taken into account in assessing the homogeneity of major taxonomic groups. It may be argued that two independent groups derived from a remote common ancestry might have followed identical evolutionary trends, leading to end-products not morphologically distinguishable. The answer to this argument is that, on the basis of the natural selection of random variations, the genetic probabilities are entirely against such a proposition, and in any case paleontology provides no evidence for extreme parallelism of this sort. So far as the Hominoidea are concerned, it is, of course, theoretically possible that this group may have given rise in the past to other evolutionary radiations besides the Pongidae and Hominidae. But, again, if this is so, no fossil evidence of any such radiation has yet been found.

height; relative displacement forward of the occipital condyles; restriction of nuchal area of occipital squama, associated with low position of inion; consistent and early ontogenetic development of a pyramidal mastoid process; reduction of subnasal prognathism, with ultimate early disappearance (by fusion) of facial component of premaxilla; diminution of canines to a spatulate form, interlocking slightly or not at all and showing no pronounced sexual dimorphism; disappearance of diastemata; replacement of sectorial first lower premolars by biscuspid teeth (with later secondary reduction of lingual cusp); alteration in occlusal relationships, so that all the teeth tend to become worn down to a relatively flat even surface at an early stage of attrition; development of an evenly rounded dental arcade; marked tendency in later stages of evolution to a reduction in size of the molar teeth; progressive acceleration in the replacement of deciduous teeth in relation to the eruption of permanent molars; progressive "molarization" of first deciduous molar; marked and rapid expansion (in some of the terminal products of the hominid sequence of evolution) of the cranial capacity, associated with reduction in size of jaws and area of attachment of masticatory muscles and the development of a mental eminence.

It is to be noted that this provisional definition of the family Hominidae is not intended to be exhaustive, but merely representative of some of its main distinguishing features. It is also to be noted that all the characteristic evolutionary trends have not necessarily proceeded synchronously; as we have already emphasized, paleontological evidence of evolutionary sequences in general show that they not uncommonly proceed at different rates. But by an analysis of the total morphological pattern of a fossil hominoid (provided that sufficient data are available) it should be possible, even in relatively early stages of their initial segregation and divergence from one another, to determine whether such a fossil is representative of the evolutionary sequence already committed by incipient changes to the developmental trends characteristic of the Hominidae, or to those characteristic of the Pongidae.

For comparison with the Hominidae, the Pongidae may be defined in the following terms.

Family Pongidae A subsidiary radiation of the Hominoidea distinguished from the Hominidae by the following evolutionary trends: progressive skeletal modifications in adaptation to arboreal brachiation, shown particularly in a proportionate lengthening of the upper extremity of a strong opposable hallux and modification of morphological details of limb bones for increased mobility and for the muscular developments related to brachiation; tendency to relative reduction of pollex; pelvis retaining the main proportions characteristic of quadrupedal mammals; marked prognathism, with late retention of facial component of premaxilla and sloping symphysis; development (in larger species) of massive jaws associated with strong muscular ridges on the skull; nuchal area of the occiput becoming extensive, with relatively high position of the inion; occipital condyles retaining a backward position well behind the level of the auditory apertures; only a limited degree of flexion of basicranial axis associated with maintenance of low cranial height; cranial capacity showing no marked tendency to expansion; progressive hypertrophy of incisors with widening of symphysial region of mandible and ultimate formation of "simian shelf"; enlargement of strong conical canines interlocking in diastemata and showing distinct sexual dimorphism; accentuated sectorialization of first lower premolar with development of strong anterior root; postcanine teeth preserving a parallel or slightly forward divergent alignment in relatively straight rows; first deciduous molar retaining a predominantly unicuspid form; no acceleration in eruption of permanent canine.

Again it is to be noted that these evolutionary trends have not all proceeded at the same rate, nor have they all been realized to the same degree at the same stage of evolution. For example, there is now good evidence that in the Miocene the dental morphology characteristic of the Recent Pongidae had already been acquired (except for the hypertrophy of the incisors and the associated development of a "simian shelf" in the mandible); but the limb skeleton at that time still retained many primitive features suggesting quadrupedal locomotion of the cercopithecoid type. It seems probable, indeed, that the extreme specializations of the limbs for arboreal brachiation may have been a relatively late development in the evolution of the Pongidae. It has actually been argued that these Miocene hominoids are not to be regarded as pongids in the proper sense of the term, since they did not show some of the extreme specializations that are characteristic of the modern anthropoid apes. But this is to take much too narrow and static a view of taxonomic nomenclature. In so far as the term "Pongidae" refers to the subsidiary radiation of the Hominoidea which culminated in the development of the modern anthropoid apes, it must include all those types representative of the earlier phases of pongid evolution after this group had become definitely segregated from the Cercopithecoidea. Studies of comparative anatomy make it certain that the ancestral stock from which the modern anthropoid apes arose must have shown just such a combination of characters of an intermediate kind as those found in the Miocene hominoids; and a critical examination of the latter also makes it clear that they had already become definitely segregated from the Cercopithecoidea and that most of the known types were committed (so to speak) to the evolutionary trends characteristic of the Pongidae.

13 *The Evolutionary Significance of Variation and Varieties of "Neanderthal" Man*

F. Clark Howell

THE EDITOR OF THE *Readings* KEEPS ASKING HIMSELF WHY HE IS REPRINTING *this article with whose conclusions he is not in full agreement. The disagreement does not reflect on his admiration for Dr. Howell; indeed, it is Howell's scrupulous attention to detail and superb control of the data that has finally motivated the retention of this piece. What then the difficulty? It lies in Howell's rejection of a "Neanderthal" phase in human evolution. Certainly we must agree with him that variability from one group to another was marked. But it seems to us that there is utility in the grand designation "Neanderthal" which calls attention to uniformities of anatomy spread rather wide during a particular period. It also assists in the assimilation of additional fossils of Neanderthal type, such as those found at Mapa and Ch'angyang in China since Howell wrote this piece.*

All of this goes to show that in the roster of fossil ancestors of man there are no creatures more fascinating than those loosely classified as H. neanderthalensis. *The popular view of these fossils is revealed in modes of speech, when we refer to "Neanderthal" attitudes in politics; these fossils*

SOURCE: *The Quarterly Review of Biology*, Vol. 32, No. 4 (1957), pp. 330–343. Reprinted with the permission of the author and the publisher.

The author (b. 1925) is Professor and Chairman of the Department of Anthropology at the University of Chicago. He is a specialist on human evolution and has concentrated on the "Neanderthal problem." In 1963 he edited *African Ecology and Human Evolution*.

*have also made their imprint in literature, as in the novels of William
Golding and others. Most popular treatments assume that the Neanderthals were bow-legged, stoop-shouldered, jut-jawed, low-browed sub-
humans who held the evolutionary stage until they were driven to extinction by clean-cut* H. sapiens *types, such as Cro-Magnon, in one of the
world's earliest examples of genocide. Actually, there is reason to believe
that this view is hopelessly in error, that the genocidal conflict is mostly a
projection of our world rather than a reconstruction of theirs, and that
much of the Neanderthal gene pool survives in modern populations.*

*That the foregoing simplification has many flaws and difficulties
should occur immediately to the reader of the selection that follows. He
will learn quite soon that the argument presented by Dr. Howell does not
rest upon superficialities, but upon the most penetrating analysis of a
comparative anatomical sort. The purpose of having students read the article is not to worry about these anatomical details, however, but to see
what goes into the forging of a professional scientific opinion.*

A hundred years ago, in August, 1856, Johann Carl Fuhlrott, then a
professor at the Realschule in Elberfeld (Germany), was given fourteen
pieces of a human skeleton encountered by workmen during the removal
of deposits of earth accumulated in the Feldhofer Cave. The cave was
situated in the steep limestone cliffs of the gorge of the Neander valley,
some sixty feet above the small stream of Düssel, eleven kilometers east of
Düsseldorf. The gorge, and the valley to the north, named for the German Reformed Church composer and poet Joachim Neander (1650–
1680), had long been a favored spot for week-end outings, and excursion-
ists were provided with a charming booklet which described its scenic
beauties and local natural history. Since 1921 it has been a monument
under the protection of the Naturschutzvereins Neandertal; the cave has
long since disappeared through limestone quarrying activities.

The controversy which arose after Schaaffhausen's description of the
human remains, particularly after it was translated by George Busk and
published in English (1861), is well known. There were those workers
like Schaaffhausen and Huxley who recognized the skeleton to be that of
a normal human individual, although of an ancient variety. King, although he subsequently changed his mind, thought it was less closely related to modern man and introduced the specific designation, *Homo neanderthalensis.* Others, like Blake, Mayer, and Virchow, were convinced
that its special morphology was pathological and due in particular to
rickets. Subsequent discoveries, especially those in Belgium at the cave of
Spy and in southern France at the cave of La Chapelle-aux-Saints and the
shelter of La Ferrassie fully confirmed the normalcy of this human variety whose distinctiveness was a phylogenetic rather than a pathologic
phenomenon.

It is in general true that most workers of the last century who were interested in the skeletal remains of early man were primarily concerned with the Neanderthal remains as representative of a link intermediate between living men and the recent African apes. Before, and even for some considerable time after the Neanderthal discovery there was preoccupation with a sort of horizontal hierarchical arrangement of living human groups as a spectrum from least to most "primitive," the latter approximating most closely to the living pongids. With the dearth of fossil human skeletal remains, and an inadequate knowledge of Pleistocene stratigraphy and time, it was impossible then to appreciate the evolutionary significance of these earlier human discoveries. The fact that there was a lack of fossil animal or cultural associations in the case of the type specimen from the Neander gorge served only to confuse and obscure the situation. With increasing knowledge of the geological age and geographical distributions of the various Neanderthal peoples, and the recovery of fossil human remains from earlier and later horizons, it is possible at last to assess more adequately their evolutionary importance.

The term "Neanderthal" has been greatly extended beyond its initial usage. It pertained originally only to the type specimen and came to be firmly established as a designation for a certain extinct variety of man. It received a temporal connotation only with the recovery of the two human burials in the cave of Spy which were associated with a so-called cold or subarctic fauna comprising a number of extinct species (or forms no longer found in the region). As discoveries multiplied in future years the term was applied to human remains from regions outside of western Europe and from earlier geologic horizons. It has been applied loosely to fossil human remains from western Asia and northern Africa, and even the tropics and subtropics of the southern hemisphere of the Old World! The practice has shown no signs of passing out of fancy. It has been particularly unfortunate since it has tended to categorize certain Pleistocene hominids so that posing meaningful inquiries as to their affinities and phylogenetic significance was automatically precluded. In fact, the first step in this direction was taken by King when he introduced a specific designation, *neanderthalensis*, for the skeleton from the cave in the Neander gorge.

One result has been the growth of a great controversy, still very much alive, as to whether there might have been a "Neanderthal" phase or stage in the evolution of modern man. This view was strongly supported by Hrdlička and Weidenreich, to mention only two that are well known. Unfortunately, this point of view has still to be meaningfully expressed in terms of modern evolutionary theory. Opponents of this viewpoint have argued that "Neanderthals," broadly speaking, were merely an evolutionary blind-alley, a divergent offshoot in man's phylogenetic history with its roots far back in the Pleistocene. The use of the appellation

"Neanderthal" for a fossil hominid would thus automatically exclude the human remains in question from having any direct evolutionary significance for modern human origins.

Actually, this too simple dichotomy is no longer either useful or attractive, in view of present understanding of the hominid fossil record. It is no longer necessary to think of simple morphological stages of human evolution during the earlier Upper Pleistocene, as has been done commonly in the past. There is now sufficient fossil evidence from clearly defined time levels, to permit some observations on samples of human populations from circumscribed geographic regions of the European and western Asian continental land mass. An attempt will be made here to outline the major aspects of the Neanderthal problem on the basis of present paleoanthropological knowledge, with particular reference to the question of variation and varieties within the peoples called Neanderthal.

Early Neanderthals

The first peoples who are recognizably Neanderthals have been found in the earliest stage of the Upper Pleistocene, the Last Interglacial (Eemian=Riss/Würm). Their distribution seems to have been exclusively (or at least primarily) Eurasian, extending from south-central and western Asia into, and throughout, Europe. The human skeletal remains available from this time are, however, both scant and quite scattered over this area. With the exception of one site (Krapina) there is no adequate series of specimens from any single locality; morphological studies must be based of necessity not only on fragmentary remains, but often poor preservation of a single individual. What is available to the human paleontologist is a glimpse of segments of early Neanderthal populations from southern Uzbekistan (Teshik-Tash), Palestine (et-Tabūn Eb, probably ez-Zuttiyeh), Croatia (Krapina), Slovakia (Ganovcé), Thuringia (Ehringsdorf), and western-central Italy (Saccopastore).

Mediterranean Africa is still too poorly known to permit an assessment of its racial composition at this time. However, it seems very likely from other paleoanthropological and mammalian paleontological evidence that some variety of (early) Neanderthal peoples also occupied that area.

Two sites in Mediterranean Africa have yielded skeletal remains attributed to "Neanderthal" man. These are: Haua Fteah in Cyrenaican Libya and the Mugharet el-Aliya (Tangier, Morocco); in both instances the remains were associated with a Mousterian industry of Levallois facies. The remains, consisting of upper and lower jaw fragments, are too incomplete to determine certainly the affinities of these North African prehistoric peoples; they would seem to have been with the broadly contemporaneous southwest Asian Neanderthals.

The area south of the Sahara seems to have been racially distinct, judging from the somewhat younger human skeletal remains from the sites of Eyasi, Broken Hill, Saldanha, and Florisbad. Thus, Neanderthal penetration did not pass south of the Sahara Desert. This was surely an effective barrier to early man during the Last Interpluvial (Interglacial) stage, although probably much less of a barrier during the Penultimate and Last Pluvial (Glacial) stages.

The origins of these early Neanderthal peoples are still completely obscure. It is not yet possible to ascertain (1) whether they were new occupants of the European continent, spreading northward and westward from southern and western Asia, perhaps as a result of the major amelioration of glacial climate at the end of the Middle Pleistocene, or (2) whether they represented an indigenous development within the European continent. The problem of origins cannot be settled until something more is known of the peoples of the European Third Glacial stage. It is altogether possible that the human mandible from Montmaurin (Haute-Garonne), as well as the cranial fragments from Fontéchevade (Charente), derive from this time; however, both are commonly regarded as of Last Interglacial date. The cranial morphology of the peoples of the preceding Great Interglacial stage is now fairly well known from the remains discovered in central and western Europe, at Steinheim and Swanscombe, and in the Maghreb of northwest Africa, at Ternifine; there are also the slightly younger remains, dated to the base of the Penultimate Pluvial, from Rabat and Sidi Abderrahman. There is little indication of specifically Neanderthal morphology in any of these specimens. The masticatory apparatus, both mandible and dentition, was quite primitive, judging from the remains from the Maghreb (and the Montmaurin mandible), while the occipital area of the cranial vault was fundamentally more modern in its morphology. It is altogether likely, however, that important human evolutionary changes were taking place during the Penultimate Glacial stage. A major advance could be made towards a solution of the problem of Neanderthal origins with the discovery of adequate skeletal remains from this time level.

Only the cranial morphology of the early Neanderthals of Europe is fairly well known, on the basis of the two Saccopastore skulls and the series of broken and mutilated specimens from Krapina. Another fairly complete cranium (No. 3) from Kaempfer's Quarry, Ehringsdorf (Thuringia) was somewhat inaccurately restored by Weidenreich. Kleinschmidt made a more correct restoration which clearly reveals the basic similarity to the specimens from Saccopastore. The series from Krapina, as well as earlier discoveries (Nos. 1, 2) at Ehringsdorf include not only specimens of the adult jaws and dentition, but juvenile cranial and mandibular fragments which permit some inferences on early Neanderthal growth and maturation. There are fairly numerous, but incomplete postcranial fragments from Krapina, an incomplete femur from et-Tabūn Eb (Mount Carmel), and juvenile postcranial fragments (which are largely useless) from Ehringsdorf (No. 2) and Teshik-Tash. However, the postcranial skeleton of these peoples is still really very poorly known.

These peoples differed in cranial morphology from the succeeding classic Neanderthals in a number of features. The most important are: (1) smaller cranial capacities, (2) shorter cranial lengths and narrower widths, (3) more highly arched vaults and expanded occipital bones with a tendency to produce an external occipital protuberance associated with a small occipital torus, (4) a tympanic plate with more vertically oriented anterior portion and less robust posterior portion, (5) shorter and more flexed cranial bases, (6) smaller facial skeletons, (7) suprafacial toral structures tending to separate into medial and lateral elements, and (8) more antero-lateral orientation of malar bones, with clear demarcation between malar and maxilla, and tendency for depression of the supracanine region (canine fossa formation). The postcranial skeleton exhibits features which are in general more anatomically modern than was the case in the distinctive classic Neanderthal group. Thus, the long bones were relatively more gracile, the humerus relatively straight, the radius only slightly curved (but with the long neck and backward situated bicipital tuberosity of the classic Neanderthals), the ulna quite straight and slender (but with the enlargement of the olecranon incipiently classic Neanderthal), and the femur with relatively straight shaft, moderate subtroachanteric flattening, and lack of enlarged extremities. Similarly, the characteristic morphology of the axillary border of the scapula was not typically of the classic Neanderthal variety (with its prominent dorsal sulcus and pronounced axillary crest), although there was already an approach to this form in some Krapina specimens.

Many features of early Neanderthal morphology, both cranial and postcranial, are incipiently classic Neanderthal. However, the general morphological pattern of these early Neanderthal peoples bore a close resemblance to that of anatomically modern man, a fact which indicates again the special character of classic Neanderthal morphology. Actually this is not altogether unexpected, at least in Europe, if consideration is given to the peoples of the Great Interglacial stage, as represented by the Steinheim and Swanscombe remains. These specimens illustrate very clearly that the still small-brained handaxe-making peoples of that time had already approached a basically modern morphological pattern in certain features of the braincase (and middle face), although the masticatory skeleton (and related anterior region of the vault) was still somewhat primitive. [This is equally true for the child from Teshik-Tash which, according to the careful description of Gremiatskii, is considerably less anatomically modern than Weidenreich first suggested.] The evidence would now seem to indicate that "neanderthalization," if one may use this phrase, was a continuing and strictly European phenomenon.

Our knowledge of human races and their distributions in Eurasia during the initial part of the Last Glacial stage is considerably better than for the preceding interglacial. However, fossil samples of such populations are still relatively small, except for southwestern Europe and the Levant coast. Nevertheless, an examination of the evidence at hand reveals quite clearly differences in skeletal morphology between southwestern Europe on the one hand, and eastern Europe and western Asia on the other.

The people who occupied the western and southern parts of Europe during the earlier phase of the Last Glaciation have been termed classic Neanderthals. The holotype for the population is the partial skeleton found in 1856 in the Feldhofer cave in the Neander gorge. Two other specimens attributable to the group, an adult skull from Forbes Quarry (Gibraltar) and a child's skull from the cave of Engis (Belgium), were found earlier and went unrecognized for some years until the discovery at the Neanderthal proper. This group is well known from a number of specimens from western Germany, Belgium, southern France, Spain, and western Italy.

Sites which have yielded classic Neanderthal skeletal remains are: *Germany:* Neanderthal; *Belgium:* Bay-Bonnet, Engis, La Naulette, Spy; *Channel Islands:* St. Brelade (Jersey); *France:* Malarnaud (Ariège); La Chaise, La Quina, Petit-Puymoyen (Charente); La Chapelle-aux-Saints (Correze); Genay (Côte d'Or); Combe Grenal, La Ferrassie, Le Moustier, Pech de l'Azé (Dordogne); Monsempron (Lot-et-Garonne); Hyena and Wolf Caves, Arcy-sur-Cure (Yonne); *Spain:* Bañolas, Cova Negra, Gibraltar (Forbes Quarry, Devil's Tower), Piñar; *Italy:* Fossellone and Guattari Caves (Monte Circeo), Santa Croce di Bisceglie.

The classic Neanderthals differed from the early Neanderthals in a number of aspects of cranial morphology, both in the braincase and the facial skeleton. The classic Neanderthals were characterized by: larger brains; long, low, and wide cranial vaults with a high frequency of post-lambdoidal flattening (due to the pattern of growth and closure of this suture); less flexed cranial bases; more sharply angulated occipital bones with relatively heavier occipital tori; more horizontal orientation of the tympanic plate with heavy anterior and posterior portions; larger facial skeletons (large, round orbits, large nasal aperture, marked interorbital space); semicircular supraorbital tori with fused medial and lateral elements; and shelving of maxilla into malar, with no demarcation between these bones, a convergence of the maxillary walls, and lack of supracanine hollowing (canine depression).

This distinctive cranial morphology of the classic Neanderthals was the result of a characteristic pattern of ontogenetic development and growth. This pattern can be analyzed in some detail, since infant (*Pech de l'Azé*), child (*Gibraltar 2, La Quina 18*), and adolescent (*Le Moustier*) individuals provide a fair cross-sectional series for comparison with adults. Fortunately, a well-preserved early Neanderthal child's cranium (*Teshik-Tash*) is known, and it reveals a quite distinctive morphology when compared with a classic Neanderthal child (*La Quina 18*) of similar dental age. An eastern European Neanderthal child (*Subalyuk*), contemporaneous with the classic Neanderthals of western Europe, bears a closer morphological similarity to the early Neanderthal from Teshik-Tash than to the classic Neanderthal variety. This is a point of considerable importance in understanding the evolutionary origin and significance of the classic Neanderthal peoples.

The classic Neanderthal adult postcranial skeleton is quite well known from a series of seven partially partially preserved individuals (La Chapelle, La Ferrassie 1, 2, La Quina 5, Spy 1, 2, and the type Neanderthal remains) from five sites; the adolescent skeleton is represented by a young male from Le Moustier. Since the early Neanderthals are known largely only by their skulls and dentition, the Krapina remains being the exception, it is difficult to make comparisons of the postcranial skeleton with the classic Neanderthal group. The Krapina series would suggest that there were certain slight differences, but it must be remembered that no early Neanderthal postcranial remains are known from southwestern Europe. At any rate the differences are probably no more than those between distinctive modern human populations. The classic Neanderthals did differ in postcranial morphology from anatomically modern populations but, as Patte has very clearly demonstrated in his excellent synthesis of the comparative data, these differences were much less marked than some writers in the past have been led to believe. Moreover, and contrary to the conclusions of some earlier workers, the classic Neanderthal postcranial skeleton is basically modern human in over-all morphology; it bears no phylogenetically significant resemblance to that of the non-hominid higher primates. Such features were stressed by Boule in his description of the "old man" (actually probably under 40 years of age!) of La Chapelle-aux-Saints, but Schwalbe and others have shown that this interpretation is untenable.

The classic Neanderthals were fairly short, stout, and powerfully built people. Some of the especially interesting and characteristic features of their postcranial skeleton are: generally low vertebral bodies with large transverse and spinous processes; a broad upper thorax; a long, fairly slender, well-curved clavicle with large anticular extremities; scapula with a prominent dorsal crest on the axillary border and a well-developed dorsal marginal sulcus, and a prominent upwardly inclined scapular spine with large rounded notch; a relatively short, but robust humerus with prominent muscular insertion areas, large head and distal extremity, weak humeral torsion, large epitrochlea and paratrochlear crest, and a large condylo-diaphysial angle; a relatively low (70.–76.) antibrachial (radio/humeral) index; a short, robust forearm with rather high arm (humerus/ulna) angle, marked (radius) to considerable (ulna) curvature, large proximal and distal extremities, radius with great relative length of neck and distal situation of salient bicipital tuberosity, marked proximal flattening (platolenia) of the ulnar diaphysis, marked height of the olecranon and large, sloping coronoid process; a hand with robust, large-headed metacarpals and short phalanges; very massive femora with slight to very pronounced shaft curvature, no pilaster and only slight to absent linea aspera, considerable platymeria, low angulation and little flattening of the neck, very large head (compared to physiologic length) and greater trochanter, frequent development of a third trochanter and hypochanteric fossa, large distal extremity (compared to physiologic length) with broad, deep patellar fossa, condyles usually of about the same size or with the external *smaller* than the internal; a very low (74.–79.) crural (tibio/femoral) index; a very robust, eurycnemic tibia, large proximal extremity with retroverted tibial plateau, straight or slightly concave surface of the lateral condyle, large distal extremity, quite straight angle of the articular surface for the astragalus, high frequency of (external) squatting facets; very robust, curved fibula with large extremities and subcylindrical (rather than fluted) shaft form; a large, broad, and high astragalus with short head and neck, quite marked deviation of the talar head, long trochlea with large posterior compared to anterior breadth, high frequency of trochlear squatting facets, very broad and obliquely situated internal malleolar facet which is larger than the external facet; a large (broad and long), massive calcaneus with very long heel; and very robust metatarsals, very thick and short phalanges.

Where there is sufficient evidence to permit accurate relative dating (as there is at a considerable number of occupation and burial sites) it has been established that the classic Neanderthals were confined to the initial damp and cold phase of the Last Glacial stage (= Early Würm), i.e., throughout the time of the accumulation of the first two Recent Loesses of the western European succession. For reasons still unknown, the group disappeared completely from the record sometime during the subsequent, major (Göttweiger or Fellabrunner) interstadial phase. At this time anatomically modern peoples of the Cro-Magnon variety, with a quite different stone-working technique (punched blades and the prismatic core) and tool-kit, penetrated into westernmost Europe from regions farther eastward, probably the hilly country of southeastern Europe. Some workers, for example Zeuner, have maintained that at some sites (St. Pierre les Elbeuf on the Somme River, Grotte Guattari at Monte

Circeo) there is evidence of classic Neanderthal survival throughout this interstadial phase and even into the subsequent cold stadial (= Main Würm). However, in the case of the loess sections there is no evidence to support this inference, since Upper Paleolithic blade-tool industries clearly appear toward the close of the interstadial and are exclusively present in the subsequent Main Würm stadial, the time of the western European Aurignacian. Thus, it is possible to establish the time of classic Neanderthal disappearance quite closely, although the cause or causes for such disappearance is still a hotly argued issue in paleoanthropology. There is no clear-cut evidence which would indicate that the classic Neanderthals either (1) lived contemporaneously with the earliest of the Cro-Magnon people (who were probably responsible for the Chatelperronian industry) or (2) that they interbred with the latter people. However, both possibilities have been suggested by some workers.

The classic Neanderthals were apparently restricted in distribution only to southwestern Europe. The main centers of occupation were the sheltered and well-watered valleys of southern France and similar parts of the Iberian and Apennine peninsulas. These were regions outside the main periglacial zone of permanently frozen ground and tundra vegetation. It is well established, however, that there was at least sporadic classic Neanderthal penetration, perhaps seasonally for hunting and collecting purposes (and with attendant alterations in tools and techniques of manufacture), into adjacent, more northerly parts (including southern Belgium, northern France, and the Rhineland). Such penetration probably took place during the (two) more humid and cool phases of climate which preceded the very windy and dry maxima of the Early Last Glacial when the first two Recent Loesses were accumulated. There is no evidence of human occupation in the loesses proper when those zones supported only an herbaceous vegetation with sparse dwarf trees and bushes of the subarctic variety and a fauna comprising largely steppe rodents and the like.

There remains the question of whether classic Neanderthals also occupied the Alpine forelands of central Europe and the regions farther to the east. The question is still difficult to answer. The foreland region has failed to provide human skeletal remains in association with the local Mousterian industry (often an Almühlian facies with fine leaf-shaped points). There are Mousterian sites in the limestone hills (Jura) of southern Württemberg and Bayern, but they are far from common and, in fact, date largely from the end of the Early Last Glacial into the main interstadial. Human occupation would appear to have been uncommon and sporadic here during the early stadial phase, and there is no evidence that *classic* Neanderthals occupied the region.

Mousterian sites are only rarely present in the open loess lands of the Danubian basin and, more commonly, in the hilly country of Moravia and

Slovakia (including the adjoining Bükk mountains to the south) and the foothills of the Carpathian chain. There are special facies of the Mousterian industry in this easterly region, but these are still rather poorly known and have not been compared with those of other regions. Human skeletal remains, usually referred to a Neanderthal people, have been recovered from two sites in this easterly area, Šipka cave in northern Moravia and Subalyuk cave in the Bükk mountains (Hungary). Both sites date from the Early Last Glacial.

Mottl has suggested that the Subalyuk remains date from the later part of the Last Interglacial stage. However, and as Gross has also noted, both the faunal and the stratigraphic evidence (as well as the associated late Mousterian industry) testify to the steppe conditions which prevailed in this region in the Early Last Glacial.

The nature and preservation of the skeletal material leaves much to be desired, but the morphological evidence seems to suggest that the peoples were not classic Neanderthals. Instead they resembled more closely the early Neanderthals of the preceding interglacial. Apparently early Neanderthal peoples persisted, both in eastern Europe and southwestern Asia, into the Early Last Glacial (Pluvial).

East-central and eastern Europe were not particularly isolated during the Early Last Glacial. Most of the plains and low country were steppe lands which supported a rich grazing fauna (fully exploited by the subsequent Upper Paleolithic peoples); hilly regions and enclosed valleys were largely wooded. There were no major natural obstacles, climatic or otherwise, to prevent population shifts as bands moved from territory to territory, nor to hinder free genetic interchange over this region, the regions bordering the Black Sea and southwestern Asia. It would seem that there was broad racial continuity at least as far east as the Crimea and southward into the Levant. This is suggested by Neanderthal remains from the site of Kiik-Koba and those from the site of et-Tabūn (Mount Carmel).

The European early Neanderthal remains, although not numerous and far from well preserved, suggest very strongly that the distinctive classic Neanderthal skeletal morphology had its roots in the Last Interglacial. The evidence would seem to indicate, as the writer has concluded elsewhere, that the classic Neanderthals were a final local evolutionary development in the western European *cul-de-sac*. The field evidence also suggests that a discontinuity in human distribution was very likely present through the central European periglacial corridor. This discontinuity would have had a profound effect in terms of gene flow, since western and southern Europe would have constituted circumscribed breeding areas for Neanderthal peoples. The classic Neanderthals would thus have become a stabilized variety only during the initial phase of the

Last Glacial, due to isolation and perhaps in response to the imposed rigors of a harsh subarctic climate imposing severe selective pressures.

Southwest Asian Neanderthals

Seven sites in five southwest Asian localities have yielded human skeletal remains which have been attributed to a variety of Neanderthal man.

Southwest Asian sites which have yielded remains attributed to a variety of "Neanderthal" man are: (1) M. ez-Zuttiyeh, a cave near the northern shore of the Sea of Galilee (2) M. et-Tabūn, a cave, and (3) M. es-Skhūl, a rock shelter, both in the Wadi el-Mughara on the western slopes of Mount Carmel (4) Shukbah, a cave in the Wadi en-Natuf, northwest of Jerusalem (5) Djebel Qafzeh, a cave in Galilee, south of Nazareth (6) Shanidar, a cave in southern Kurdistan (7) Bisitun, a cave near Kermanshah in western Iran. Since this was written further adult skeletons have been found by Ralph Solecki in Shanidar cave during the 1957 season.

In all cases (save perhaps that of the specimen from M. ez-Zuttiyeh, see below) these were associated with a local Mousterian industry of Levallois facies. The best known of these, from the caves on the Mount Carmel, have had a very mixed reception by students of human paleontology. Paleoanthropologists have failed to reach a reasonable consensus as to their affinities with the several sorts of European Neanderthal people, and there is not yet any agreement as to their broader phylogenetic significance.

This lack of agreement has been due to some extent to misunderstandings as to the relative geological age of the so-called Levalloiso-Mousterian industry (and associated fossil men) in this area. At Mount Carmel the remains from et-Tabūn (level C) and es-Skhūl (level B) were assumed by McCown and Keith to be "contemporaneous in a moderately narrow sense" and thus to represent a single variable population. These prehistoric people were presumed to date from the closing phases of a dry and warm interpluvial which was considered to correspond to the European Last Interglacial stage. Thus, the Mount Carmel people would have been broadly contemporaneous with the European early Neanderthals. This conclusion is not supported by the field evidence, however. A careful examination of the stratigraphic and faunal data leaves no doubt that the human skeletal remains are of Early Last Pluvial age. Other Levant Levalloiso-Mousterian sites with human skeletal remains (ez-Zuttiyeh probably excepted) are of the same age. Thus, these Neanderthal peoples were not contemporaneous with early Neanderthals, but with the classic Neanderthals of southwestern Europe. The relative age of the southwest Asian Neanderthals is a matter of considerable consequence in understanding their phylogenetic significance.

Three major interpretations of their evolutionary significance have been offered. McCown and Keith concluded that at Mount Carmel there were the "remains of a single people, the Skhūl and Tabūn types being but the extremes of the same series, there being intermediates between the extremes." This was due, in their opinion, to "an evolutionary divergence," since the Mount Carmel people "were in the throes of evolutionary change." Although these authors found the people from the shelter of Skhūl to bear a closer resemblance to the Cro-Magnon people of the European Upper Paleolithic, the former were not, in their opinion, directly ancestral to these anatomically modern men ("the Mount Carmel people are not the actual ancestors of the Cromagnons but Neanderthaloid collaterals or cousins of the ancestors of that type"). [This conclusion, which has not been entirely clear to some workers (including the writer), is clarified by Keith's remark that he and McCown believed "that at the period earlier than that represented by the fossil Carmelites, and farther towards the east, a local group of Neanderthalians began to evolve in a Caucasian direction and that these Carmelites represent a later phase of this movement."]

This interpretation has been opposed by some other workers. Ashley Montagu was the first to offer hybridization as an alternative explanation, one which McCown and Keith had indeed considered but rejected. He was convinced that "any other theory would have to assume the spontaneous mutation of far too many genes, or far too great a change in gene variability, to render such a theory tenable." Hooton agreed with this conclusion, finding McCown's and Keith's interpretation "both ambivalent and ambiguous," and lent his support to this alternative hypothesis. Dobzhansky added the weight of a geneticist when he stated that the Mount Carmel population was "a result of hybridization of a Neanderthaloid and a modern type, these types having formed earlier in different geographic regions." This proved, in his opinion, that "the Neanderthal and the modern types were not isolated reproductively, and hence, were races of the same species rather than distinct species." Most recently Weckler has attempted to extend this interpretation into a broad (but farfetched!) explanation of human evolution in the Pleistocene.

Both the theory of evolutionary divergence (as framed by McCown and Keith) as well as that of hybridization have recently been rejected by Le Gros Clark. He has suggested that the people of the Mount Carmel caves "appear to represent a transitional stage leading from pre-Mousterian *Homo sapiens* to the later establishment of the definitive species *H. neanderthalensis*." This conclusion would seem to imply that all European Neanderthals of the Last Interglacial, and southwest Asian Neanderthals of the subsequent Early Last Pluvial, constituted merely an incipient stage in a unilinear Neanderthal development, terminated by an aberrant and specialized paleospecies which failed to survive the Early Last Glacial.

These divergent opinions reflect the uncertainty (and misunderstanding) which surrounds the people of the southwest Asian Mousterian. The problem is seriously in need of re-examination and an alternative explanation will also fit the facts. Several matters can probably be resolved only by the discovery in the Levant of additional human skeletal remains in a stratified series of Mousterian occupation levels. It would be especially useful if additional remains were to be found with an Acheulian of Yabrudian facies (ex-Micoquian), like that in et-Tabūn level E, and with a Mousterian of Yabrudian facies, like that present at Yabrud (Shelter I) on the slopes of the Anti-Lebanon mountains. In both cases, but at different time levels, there is evidence of what might have been extraneous cultural influences penetrating into this region from a still unknown source and responsible for the introduction of an Upper Paleolithic blade-tool typology. It seems very likely to the writer that important structural changes were taking place in human populations of the Levant during the Early Last Pluvial. These were of primary significance for the evolutionary origin of subsequent anatomically modern peoples of the European Upper Paleolithic.

Early Neanderthal peoples, not unlike those from Europe (Ehringsdorf, Krapina), were probably present in the Levant as early as the Last Interpluvial (Interglacial). This conclusion is founded on very tenuous evidence: an incomplete shaft of a femur (level Ea) and an isolated, worn lower right molar (level Eb) from the rich Acheulian of Yabrudian facies occupation zone in the cave of et-Tabūn at Mount Carmel. These people also resembled the succeeding inhabitants of the cave responsible for the Mousterian of Levallois facies industry (level C). The cranio-facial fragment from ez-Zuttiyeh (Galilee) offers more substantial evidence. These remains are usually assumed to have been associated with a Mousterian industry of Levallois facies, but Garrod has directed attention to the fact that they derived from the basal occupation zone of the site where hand-axes, suggestive of an Acheulian of Yabrudian facies industry, were present. In his original description of the specimen Keith found "details in which the Galilean type differs from the Neanderthal varieties which have been discovered in Europe hitherto"; but, at the time, he was reluctant to decide on the basis of the material available whether these were of racial significance or merely individual variation. Subsequently, Keith affirmed that "the ancient Galilean was not the pure Neanderthal type, but a variant of the type. . . ." This specimen, as McCown and Keith have shown, closely resembled the skeletal remains from the Mousterian of Levallois facies horizon (level C) at et-Tabūn.

Aside from a nearly complete (female) skeleton, this level (C) yielded only another isolated (male) mandible and five other small portions of the upper and lower limbs of further individuals. These remains, not sufficiently numerous to reveal the range of variation of the population which they represent, closely resembled the European early Neanderthals. They differed markedly, both in cranial and postcranial morphology, from the classic Neanderthal peoples of western Europe. As in the case of European early Neanderthals, there were a number of features which approached and even at times duplicated the morphology of anatomically modern man.

Keith and McCown were first led to distinguish two distinct morphological "types" in the human remains from the sites in the Wadi el-Mughara: the "Skhūl type," a majority of whose features were "those which we find in the modern races of man, the native races especially"; and the "Tabūn type," which although having an "undoubted kinship with the Skhūl type of humanity," was basically "Neanderthaloid" and "more akin to the Krapina Neanderthaloids." In their final report this opinion was modified and the idea of two distinctive types was abandoned. McCown and Keith still stressed that "the range in form . . . is unexpectedly great" in the series from the two sites. Nonetheless, they regarded these as "the remains of a single people, the Skhūl and Tabūn types being but the extremes of the same series, there being intermediates between these extremes." More recently McCown has reiterated the reasons for accepting this point of view.

The morphology which characterized the female skeleton (I) from the et-Tabūn cave was also present in some of the people of es-Skhūl. This is exemplified in Sk. VI (comprising a crushed part of the cranium and mandible and some parts of the post-cranial skeleton, but a badly crushed cranium and mandible); and it was most evident in the bones of the extremities. The remains of other individuals, particularly the well-preserved skeletons of Sk. IV, V, and IX, exhibited in both cranial and post-cranial morphology a majority of features which were anatomically modern in nearly all respects. In fact, the population of es-Skhūl exhibits all the necessary morphological attributes of an ancestral proto-Cro-Magnon people. This is true in spite of the presence within the population of a range of variation which overlapped that of early Neanderthal peoples. Moreover, the characteristic morphological pattern of the people of es-Skhūl was not an isolated phenomenon in the Levant. It can be duplicated in all significant details among the skeletal remains from the cave of Djebel Qafzeh (Galilee). These were found with the same Mousterian of Levallois facies association and also date from the same late part of the Early Last Pluvial. This series, comprising mostly skull and jaw fragments of five individuals, and which is still to be published, fully confirms the significance of the primitive, anatomically modern, morphology of the people of es-Skhūl.

There is no definite proof that the human remains from et-Tabūn (level C) and from es-Skhūl (level B) were contemporaneous and, therefore, representative of the *same* interbreeding population. Although both were of Early Last Pluvial age, geological and faunal evidence would suggest that the people from the es-Skhūl cemetery lived slightly later than did their counterparts of the et-Tabūn Levalloiso-Mousterian. However, the important problem is whether the range of variability was roughly the same in both series or had a different mean and merely overlapped in each instance. The suggestion is that the es-Skhūl population tended toward more anatomically modern morphology, although there was overlap with the et-Tabūn people at the other extreme of the range. If this is in fact the case, then there would appear to have been a trend in this region within the Early Last Pluvial toward increasing "sapiensization." The matter cannot yet be settled, since the et-Tabūn cave yielded too few human remains compared with the series from the es-Skhūl shelter (a total of ten individuals, some very incomplete, of both infants and adults, as well as sixteen other district isolated fragments), but must remain until larger skeletal series are available from this range of time in the southwest Asian area.

The rock shelter of Starosel'je, southern Crimea, has recently yielded infant human skeletal remains dating from the Early Last Glacial. It was associated with a Mousterian industry like that at Kiik-Koba (upper level), predominantly made up of side-scrapers and some small hand-axes, with traces of an incipient blade-core technique. The skull can be quite well reconstructed, but the post-cranial skeleton is so poorly preserved as to be useless. The Starosel'je individual may have suffered from hydrocephaly (although Prof. G. F. Debetz informs the author that this is doubtful), but nonetheless in the structure of the facial skeleton (as well as details of the vault) it resembled the morphological pattern of anatomically modern man. This discovery provides further evidence of quite anatomically modern people among the "Neanderthal" folk of southwest Asia and adjacent regions.

Conclusions

During the first quarter of this century some students of human paleontology, especially Schwalbe, Boule, Adloff, and Keith, were inclined to exclude any "Neanderthal" peoples from the direct ancestry of anatomically modern man. In general four main arguments were advanced to support this conclusion: (1) a morphological hiatus of specific taxonomic significance existed between Neanderthal and anatomically modern peoples; (2) Neanderthal peoples were too specialized to be included among the forerunners of anatomically modern peoples; (3) time was too short to allow for the evolutionary transformation of Neanderthal man into an anatomically modern form (as represented by the first of the European Upper Paleolithic peoples); and (4) anatomically modern man, as *proven* by the fossil record, had a great Pleistocene antiquity and this demonstrated the separateness of Neanderthal and anatomically modern human lineages over a long span of time.

The first two points are closely related. It is unquestionably true, as was shown by a number of the workers cited earlier, that *some* Neanderthal peoples were characterized by a very special pattern of skeletal morphology. However, these classic Neanderthals constituted only one of several groups of peoples of different geographic and temporal distribution which have been labeled Neanderthal. The unfortunate tendency to apply this designation to a multiplicity of Upper Pleistocene peoples (even at times to Middle Pleistocene peoples!), without proper appreciation for earlier definitions and understandings, has only resulted in confusion. Other human groups labeled Neanderthal, including both the early Neanderthals of the Last Interglacial and the Levant "Neanderthals" of the Early Last Pluvial, differed markedly in their morphology from the classic Neanderthals of southwestern Europe. In each case these differences were in the direction of anatomically modern human morphology.

The third point has constituted a stumbling-block to paleoanthropologists for at least half a century. It is pertinent only so long as it refers to evolutionary transformation from classic Neanderthal peoples to succeeding Upper Paleolithic peoples *in the western European area.* The writer is not aware of any thoughtful worker in the field in the past half century who has specifically advocated this position. Yet the confusion does exist in general anthropological literature and, more importantly, it implies that any peoples labeled Neanderthal could only have represented an extinct segment of humanity. In a broader context, however, this point is not relevant. Only the fossil record can afford direct evidence which would give an indication of evolutionary rates and the time necessary for any such transformation. With our present lack of understanding of the genetic basis of nearly all morphological attributes, it is impossible to argue a priori that there was or was not sufficient time for such change to have occurred (*unless* it can be established that a very high degree of specialization was present). It is quite apparent that a great deal more must be known from the fossil record, both of temporal and spatial variation, before such arguments can have any real weight.

The final point is of particular importance, since some workers in the past and a number still at the present time attach to it a special relevance. Sir Arthur Keith was the most outspoken proponent of the point of view which advocated the great antiquity of anatomically modern man and he only abandoned it toward the end of his long and fruitful life. It is necessary to emphasize that it was always based on evidence which was either dubious or downright flimsy and equivocal. Students of the evolution of other mammalian groups have surely been more critical of their primary evidence than human paleontologists have been, in this instance. Critical reevaluations of the primary evidence or greatly improved or new methods of determining the relative age of fossil bones have conclusively shown in recent years that nearly every shred of evidence which was marshalled at one time or another to support this theory was either ill-appraised or fraudulent.

This theory of longstanding human polyphyletism was seriously undermined by these revelations, but it has not yet been completely abandoned. In recent years it has been modified and reframed by several workers, notably Vallois and Heberer; Le Gros Clark has also supported the same general viewpoint, although phrased in a somewhat different taxonomic framework. One of the most elaborate and imaginative efforts to spell out the course of human evolution using such a theory as a point of departure has been made by Weckler.

The fossil materials which now lend any support to this theory are indeed rare. Two incomplete human crania, one from a gravel pit at Swanscombe (Thames River) and another from the cave of Fontéchev-ade (Charente), furnish the only evidence for the so-called "pre-sapiens" lineage. The evidence itself is equivocal and ambiguous, as has been pointed out by several workers including Roginskii, Sergi, Breitinger, and the author. The parieto-occipital fragment from Swanscombe does not prove that an ancient anatomically modern human variety existed at the time of the Great Interglacial; it does confirm the presence in western-most Europe of a human variety closely resembling that recovered from the gravels at Steinheim (a.d. Murr, Württemberg) which is of the same age. In his comparative study of the Swanscombe remains Morant pointed out that, "as far as can be seen, the Swanscombe and Steinheim skulls were quite similar, and it is not unlikely that they represent the same Acheulian group." Moreover, the recent discoveries of mandibles and teeth at Ternifine (Algeria) and Sidi Abderrahman (Morocco), as well as the earlier find of a mandible and maxilla at Rabat (Morocco), clearly oppose such a theory. These skeletal remains buttress the Steinheim-Swanscombe materials as evidence of anatomically non-modern peoples having been responsible for the widespread Acheulian stone industry. This conclusion is further supported by the morphology of the mandible from Montmaurin (Haute-Garonne). It also, in the writer's opinion, tends to contradict the view that the fragmentary and distorted Font-échevade remains were those of a primitive form of anatomically modern man.

The Fontéchevade remains, probably two individuals represented respectively by a distorted and incomplete skullcap (no. 2) and a small fragment of frontal bone (no. 1), constitute the only evidence which might favor the theory that an incipiently anatomically modern group was present in the basal Upper Pleistocene (or terminal Middle Pleistocene, as the remains may be of Penultimate Glacial age). Since (at that time) nearly all parts of Europe were occupied by early Neanderthals (or their forerunners), this would imply that several distinct forms of man were present in the same general area. To remain distinct, and such has been clearly implied in the designation "pre-sapiens," genetic interchange must have been prohibited or at an absolute minimum; otherwise such

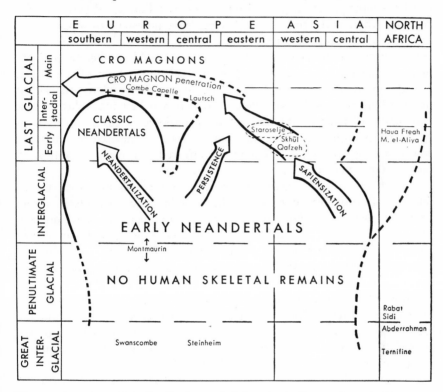

Temporal and spatial distribution of "Neanderthal" peoples of the upper Pleistocene and of their Middle Pleistocene forerunners.

differences would have disappeared as a consequence of hybridization. If these groups were populations (demes) of the same species, with a common evolutionary origin, but an isolated development, presumably there would have been attendant fusion into a single variable population as they came together. Otherwise, these must have represented distinctive sympatric species which led dissimilar ways of life and were characterized by habit and behavioral differences, so much so that interbreeding did not customarily occur.

The writer is unable to find any paleoanthropological evidence which would favor this conclusion. Such an explanation might appear more likely if this was a case of a distinctive geographic area where a particular species had developed through isolation. The evidence of the fossil record indicates that (until the main interstadial of the Last Glacial) the area was extensively occupied by Neanderthal peoples. If such Neanderthal peoples, and their anatomically non-modern forerunners (Steinheim-Swanscombe, Montmaurin), were indigenous to the European area any "pre-sapiens" peoples must have had an origin elsewhere and have subsequently expanded into (western) Europe. Where was this area and where is the fossil and other evidence necessary to support such an hypothesis? Actually, the Fontéchevade human remains themselves are not fully conclusive as to whether these were "anatomically modern" or represented a variety of early Neanderthal. In the light of this fact it would appear judicious to resist founding a far-reaching theory of modern human evolution on evidence which is at best inconclusive. One is reminded of Jepsen's admonition "that genealogical trees for fossils must be strong enough to support the opinions they are devised to symbolize and that large branches shouldn't be inferred too readily from small morphologic evidences."

With the steadily increasing breadth of the hominid fossil record human paleontologists must reexamine certain basic concepts in earlier studies of man's evolution. Older ideas of simple rectilinear development, whether uniphyletic or biphyletic, are no longer either useful or justifiable. These are in fact merely another version of the familiar family tree which, in its usual form, fails to take into consideration the distribution of human populations in space and time, their variability, and their biological and cultural adaptations to changing Pleistocene environments. Nor has sufficient attention been devoted to the problems of competition and territoriality in such early hunter-gatherers, both of which are of the utmost significance for any simple biphyletic account of the origins of the anatomically modern varieties of man.

Peoples who have been labeled "Neanderthal" are of particular importance in human evolutionary studies because of their temporal distribution and their spatial range. The concept of a "Neanderthal" phase or stage of man's evolution is no longer useful since there was marked variability from one such group to another. Frequently, as in the case of certain human remains from southeast Asia (Solo man) and southern Africa (Broken Hill, Saldanha, Florisbad men), the application of the designation "Neanderthal" has obscured rather than clarified the real nature and importance of the human skeletal materials. In this paper an attempt has been made to outline some of the present understandings about Neanderthal peoples and to stress the need for their careful study and reevaluation if studies of man's evolution are to proceed along potentially fruitful directions.

14 The Human Brain in Evolutionary Perspective

Ralph L. Holloway, Jr.

THE BRAIN IS INVARIABLY AT THE CENTER OF INTEREST IN THE QUEST FOR *understanding of human evolution, yet the curious thing is that so little is known about it, particularly in evolutionary perspective. Ralph Holloway is one of the young physical anthropologists who view human evolution as a complex synthesis of factors, taking into account in their studies such things as genetics, ecology, fossil record, comparative anatomy and physiology, and the affects of cultural participation. As a result of the multiplexity of evidence brought to bear on his analysis of the problem of human evoluton, Holloway feels uneasy about simplistic statements relating brain size to intellectual ability. This uneasiness is warranted, as there has been considerable talk of cerebral "Rubicons," that is fixed boundaries, the crossing of which differentiates "human" from nonhuman ability to think. The Holloway piece raises many more questions than it resolves, which is to be expected at our present level of understanding. The reader may have good reason to revisit it when he is considering No. I:20 on primate studies and No. I:24 on "the human revolution."*

SOURCE: Unpublished paper presented at the Sixth Annual Meeting of the New England Psychological Association, Boston, Massachusetts, November 11, 1966. Used with the permission of the author, who wishes to thank Henry Tyblor for his kindness in criticizing this paper and for his many helpful suggestions.

The author (b. 1935) is Assistant Professor of Anthropology at Columbia University. His major interests are paleoanthropology and the evolution of brain and behavior. He is especially concerned with quantifying parameters used in studies of the brain and the effects of environment on brain structure. His most recent publication is an article on cranial capacity and neural reorganization (*American Anthropologist*, 1966).

This paper attempts to present the broad outlines of the evolution of the primate brain and, in particular, raises a number of problem areas surrounding the topic of primate brain and behavioral evolution. Hopefully, it indicates some contributions that a physical anthropologist can make toward a necessarily multidisciplinary approach to the subject. Three problems are briefly discussed, and a general framework provided: (1) the continuities and discontinuities between human and nonhuman behavior; (2) the human and nonhuman neural systems which can account for behavioral specificities and repertoires; (3) the use of the fossil and archaeological record of human evolution in approaching the first two problems.

Biases

My perspective on these problems contains biases, and I think I should try to set them forth. I have tried to question them, but admit I have not yet resolved the issues satisfactorily. Hence, I regard them as biases.

1. Subhuman behavior, viewed holistically and in terms of interacting neural systems, is presently more difficult to describe than human behavior. I gain the impression, either correctly or not, that we tend to confuse the simplicity of our laboratory tests with simplicity of behavior and neural structure. While I do not deny that study of monkey behavior has heuristic value, I do not believe it gives us any evidence directly relevant to either human behavior or human evolution.

2. Human behavior is both qualitatively and quantitatively different from that of other subhuman primates. That is, human behavior is an emergent phenomenon, albeit based on more primitive anlagen existing in the primate order. Neural terminology can easily describe the matters of degree; we cannot fully describe the neurological transforms responsible for behavior of kind because we do not know the actual behavioral parameters and cannot specify the plurilocal dynamic systems which integrate the emergent with the primitive anlagen. Perhaps the preceding is straightforward to all of you. The following will probably raise a few hackles on your necks. My bias is that the faculty of symbolization, i.e., *the imposition of arbitrary form upon the environment, and social rules for the generation of such forms*, is only one aspect of the difference of kind. Not being a monkey or an ape, I cannot speak about self-consciousness, self-reflection, self-or-ego objectification, or commitment to self. Categories such as conceptual vs. perceptual thought, signs vs. symbols, emotionality vs. rationality, do not seem (in my bias) the transforms that focus on the essential differences between primates. My second bias, then,

is simply this: that more than symbolization separates the ape from man.

3. My third bias, and here I feel more secure empirically, is that the human brain is not an enlarged ape brain, more complex simply because it has more parts. As I have argued elsewhere, not only has the cortex enlarged, it has become reorganized. I also believe that the subcortical components have likewise become reorganized in the course of evolution, although the basic plan is naturally retained. While no new parts exist in the human brain, the interaction of essentially reorganized systems produce output(s) which are behaviorally emergent. By *reorganized*, I mean that behavioral shifts favored by natural selection of sensorimotor, emotive, and intellectual attributes have resulted through quantitative shifts of different neural systems or components. In a moment I will talk about these differences and make a plea for the kinds of data that are sorely needed.

4. A fourth bias is that a consideration of the fossil record may provide insights into problems relating to human brain and behavior. By utilizing natural selection of behavior and structure as a heuristic framework, the fossil record provides *clues* (not empirical evidence) that might be useful today for understanding brain and behavior.

Problem Areas

CONTINUITY AND DISCONTINUITY: DEGREE AND KIND

How does human behavior differ from that of nonhuman primates? Is it just a matter of having language and organizing experience symbolically? Or are there matters of motivation, objectification of ego-environment, hedonistic involvements or attachments to arbitrary clusters of percepts which integrate with the language faculty to produce human specificity? Are there also matters involving the retaining of experience and strategies for its recall that require a sort of neural binding integrated with the symbolic functioning? This is a problem area where some clear thinking would be useful to all of us. Obviously, I am making no claim here to clear thinking. I am confused about the differences between ape and human behavior. I think it is still a legitimate problem area, and that when some clear formulations are made, they will facilitate the study of the nervous system generally and do much for comparative study.

Aside from this issue, there is good agreement that symbolization is the basic process of major significance in defining human existence. The continuities far outweigh the discontinuities. Recent reviews have stressed that the normal development of behavioral repertoires in primates depends on a natural social environment where peer-group processes, mother-infant interactions, and exploration possibilities are not cramped. Play, curiosity, problem-solving abilities, and need for social contact appear to be continuous matters, as both field and laboratory studies have shown. Behavioral repertoires associated with emotional rubrics such as "fear," "pride," "happiness," "peevishness," "humor," "shame," "frustration," "anger," and even "artistic bent," have been described for apes and monkeys, the former being approached with great empathy by human observers. Whatever the true existence of these states, I am going to argue that something like *hedonistic imperative* (a pleasurable dimension of activities for activities' sake) shows an increasing importance as one goes up the primate scale. Many of these items have been explained as adaptive in the sense that they allow the animal to have wider exposure to its environment. I am going to emphasize that natural selection has favored a strategy where these behaviors are common because the animal finds an intrinsic pleasure in doing them. For the primates as a whole, the hand is an important device for gaining information about the environment as well as a means of manipulating the environment. It is a *social* as well as instrumental organ. Along with the above attributes, there are devices (behavioral patterns) devoted to social control. When we come to this subject, however, the differences between man and ape seem not only heightened, but of a new "emergent" quality. The basis for social control in man is symbolism and analogues to primate dominance patterns. The symbol systems structure the perception of both the self and others. Environments are literally created through the *productive* and *arbitrary* design features of the peculiar specific human communication system, where almost any degree of improbability is generated by the symbolic faculty (whether it be patterned insanity, kinship systems, religious and political systems, myths, or definitions of objects). Along with the created environment is a set of social rules which bind the actors to their environments in many ways. It is hard to think of any system created through the symbolic faculty that is imaginative and which lacks social controls which determine how one is to orient toward the system, or what is to occur if the proper codes are breached. These matters go considerably beyond any dominance factor based on physiological components as, for example, found in a baboon, macaque, or chimpanzee group. In other primates, attraction ties can develop where there is no biological relationship, or necessarily any developmental (ontogenetic) conditioning or exposure. Sexual selection in chimpanzees is perhaps one example of this. In the human case, these attractions can be manifold at many levels and are largely fashioned by the symbol systems. In this process another "emergence" takes place. The symbol systems structure the environments at rates potentially greater than biological reproduction, and these "environments" which have been generated select further on the organism and symbol systems. This is a process of positive feedback and is significant for the evolutionary process of *orthoselection*. An example would be the rapid brain expansion during the Pleistocene from the

Australopithecines to modern man and the generation of cultural complexity, both material and social. Most simply, man, and all his symbolic productions, is his own environment. That is, man structures his own environment, whereas, in general, nonhuman animals do not. I am now going to go into another area where I feel somewhat uncertain, but which I think should be explored if we are concerned with human behavioral specificity. I am thinking crudely, if you like, of the degree of enthusiasm or commitment to arbitrary symbolic constructs which can in the extreme case approach a religious fanaticism or insanity. It is analogous to what Lorenz has called "militant enthusiasm." This is what I referred to before as the "hedonistic imperative." It encompasses things like "art" and "beauty." It is the integration of visceral (pleasure and excitement or tonus) and logical symmetrical intellections. It includes tendencies to erect boundaries, yet breach them, and seeks closures within sets of symbolic constructs. Music, myth, pictorial and tactile acts (arts) are what I am referring to. I believe these tendencies are neurologically structured in higher primates and achieve their zenith in the case of man. I doubt that the gap between ape and man can be crossed, however, by simply talking about symbolism. Let me now turn to the nervous system.

HUMAN AND NONHUMAN PRIMATE BRAINS

Here the matter is less ambiguous. Elsewhere I have discussed a number of areas of brain reorganization in different primate species. I cannot go into full detail here, but I argue that all levels of the nervous system have been affected. It is frankly embarrassing to represent a field where behavior has for so long been reduced to a matter of birdseed volumes. In essence, anthropology, neurology, and to a lesser extent psychology each have been obsessed with "rubicon" models. A few more cubic centimeters of volume, a few more neurons, a bit more association cortex, some more frontal lobe or parietal lobe, and Presto! you have human behavior. If we are to understand the neural differences between animals, we must account for them quantitatively and piecemeal. But there is no longer any excuse for cathecting on "rubicon" models to explain behavioral differences of the order which are of most interest to us. It is the organization and interactions between all of the differences which must decide the final product.

What are the systems which have been reorganized in the course of primate evolution, and how do these relate to what has been said thus far about behavioral differences? I would like to begin with a pathological condition known as microcephaly. There are some chimpanzees, and more gorillas, who have more volume of brain than many microcephalics. Yet, one would never confuse the microcephalics' behavior with that of the apes. Some of these human beings talk—use language. Some are *productive*, in Hockett's sense. That they are seriously handicapped behaviorally is wholly obvious. Yet they retain a certain specificity regarding affect and orientation to their environment. I have suggested that they carry off these specificities with less neurons in their cortices than some healthy apes. I think neuron number alone can explain nothing but richness of repertoire and that human specificities cannot be reduced to any permutations of 2^N power. As for association cortex, whatever that *really* is, I have calculated the following: ("Association/Sensorimotor" ratios = man = 27.8; chimp = 20.0; macaque = 4.8).[1] But, if we are interested in systems interactions and regard the specificities of the output as resting upon the whole activity of the brain, we will not reduce the specificities to the A/S ratio, but instead appreciate the increased role of certain sections, such as the parietal lobe, in the whole.

At the microscopic level, the primate cortex has undergone the following changes: (1) general increase in cell size (hypertrophy); (2) a decrease in neuron density; (3) an increase in dendritic branching—this conclusion is logical, not empirical; (4) an increase in glial/neural ratio; (5) an increase in Golgi-II stellate cells. One conclusion of these findings is that a fourfold increase in gross volume does not mean an isomorphic increase in neuron numbers. Shariff's figures are unambiguous on this account: man = 6.9 x 10^9; chimpanzee = 5.5 x 10^9; macaque = 2.5 x 10^9. Of course, they require replication. At a more molar level, the human cortex has differentially expanded, particularly in the temporal and parietal areas, a fact long appreciated. The behavioral effects of this reorganization have been discussed further by Dr. Geschwind in terms of the infraparietal lobule, non-limbic to non-limbic associations, intermodality transfers, and the symbolic faculty. I hope his work will not be abused by others in search of some "rubicon," and that his interesting model will be integrated with remaining neural and behavioral systems. [As an aside, it is interesting that Dart in 1925 regarded his Australopithecine as on the human line because, among other things, he thought he had found a reduction of primary visual cortex and expansion of posterior parietal area in the Taung endocast based on the position of the so-called "lunate" sulcus. Now that stone tools are known for these animals, and since language and stone tool-making probably come together in a cognitive package, and since the parietal lobule has significant involvement in sensory discrimination (tactile, visual, auditory), it is timely to reexamine that early endocast and see if the "lunate" sulcus can be identified. Certainly, by the time of Homo erectus in the lower middle Pleistocene, some 600,000 years ago, there is evidence that parietal and temporal lobes had expanded significantly. The fossil and archaeological record attests to both hunting and tool-making activities at a significant level

---

[1] These calculations are reported in a forthcoming paper to be published in the *American Journal of Physical Anthropology*. They are not true A/S ratios, since the motor cortex has not been taken into account.

which is very suggestive that the major human specificities were operative at that time, if not earlier.] I submit that the remaining expansion (from 800 to 1400 c.c.) can be accounted for by the four factors I mentioned earlier under molecular reorganization. These changes would be parallel to the changes noted by Clendinnen and Eayrs on growth hormone effects, and the work by the California Group (Rosenzweig, Krech, Bennett, Diamond) on extra-environmental-complexity-and-training (ECT) resulting in neuron hypertrophy, decreased neural density, and increased glial/neural ratio. My own work on dendritic branching in these animals suggests that this parameter increases also. The expansion could then be accounted for without vast increases in neuron number. The behavioral changes would have been in the direction of enhancing *complexity-management*, i.e., behavior of degree. Positive feedback, deviation-amplification, the generation of environmental complexity through symbolic *productivity* and increasing brain connectivity describes this aspect of human evolution.

Since time is running short, I will only briefly describe other aspects of neural reorganization. Sensorimotor abilities are reflected in enlargement of almost all cell stations or nuclei and pathways associated with these functions. The hand in particular, and hand-eye coordination are well developed. Fossil endocasts are useless here. The skeletal evidence for the Australopithecines shows an essentially Homo arrangement of the foot, hand and pelvis. These animals were not only bipedal; they used their hands and their brains to make stone tools according to arbitrary symbolic patterns. Somewhat later in time, at the Homo erectus stage, a few of the handaxes show extreme degrees of symmetry and extraordinary care in workmanship. I think it is impossible to deny that the *hedonistic imperative* was fully blown by this time.

When we come to subcortical structures associated with emotional behavioral attributes, we are embarrassed by the paucity of good quantitative comparative data. What the reorganizational changes mean functionally is anyone's guess at this time. (I am willing to cooperate with anyone interested in pursuing this matter—all I need are the brain slides.) While the evidence for subcortical components as having been reorganized in the course of primate evolution is slight, the evidence does not suggest that these components are any less important in terms of behavioral integration. I submit that the *hedonistic imperative* in the human case is more elaborate rather than less so in comparison to other primates. The cortex can both inhibit and facilitate emotional tonus by acting on limbic and hypothalamic structures. Proprioception and muscular effort, as well as intellectual concentration, can be pleasurable (and unpleasurable) tasks for the human to a degree which surpasses the ape. I submit that culture was not only adaptive, it was enjoyable, and that the generation of increasing degrees of improbability, symbolism, is an example of the *hedonistic imperative*. Stone-tool making is one example which cross-cuts, I think, the purely symbolic or cognitive, and the pleasurable. I think this integration, which is the true emergence, is reflected in the reorganization of all levels of the nervous system—the sensorimotor, the limbic, the associative areas. Note here that I am making the parietal lobe and its integration with the frontal portion (or planning sector) an important element both in the continuities and discontinuities of primate behavior. Tactile appreciation, symbolism, visual and hand coordination, auditory appreciation, and pleasure (or emotional tonus) go together.

THE FOSSIL AND ARCHAEOLOGICAL RECORD

So far, I have tried to put the sensorimotor systems, the subcortical components, and the cortex, particularly the parietal lobe, into a package integrated with symbolism and the *hedonistic imperative*. These processes, of course, are learned and played out in social environments, or private symbolic ones. Are there parameters of social environments in the human case not found in other primates? Here, I turn to the fossil and archaeological record for clues.

1. The amount of sexual dimorphism in early hominids is greatly reduced in certain structures, but heightened in others, and these others are visually and tactually based. Almost without exception, terrestrially-oriented primates show high degrees of sexual dimorphism. A concomitant feature is a heightened expression of aggression or agonistic repertoires. Can this tell us something about intragroup behavior and social cohesion, or the actors' orientations toward other actors in the group and without? (It suggests a social structuring based more on cooperative cohesive elements than overt agonisms, as seen in terrestrial primates.)

2. The stone tools, dentition, and associated animal bones at many hominid sites indicate a new adaptation strongly based on hunting. Two aspects deserve underlining: (a) cooperation of males; (b) sexual division of labor between male and female in terms of economic (and behavioral?) roles. All this suggests motivational and emotional orientations not found in other primates, as does:

3. Basic changes in sexual physiology leading to the permanent year-round receptivity of the female to the male. Was this not an adaptation necessary for the stabilization of economic and social roles in a precarious new economic pursuit-hunting? This adaptation was highly advantageous and highly successful. We are its products. So now I would like to add to the *hedonistic imperative* these areas as well: the more interesting and pleasurable aspects of sexual dimorphism, the breast, rounded contours, distribution of fat, glabrousness, and many, many symbolic constructs.

I am fully aware that all of this is speculative, and empirical support for these transformations is lacking until time machines are invented. The evidence is logico-deductive only. But these transformations did occur, and not by fiat, but through natural selection. Their organization involves more than muscles and limb-bones, hands and tools. They involve the brain. At our present juncture of thought, these above suggestions serve only as heuristic cues toward explicating (1) behavorial processes and (2) the underlying neurological concomitants of *Homo insanus.*

THE FOLLOWING selections (Nos. 15–19) are reprinted without change from the first edition of these *Readings*. The only addition is a statement bringing the UNESCO material up to date. The editor thinks it important to say why this is the only section of this book that has not undergone some alteration. The reason is simple: nothing new has been said about the matter in the intervening decade. Nothing new, that is, in a scientific sense; certainly nothing that seems to the editor to change the picture as presented in the previously selected articles. This blanket statement is also meant to include a few things written by the editor on the subject of race.

15 On the Number of Races of Mankind

Stanley M. Garn and Carleton S. Coon

BLACK, WHITE AND YELLOW. NEGROIDS, CAUCASOIDS AND MONGOLOIDS. THESE *are certainly the familiar lay-categories of race. But how significant are they? In a world in which the most exotic peoples come constantly in touch, how do we label the American Indians, the Polynesians, the people of India or the native Australians? More important, what does the obvious existence of populations which cannot be accommodated in any simple racial scheme mean for the concept of race? What is a race anyway? How many are there?*

Introduction

Physical anthropologists, taxonomists, and geneticists are, with few exceptions, agreed that the genus *Homo* is represented by but one polytypic species to which all living races belong. They are also agreed

SOURCE: *American Anthropologist*, Vol. 57 (1955), pp. 996–1001. Reprinted with the permission of the authors and the publisher.

Professor Garn (b. 1922) is Chairman of the Physical Growth Dept., Fels Research Institute, and teaches at Antioch College. A productive researcher in several fields, he is a co-author, with Carleton Coon and Joseph Birdsell, of *Races* (1950).

Carleton S. Coon (b. 1904) was Curator of Ethnology of the University Museum of the University of Pennsylvania and Professor of Anthropology at that university until his retirement in 1963. Among the dwindling group of anthropologists whose expertise extends beyond a single subdiscipline, he has made contributions to both physical anthropology and ethnology. Among his books are *The Races of Europe* (1939), *Caravan* (1951), *The Story of Man* (1954) and *The Seven Caves* (1957). His most recent book (with Edward E. Hunt, Jr.) is *The Living Races of Man* (1965).

that there are races or equivalent taxonomic units sometimes designated by other names. But there is considerable seeming disagreement as to how many races there are. Different taxonomies have listed as few as two races and as many as two hundred. Of two books on race that appeared in 1950, one distinguished six races, including a hypothetical Early European race, while another described thirty races. Such divergences have not simplified the problem of teaching about race, nor have the reasons for the discrepancies always been made clear.

Actually, what seems to be a disagreement of considerable magnitude narrows down to a lack of agreement on just what taxonomic unit is properly designated as a race in man. What Boyd calls a race is a geographical unit, and Boyd's system of races admittedly resembles the "stocks" or "divisions" recognized by other workers. On the other hand, the populations listed as races by Coon, Garn, and Birdsell merit no special label in Boyd's system. Inescapably, applying the term "race" to the larger taxonomic unit results in a smaller number of "races," while restricting the term "race" to the smaller unit yields a larger number of races. There, and in a nutshell, lies the gap between four and forty races.

Agreement as to which taxonomic unit properly constitutes a race in man is not easily achieved at this time. Carolus von Linnaeus, the great classifier, and Blumenbach (whose taxonomy is most famous of all) both distinguished a small number of geographically delimited races. The rule of priority, therefore, favors the larger geographically defined taxonomic unit. But usage—the usage of the last century and, particularly, the usage of population genetics—favors restricting the term "race" to the breeding or Mendelian population. Thus we are confronted with two somewhat different concepts of race and no acceptable rule to resolve the conflict in favor of one or the other.

Fortunately, however, it is possible to retain both meanings while moving in the direction of simplicity and clarity. For there are collections of human populations having an obvious similarity and contained within particular geographical limits. Such a collection is properly a *geographical race,* as the term has been used by Rensch, Mayr, and others. And there are the populations themselves, or *local races,* corresponding to the units that are subject to investigation. If we simply state whether we are referring to geographical races, of which there are a small number, or local races, of which there are many, the discrepancies mentioned above largely cease to exist.

Geographical Races

A geographical race is, in simplest terms, a collection of (race) populations having features in common, such as a high gene frequency for blood group B, and extending over a geographically definable area. In man, as in other widely ranging mammals, the geographical limits often correspond to continental areas. This is due to the fact that seas, oceans, and major mountain chains are more effective barriers to migration and "geneflow" than are rivers and smaller land elevations.

The human stocks or divisions, recognized by many anthropologists, and the races of Linnaeus, Blumenbach, and Boyd are equivalent to geographical races as defined here. They include for the most part numbers of populations, the populations have many features in common, and the geographical areas correspond to the continents or to major island groups. There is much similarity between the areas inhabited by the different geographical races of man and the geographical regions drawn up by Wallace (1876) for other mammals. It is especially instructive to note that those human populations whose taxonomic status has been most in doubt inhabit areas where, following Wallace, we might expect separate geographical races. Examples are the Bushmen-Hottentot, who have been classified in and out of the Negro category, the non-Negrito Australian aborigines, and the Eskimo of panarctic or circumpolar distribution. However, we need not expect precise accord between geographical areas and geographical races in such an adaptable and footloose species as man. Rather we mean to stress the fact that the taxonomic unit immediately below the species is best defined as a geographical race.

Local and Microgeographical Races

In contrast to geographical races, which are assemblages or collections of local race-populations and whose marginal members may be somewhat in dispute, there are also the populations called local races in the present terminology. These are units that can be subjected to study, and these are the units that change most in evolutionary time. In many cases such local races can be identified, not so much by average differences, but by their nearly complete isolation.

Yet, in more densely populated areas, neatly circumscribed and reproductively isolated populations may be hard to find. Europe, in contrast to the Americas in early colonial times, consists of a single sheet of humanity. And yet there are systematic differences as we proceed in any direction, and there are human islands where particular morphological or serological traits are especially common or unusually rare. Sheer weight of numbers, like distance and geographic barriers, serves to effect partial isolation and to preserve long-standing genetical differences. What we find in Europe, in particular, is not neatly defined local races but rather microgeographical races which differ only qualitatively from local races.

A note should be added about those local race-populations formed in historic times as a result of admixture between different populations. Despite their recent and known orgins, they constitute races just as good as those of greater antiquity and whose origins are shrouded in ignorance. Setting these recently formed races aside as "mixed" races does emphasize the existence of investigative problems peculiar to them, but it is not only an indefensible taxonomic practice but makes us appear more certain than we are about the origins of the older human groupings.

Relationship between Local and Geographical Races

In an earlier taxonomic day it was the fashion to assign, or to try to assign, every population to an appropriate geographical race. This effort was due in part to a desire for taxonomic neatness—a compulsive trait—and in part to the incorrect assumption that a taxonomy need also serve as a phylogeny. As a result there have been some blatantly incongruous assignments, such as putting Australian aborigines in the Negro category, and some needlessly complicated categories for groups of presumed hybrid origin.

Europe, to be sure, is a special case. Except perhaps for the migrant gypsies and the formerly isolated Lapps, all local and microgeographical races in Europe do fit into a single European geographical race. The Americas constitute a second area where all purely indigenous local races can be assigned to an American or Amerindian geographical race. But in the rest of the world there are numerous populations that cannot be contained in a tidy system of three to seven geographical races. And, apart from compulsiveness, there is no compelling need to do so.

The aboriginal Australians constitute one such example. Sometimes granted a geographical race of their own, they have been assigned to the Negro category (on the basis of skin color) and again to the White category (on the basis of facial form and, occasionally, light hair color). These men of the bush have been shuttled between Negro and White in different taxonomies, upon the didactic assumption that they must be one or the other. Likewise, the hunters of the Kalahari, often placed in the Negro category, occasionally have been assigned to the Mongoloid group on the basis of an assumed yellow skin pigment that has never been demonstrated! In similar fashion other populations, such as the Ainu, have rested uneasily, being out of place in their present geographical area yet not acceptable candidates for membership in a European geographical race.

In addition to these rather isolated, small, and scattered populations, it is in India that the either-or system of assignment has led to the most serious problem. The millions in India do have a rather high gene frequency for B, yet (as Boyd now accedes) they are not Mongoloid. They are not Negroid either, despite a generally high skin melanin concentration, nor are they Caucasian in Blumenbach's sense. While India does merit a geographical race of her own, the lesson from India is that every population can not be tagged in a simple system of but a few "major races" or "stocks."

On the Number of Races of Mankind

Returning to the central theme of this paper, it is possible to achieve agreement on the number of races of mankind, once we distinguish between geographical races and local and microgeographical races. If a geographical race is defined as a collection of similar populations inhabiting a broad continental area or island chain, then the number of geographical races of man is approximately six or seven. And, if the local race is equated with the Mendelian population, then the number of local and microgeographical races is upwards of thirty.

Clearly one can recognize a European and Western Asiatic geographical race conforming to Blumenbach's category "Caucasian." There is a Northern and Eastern Asiatic geographical race, encompassing a very large number of local races. That there is an African geographical race goes without saying, as does the existence of an Indian geographical race. Micronesia and Melanesia merit a separate category, and the same is true for Polynesia. But the Americas constitute a particular problem. Anatomically the aboriginal Americans resemble Asiatics closely; serologically the dissimilarities are many. Since a taxonomy need not solve the complicated problem of origins, granting the twin Americas separate status seems advisable, and the number of geographical races here listed is thus raised to seven.

As to the smaller taxonomic unit, our enumeration depends on the minimum size of the population units we wish to consider (in the case of local races) and on the minimum degree of difference we choose to emphasize (in respect to microgeographical races). Regarding the Pitcairn Islanders and the inhabitants of Tristan da Cunha, though their numbers are small and their origins recent and "hybrid," both constitute happily breeding and effectively isolated local races. There are other local populations, like the Cowrie-shell Miao and the Lolos, the now extinct Tasmanians, or the British Colored (chiefly located in Liverpool), that may not be listed as races in an elementary textbook yet constitute perfectly good biological races. In fact it is rather shocking to see that American anthropologists, familiar with the large number of American populations, have failed to support the claims of these to racial status. For a realistic census of local races, starting at Point Barrow and ending in the Fire Islands, would come close to exhausting our minimum race list of thirty.

Microgeographical races pose the problem they always have—a problem long antedating the term. For in a large continuously inhabited continental area, where individual mobility is small relative to the size of the total population, there may be distinct regional differences without either geographical barriers or group endogamy to help in delimiting the "population." Thus for Europe various taxonomies have ranged from a simple dichotomous system, involving a Northern or "Nordic" and a Southern or "Latin" race, to systems utilizing all of the permutations of the Van Eikstadt taxonomy. To the extent that local differences within large populations are considered, rather than abstracted or idealized types, there is equal justification for finer or coarser divisions when dealing with microgeographical races.

Counting up the number of geographical races is comparatively simple, because there are a limited number of continents and islandic chains, and different human groups have radiated through and exploited each of them. A count of local and microgeographical races, however, is a more difficult procedure. Not only are we currently unable to enter into a very large section of the world, where many populations remain unstudied, but we have been remiss in investigating race-populations within our own national borders. These observations, plus the foregoing, should make it clear that in regard to the number of local and microgeographical races of man, the count is thirty *plus*. And the "plus" represents an indeterminate number at least as large as the thirty.

Conclusion

It has been the purpose of this paper to point out that no major discrepancy exists between one taxonomic system listing only six human races and a second system enumerating thirty, once the taxonomic units are adequately defined. Taking first the larger taxonomic unit, the geographical race, well under ten such geographical races seem sufficient in the present state of knowledge. The smaller taxonomic units, the local and microgeographical races, are of necessity more numerous. Local or microgeographical races, isolated by distance or by numbers and corresponding more nearly to Mendelian populations, are but barely represented by a taxonomy listing as few as thirty such "races."

Since adequate data are in many cases lacking, every local race cannot be assigned to an appropriate geographical race. While this frustrates attempts at a nicely tidy taxonomy, functioning as a phylogeny as well, the study of race and the investigation of ongoing evolution in man are in no way hampered. Rather it centers attention on the fact that geographical races are to a large extent collections of convenience, useful more for pedagogic purposes than as units for empirical investigation. Local and microgeographical races, on the other hand, not only are susceptible to direct study but also afford insight into the evolutionary mechanisms still at work in shaping man. For such purposes a complete enumeration of the number of races of man is needless. A numerically small, out-of-the-way population of recent and hybrid origin may prove more informative than a large Western population extending backward to the dawn of European civilization.

16 Climate and Race

Carleton S. Coon

TOWARDS THE CLOSE OF HIS CAREER, EARNEST HOOTON, A FAMOUS PHYSICAL *anthropologist, revised one specific element in the definition of race with which he had worked for thirty years. Originally he had defined a race as a large population which, though showing individual variation, tended to be alike in physique and physiology. The common physical traits were assumed to be the result of shared heredity and were supposed to be primarily non-adaptive. It is the last phrase that Hooton finally removed from his definition of race, though not all of his colleagues have since followed suit.*

A non-adaptive trait is one which is absolutely neutral under all practical conditions which its bearer may meet. It neither advances the organism's chances to live and reproduce nor does it diminish them. Definitions of race that utilize the concept do so in order to stabilize their categories: if the criteria are not subject to external influence, they are relatively immune to change. The resulting racial categories are rigid and immobile; it is not accidental that they reflect certain contemporary racist views. Political and ethical questions to the side, however, we note that the static concept of race based upon non-adaptive characters has two very great weaknesses. First, it places the biological classification of human varieties in limbo, cut off from the main stream of evolution and its processes and therefore detached from the main stream of modern science. Second, many of the classically accepted non-adaptive traits have been reexamined and now are believed to be adaptive in a variety of subtle ways.

The problem of the causal relations between adaption and the

SOURCE: Harlow Shapley (ed.), *Climatic Change* (Cambridge: Harvard University Press, 1954), pp. 13–34. Reprinted by permission of the author and publisher.
For biographical data on the author, see I:15.

existence of human races is still poorly explored and controversial. The author of the following selection has never been adverse to controversy and sets down his hypotheses and speculations in the context of a broad knowledge of the subject.

Three-quarters of a century ago, in 1877, J. A. Allen, a zoologist at the American Museum of Natural History, wrote, in an article reprinted, like this one, in a Smithsonian Annual Report: "The study of man from a geographical standpoint, or with special reference to conditions of environment, offers a most important and fruitful field of research, which, it is to be hoped, will soon receive a more careful attention than has as yet been given it." Allen's paper dealt with geographically correlated variations in North American animals and birds, on three axes: color, general size, and the relative size of the peripheral parts; or more simply, color, size, and form. The first of these had already been studied in 1833 by Gloger, the second by Bergmann in 1847. Only the third was new with Allen. Wholly apart from the study of man, few scientists in the zoological field have concerned themselves, since Allen's day, with the subject of geographical variations within species. An outstanding exception is Rensch who, during the late twenties and thirties tested these rules and added several observations of his own; but even with this work available, Ernst Mayr was moved to state: "The study of these ecological correlations and the establishment of definite rules is such a new field that we may consider ourselves at the beginning of the work."

If, 64 years after Allen's statement, an authority of Mayr's stature could say that we were at the beginning of the work, it is clear that up to 11 years ago this aspect of biology had been greatly neglected, and such is still the case. During those 64 years the study of biology passed through several phases of emphasis. First was the Darwinian epoch, in which Allen's work could clearly be rejected as Lamarckianism, and then came the era of genetic orthodoxy, during which it could be tossed into the bin of discredited interests, for at this time it was fashionable to call people interested in taxonomy, naturalists. Mayr himself, probably more than any other man, has brought taxonomy back into the biological social register. He has shown how essential the study of systematics is to a comprehension of the total life process. Although his interest in ecological rules does not represent a complete rediscovery, as Morgan rediscovered Mendelian genetics, yet his emphasis on this aspect of biology may turn out to be an equally important landmark in biological history.

If the study of ecological rules has been neglected by biologists, physical anthropologists have slighted it even more. The study of race in man has been influenced not only by biological fashion but also by current political ideologies. In each country of Europe, as in America, and in some African and Asiatic nations, a small but persistent group of men has continued to pile up objective data on the metrical and morphological characters of human beings. In some European and Asiatic countries, before World War II, politicians and propagandists concocted theories of racial superiority and inferiority with which to bolster their political schemes. In other European countries corresponding politicians and propagandists interested in internationalism brewed up opposite theories: first, to the effect that all races are equal in every respect, and second, to deny the existence of races at all. In America we have followed both of these fashions in turn. Each has served the political motives of its period. The second movement, unfortunately for the progress of science, is still with us. So strong is the feeling against thinking or talking about race that the study of the facts of race itself is nearly at a standstill. But fashions come and go. What is laughed at in one decade becomes the rage in another. Perhaps our turn will come.

Just as Rensch was the only voice crying in the zoological wilderness, the combined plea of three men, Garn, Birdsell, and myself, raised, in 1949, a feeble noise in the desert of physical anthropology. In our small and conceptually indiscreet book "Races" we suggested that some of the racial variations in man may be due to adaptations, by mechanism or mechanisms unknown, to extremes of environment. At the time we wrote it I, at least, had never heard of Allen, Gloger, Bergmann, or Rensch. It was only in a review of our book by Dr. M. T. Newman that I learned of their work. Since then I have found a little time to read what these zoologists have written, and to think about how their findings may possibly apply to man. Just this small amount of contemplation has made it abundantly clear that if a person is to study the racial variations in man in terms of ecology, he must be a superscientist, thoroughly conversant not only with his own subject, including anatomy, but also with physiology, particularly heat-and-sweat physiology, nutrition and growth, radiation physics, optics, body mechanics, genetics, and cultural anthropology in time and space. With all due respect to my colleagues I know of no one individual who can meet these qualifications. Hence it looks as though Allen's prediction would have to be still further delayed.

Still the problem can be stated. According to the modern concept of species formation expounded by Mayr and others, most animal species are polytypic—that is, they extend over a varied geographical range, and in a number of observable characteristics the local populations vary gradually from one end of the spatial range to another. A minority of species is monotypic—that is, lacking in geographical variation in any known character. Monotypic species are usually confined to small and isolated areas. Man is a polytypic species. Cases of genuine isolation, like that of the Polar Eskimo, are rare and probably of short duration. Like other polytypic species man varies from place to place, and the different forms which his variations take seem, in some, but not all, instances, to follow the same ecological rules as do those of other warm-blooded animals. Three of these rules, the longest known, concern us here.

1. *Gloger's rule.* "In mammals and birds, races which inhabit warm and humid regions have more melanin pigmentation than races of the same species in cooler and drier regions; arid regions are characterized by accumulation of yellow and reddish-brown phaeomelanin pigmentation." "The phaeomelanins are subject to reduction in cold climate, and in extreme cases also the eumelanin" (polar white).

2. *Bergmann's rule.* "The smaller-sized geographic races of a species are found in the warmer parts of the range, the larger sized races in the cooler districts."

3. *Allen's rule.* "Protruding body parts, such as tails, ears, bills, extremities, and so forth, are relatively shorter in the cooler parts of the range of the species than in the warmer parts."

The rest of this paper will be devoted to an inquiry into the possible application of these three rules to man. They cannot be called laws in the sense of Newton's Law or the Second Law of Thermodynamics, although these two, and other well-established physical principles, no doubt contribute to whatever validity they may be shown to possess. That no one simple law is involved in any instance is shown by Rensch's discovery that these three rules, along with several others of his own formulation (Rensch's clutch rule and hair rule, for example) are subject to 10 to 30 percent of exceptions. They cannot be called laws, because controls have not been sufficiently established to eliminate outside functions, and because not enough experiments have been made. However, a hibernating animal that defies Bergmann's rule is no more a valid exception to it than a helicopter is to the law of gravity; if all exceptions were run to the ground and all leads followed, the physical basis for these observations could in each case be established, or the rule refuted.

With man we have several advantages, and one disadvantage. We are dealing with a single species, or *rassenkreis,* to use Rensch's term, that is extremely numerous for a mammal and that covers a larger geographical area than that of almost any other mammal. More human beings have been "collected" than any other kind of fauna. Our measurements, while far from adequate, are relatively numerous. Another advantage is that we know quite a lot about the history of man. One principal disadvantage is that man possesses culture. In addition to his enormous capacity for physical adjustment to many climates, he has developed artificial adaptive aids, such as the use of fire, shelter, clothing, food preservation, and transportation, which have permitted him to occupy every single part of the land surface of the world except the Greenland and Antarctic icecaps, and by means of which he is already looking for further conquests in other planets and outer space. There neither Gloger, nor Bergmann, nor Allen can help him.

For the best part of a million years, some kind of man has existed, probably occupying not one but several environments, and during his evolutionary life span the climates of most, if not all, of the regions in which he has lived have been altered, in most cases more than once. As part of the cultural growth of man, two principal evolutionary shifts have been achieved. The brain has gone through two major changes in size, quite independently of body size, by means of two consecutive doublings of the cortical area. This means that two major steps in human evolution may have taken place since the ancestors of man became erect bipedal primates feeding themselves with their hands. This further means that some, if not all, of the climatically adaptive changes which distinguish modern races from one another may have been acquired in stage 1—or stage 2 of this process, rather than in stage 3, the modern level of potential cerebration. The late Franz Weidenreich postulated that the Mongoloid face began with *Sinanthropus* in stage 2. Whether or not he was correct, that anatomist was prepared to accept the thesis of presapiens raciation, and the concomitant thesis of multiple evolution from an earlier evolutionary level. Whether or not one or several human stocks made this jump, we do not know, but for present purposes the latter possibility must be taken into consideration.

We must not, however, assume that any or all stocks which passed through the first two cerebral size stages to the third were any more apelike in many respects than the reader. Schultz has shown that some of the features which distinguish man from his fellow occupants of the great primate house are more conservative and ancient in man than in the apes. For example, the heavy hair on the human scalp is also present in the newborn chimpanzee, which has hair elsewhere only on its eyelids, eyebrows, and arms. The erect position of the head on the top of the spine, with the position of the face and orbits below the brain case, is another example of what Schultz calls ontogenic retardation, or conservatism, rather than using the less palatable and perhaps less truthful, if commoner, word, fetalization. The human position of the great toe falls also in this class of phenomena, while the smaller size of the other toes is due to shortening rather than to an increase of the length of the big toe itself. Furthermore, we cannot assume that all earlier human types had big teeth and prognathous jaws. The gibbon's face is no larger in proportion to its brain and body than that of man. The siamang, in a few examples, has a chin.

In the basic evolutionary characters all men are equally human as far as we can tell; if some races resemble one or another of the anthropoids in some particular feature, that may mean only that that particular race is more specialized, more differentiated from the common stock, than the others. No earlier evolutionary status is necessarily implied, at least until we know all the pertinent facts.

Schultz has shown that among the apes just as much variation is seen as among men, if not more. He says that the "skin color of the chimpanzee varies from black to white . . . the writer has the body of a young chimpanzee, born of black haired parents, which had straw-colored hair at birth, and later this color changed to a reddish tint. . . . Giants and pygmies have developed among chimpanzees and orang-utans, and long-armed and short-armed varieties among gorillas. . . . Of the great apes . . . each has a very limited distribution, in contrast to man, yet each has produced several species or subspecies which are morphologically but not geographically as different from each other as the main races of man."

Schultz's statement shows that many of the differences between men which we consider racial also occur individually and racially among the apes. This means that the early human forms must have possessed the capacities for these same variations, some of which can, therefore, be very ancient and can go back to the earlier evolutionary stages. In other words, a Negro may have become black before he became a man, a Nordic's ancestor blond and blue-eyed while his brain was still half its present cortical surface size. The evidence used in this paper does not favor any such interpretation, but neither does it render it impossible.

Taking up Gloger's rule, first, we find that it was originally formulated to account for the color of feathers and fur, rather than skin. Birds and beasts of humid forested regions, in the cooler latitudes as well as in the Tropics, tend to adopt sombre colors; the association is with humidity and shade, rather than with temperature. Since individual birds and animals have been seen to grow darker or lighter when carried from one environment to another, it is clear that whatever influence produces this effect reflects a genetic capacity of considerable latitude. At any rate, it does not apply to man. His color variation is primarily concerned with the skin, which in a precultural state must have been wholly, except for the scalp, exposed to the elements, as in some racial and cultural situations it still is.

Speaking very broadly, human beings have three kinds of skin. One is the pinkish-white variety that burns badly on exposure to the sun and fails to tan. Such skin is found in a minority of individuals in the cloudy region of northwest Europe, among descendants of the inhabitants of this area who have migrated elsewhere, and among albinos anywhere. It is quite clearly defective skin; and causes its owners trouble anywhere anytime they step out of the shade. Clothing, lotions, wide-brimmed hats, and sun glasses help to mitigate its deficiency. Luckily for the rest, relatively few of mankind possess it.

At the opposite extreme is black or chocolate-brown skin, familiar as the integumental garb of the full-blooded Negro. Persons who wear skin of this type are the same color all over, except for their palms and soles. As I discovered in Ethiopia, the unexposed skin is sometimes even darker than the portions exposed to the sun such as the hands and face, perhaps owing to an increased thickening of the horny layer in contact with solar radiations. Once this layer has thickened, man with this kind of skin can travel anywhere without fear of the sun; he can roll up his sleeves, toss off his shirt, or run naked in any climate where he or any other human would not be hindered by the cold. Negroes have gone to Alaska and to the North Pole.

In between is the range of integumental color possessed by the majority of mankind, belonging to skins which, although appearing as white, olive, yellowish, reddish, or brown, have one feature in common. The skin that is covered by clothing, if any, is relatively light. Exposed areas, if the light is strong enough, tan. In some populations this tanning can approach the darkness of the black-skinned peoples. However, skin that can tan can also bleach. Peoples who live in mid-latitude regions where the air is dry and the sky cloudless in summer, while in winter dampness and clouds are the rule, can shift their skin color with the seasons. This capacity for developing pigment in response to light and losing it when the light is gone is probably the original genetic situation with man.

The physiological advantages of the second and third types of pigment are easy enough to see. They concern entirely, as far as we know, ultraviolet radiation. The UV scale runs from about 2,400 to 3,900 Ångstrom units, where it joins the lower end of the range of visible light. Actually, although shorter waves are produced artificially by lamp makers, all solar radiation under about 2,900 units is filtered out by the earth's atmosphere and has nothing to do with the adaptive character of the human skin. Through the remaining thousand-unit range, UV radiation penetrates exposed skin to irradiate some of the subcutaneous fats, thus producing vitamin D, which is of benefit to the system.

However, those rays which are concentrated in an extremely narrow peak near the short end of the range, and centered at 2,967 units, can damage the unpigmented skin if the sky is clear, the sun overhead, and if the exposure is prolonged past a critical time limit. Sunburn, erythema, prickly heat, and sunstroke can follow. However, the hazard carries its own cure, for if the skin is exposed for short periods it will tan. The pigment so acquired absorbs the UV radiation concentrated at this critical peak and converts it into radiant heat, which the skin then loses through the normal processes of radiation, convection, and sweating, along with other heat produced by the metabolism of food within the body. The pigment granules do not interfere with UV penetration along the rest of the scale, and thus vitamin D production can continue. Tanned skin is thus useful in regions where the peak of UV radiation is seasonal, since in the season of reduced light the skin bleaches and permits the maximum of irradiation.

In contrast to the genetic capacity for change inherent in skin that tans, black skin is constant. In the distant and naked past, it must have had a clear advantage in the Tropics over tannable skin. That advantage remains to be discovered experimentally. Geographically speaking, peoples with black skin who are known to have lived in their present habitats since the rather mobile dawn of history live in regions close to the Equator where UV is strongest. They inhabit the forests and adjacent grasslands of central Africa. The second great center is Melanesia, including Papua and northern Australia. They also include the extinct (in the full-blooded state) Tasmanians. In between Africa and Melanesia fringes of land and islands hold connecting links; southern India, Ceylon, the Andamans, the Malay Peninsula, and the Lesser Sundas contain black-skinned peoples, as do some of the islands of the Philippines.

Except for Tasmania, whose inhabitants had obviously migrated there from a region of lower latitude, these areas are all within 20° of the Equator, and most of them are within 10°. In all of them there is little seasonal change. Aside from these uniformities, they represent a variety of environments, including shady forests, grasslands, deserts, and coast lines. Since we have a good idea what black skin is good for, we can discover no particular reason for it in the forests. Bright equatorial sun is, however, a problem in grasslands, deserts, and on the water.

Returning to the rest of the animal kingdom, we find that grassland and desert mammals are generally light or tawny colored. This is true of animals whose skins are protected by hair. A few animals, however, are naked like man, and these are black or dark gray. They include the elephant, rhinoceros, hippopotamus, buffalo, and certain types of pig. These animals reach their peak of numbers and development in the grasslands or desert fringe; except for the rhino they enter the forest, where they are fewer and less favored. Their color, carried in from the sunlight, is neither an advantage nor a disadvantage in the shade.

In Africa the blackest Negroes live in the grasslands. In the forest we find two kinds of people: Pygmies, who are not completely black, and Negroes. The Pygmies hunt, the Negroes farm. The two exchange products. Since the Negroes make the arrowheads and nets with which the Pygmies hunt, the latter would have a hard time living without either these implements or the plantains which the Negroes give them for food. Furthermore, the food plants which the Negroes cultivate are of southeast Asiatic origin, and they could hardly have been introduced later than the first millennium B. C. Since southern India got iron during this same millennium, and the motive which brought people across the Indian Ocean to Africa was a search for iron, it is unlikely that the Negroes entered the forest to live much before the time of Christ. If we look at Melanesia we see again that the forest is poor in game, the principal animal being the pig, escaped from domestication. The pig came in with agriculture, and neither can have been introduced much before the first millennium B. C. Therefore, the present black-skinned populations of these two tropical forest areas must be historically recent; black skins go with grasslands or deserts and have entered forests in numbers only with agriculture. In the Belgian Congo the forest Negroes are decreasing in numbers while the Pygmy population remains constant. If we look back to the Pleistocene, we see that the glacial advances and retreats in the north were accompanied by a succession of pluvial and interpluvial periods in the Tropics. At least once the Sahara was blooming with grass and flowers, and at other times the forest was reduced to a fraction of its present area.

Why, one may ask, did not black skins develop in the Americas, where land within 10° of the Equator runs along a course of 4,000 miles? The answer, which is geographical, confirms our interpretation of black skins in the Old World. The coast of Ecuador is heavily forested. Open country begins at the Peruvian border, 4° south of the Equator, whence it continues to the forest zone of Chile. The coastal desert averages only 20 miles wide. Owing to the combination of the mountains behind and the cold Humboldt Current in front, the air is cool, the humidity high, the sky usually overcast, and little solar radiation gets through. Moving up into the highlands, we should expect a double concentration of UV at 10,000 feet, where one-sixth more solar radiation penetrates the atmosphere than at sea level. However, the region of Quito, which is on the Equator, is frequently cloudy; the year has two rainy peaks. Thunder, Brooks says, is heard on 99 days each year. Since the air is also cold, the Indians cover up as much of their skin as possible. At 17° farther south, on the shores of Lake Titicaca, less rain and clouds appear, but the humidity is moderately high. Americans with untannable blond skins suffer intensely. The Indians, who wear broad-brimmed hats as well as the usual heavy clothing, tan to a deep reddish brown on exposed parts.

Moving eastward we find most of the Amazonian countryside heavily forested. Indians, Negroes, Whites, and all shades between get along with equal ease as far as UV is concerned. However, between the great river system in Brazil, the Guianas, and Venezuela are patches of savannah, precisely the kind of country in which black-skinned animals and men luxuriate in Africa. However, these patches are small and not long ago may have been smaller. They support no tempting animal life as in Africa, and the few Indians who got out there are refugees from the forests that line the streams. There is no evidence of any earlier population in this region at all. From all these considerations no reason appears for a black-skinned population to have developed in the Americas. The relative antiquity of man in the two hemispheres is therefore beside the point.

While Gloger's rule appears to cover variations in the response of the human skin to UV, both Bergmann's and Allen's rules are cut to fit the other end of the scale, radiant heat. Unlike UV, radiant heat both enters and leaves the body, which is physiologically well adapted to maintain an even temperature under extreme environmental conditions. Clothing, shelter, and fire also help, but not to the exclusion of physiological adaptation.

Bergmann's rule, that warm-blooded animals of a given polytypic species will be larger in the colder and smaller in the warmer portions of its ecological range, is based on the physical fact that the larger a body, all else, including shape, being equal, the smaller the ratio of skin surface area to bulk, one being a square, and the other a cube. Since most of the heat loss comes through the skin, the larger the animal, all else being equal, the easier the process of keeping it warm. Other factors, some of which will be dealt with presently, enter into this picture, and if they and others still to be determined did not, it would be more than a rule.

The simplest test of Bergmann's rule is to compare mean body weight of different human populations with climate as expressed by latitude. In Europe a regular cline is found between the peoples of the northwest, as the Irish with 157 pounds and the Finns with 154, down to the Spaniards with 132 and the racially white Berbers of Algeria with 124 pounds. In Asia the Mongoloid peoples show the same tendency, with the North Chinese weighing 142 and the Annamites 112 pounds, respectively. In America the Eastern Aleuts average 150 pounds, a level maintained by most of the Indians of the northern United States and Canada, while the Maya of Central America tip the scales at only 119 pounds. In South America weight rises with altitude and latitude to a peak among the bulky Indians of Patagonia and the grasslands of Tierra del Fuego. The equatorial Andamanese weighed only 98 pounds, the Kalahari Bushmen 89. The Baluba, a non-Pygmy Negro tribe of the Belgian Congo, average only 118 pounds, which seems to be par for tropical rain forests. In Polynesia, where offshore breezes make heat loss no problem, weights are high, as they are in cool New Zealand. Polynesian figures range from 140 pounds upward. Indonesians, to whom Polynesians are supposed to be related, are 20 to 30 pounds lighter. Their islands are hotter.

It can be easily demonstrated that changes in body size may take place in a single generation. Whatever genetic mechanisms control weight permit a useful capacity for variation. Man's size is as plastic as his tannable skin color and as automatically regulated. Anyone who has visited the Lower Amazon country has seen that the Brazilian citizens in that tropical forest are of one size, whatever their hair form, skin color, or cast of facial features. At least three racial stocks are concerned, the Mediterranean, Negro, and American Indian. All come out the same size. Farther south representatives of these same three stocks are much larger.

One other environmental factor affects body size, causing different populations within a given climatic zone to vary within their limits of tolerance. That is nutrition. In my North Albanian series I found that the tribesmen living on food raised on granitic soil were significantly smaller than those who walked over limestone, thus confirming the results of French investigators more than half a century earlier. Trace elements are important, and so are feeding habits. In a Moroccan village studied by Schorger the boys were given almost no meat until they reached the age of 14, at which time they were expected to work. From then on they ate with the men, whose diet included animal proteins. At that point their growth was relatively rapid. A main diet of polished rice goes with small people; we do not know how big they would have been if they had eaten other foods in a hot climate.

Most striking of all the size differences in man are those between the Pygmy peoples of Africa, the Indian Ocean countries, Indonesia and Melanesia, and normal human beings. However, the Pygmies are not much smaller than some of the people of the Amazon Valley. In all these selvas the leaching of the soil through excessive rainfall is held responsible, through the agency of washing out of trace elements. But man is not the only pygmy in the forest. In Africa the elephant, hippopotamus, buffalo, and chimpanzee all have pygmy counterparts. What affects man there cannot be cultural; it is of universal mammalian application, since the animals mentioned eat the whole range of available foodstuffs and are exposed to the same range of temperature, humidity, and solar radiation.

Along with size comes the question of basal metabolism. Although questions have arisen about coordinating techniques, still the geographical distribution of the results follows a Bergmannian pattern. The norm is set for Europe and the northeastern United States; rates more than 10 percent above normal are found among the Eskimo, who reach 30 percent of excess, the Ojibwa Indians of the Great Lakes region, and the Araucanians of southern Chile. Rates 10 percent and more below the norm are found among Australian aborigines and inhabitants of the hotter parts of India, Australia, and Brazil. Americans in New Orleans are also below par. This needs a lot of checking and controlling, but despite two exceptions the trend is clear. Furthermore, like alterations of pigment and gross size, changes in basal metabolism can in some cases be acquired.

That basal metabolism should change with climate makes sense, as does the whole mechanism of heat control in man. Here we enter a field where many physiologists have brutalized themselves and their friends for the sake of science; one investigator writes that he and his team even took the rectal temperatures of porcupines in the Talkeetna Mountains of Alaska at −22° F. Others thrust thermocouples into their own flesh, piercing their palms and wrists to the depth of the bone. Still others consented to be locked in sealed chambers from which heat and oxygen, alternately, were withdrawn, while a few pedaled themselves nearly to death on bicycles. As a result of this self-sacrifice we are in a position to evaluate Allen's rule in man.

Being a warm-blooded animal is a great advantage. It permits one to move and act at nearly all times in nearly all places, instead of scampering feverishly for shade or waiting for the chill to burn off before moving. However, the process of keeping the internal organs at a temperature of 98.6° F. has its problems too. This temperature can fall to 77° F. or rise to 110° F. before death intervenes, but variations of half these magnitudes are serious, particularly on the high side, for man can lose heat more safely than he can gain it. Even when he is trying to keep warm, man loses a certain amount of heat functionally in evaporation of moisture through the palms, soles, axillae, and pubic regions, just to keep tactile and hinge areas ready for action.

As long as the temperature of the outside environment is below 83° F., the body normally loses heat by radiation and convection. At 83° F. it begins to sweat, and the surface of the body grows increasingly moist, until at 93° F., in a saturated atmosphere, the whole body is covered, water is dripping off the surface, and the perspiration fails to do its work, which is to cool the surface of the skin by evaporation. At this point, if the temperature rises without a drop in humidity, trouble is near. However, in dry air only 40 percent of the body surface is normally wet at 93° F.; at blood temperature the ratio is 50 percent, and a complete coverage, in the American human guinea pig, is not attained until 106°F.

The evaporation of sweat is the principal means by which the body loses its radiant heat. Experiments have shown that a resting man at 122° F. and a humidity of 44 percent will lose 1,798 grams of sweat per hour; a working man, in a humidity of 35.6 percent saturation, will lose 3,880 grams per half hour, or half his normal blood volume, at a cooling potential of 25 to 30 times the normal resting metabolism. Needless to say such a liquid turnover requires him to drink gallons of water and also taxes his heart. It is greatly to the advantage of human beings living under conditions of extreme heat to avoid this circumstance as much as possible.

Such heat is found largely in the deserts of the world which lie on either side of the Equator, on the Tropics of Cancer and Capricorn. Chief among them are the Sahara, the Arabian, Persian, Thar, Kalahari, Australian, Argentine, Chilean, and Colorado Deserts. Of these the Turkestan, Gobi, Argentine, and Colorado Deserts lie farthest from the Equator. Characteristic of deserts is a great diurnal variation in temperature, and often a seasonal one as well. On a hot day the mercury may fall to 71° F. at 5 a. m., reach the critical sweating point of 93° F. at 10:15 a. m., hit a peak at 108° F. at 2 p.m., and fall to 93° F. again at 7:45 p.m. A hunter, who has nothing to work with but his own body and a bow and arrows or a handful of spears, will be up before daylight, and he will be on his way by the time the coolest point of the daily cycle will have been reached. He will be able to go out to his hunting ground before the heat bothers him, and if he is lucky he can make his kill early and take his time on the way home before or during the heat of the day. If he is on a 2- or 3-day hunting trip, he can nap under a bush in siesta time, and return on another morning. An Arab who is herding camels or conducting a caravan will travel by the light of the moon and stars and sleep under a lightproof black tent in the middle of the afternoon. In Middle Eastern desert countries even truck drivers prefer to work at night, to save their tires as well as their own systems. If forced to do so, a desert-dwelling human being can walk in the heat of the day, but if he confines his traveling to the nighttime he can go three times as far, without water, before collapsing.

Animals that live in the desert belong to two classes, those that can do without water and those that use it to cool the body through evaporation. The first category includes especially a number of rodents, which derive water from desert vegetation and can even extract it metabolically from dry seeds. Such animals have no water to spare; they hide behind or under rocks or bushes during the heat of the day, or burrow far underground, in some cases pulling stoppers of earth in behind them. When the surface ground temperature is $122°$ F. it may be only $83°$ at a depth of 1 foot 3 inches, while at 6 feet it may fall as low as $68°$ F., with considerable humidity. Animals that hide during the day to save water will die when forced to spend a few hours in the bright sun in the heat of the day.

The other class of animals is composed of larger forms, such as the camel, oryx, and addax, which are able to hold up to a fifth of their body bulk in stored water and to utilize it gradually. In this sense they are no better off than a man weighing 120 pounds carrying a 5-quart canteen. In cool spring weather they are at an advantage over the man, however, for they can derive their moisture from herbage; only in the hot and barren season do they depend on their speed to carry them to water. In addition to their water-holding capacity, these animals have something else in common. They all have long legs and necks and are extremely gracile for their weight. Their bones are long, fine, and hard; their musculature light. In treeless country they can make high speeds. Even the cat family has its desert representative, the long-legged cheetah, which is said to be the fastest runner of all living things.

Man in the desert is also light and gracile. He too needs to be able to travel far on a small heat load. But his animal companions have buff-colored hairy coats, which reflect solar light; it is unlikely that they lose their heat in this fashion. Man must lose it through his skin surface, and the more surface he has per unit of weight the better. The more he can lose through radiation and convection the less he has to sweat, and the more skin surface he can use for evaporation the higher the temperature he can stand. The smaller his bulk, the less the load on his heart. The shape of his body takes on added importance as we realize that all parts of its surface do not lose heat equally. The back of his hand has about 400 sweat glands to the square centimeter, the forehead 200, and the cheek as few as 50. The hands, which comprise 5 percent of the body surface on normal Americans, lose 20 percent of the heat of the body by evaporation.

When a man begins to perspire, moisture appears first on his forehead, neck, some of the larger areas on the front and back of his trunk, the back of the hand, and the adjacent part of the forearm. The head and neck must lose heat rapidly for they have the brain to keep in thermal equilibrium, and if the head is globular in form, it has the worst possible shape for heat loss. Old World hot-desert peoples are narrow headed. After this the cheek, the lateral surfaces of the trunk, and the rest of the extremity surfaces begin, but these regions sweat much less. Sweating is always slight to moderate on areas rich in subcutaneous fat, such as the cheek and the gluteal and mammary regions. The inside of the thighs and armpits sweat even less, since they face in and not out and are in a poor position for heat loss. The palms and soles, which perspire at lower temperatures, lose the least of all in periods of stress.

The chief burdens then are on the neck and head, which have purely local duties, and on the hands and forearms, which act as radiators for the whole body. It has been shown that the average human body (American) loses heat after the fashion of a cylinder averaging 7 cm. in diameter. While the head and trunk are bulkier than this, the forearms and hands resemble even smaller cylinders, and the fingers and toes even smaller yet. Now heat loss increases as the square of the diameter of the cylinder decreases. Hence the survival value of long, tapering forearms and fingers in a dry, hot place becomes self-evident.

One of the racial peculiarities of Negroes is long arms, with particular emphasis on the length of the forearm, and large hands with long fingers. Forest Negroes often have relatively short legs, but we have seen that the legs have much less to do with heat regulation than the arms. The Nilotics and Somalis and Masai and other black-skinned peoples of the Sahara, Sudan, and the Horn of Africa have long skinny legs and long gracile necks; no case of adaptation to a given environment situation could be clearer. The same is true of South Indians, Ceylonese Vedda, most Melanesians, and the Australian aborigines of the desert, as well as of white Australians from Queensland. The Bushman of the Kalahari is extremely slender; of the inhabitants of the American deserts information is defective. At any rate, as far as we know, the desert portion of Allen's rule holds for man, for obvious reasons. The mechanism of change is less obvious.

The other end of Allen's rule applies to adaptation to cold. Naked savages can live without much clothing in temperatures down to the freezing point. Several technical experiments have been performed on Australian aborigines sleeping naked in the desert when the night temperature fell to the frost point. These people keep rows of small fires burning and sleep between rows. Parts of their skin surface becomes quite cold, others hot. They seem to be able to absorb radiant heat from the fires on some parts of their skin surface in all of which the venous blood is at a minimum. Thus they survive until morning. In the daytime the air temperature rises rapidly.

The Yaghans, canoe Indians of Tierra del Fuego, paddle nearly naked in their boats in foggy channels, in an environment where year-round temperatures hover above and about freezing point. Darwin saw a naked woman nurse a naked baby while sleet melted on her body, and a group of Yaghans who drew up to the outer glow of the explorers' fire sweated profusely. The Ona, foot Indians of the plains on the northern part of the island, wore guanaco skin robes and moccasins, and slept behind skin windbreaks in the snow. The Chukchi of Siberia, who wear Eskimo-style clothing, like to remove their shirts to cool off, and Bogoras saw Chukchi women thrust lumps of snow between their breasts for the same purpose.

The mechanism of heat loss in cold conditions will explain this. When the environmental temperature falls the body stops sweating at 83° F., and heat loss is accomplished wholly by radiation and convection. Venous blood, which has been returning from the back of the hand through superficial blood vessels on the arm, is rerouted; vasoconstriction shuts off this road, and vasodilation opens alternate channels through deep-lying veins which surround the artery. The chilled venous blood returning to the heart cools the arterial blood, so that it will have less heat to lose, and the heat gained by the venous blood is carried to the heart. Thus heat loss through the hand and arm is reduced to but 1.5 percent of the body's total at higher temperatures. The amount of blood that flows through 100 cc. of fingertip tissue falls from a maximum of 120 cc. to 0.2 cc. per minute. The arm itself becomes an insulator in depth.

At an air temperature of 73° F. a naked American with a rectal temperature of 97° will show the following skin temperatures: head, 94°; trunk, 93°; hands, 86°; feet, 77°. Deep thermocouple work has shown that the hands and wrists chill to the bone literally. However, when the temperature of the extremities falls below a point between 41° and 50° F., vasoconstriction ceases, and peripheral bloodflow is accelerated, to keep the extremities from freezing. What this means racially is that a person of north European ancestry can afford to have big bony hands which help keep him cool in hot weather, because at the winter temperatures at which he operates, particularly when clothed, the size of his hands makes no difference in heat economy; they are simply shut off from the heat system, like an empty room.

It is a matter of casual observance that most Mongoloids have small and delicate hands and feet, short distal segments of both upper and lower limbs, and short necks. However, recent studies of the Eskimo have shown that despite expectation these people have large hands. It is believed, although the material proving this has not yet been published, that racial differences in venous patterns exist, which would account for the Eskimo hand as well as for the ability of the Australian aborigine to sleep in the cold without clothing.

Turning to the Eskimo foot, which is small as expected, it is common knowledge that his excellent boot keeps this extremity warm, as long as it is dry. Water can leak in through the stitch holes if the sinew is not preswollen, and it can also come from sweat induced through exertion. A wet boot affords little insulation, and some Eskimos freeze their toes. Similarly the hand is here a liability; as Quartermaster Corps researchers have shown, it is almost impossible to keep a hand warm in the best of mittens when the body is at rest outdoors in very low temperatures. Eskimos bring their arms and hands in next to the body skin, leaving sleeves dangling, when they can.

Ears, nose tips, and other protrusions need special protection; with the fall of the glass the amount of blood sent to the ears increases greatly, and a relatively great loss occurs at this vulnerable point. Polar and subpolar people are invariably described, in the prime of the individual, as being well equipped with subcutaneous fat. This fat is especially well developed on critical spots, such as the cheek, wrist, and ankles. One centimeter of fat is given the same insulation rating as a complete suit of winter clothing. The healthy Negro living in a hot country carries almost no subcutanous fat. His superior performance in the desert, compared to Whites of the same age and weight, has been demonstrated.

In summary, adjustment to the cold requires large body mass, short extremities, much fat, deep vein routing, a high basal metabolism, or some combination of these five features. Adjustment to the heat requires small body mass, attenuated extremities, little fat, extensive superficial vein routing, a low basal metabolism, and a greater number of sweat glands per unit of surface area. Possibly the role of melanin in starting the skin to sweat at a lower threshold by conversion of UV to radiant heat may be added. Any combination of these seven may be involved. The type or types of physique most suited to cold resistance are exactly those which, the doctors tell us, are most likely to suffer from heart trouble, and so it is a lucky thing that adjustment to the cold does not place an extra load on the heart. Heat-adapted physiques are those best calculated to stand the extra heart load which they receive.

So far we have been thinking about heat loss from the skin, but calories also leave the body through the lungs. In hot weather the heat loss from the lungs through respiration is negligible and of little help to the suffering organism, but as the mercury drops this source of leakage becomes serious, reaching 50 kg. calories per 1,000 liters of expired air in extreme cold. Not only does this affect the total heat load of the body, but it subjects the nasal passages to heavy chilling. To what extent the Mongoloid face, inside and out, may compensate for this by its special architecture remains to be discovered.

One other climatic hazard which human beings have faced and overcome is that of reduced oxygen at high altitudes. Dill and his associates have found that the inhabitants of the Andes have become able to live and work at 17,500 feet and more, through the fact that their blood carries a much higher concentration of red corpuscles than of people at sea level. At the same time they need more air, which they obtain through more efficient automatic breathing control as well as the larger lungs. The requirements for physique in high altitude resemble those for cold. Perhaps it is no coincidence that the two great high-altitude plateaus of the world, the Andean and the Tibetan, are inhabited by Mongoloid peoples who greatly resemble each other.

This paper does not pretend to cover, even in outline, all the more obvious adaptive variations in man in the fields of color, size, and form. No attempt has been made to deal with the eye or the hair. Little attention has been paid to genetics, in the belief that before we can discover the biological techniques by which a set of variations is inherited we should first describe the variations themselves. Since blood groups are believed to be nonadaptive, they have been temporarily ignored.

Since I started this racial heresy in 1946, when I wrote the first draft of what was to be expanded into the book "Races," with the help of Garn and Birdsell, many others who possess special technical skills, and whose interests are focused in other than purely racial channels, have been working on important aspects of the problem. Garn is conducting experiments with metabolism and body heat at the Fels Institute, Yellow Springs. Ancel Keys and Josef Brožek, in Minneapolis, have independently studied the basic components of the human body, with special emphasis on its fat content. Russell Newman, Phillip Wedgewood, and Paul Baker have been devising techniques for the same purpose in Lawrence, Mass., and conducting interracial studies of physiological tolerance for the Armed Forces. Various other Army and Air Force scientists, and their Canadian colleagues, have been working on basic differences in anatomy and physiology between Eskimos, Indians, Whites, and Negroes.

Our subject is acquiring dignity, and results are being produced. We are now on the road to learning the basic facts about race in man, facts of which no one should be proud or ashamed. In an atom-age world in which men of all races are coming into increasing contact with one another on a basis of equality and cooperation, a knowledge of what a wonderfully adaptive thing the human body is, is a much healthier commodity than the recently traditional hide-race point of view.

17 Race and Evolution

Stanley M. Garn

MANY WHO HAVE NO DIFFICULTY IN ASSIMILATING THE CONCEPT OF EVOLU-
*tion with regard to the development of life and even of the emergence of
man among the primates compromise the fundamental postulate of evolution by limiting its action to the past. Typical is the view that man was
the last product of evolution—that evolution ceased once man, presumably
its goal, was achieved. It is quite easy to believe this. Not only does it
flatter ourselves, but we bolster it with strategic definitions and classifications. The interpretation of fossil hominids as rigid types existing only to
lead the way to man fits smugly into this view, and the idea of archetypal
races continues to reinforce it.*

*We have seen, however, that much evidence can be marshalled
against this static view (e.g., Nos. 11, 13, 15, 16). Here, by way of
summary, is a statement which, starting with a more fluid concept of
modern race, challenges some traditional assumptions about our fossil
ancestors.*

Introduction

Until rather recently race in man was held to be fixed, unchanging,
and static, stable over long periods of time, except in the event of "admixture." And in similar fashion the criteria of race, the natural characteristics that distinguish one race from another, were also considered as con-
stants, neither adaptive nor inadaptive, but adaptively netural.

Franz Boas opened a new chapter in physical anthropology by
demonstrating the plastic nature of those metric traits once extensively
used as taxonomic criteria. But to Boas, race itself was fixed, a race being
"a stable type reaching into deep antiquity."

SOURCE: *American Anthropologist*, Vol. 59 (1957), pp. 218–224. Reprinted with the
permission of the author and the publisher.
For biographical data on the author, see I:15.

Earnest Hooton did more than anyone else to spur popular interest in human evolution. Yet in the first edition of *Up from the Ape,* and for some years afterward, he insisted upon nonadaptive bodily characters as racial criteria.

It is not surprising, therefore, that the blood groups were first extolled as of particular taxonomic value on the basis of supposed adaptive neutrality. Blood groups were hereditary, free from environmental modification, and there was no reason to suppose that A had any advantage over B, or disadvantage compared to O. Seemingly, blood groups were the answer to the taxonomist's prayer.

Now the concept of static race and of stable racial criteria had, on the surface, much to recommend it. In particular, the reconstruction of racial history and the analysis of race-mixture appeared quite simple, if race itself did not change. To trace a race you merely had to find similar skeletons further back in time. And to compute racial admixture, simple mathematics answered how much p and how much q would—in genic matrimony—yield a given proportion of p and q (assuming no exceptions to the Hardy-Weinberg rule).

Yet the notion of stable races and of inadaptive racial criteria led to a logical impasse. If races do not change, how did races come to be? And if skin color, body proportions, hair form, or gene frequencies are not subject to natural selection, how is it that races now differ from each other, often to so great an extent? It is this logical impasse that led Hooton to change his opinions, as described in the revised edition of *Up from the Ape.*

There is no escape from this impasse, only a devious detour. All that could be done was to place the origin of the geographical races of man as far in the past, and in the most remote areas, as possible. Whites, Blacks, Yellows—all were derived from archeologically inaccessible sections of Asia. Some taxonomists hopefully looked to the Upper Cave at Choukoutien for early Mongoloids and nascent Melanesians, presumably strictly endogamous then. And Gates (following an extreme line of reasoning) assigned to the geographical races of man an antiquity older than mankind itself.

Today, as we investigate evolutionary mechanisms at first hand, as we demonstrate drift and compute rates of selection, we may wonder at the seeming reluctance to admit race as a part of human evolution. Retrospectively, it may seem strange that men who devoted their lives to human evolution at the species level should have balked at accepting evolution at the racial level. Here, perhaps, one may blame Darwin, the father of evolution, himself. For pre-Darwinian evolutionists, like Blumembach, Buffon, and Kant, readily accepted race as a product of local evolution, while Darwin (in his *Descent of Man*) toyed with the possibility that the differences between human races were due to evolution, and then recoiled from the obvious. Not until the evolutionary nature of race was firmly accepted by entomologists, mammologists, and herpetologists, did anthropologists regain the interest in the evolution of human races held by naturalists 250 years ago.

Evidence for Recent Evolution in Man

In truth, acceptable evidence for ongoing evolution in man was extraordinarily hard to come by. No trend comparable to the phenomenon of "industrial melanism" in butterflies could be demonstrated. And no human trait had proven adaptive value, comparable to coat color in geographical races of mice. Almost by default the evidence was against recent hominid evolution, and in consequence the notion of static race and neutral taxonomic traits seemed the wiser assumption to follow.

Many evolutionary "trends" have been suggested for recent man. But apparent trends, like agenesis of the third molar and changes in the digital formula, were obtained by sampling different populations and not by following one population through recent time. Nearest to a satisfactory trend is the undoubted shift toward round-headedness exhibited by contemporary populations. Now it is possible that brachycephaly has some adaptive value under modern conditions of life. Yet the trend toward round-headedness may simply reflect a growth response to more adequate nutrition: in this event brachycephalization cannot be termed an evolutionary trend at all.

Again, there is every reason to believe that many human differences have adaptive value in climatic extremes. Just as the reduced mass and increased peripheries of the desert fox, and the extra insulation of the arctic seal represent genetic adaptations to desert and freezing temperatures respectively, variations in the human surface-mass ratio follow expected climatic lines. The degree of melanin deposition in man also bears a statistical relationship to mean ultra-violet intensities. And desert men tend to small overall size, an expected finding since the smaller man has a better capacity to throw off heat. In short, a great many racial differences seem to relate to the geographical histories of the particular races in question.

But it is one thing to prove either logically or experimentally that a given trait may be beneficial, and another thing to demonstrate survival value. Given a sunlamp and a timer one can easily show that the Negro is slower to reach erythema and subsequent discomfort. Given a tank of cold water and a thermocouple it is no trick to show that Eskimo skin temperatures remain higher and that peripheral blood flow is twice that of whites. But to clinch the argument, selective survival must be demonstrated; the possessors must be differentially represented in the next generation. Such has not been demonstrated for any morphological trait useful in distinguishing one race-population from another.

The first break came in 1940 with the discovery of the "Rhesus factor"—the Rh series of alleles. Here for the first time one could demonstrate a common gene having adaptive value, and its relatively inadaptive alleles. For our purposes, the implications to neonatal mortality and the medical aspects of the problem are dwarfed by the simple realization that the present Rh gene frequencies need not have obtained in the past. There must have been a time when the Rh$^+$ and Rh$^-$ alleles for whites more nearly approached 50-50 than the present 85-15. And for some future time, unless replacement transfusions can brake this line of evolution, we might predict an American white population nearly homozygous for the more common (Rh positive) alleles.

More recently, evidence has accumulated that incompatibilities in the classical A-B-O system may also result in fetal deaths and neonatal loss. One can see, for the first time, possible advantages of population homozygosity as far as successful reproduction is concerned, even though heterozygosity may be desirable from the standpoint of species survival. The important conclusion is that the blood group genes, once extolled as particularly neutral, have proven to be far from neutral. And more important, blood group gene frequencies as we know them now may be purely temporary, no accurate indications of past conditions.

Counteracting or reinforcing these selective trends may be the relationships between the A-O-B blood groups and some common organic diseases. Though O is differently favored at or before birth, the apparent linkage between O and ulcers suggests that O may be relatively inadaptive later in life. On the other hand the dominant alleles, represented by the genes p and q, seem to be associated with other noninfectious disorders such as gastric carcinoma. Taken as a whole, we can visualize one human population moving rapidly toward an excess of O, and another building up in the B factor year after year. Maternal-fetal incompatibilities plus differential adult survival could well yield the kind of differences in blood group frequencies we know for the races of man today. The net results of such trends may be (like drift) trivial as far as species evolution is concerned. But racial differences are trivial in comparison to species differences, and it is the phenomenon of race we are considering here.

The most dramatic example to date is that of Thallasemia major, the so-called Mediterranean anemia. Here, though the gene is strikingly disadvantageous in the homozygous state, gene loss is more than balanced by relative resistance to malaria exhibited by the heterozygote. As a result, people in malaria zones differ remarkably from their less steamy neighbors in the frequency of this gene. Here is an example of local evolution, proceeding at a very rapid pace. And here, evolution is not unrelated to temperature changes and to the mean annual rainfall. Drop the annual temperature but a few degrees, reduce the rainfall a few inches (or use DDT) and the recessive carrier ceases to be at an advantage. Conversely, there must have been periods in the past when the gene for Thallasemia was more widely distributed in Mediterranean countries than it is now. And the related sickling gene may have been more extensively distributed in Africa during periods of heavier rainfall.

Let it not be assumed that blood-group genes or genes affecting the blood alone have adaptive value in man. Our present sampling of knowledge is an accidental by-product of widespread blood-typing, and of the ease with which some haematological studies can be made. It is quite likely that all of the traits in which peoples differ have adaptive value. It is likely that the recessive carrier of Morquio's syndrome, the genetic diabetic, and the hypertensive and the coronary-prone individual all possess certain unique advantages over their fellows. Were skin color, hair form, and bone lengths regularly recorded in relation to the more common diseases (as is cholesterol level today), the probabilities are great that they too would cease to be considered neutral in regard to human welfare.

There is now excellent evidence that under our noses (and often without outward signs) races have been changing. Evolution has been taking place, often to an appreciable degree, since the *Origin of Species* first appeared on British bookstands. Genes and traits that once seemed as neutral as a Swiss diplomat, may now be listed among those having proven adaptive value. In short, we must now acknowledge the fact that races do change, and that the criteria that (temporarily) distinguish one race from another, are only temporarily suited to that purpose. These two conclusions, now demonstrated in fact as well as in theory, have tremendous bearing on our studies of man.

Race and Evolution

With what we know now, two conclusions are quite inescapable. First, human races—like higher taxonomic units—are subject to evolutionary change. Second, the particular traits by which races distinguish themselves are subject to natural selection, and therefore do not have eternal taxonomic value. In retrospect, all of the characters used in constructing a classification of man must have been grist in the evolutionary mill.

Now we cannot have change and no change simultaneously. Present frequencies of blood groups or of morphological traits are, at best, interim reports of present conditions. They need not be identical to frequencies in the recent or remote past, and they need not predict gene or trait frequencies in the future. Traits now common may once have been rare, and vice versa. Only a rash worker would care to estimate how common the sickling trait was a few hundred years ago. It would be equally rash to estimate the incidence of shovel-shaped incisors, transitional vertebrae, or suture-bones in the days of the Caesars.

As a consequence, the search for ancestors becomes far more difficult than it once seemed. It is not necessary to assume that ancestral Amerindians were derived from a B-free population (with the implied late appearance of B); they may have lost it in transit. But it is equally likely that B had adaptive value in Asia, but none in America. By the same token, the absence of a sickling-trait among the Veddoids does not prove that there existed no ancient linkage with Africa. As soon as we accept changes in gene frequencies, we can no longer employ present frequencies as certain indications of past events.

While this obvious corollary admittedly pulls the rug from beneath our more cherished reconstructions, evidence for changing race may free us from the burden of prefabricated and hypothetical ancestors. If blondism is adaptive in a particular climatological zone, all-blond *echt*-Nordics need not be invoked to explain blondism in the Baltic. And if Rh-(cde) is adaptive in certain times and places, then the Basques may have attained their serological uniqueness with no help from (still) hypothetical "Early Europeans." Not too long ago local and geographical differences among American Indian populations were explained by a bewildering number of unverifiable migrations. Admitting the possibility of local evolution in the Americas has cleared the air, though demanding a new set of proofs instead.

In the past "intermediate" populations have been attributed, almost exclusively, to hybridization. Without denying this oldest human accomplishment, contemporary evolutionary genetics provides an alternative explanation. Suppose that melanism is adaptive in the tropics, and blondism in the North. In between we would expect, as a result of competing rates of selection, intermediate coloration, a simple example of balanced polymorphism. Then, there are numerous populations whose intermediate status has given them the rank of triple or even quadruple-hybrids. In some cases the explanation of multiple origins can be justified on the basis of historical and archeological evidence. But even where such documentation is complete, balanced polymorphism may be responsible for the continuance of the various parental genes. And in other cases, the triple-hybrids may not be "hybrids" at all.

The fact that a race can change markedly in the course of a few score generations complicates our search for ancestors, especially those more remote. If we cannot be sure that contemporary Ainu, to take an extreme example, really resemble their pre-Neolithic ancestors, how about long-term reconstructions of our phyletic line? Need a trait in Chancelade be ancestral to a similar trait in the Greenland Eskimo? Need shoveling of the incisors in *Pithecanthropus* have any bearing on similar dental formations in contemporary Chinese? And further, admitting rapid change over the centuries, need all so-called "Neanderthals" be peas from the same genetic pod?

Contemporary evolutionary studies have opened wide Pandora's box. Yet the situation need not be disheartening to the adventurous student of man. While some genes may be subject to rapid selection, others may be very close to adaptive neutrality. It may be possible to prepare a list of almost-neutral genes, for the specific purpose of phyletic reconstruction. Yet there will always be doubts. We have no assurance that the neutral gene of today will not prove adaptive tomorrow. Reconstructions of racial history, or the history of our species, may always be marked by uncertainties which even the most complete skeletal record can never totally resolve.

At the same time, if we are confronted with change rather than static conditions, it is change that we must study, considering it a challenge to research rather than an obstacle to progress. There is a whole series of challenges, first documenting change (and this we have scarcely begun to do) and then explaining it (which may require a major excursion into medical genetics). The older, static, unchanging concept of race was essentially self-limiting. Once all the pigeon-holes were filled, there would have been nothing more to do. With changing race and adaptive traits, we have our job cut out for generations to come.

18 Race Differences: The Present Position of the Problem

Otto Klineberg

IN THE PREVIOUS SELECTIONS, RACE HAS BEEN TREATED PURELY FROM THE *point of view of physical anthropology. Race differences in that case referred to patterned variations in physical character as determined through controlled observation and measurement. In the following selection, however, race differences mean something else. It refers to variations in intelligence and personality, not between individuals but between large populations which are distinguished by separate and distinct heredity.*

Inclusion of this selection at this juncture can be defended on two primary grounds. First, the matter is vital to our own culture at this time; it cannot and should not be avoided. Second, certain aspects of a person's psychological constitution are as much part of the biological order as the fact that he sees or walks or uses his genital organs. The difficulty is that a considerable portion of the psychological constitution, particularly those

SOURCE: *International Social Science Bulletin*, Vol. 2, iv (1950), pp. 460–466. Reprinted by permission of the author and UNESCO, the publisher.

The author (b. 1898) is Professor of Psychology at the Sorbonne in Paris. Though his primary interests have been in studies of intelligence and social aspects of mental health, he has done ethnographic field work and maintains serious anthropological interests. Among his books are *Race Differences* (1935), *Social Psychology* (1948) and *Race and Psychology* (1951).

aspects which comprise the personality and dictate concrete acts of behavior, has only a partial and tenuous rooting in biology. These facts reflect culture, a discrete and nonbiological order of phenomena (see Nos. I:3 and II:2–4. The most obvious differences between peoples: differences of language and accent, differences in musicality and sense of rhythm, differences in ideas of personal cleanliness and god, etc., have no fundamental relation to physical type. But what of other kinds of difference that are often alleged to distinguish the races? What, for example, of intelligence and learning ability, so important in contemporary racist controversy? This is a question for psychologists, not physical anthropologists. The findings of several decades of controlled testing and analysis were instrumental in bringing the United States Supreme Court to its historical opinion on desegregating the schools. No scientist has contributed more to our understanding in this matter than the author of the following selection.

The Unesco 'Statement on Race' adopts a clear and unequivocal position regarding the measurement of psychological differences between racial groups.

It states:

It is now generally recognised that intelligence tests do not in themselves enable us to differentiate safely between what is due to innate capacity and what is the result of environmental influences, training and education. Wherever it has been possible to make allowances for differences in environmental opportunities, the tests have shown essential similarity in mental characters among all human groups.

This statement was prepared and approved by a group of scholars who had long been associated with research and writing in this field, and who undoubtedly had an adequate background of information to justify their conclusions. They could not, however, within the obvious space limitations of such a statement, give more than a glimpse into that background. The purpose of the present article is to supply some of the facts which justify the position taken, and to indicate some of the recent developments which have strengthened the conviction that this is the only position which is scientifically tenable.

Before entering into details concerning the relevant research, it may be worth while to note the striking change which has occurred in the thinking of many scientists who have concerned themselves with this problem. The reasons vary, but the fact is significant. To take one example, Howard W. Odum, Professor of Sociology at the University of North Carolina, published in 1910 a volume on *Social and Mental Traits of the Negro,* in which he expressed the definite conviction that Negroes were inherently inferior to whites, and that they should be given the kind of education which was adapted to their poorer mental equipment. In 1936, Odum wrote an article on 'The Errors of Sociology,' published in Volume XV of the journal of *Social Forces*. Among these errors Odum lists 'the assumption that races are inherently different rather than group products of differentials due to the cumulative power of folk-regional and cultural environment'.

In 1923 the late C. C. Brigham, Professor of Psychology at Princeton University, published *A Study of American Intelligence*, in which he reported his analysis of the results obtained through the application of intelligence tests to more than a million recruits in the American army in the first world war. Since these recruits included many immigrants and sons of immigrants, as well as Negroes, Brigham compared the results obtained by various ethnic groups and found that whites were on the average superior to Negroes; among the whites, North Europeans (Nordics) were superior to Central Europeans (Alpines) who in turn were superior to South Europeans (Mediterraneans). The assumption was made that the tests measured differences in native intelligence. This study of Brigham's was widely read and frequently quoted; the suggestion has been made that it was a factor in determining the immigration policy of the United States.

Brigham himself changed his mind only a few years later about the meaning and significance of his analysis. As the result of a statistical study of the relationship between the various parts of the intelligence tests applied, he concluded that the method used was not scientifically sound. In an article on 'Intelligence Tests of Immigrant Groups', published in the *Psychological Review* in 1930, he wrote: 'As this method was used by the writer in his earlier analysis of the Army tests as applied to samples of the foreign-born in the draft, that study with its entire superstructure of racial differences collapses completely.' Brigham points out also that language difficulties may also have played a part, since many of the groups tested were bilingual, or spoke their own native language much better than they did English.

After a careful survey of all the factors involved, Brigham concluded that 'comparative studies of various national and racial groups may not be made with existing tests' and that 'one of the most pretentious of these comparative racial studies—the writer's own—was without foundation'.

One final example of the change in point of view may be of interest. Florence L. Goodenough, Professor of Psychology at the University of Minnesota, published an article in 1926 in the *Journal of Experimental Psychology* on 'Racial Differences in the Intelligence of School Children'. She used her own 'Draw-a-Man' test, in which achievement is measured in the terms of how accurately a man is drawn, with regard to the aesthetic qualities of the drawing. Since the test makes no use of language or "information', she believed it could be regarded as a test of native intelligence, independent of culture or previous experience. She reported that her groups differed in economic background, but she regarded this as irrelevant to her results. She wrote: 'It seems probable, upon the whole, that inferior environment is an effect at least as much as it is a cause of inferior ability . . . The person of low intelligence tends to gravitate to those neighbourhoods where economic requirement is minimal . . . His children inherit his mental characteristics.' In other words her conclusion was that there are racial differences in native ability, and that the results of the application of an intelligence test reveal the existence of such differences.

Very recently (September 1950) Professor Goodenough, writing with Dale B. Harris on 'Studies in the Psychology of Children's Drawings' in the *Psychological Bulletin*, reviews many of the investigations made with the 'Draw-a-Man' test, and concludes that there is definite indication of the influence of culture and previous training on the results obtained. The test is not so 'culture-free' as was formerly believed. Goodenough and Harris state in this article that they 'would like to express the opinion that the search for a culture-free test, whether of intelligence, artistic ability, personal-social characteristics, or any other measurable trait is illusory, and that the naive assumption that the mere freedom from verbal requirements renders a test equally suitable for all groups is no longer tenable'. In a footnote Goodenough states that her earlier study reporting differences among the children of immigrants to the United States 'is certainly no exception to the rule. The writer herby apologizes for it!'

These honest and courageous admissions on the part of three distinguished scholars are mentioned here because they represent in clearest form the development which has taken place in this whole field of inquiry. When the tests were applied to representatives of different ethnic groups, it was usually in the belief that the method was capable of measuring native ability, and that the results could be so interpreted. Voices of caution and criticism were raised from the beginning, and, among psychologists at least, they were in the minority. The history of the mental testing of ethnic or racial groups may almost be described as a progressive disillusionment with tests as measures of native ability, and a gradually increasing realization of many complex environmental factors which enter into the result.

Such factors have been described in several previous publications, and they will merely be listed at this point. They include previous schooling; socio-economic level; degree of familiarity with the language used; experience with the kind of problems which enter into the tests; experience with tests in general; motivation, or desire to do well; rapport with the investigator; speed or tempo of activity; physical well-being; etc. Some of these factors affect one group, others another; taken together, they indicate how impossible it is to speak of a culture-free test.

One approach which was designed to avoid the above difficulties is represented by the study of very young children, presumably before they have been subjected to any influences from the social environment. This was attempted by Myrtle B. McGraw in 1931, in 'A Comparative Study of a Group of Southern White and Negro Infants', published in *Genetic Psychology Monographs*. She studies white and Negro infants in the first year of life, administering to them the 'Baby Tests', devised by Hetzer and Wolf under the direction of Charlotte Buehler at Vienna. The results showed the white babies to be on the average definitely superior to the Negro. The author concludes: 'It is significant that with even the very young subjects, when environment factors are minimised, the same type and approximately the same degree of superiority is evidenced on the part of the White subjects as that found among older groups.'

The difficulty with this conclusion is that environmental factors, even at this early age, are by no means 'minimized'. The performance of an infant on the Baby Test is markedly influenced by general physical development, which in turn depends on adequate nourishment. In this respect the Negro children were definitely at a disadvantage. They came from homes that were economically inferior, and they were relatively deficient in weight. These facts are not irrelevant simply because the children are young; on the contrary, the linkage between physical and mental development should be at least as striking at the beginning of life as later.

This interpretation is supported by a more recent study of Negro and white babies at New Haven, Connecticut, by B. Pasamanick, under the direction of Professor Arnold Gesell of Yale University. The results are reported in an article 'A Comparative Study of the Behavioral Development of Negro Infants', published in the *Journal of Genetic Psychology* in 1946. In this study the Negro infants revealed a physical and psychological development equal to that of the whites; the tests used showed no significant differences between the two groups. The investigator points out that, as a result of careful dietary controls introduced during the war, the Negro mothers in this group received adequate nourishment, and in fact were not markedly different from the white mothers in this respect. The general economic level of the Negro group had also improved as a consequence of the opportunities opened up by defence industries. These Negro infants started out, physically, on equal terms with the whites. They also, in parallel fashion, showed no inferiority or retardation in psychological development. With the equating of environmental opportunities, the difference between the two groups disappeared.

This last statement is crucial to the whole problem, and is in need of considerable amplification. If it can be adequately demonstrated that the removal of environmental inequalities really brings with it the elimination of inferiorities in test performance, the issue will have been settled. It will no longer be possible to base the argument for inborn racial differences on the results of the intelligence tests. The situation of the American Negro and the American Indian furnishes the most critical and at the same time the most adequate data for evaluating the point of view which is here being developed.

The American Negro has been studied by means of various psychological tests in various parts of the United States. Some years ago, the writer (in *Characteristics of the American Negro* 1944) made a survey of all the available research data, and concluded that, on the average, American Negroes obtained an intelligence quotient of about 86, as compared with the norm of 100 for the general population. This points to a substantial inferiority on the part of the Negro. It was at the same time striking to note the tremendous range of scores obtained by the various groups of Negro children examined. One, a rural group in Tennessee, showed an average Intelligence Quotient of 58; at the other extreme, a group in Los Angeles, California, turned out to be superior to the average white population with a score of 105. This remarkable range is in keeping with our hypothesis of environmental determination. In rural Tennessee the Negroes came from an exceedingly inferior economic level of the population and attended inadequate, segregated schools. In California they suffered little discrimination, had improved their economic status and attended the same schools as did the white children.

A direct attack upon this problem was made by J. Peterson and L. H. Lanier, who in 1929 published their 'Studies in the Comparative Abilities of Whites and Negroes', in *Mental Measurement Monographs*. They suggested that 'a useful check on the reliability of a given race difference obtained in any locality and under any specific set of circumstances is to take what seem to be fairly representative samplings from widely different environments and to compare the various results as checks upon one another with a view to determining just which factors persistently yield differences in favour of one or the other race'. With this in mind they compared the Negro and white boys in three different cities, Nashville (in Tennessee), Chicago and New York. The results showed that in Nashville, which is in a southern state where Negroes do not have opportunities equal to those of whites, the white boys were markedly superior; in Chicago there was a slight difference in favour of the whites; in New York there were no significant differences between the two racial groups. These results are not difficult to understand if our hypothesis concerning the importance of environment factors is correct.

The authors, however, suggest another explanation of their findings. They believe that a process of 'selective migration' has occurred; that is to say, the most energetic and intelligent Negroes have left the south in order to find new homes and a better life in the north. That would mean that the northern Negroes did well on the tests not because they lived in a superior environment, but because they were innately superior to start with. Peterson and Lanier speak of New York as showing 'a selectiveness of the best genes in the negroes' as a consequence of this type of migration.

Since no conclusive evidence was presented in favour of this hypothesis of selective migration, the present writer became convinced a number of years ago that a more direct attack upon the problem was required. The results of his investigations, carried out with the co-operation of a number of advanced students at Columbia University, are presented in detail in *Negro Intelligence and Selective Migration*, published in 1935. The two principal methods were used. The first was to see whether there was any indication that those Negroes who migrated were in any way superior to those who remained in their own native localities. A careful search through the school records in several southern cities, and a detailed statistical comparison of the school marks obtained by the migrants and the non-migrants respectively, showed no significant differences between the two groups. In other words, there was no evidence to indicate that those who migrated were 'selected' for their superior ability.

The second approach attempted to study more directly the effect of a superior environment (in this case of New York City) on the test scores of Negro children who had come to New York from the south. If the environment exerts an influence, this should reveal itself in an improvement in test scores at least roughly proportionate to the length of time these children had lived in New York. This is precisely what the results showed. A number of different tests were applied to groups of Negro boys and girls, and in general it was found that there was a close (though by no means perfect) correspondence between test scores and length of residence in New York. Those who had lived there the longest obtained on the average the best scores; those who had recently arrived from the south, the poorest. The conclusion appears clear and unequivocal. It is verified by similar studies in the case of Washington and Philadelphia (the latter study is as yet unpublished). The hypothesis is justified that, as the environmental discrepancies are reduced, the differences in test results are reduced correspondingly. There is nothing to support the contention that an alternative hypothesis, like that of selective migration, is equally capable of explaining these findings.

In the case of American Indians, the relevant material is somewhat different. In general, the test scores obtained by American Indians are inferior to those of Negroes. On the average, Indian intelligence quotient is in the neighbourhood of 81. This result is not difficult to explain or understand. Not only do most American Indians occupy an inferior economic position in comparison to the rest of the population, in addition, their whole background and culture are so different from that of white Americans, that it can hardly be expected that they should do equally well on tests that have been standardized on the latter group. Their relative unfamiliarity with English constitutes still another handicap; it has been demonstrated, for example, that Indian children do much better on performance tests (in which no language ability is required) than on the usual variety of linguisitic tests.

On the more positive side, the late professor T. R. Garth of the University of Denver, attempted to discover what would happen if American Indian children were placed in a superior environment. In 1935 he published in the *Psychological Bulletin* a note on the foster Indian child in the white home. He reported that a group of such foster children obtained an average intelligence quotient of 102, which is certainly a remarkable improvement over the general Indian score of 81. This result would be conclusive evidence of the effect of the environment on group differences, if it were not for the possibility that those Indian children who were living in white homes were exceptional. It may be that when white families take Indian children into their homes, they choose those who have superior intelligence. This is the hypothesis of 'selection' in a different context and in another form. Professor Garth attempted to answer this criticism by testing also brothers and sister of these foster children; these brothers and sisters had not been taken into white homes, and were still living on the 'reservation'. They obtained an average intelligence quotient of only 87.5. This suggests that the superiority of the foster children is in fact due to their more favourable environment opportunities, but the proof is not complete.

There is, however, one other line of evidence which appears to be completely convincing. It is represented by the study made by Professor J. H. Rohrer of the University of Oklahoma, 'The Test Intelligence of Osage Indians', published in the *Journal of Social Psychology* in 1942. The Osage Indian children live under social and economic conditions which are quite comparable to those of the white children with whom they were compared. This is largely due to the fortunate accident that on the land which was ceded to them by the American government as a reservation, oil was later discovered. As a consequence these Indians became relatively well-to-do, and were able to create for themselves and their families living conditions far superior to those of other American Indian communities. With this fact in mind, it is illuminating to look at the results obtained by Rohrer. On one test, the Goodenough 'Draw-a-Man', which was a non-language test, the white children obtained an average intelligence quotient of 103, and the Indian children 104. On a second test, which uses language, the white score was 98, the Indian 100 (These differences are so small as to be insignificant.) There can be no doubt in this case that when American Indian children have environmental opportunities comparable to those of whites, their apparent inferiority disappears completely.

Nor can this result be explained by selection. It was *after* they had been given their land that oil was discovered, they did not seek out this particular region, they exercised no real choice in the matter. They were lucky; and their good luck gave them opportunities denied to others. This is reflected not only in their economic success, but also in their success in solving the problems presented by the intelligence tests. The conclusion is inescapable that, given equal opportunities, the American Indian children perform as well as any others.

That is where the matter rests now. The net result of all the research that has been conducted in this field is that there is no scientific proof of innate racial differences in intelligence; that the obtained differences in test results are best explained in terms of factors in the social and educational environment; that as the environmental opportunities of different racial or ethnic groups become more similar, the observed differences in test results also tend to disappear.

Other approaches to the problem of psychological race differences have yielded similar conclusions. When tests of temperament or personality are used, the same considerations apply; groups differ, of course, but evidently as the result of the cultural and social influences which have played a part, and not as the result of race or biology. The argument from the cultural contributions of a particular ethnic group to the inborn racial characteristics of that group falls down for many reasons: cultures may vary while race remains unchanged, the same culture may be found in groups of different race, what looks like a superior cultural contribution from one point of view may seem much less significant when another criterion is applied, etc. Studies of race mixture are similarly inconclusive, since individuals of mixed racial heredity cannot be from those of 'pure' race. Finally, there is no evidence that some racial groups are biologically more 'primitive' or undeveloped than others.

This does not mean that heredity plays no part in the determination of behaviour. On the contrary, there is good evidence that 'individuals' and 'families' may be distinguished from others in terms of heredity as well as acquired characteristics. As regards large racial groups, however, there appears to be about the same range of hereditary capacities in one group as in another. The fact that differences in behaviour between such groups obviously exist, is no proof that they exist because they are inborn.

There is ample reason, therefore, in the light of the accumulated scientific knowledge accepted by the overwhelming majority of social and biological scientists, to concur in the conclusions of the Unesco 'Statement on Race':

According to present knowledge, there is no proof that the groups of mankind differ in their innate mental characteristics, whether in respect of intelligence or temperament. The scientific evidence indicates that the range of mental capacities in all ethnic groups is much the same.

19 Revised Version
of the UNESCO
Statement on Race

Harry L. Shapiro

AGREEMENT AMONG A GROUP OF SCHOLARS AND SCIENTISTS ON ANY SUBJECT *of ongoing research is difficult to achieve. All the more significant then is the UNESCO Statement on Race which was prepared through the concerted action of twelve distinguished scientists from six different countries.* Published in the United States in the American Journal of Physical Anthropology, *it represented the consensus of informed opinion on race in 1951. In 1966 a supplement was approved by an equally distinguished committee of twenty-two scientists, and this supplement, here attached to the 1951 statement, is the only addition or change made in the treatment of race in this revision of the* Readings.

Under the date of July 18, 1950, the United Nations Educational, Scientific and Cultural Organization issued a formal statement designed to represent an authoritative and scientific declaration on race. At a conference held in Unesco House, Paris, in December, 1949, the content of the document had been discussed and agreed upon by a panel consisting of the following distinguished scholars:

Professor Ernest Beaglehole, New Zealand
Professor Juan Comas, Mexico

SOURCE: *American Journal of Physical Anthropology*, Vol. 10 (1952), pp. 363–368. Reprinted with the permission of the author and the publisher.
  The author (b. 1902) is Curator of Anthropology at the American Museum of Natural History and Adjunct Professor of Anthropology at Columbia University. With interests ranging from human evolution to Polynesian ethnography, Professor Shapiro is noted as an authority on racial blending, which he has studied in Pitcairn Island, Hawaii and elsewhere. Among his books are *Heritage of the Bounty* (1936), *Migration and Environment* (1939) and *Aspects of Culture* (1956).

Professor L. A. Costa Pinto, Brazil
Professor Franklin Frazier, United States
Professor Morris Ginsberg, United Kingdom
Dr. Humayun Kabir, India
Professor Claude Levi-Strauss, France
Professor Ashley Montagu, United States (Rapporteur)

Its final form was prepared by Professor Ashley Montagu, who had the benefit of the advice of

Professor Hadley Cantril	Professor Otto Klineberg
Professor E. G. Conklin	Professor Wilbert Moore
Professor Gunnar Dahlberg	Professor H. J. Muller
Professor Theodosius Dobzhansky	Professor Gunnar Myrdal
Professor L. C. Dunn	Professor Joseph Needham
Professor Donald Hager	Professor Curt Stern
Professor Julian S. Huxley	

This statement on race was solicited by Unesco as part of its campaign to combat the evils of racism. This is a function which Unesco regards as one of its fundamental purposes. At its organization in 1945 it was specifically charged with this task, which was later reaffirmed by various resolutions adopted by the General Conference in 1948 and 1949. In the latter year the General Conference definitely committed Unesco "to study and collect scientific materials concerning questions of race," "to give wide diffusion to the scientific material collected," and "to prepare an educational campaign based on this material."

Since the concepts and notions about race that are current in the world are extraordinarily diverse and frequently ill-founded, Unesco was confronted with the necessity of securing a precise statement on the subject by specialists which would (1) represent the best scientific opinion and (2) set up a corpus of general agreement.

The publication of the Statement, which it was hoped would achieve these ends, met however with considerable criticism from professional students, particularly in England and France. There were at first no published comments on the part of American physical anthropologists. This apparent failure to react favorably or otherwise to the Statement may, I think, be attributed to its inadequate distribution among American specialists on race.

Since Unesco's purpose is to obtain, if possible, a declaration widely acceptable to recognized authorities and not to defend or support any particular document, Dr. Alfred Métraux, who is in charge of Unesco's activities in this matter, decided to call a second conference to reconsider the entire subject and attempt to frame another statement on race that might prove more acceptable without sacrificing the highest standards of scientific objectivity. Since one of the objections to the first statement was the relative paucity on the panel of specialists on the biological aspects of race, every effort was made to secure a representative roster. This, incidentally, did not prove as simple as might be supposed. The group which met for 5 days, June 4 to June 8, 1951, at Paris, included the following:

Physical anthropologists

Professor R. A. M. Bergman, Netherlands Anthropological Society, Amsterdam

Professor Ashley Montagu, Rutgers University, New Brunswick, New Jersey

Dr. Eugène Schreider, Laboratoire d'Anthropologie Physique, Institut de Paléontologie humaine, Paris

Dr. Harry L. Shapiro, Chairman, Department of Anthropology, American Museum of Natural History, New York

Dr. J. C. Trevor, University Lecturer in Anthropology, Faculty of Archaeology and Anthropology, Cambridge (U.K.)

Dr. Henri V. Vallois, Professor au Museum d'Histoire naturelle, Directeur du Musée de l'Homme, Paris

Professor S. Zuckerman, Department of Anatomy, Medical School, University of Birmingham

Geneticists

Professor Gunnar Dahlberg, Director, State Institute for Human Genetics and Race Biology, University of Uppsala, Sweden

Professor L. C. Dunn, Department of Zoology, Columbia University, New York

Professor J. B. S. Haldane, Department of Biometry, University College, London

Professor Hans Nachtsheim, Institut für Genetik, Freie Universität, Berlin

Serological anthropologist

Dr. A. E. Mourant, Director, Blood Group Reference Laboratory, Lister Institute, London

Professor Henri Vallois was elected chairman and Professor Leslie C. Dunn rapporteur. The discussions were carried on in French and English, with the translations expertly managed by experienced Unesco linguists.

As a participant I can vouch for the painstaking and detailed effort that went into the work of the conference. The statement as it took shape does not, of course, represent fully the ideas nor the characteristic language of any one of us. In the very nature of the circumstances it could only form a kind of core of common agreement expressed in carefully considered terms. The fact that the individuals in a group as large as this, representing so many different points of view, did not in the end balance each other off, speaks strongly for the positive conclusions upon which they could agree. This must be kept in mind in reading the statement finally adopted. . . .

The statement adopted at Paris, June, 1951, was subsequently critically reviewed by Professor Julian Huxley and Professor Theodosius Dobzhansky and revised by subsequent consultation with various members of the panel, and in the light of suggestions from other anthropologists and geneticists. All changes were approved by the members of the panel. Professor Leslie C. Dunn as rapporteur had the difficult task of preparing the statement which is given below. This final version was approved by the panel as of May 26, 1952.

STATEMENT ON RACE, 1951

1. Scientists are generally agreed that all men living today belong to a single species, *Homo sapiens,* and are derived from a common stock, even though there is some dispute as to when and how different human groups diverged from this common stock.

The concept of race is unanimously regarded by anthropologists as a classificatory device providing a zoological frame within which the various groups of mankind may be arranged and by means of which studies of evolutionary processes can be facilitated. In its anthropological sense, the word "race" should be reserved for groups of mankind possessing well-developed and primarily heritable physical differences from other groups. Many populations can be so classified but, because of the complexity of human history, there are also many populations which cannot easily be fitted into a racial classification.

2. Some of the physical differences between human groups are due to differences in hereditary constitution and some to differences in the environments in which they have been brought up. In most cases, both influences have been at work. The science of genetics suggests that the hereditary differences among populations of a single species are the results of the action of two sets of processes. On the one hand, the genetic composition of isolated populations is constantly but gradually being altered by natural selection and by occasional changes (mutations) in the material particles (genes) which control heredity. Populations are also affected by fortuitous changes in gene frequency and by marriage customs. On the other hand, crossing is constantly breaking down the differentiations so set up. The new mixed populations, in so far as they, in turn, become isolated, are subject to the same processes, and these may lead to further changes. Existing races are merely the result, considered at a particular moment in time, of the total effect of such processes on the human species. The hereditary characters to be used in the classification of human groups, the limits of their variation within these groups, and thus the extent of the classificatory sub-divisions adopted may legitimately differ according to the scientific purpose in view.

3. National, religious, geographical, linguistic and cultural groups do not necessarily coincide with racial groups; and the cultural traits of such groups have no demonstrated connection with racial traits. Americans are not a race, nor are Frenchmen, nor Germans; nor *ipso facto* is any other national group.

Muslims and Jews are no more races than are Roman Catholics and Protestants; nor are people who live in Iceland or Britain or India, or who speak English or any other language, or who are culturally Turkish or Chinese and the like, thereby describable as races. The use of the term "race" in speaking of such groups may be a serious error, but it is one which is habitually committed.

4. Human races can be, and have been classified in different ways by different anthropologists. Most of them agree in classifying the greater part of existing mankind into at least three large units, which may be called major groups (in French *grand'races*, in German *Hauptrassen*). Such a classification does not depend on any single physical character, nor does, for example, skin color by itself necessarily distinguish one major group from another. Furthermore, so far as it has been possible to analyze them, the differences in physical structure which distinguish one major group from another give no support to popular notions of any general "superiority" or "inferiority" which are sometimes implied in referring to these groups.

Broadly speaking, individuals belonging to different major groups of mankind are distinguishable by virtue of their physical characters, but individual members, or small groups, belonging to different races within the same major group are usually not so distinguishable. Even the major groups grade into each other, and the physical traits by which they and the races within them are characterized overlap considerably. With respect to most, if not all, measurable characters, the differences among individuals belonging to the same race are greater than the differences that occur between the observed averages for two or more races within the same major group.

5. Most anthropologists do not include mental characteristics in their classification of human races. Studies within a single race have shown that both innate capacity and environmental opportunity determine the results of tests of intelligence and temperament, though their relative importance is disputed.

When intelligence tests, even non-verbal, are made on a group of non-literate people, their scores are usually lower than those of more civilized people. It has been recorded that different groups of the same race occupying similarly high levels of civilization may yield considerable differences in intelligence tests. When, however, the two groups have been brought up from childhood in similar environments, the differences are usually very slight. Moreover, there is good evidence that, given similar opportunities, the average performance (that is to say, the performance of the individual who is representative because he is surpassed by as many as he surpasses), and the variation round it, do not differ appreciably from one race to another.

Even those psychologists who claim to have found the greatest differences in intelligence between groups of different racial origin, and have contended that they are hereditary, always report that some members of the group of inferior performance surpass not merely the lowest ranking member of the superior group, but also the average of its members. In any case, it has never been possible to separate members of two groups on the basis of mental capacity, as they can often be separated on a basis of religion, skin color, hair form or language. It is possible, though not proved, that some types of innate capacity for intellectual and emotional responses are commoner in one human group than in another, but it is certain that, within a single group, innate capacities vary as much as, if not more than, they do between different groups.

The study of the heredity of psychological characteristics is beset with difficulties. We know that certain mental diseases and defects are transmitted from one generation to the next, but we are less familiar with the part played by heredity in the mental life of normal individuals. The normal individual, irrespective of race, is essentially educable. It follows that his intellectual and moral life is largely conditioned by his training and by his physical and social environment.

It often happens that a national group may appear to be characterized by particular psychological attributes. The superficial view would be that this is due to race. Scientifically, however, we realize that any common psychological attribute is more likely to be due to a common historical and social background, and that such attributes may obscure the fact that, within different populations consisting of many human types, one will find approximately the same range of temperament and intelligence.

6. The scientific material available to us at present does not justify the conclusion that inherited genetic differences are a major factor in producing the differences between the cultures and cultural achievements of different people or groups. It does indicate, on the contrary, that a major factor in explaining such differences is the cultural experience which each group has undergone.

7. There is no evidence for the existence of so-called "pure" races. Skeletal remains provide the basis of our limited knowledge about earlier races. In regard to race mixture, the evidence points to the fact that human hybridization has been going on for an indefinite but considerable time. Indeed, one of the processes of race formation and race extinction or absorption is by means of hybridization between races. As there is no reliable evidence that disadvantageous effects are produced thereby, no biological justification exists for prohibiting intermarriage between persons of different races.

8. We now have to consider the bearing of these statements on the problem of human equality. We wish to emphasize that equality of opportunity and equality in law in no way depend, as ethical principles, upon the assertion that human beings are in fact equal in endowment.

9. We have thought it worth while to set out in a formal manner what is at present scientifically established concerning individual and group differences.

(a) In matters of race, the only characteristics which anthropologists have so far been able to use effectively as a basis for classification are physical (anatomical and physiological).

(b) Available scientific knowledge provides no basis for believing that the groups of mankind differ in their innate capacity for intellectual and emotional development.

(c) Some biological differences between human beings within a single race may be as great as or greater than the same biological differences between races.

(d) Vast social changes have occurred that have not been connected in any way with changes in racial type. Historical and sociological studies thus support the view that genetic differences are of little significance in determining the social and cultural differences between different groups of men.

(e) There is no evidence that race mixture produces disadvantageous results from a biological point of view. The social results of race mixture, whether for good or ill, can generally be traced to social factors.

1966 ADDITION: BIOLOGICAL ASPECTS OF RACE

The undersigned, assembled by Unesco in order to give their views on the biological aspects of the race question and in particular to formulate the biological part for a statement foreseen for 1966 and intended to bring up to date and to complete the declaration on the nature of race and racial differences signed in 1951, have unanimously agreed on the following:

1. All men living today belong to a single species, *Homo sapiens*, and are derived from a common stock. There are differences of opinion regarding how and when different human groups diverged from this common stock.

2. Biological differences between human beings are due to differences in hereditary constitution and to the influence of the environment on this genetic potential. In most cases, those differences are due to the interaction of these two sets of factors.

3. There is a great genetic diversity within all human populations. Pure races—in the sense of genetically homogeneous populations—do not exist in the human species.

4. There are obvious physical differences between populations living in different geographic areas of the world, in their average appearance. Many of these differences have a genetic component.

Most often the latter consist in differences in the frequency of the same hereditary characters.

5. Different classifications of mankind into major stocks, and of those into more restricted categories (races, which are groups of populations, or single populations) have been proposed on the basis of hereditary physical traits. Nearly all classifications recognize at least three major stocks.

Since the pattern of geographic variation of the characteristics used in racial classification is a complex one, and since this pattern does not present any major discontinuity, these classifications, whatever they are, cannot claim to classify mankind into clear-cut categories; moreover, on account of the complexities of human history, it is difficult to determine the place of certain groups within these racial classifications, in particular that of certain intermediate populations.

Many anthropologists, while stressing the importance of human variation, believe that the scientific interest of these classifications is limited, and even that they carry the risk of inviting abusive generalizations.

Differences between individuals within a race or within a population are often greater than the average differences between races or populations.

Some of the variable distinctive traits which are generally chosen as criteria to characterize a race are either independently inherited or show only varying degrees of association between them within each population.

Therefore, the combination of these traits in most individuals does not correspond to the typological racial characterization.

6. In man as well as in animals, the genetic composition of each population is subject to the modifying influence of diverse factors: natural selection, tending towards adaptation to the environment, fortuitous mutations which lead to modifications of the molecules of deoxyribonucleic acid which determine heredity, or random modifications in the frequency of qualitative hereditary characters, to an extent dependent on the patterns of mating and the size of populations.

Certain physical characters have a universal biological value for the survival of the human species, irrespective of the environment. The differences on which racial classifications are based do not affect these characters, and therefore, it is not possible from the biological point of view to speak in any way whatsoever of a general inferiority or superiority of this or that race.

7. Human evolution presents attributes of capital importance which are specific to the species.

The human species, which is now spread over the whole world, has a past rich in migrations, in territorial expansions and contractions.

For long millennia, progress made by man, in any field seems to have been increasingly, if not exclusively, based on culture and the transmission of cultural achievements and not on the transmission of genetic endowment. This implies a modification in the role of natural selection in man today.

On account of the mobility of human populations and of social factors, mating between members of different human groups which tend to mitigate the differentiations acquired, has played a much more important role in human history than in that of animals. The history of any human population or of any human race, is rich in instances of hybridization and those tend to become more and more numerous.

For man, the obstacles to inter-breeding are geographical as well as social and cultural.

8. At all times, the hereditary characteristics of the human populations are in dynamic equilibrium as a result of this inter-breeding and of the differentiation mechanisms which were mentioned before. As entities defined by sets of distinctive traits, human races are at any time in a process of emergence and dissolution.

Human races in general present a far less clear-cut characterization than many animal races and they cannot be compared at all to races of domestic animals, these being the result of heightened selection for special purposes.

9. It has never been proved that inter-breeding has biological disadvantages for mankind as a whole.

On the contrary, it contributes to the maintenance of biological ties between human groups and thus to the unity of the species in its diversity.

The biological consequences of a marriage depend only on the individual genetic make-up of the couple and not on their race.

Therefore, no biological justification exists for prohibiting intermarriage between persons of different races, or for advising against it on racial grounds.

10. Man since his origin has had at his disposal ever more efficient cultural means of non-genetic adaptation.

11. Those cultural factors which break social and geographic barriers, enlarge the size of the breeding populations and so act upon their genetic structure by diminishing the random fluctuations (genetic drift).

12. As a rule, the major stocks extend over vast territories encompassing many diverse populations which differ in language, economy, culture, etc.

There is no national, religious, geographic, linguistic or cultural group which constitutes a race ipso facto; the concept of race is purely biological.

However, human beings who speak the same language and share the same culture have a tendency to inter-marry, and often there is as a result a certain degree of coincidence between physical traits on the one hand, and linguistic and cultural traits on the other. But there is no known causal nexus between these and therefore it is not justifiable to attribute cultural characteristics to the influence of the genetic inheritance.

13. Most racial classifications of mankind do not include mental traits or attributes as a taxonomic criterion.

Heredity may have an influence in the variability shown by individuals within a given population in their responses to the psychological tests currently applied.

However, no difference has ever been detected convincingly in the hereditary endowments of human groups in regard to what is measured by these tests. On the other hand, ample evidence attests to the influence of physical, cultural and social environment on differences in response to these tests.

The study of this question is hampered by the very great difficulty of determining what part heredity plays in the average differences observed in so-called tests of overall intelligence between populations of different cultures.

The genetic capacity for intellectual development, like certain major anatomical traits peculiar to the species, is one of the biological traits essential for its survival in any natural or social environment.

The peoples of the world today appear to possess equal biological potentialities for attaining any civilizational level. Differences in the achievements of different peoples must be attributed solely to their cultural history.

Certain psychological traits are at times attributed to particular peoples. Whether or not such assertions are valid, we do not find any basis for ascribing such traits to hereditary factors, until proof to the contrary is given.

Neither in the field of hereditary potentialities concerning the over-all intelligence and the capacity for cultural development, nor in that of physical traits, is there any justification for the concept of "inferior" and "superior" races. The biological data given above are in open contradiction to the tenets of racism. Racist theories can in no way pretend to have any scientific foundation and the anthropologists should endeavour to prevent the results of their research from being used in such a biased way as to serve nonscientific ends.

PROF. NIGEL BARNICOT, Department of Anthropology, University College, London (U.K.)

PROF. JEAN BENOIST, Director, Dept. of Anthropology, U. of Montreal (Canada)

PROF. TADEUSZ BIELICKI, Institute of Anthro., Polish Academy of Sciences, Wroclaw (Poland)

DR. A. E. BOYO, Head, Federal Malaria Research Institute, Dept. of Pathology & Haematology, Lagos University, Medical School, Lagos (Nigeria)

PROF. YAKOV Y. ROGUINSKI, Head, Chair of Anthropology, Moscow University (USSR)

PROF. CARLETON S. COON, Curator, the University Museum, U. of Pa., Philadelphia, Pa. (USA)

PROF. GEORGHI F. DEBETZ (Chairman of the meeting), Institute of Ethnography, Academy of Sciences, Moscow (USSR)

MRS. ADELAIDE G. DE DIAZ UNGRIA, Curator, Museum of Natural Sciences, Caracas (Venezuela)

PROF. ROBERT GESSAIN, Director, Centre of Anthropological Research, Musee de l'Homme, Paris (France)

PROF. SANTIAGO GENOVES (Vice-Chairman of the meeting), Institute of Historical Research, Faculty of Science, University of Mexico (Mexico)

PROF. JEAN HIERNAUX (Scientific director of the meeting), Laboratory of Anthropology, Faculty of Sciences, University of Paris (France); Institute of Sociology, Free University of Brussels (Belgium)

DR. YAYA KANE (Vice-Chairman of the meeting), Senegal National Centre of Blood Transfusion, Dakar (Senegal)

PROF. RAMAKRISHNA MUKHERJEEE (Vice-Chairman of the meeting), Research Professor of Sociology, Indian Statistical Institute, Calcutta (India)

PROF. BERNARD RENSCH, Zoological Institute, Westfalische Wilhelms-Universitat, Munster (Federal Republic of Germany)

PROF. YAKOV Y. ROGUINSKI, Head, Chair of Anthropology, Moscow University (USSR)

PROF. FRANCISCO M. SALZANO, Institute of Natural Sciences, Porto Alegre, Rio Grande do Sul (Brazil)

PROF. ALF SOMMERFELT (Vice-Chairman of the meeting), Honorary Pro-Rector, Oslo U. (Norway)

PROF. JAMES N. SPUHLER (Vice-Chairman of the meeting), Department of Anthropology, University of Michigan, Ann Arbor, Michigan (USA)

PROF. HISASHI SUZUKU, Dept. of Anthropology, Faculty of Science, University of Tokyo (Japan)

PROF. J. A. VALSIK, Department of Anthropology & Genetics, J. A. Komensky University, Bratislava (Czechoslovakia)

DR. JOSEPH S. WEINER, London School of Hygiene & Tropical Medicine, University of London (U.K.)

DR. VSEVOLOD P. YAKIMOV, Director, Institute of Anthropology, Moscow Unisity (USSR)

OTHER ASPECTS OF PHYSICAL ANTHROPOLOGY

20 Field Studies of Old World Monkeys and Apes

Sherwood L. Washburn, Phyllis C. Jay and Jane B. Lancaster

FOR ALL OF THE INTEREST IN MONKEYS AND APES, IT IS SURPRISING HOW *little was known in a scientific way about these animals until very recently. In the past decade this has been sharply reversed, and the most notable extension of knowledge has been in the most difficult area of all —the natural habitats of the species in question.*

Increase in data and analyses relating to nonhuman primate individual and social behavior has led some scientists to question some of the uses to which this primate material is being put in the explication of the evolution of human culture and society. Nonetheless, primate studies have excited

SOURCE: *Science*, Vol. 150, 3703 (December 17, 1965), pp. 1541–1547. Copyright 1965 by the American Association for the Advancement of Science. Reprinted with the permission of the authors and publisher.

Sherwood L. Washburn (b. 1911) is Professor of Anthropology at the University of California. Specializing in primatology and experimental physical anthropology, he is editor of the *American Journal of Physical Anthropology*.

Phyllis C. Jay (b. 1933) is now Assistant Professor of Anthropology, University of California at Berkeley, and has conducted studies of Indian langurs.

Jane B. Lancaster (b. 1935) whose major research interest is primate social behavior, has recently published a study of the annual reproductive cycle of monkeys and apes.

great interest and have changed some, perhaps many, of our concepts of that evolution. A recent summary of the field, prepared by scientists who have been active in its development, follows. It is interesting to compare this selection with an earlier article by Marshall Sahlins (No. II:16).

For many years there has been interest in the evolutionary roots of human behavior, and discussions of human evolution frequently include theories on the origin of human customs. In view of the old and widespread interest in the behavior of our nearest relatives, it is surprising how little systematic information was collected until very recently. At the time (1929) Yerkes and Yerkes collected data for their book on the great apes, no one had devoted even one continuous month to the systematic study of the behavior of an undisturbed, free-ranging nonhuman primate. Apparently scientists believed that the behavior of monkeys and apes was so stereotyped and simple that travelers' tales or the casual observations of hunters formed a reliable basis for scientific conclusions and social theorizing. As a part of the program of the Yale Laboratories of Comparative Psychology, Yerkes encouraged a series of field studies of the chimpanzee, the mountain gorilla, and the howling monkey. These first studies proved so difficult that Yerkes could write, in the introduction to Carpenter's study, "His is the first reasonably reliable working analysis of the constitution of social groups in the infrahuman primates, and of the relations between the sexes and between mature and immature individuals for monkey or ape." Zuckerman, quite independently, had realized the importance of field observations and had combined some field work with physiology and the older literature to produce two very influential volumes. From this beginning, only Carpenter continued to make field studies of behavior, and his study of the gibbon is the first successful study of the naturalistic behavior of a member of the family Pongidae. Hooton summarized what was then known about the primates, particularly stressing the importance of behavior and the work of Carpenter and Zuckerman.

The war stopped field work, and no major studies were undertaken for some 15 years. Then, in the 1950's, investigators in Japan, England, France, Switzerland, and the United States independently started studies on the behavior of a wide variety of free-ranging primates. For the history of science it would be interesting to examine the reasons for this burst of parallel activity. Field studies were undertaken at more or less the same time, and publications start in the late 1950's and accelerate rapidly in the 1960's. This trend is still continuing and is well shown by the pattern of frequency of citations in a recent review by Hall. The review cites the papers of Bingham, Carpenter, Köhler, Nissen, Yerkes, and Zuckerman, but there are no references to additional field studies in the period 1941–1951, and most of the references are to papers appearing in 1960 or later.

The increased interest in primates, and particularly in the behavior of free-ranging primates, has given rise to several symposiums, and results of the new studies have been published almost as soon as they have been completed. Data from the recent field studies are included in volumes edited by Buettner-Janusch, Washburn, Napier and Barnicot, and, especially, DeVore. The volume edited by DeVore is devoted entirely to recent field studies and their evaluation. It includes accounts of the behavior of five kinds of monkeys, of chimpanzees, and of gorillas. Each chapter is by the person who did the field work, and in addition there are eight general chapters. Two new journals also are devoted to primates. *Primates*, published by the Japan Monkey Centre, is now in its 5th year, and *Folia Primatologica* has completed volume 3. Carpenter's field studies and general papers have been reprinted so that they are now easily available. Southwick has published a collection of readings in primate social behavior, and Eimerl and DeVore contributed a volume on the primates to the Life Nature Library. Field studies have recently been reviewed by Jay, and proceedings of a symposium organized and edited by Altmann should appear shortly. This abundance of published material makes it hard to believe that only 2 years ago a course on primate social behavior was difficult to teach because of the lack of easily available, suitable reading material.

Obviously, with so much new data a complete review is impossible. Here we wish to direct attention to the nature of the recent field studies and to a few of their major contributions. Perhaps their greatest contribution is a demonstration that close, accurate observation for hundreds of hours is possible. Prior to Schaller's field work, reported in 1963, it was by no means clear that this kind of observation of gorillas would be possible; previous investigators had conducted very fragmentary observations, and Emlen and Schaller deserve great credit for the planning and execution of their study. A field study of the chimpanzee that seemed adequate in the 1930's now seems totally inadequate, when compared to Goodall's results. Today a field study is planned to yield something of the order of 1000 hours of observations, and the observer is expected to be close to the animals and to recognize individuals. A few years ago observations of this length and quality were thought unnecessary, if not impossible.

The importance of studies in which groups are visited repeatedly and animals are recognized individually may be illustrated by the problems they make it possible to study. For example, during one season of the year chimpanzees "fish" for termites by breaking off sticks or stiff grasses and sticking the prepared implement into a termite hole, and this whole complex of nest examination, tool preparation, and fishing is learned by the young chimpanzee. It can be seen at only one time of the year and can be appreciated only by an observer whose presence no longer disturbs the animals. Habituation to the observer is a slow and difficult process. Goodall reports that after 8 months of observations she could approach to no closer than 50 meters of the chimpanzees and then only when they were in thick cover or up a tree; by 14 months she was able to get within 10 to 15 meters of them. The problem of tool use in nonhuman primates has been reviewed by Hall, but the essential point here is that the amount of throwing and object manipulation in the monkeys (Cercopithecidae) was greatly exaggerated in travelers' tales, which were uncritically accepted, and it took years of observation in a favorable locality to reveal the complexity of this kind of behavior in the chimpanzee.

Predation

Another example of the value of continued observations is in the study of deliberate hunting by baboons. In three seasons of field work and more than 1500 hours of observation DeVore had seen baboons catch and eat small mammals, but apparently almost by chance, when the baboon virtually stepped on something like a newborn antelope and then killed it. But in 1965 DeVore saw repeated incidents of baboons surrounding, hunting, and killing small mammals.

The whole matter of predation on primates has been difficult to study. Rare events, such as an attack by an eagle may be very important in the survival of primates, but such attacks are seldom observed, because the presence of the human observer disturbs either the predator or the prey. We think that the present de-emphasis of the importance of predation on primates arises from these difficulties of observation and from the fact that even today most studies of free-ranging primates are made in areas where predators have been reduced or eliminated by man. Most predators are active at night, and there is still no adequate study of the nocturnal behavior of any monkey or ape. Predation probably can best be measured by studying the predators rather than the prey.

Recognition of individual animals is necessary for the study of many problems, from the first stages of the analysis of a social system to observations of social continuity or constancy of group membership; such observations are exceedingly difficult under most field conditions. For example, understanding of the dominance system implies repeated recognition of a number of animals under sufficiently various conditions so that the patterns of interaction become clear. Again, to be sure that a group has lost or gained a member, the observer must know the whole composition of the group.

Long-continued observations have proved to be important in many unexpected ways. For example, rhesus monkeys have been observed in several of their many very different habitats, and it has been found that young rhesus play more in cities than in some kinds of forest and play in the forest more at some seasons than at others. These differences are due in part to the amount of time which must be spent in getting food; the same forest troop may play more when fruits are available and hunger may be rapidly satified than at times of the year when the diet is composed of tiny seeds which take a long time to pick. Extracting the small seeds of sheesham pods during the months when rhesus troops spend most of their time in the sheesham trees takes many hours of the day. What might easily have been described in a short-term study as a species-specific difference of considerable magnitude turns out to be the result of seasonal and local variations in food source. It is essential to sample behavior in several habitats to gain an understanding of the flexibility of the built-in behavior patterns of a species, flexibility which precludes the need for development of new forms of genetically determined behavior to cope successfully with different habitats.

The long-term study in which many groups of a species are observed in different, contrasting localities, and in which at least some groups are known so well that most of the individuals can be recognized, will correct many false notions and will make valid generalizations possible. Although so far there have been only a few major investigations of this sort, some important generalizations seem possible.

Environment and Social Behavior

Nowhere is the extent to which the behavior of a species is adaptable and responsive to local conditions more apparent than among groups of rhesus living in India. Rhesus occur naturally in such diverse environments as cities, villages, roadsides, cultivated fields, and many types of forest ranging to altitudes of over 2400 meters. Contact with man varies in these habitats from constant and close to rare and incidental.

Where rhesus groups are subjected to pressures of trapping, harassment, and high incidence of infectious disease, groups are tense and aggression is high. These pressures are found in areas where there is most contact and interaction with man, such as in cities and at places of pilgrimage. The animals are in generally poor physical condition, and numerous old and new wounds are evidence of a high rate of intragroup fighting. Tension among groups occupying adjacent areas of land is similarly high where there is insufficient space for normal movement and behavior, and where there may be intense competition for a limited supply of food and water. This is in sharp contrast to those groups living away from man where normal spacing among groups can be effected by the means evolved by the species. In the latter environments, such as forests, the rhesus are in excellent physical condition and what aggressive behavior occurs functions to maintain stable social groups and relationships among the members of the group; wounds are substantially fewer, and disease appears to be rare.

There has been considerable controversy in discussions of the relationshïps among social groups of the same species as to whether or not the geographical area occupied by a group should be called a territory or a home range. The point we wish to emphasize is that, within one species, populations living in different habitats may act quite differently toward neighboring groups. Populations may be capable of a wide variety of behavior patterns ranging from exclusive occupation of an area which may be defended against neighboring groups to a peaceful coexistence with conspecifics in which wide overlap in home ranges is tolerated. Because local populations of a species may maintain their ranges in different ways it is necessary to investigate all variations in group spacing in diverse habitats before attempting to describe characteristic behavior patterns for any species.

Not unexpectedly, population and group composition reflect these differences in habitat and stress. Groups living on the Gangetic plains, where trapping, harassment, and disease are important factors, are smaller, and the proportion of young members is also significantly smaller. The long-term effects of pressures on different rhesus populations in northern and central India are now being investigated by a team of anthropologists of the National Center for Primate Biology.

A city presents a very different set of challenges to a rhesus group than does a forest. Often there are no trees to sleep in; living space must be shared with man and his domestic animals. Food is not available in the form common to other habitats, and monkeys may have to depend on their skill in stealing food from man. Often the food has been prepared by man for his own consumption, or it consists of fruits and vegetables pilfered from houses, shops, and streets. Garbage is picked through and edible portions are consumed. It is essential that the monkeys learn to differentiate between those humans who represent a real threat to their safety and those who are safe to approach. They must react quickly and learn to manipulate doors, gates, and other elements of the physical environment unique to their urban habitat. This is a tremendously different setting from that in which most rhesus live. City rhesus are more manipulative, more active, and often more aggressive than are forest rhesus. Clearly, the same species develops quite different learned habits in different environments.

Annual Reproductive Cycle

The belief, which has been widely maintained, that there is no breeding season in monkeys and apes gave rise to the theory that the persistence throughout the year of groups, or highly organized troops, was due to continuous sexual attraction. The evidence for a breeding season has been reviewed by Lancaster and Lee who found that in many species of monkeys there is a well-marked breeding season. For example, Mizuhara has presented data on 545 births of Japanese macaques of Takasakiyama. There were on the average approximately 90 births per year over six consecutive years. The average length of the birth season was 125 days, but it varied from 95 to 176 days. The majority of the births occurred in June and July. Copulations were most frequent in November to March and were not observed during the birth season, and in spite of this the highly organized group continues as a social unit throughout the year.

The birth season has been studied in other groups of Japanese macaques, and in general the situation is similar. There is no doubt that both mating and birth seasons are highly restricted in the Japanese macaque. The birth season is spring and summer, but its onset and duration vary considerably. If observations were limited and combined for the whole species, as they were in early studies, the birth season would appear to be much longer than in fact it is for an individual group, and it is the events within the local group, not averages of events for the species, that bear upon the role of sexual attraction in holding primate society together.

Under very different climatic conditions, in India, rhesus macaques also have a birth season, but copulations were observed in all months of the year, although probably not with equal frequency. Among rhesus on a small island off Puerto Rico births occur from January to June, and copulations are restricted to July–January. These data confirm the point that a birth season will be more sharply defined in a local group than in a species as a whole. There is a mating season among rhesus introduced on the island, but only a peak of mating in the same species in their native India. It is clear that survey data drawn from many groups over a wide area must be used with caution when the aim is to interpret the behavior of a single group. Since the birth season is an adaptation to local conditions, there is no reason to expect it to be the same over the entire geographical distribution of a species, and under laboratory conditions rhesus macaques breed throughout the year.

No data comparable to those for the macaques exist for other primates, and, since accurate determination of mating and birth seasons requires that reasonable numbers of animals be observed in all months of the year and that groups be observed in different localities, really adequate data exist for only the Japanese macaque. However, Lancaster and Lee were able to assemble data on 14 species of monkeys and apes. They found that probably the most common situation is a birth peak, a time of year at which births tend to be concentrated, rather than sharply limited mating and birth seasons. This is highly adaptive for widely distributed species, for it allows the majority of births to occur at the optimum time for each locality while maintaining a widely variable basic pattern. The birth season may be a more effective adaptation to extreme climatic conditions. There may be a birth peak in the chimpanzee, and there may be none in the mountain gorilla, but, since we have no more data than are necessary to clarify the reproductive pattern in a single species of macaque, we can conclude only that, while birth seasons are not present in either gorillas or chimpanzees, a peak is possible in chimpanzees, at least for those living near Lake Tanganyika.

Prior to the recent investigations there was a great deal of information on primate reproduction, and yet as late as 1960 it was still possible to maintain that there were no breeding seasons in primates and that this was the basis of primate society. Until recently the question of seasonality was raised without reference to a birth season as distinguished from a birth peak, or to a limited mating season as distinguished from matings throughout the year with a high frequency in a particular period.

Frequency of Mating

Obviously many more studies are needed, and one of the intriguing problems is the role of potency. Not only does the frequency of mating vary through the year, but also there appear to be enormous differences in potency between species that are reproducing at a normal rate. In nearly 500 hours of observation of gorillas, Schaller saw only two matings, fewer than might be seen in a troop of baboons in almost any single morning. The redtail monkey (*Cercopithecus ascanius*) mates rarely, but the closely related vervet (*Cercopithecus aethiops*) does so frequently. To a considerable extent the observed differences are correlated with structure, such as size of testes, and all these species seem to be reproducing at an adequate and normal rate. There is no evidence that langurs (*Presbytis entellus*) are less successful breeders than rhesus, but the langurs copulate less frequently.

Now that more adequate data are becoming available, the social functions of sexual behavior should be reinvestigated. The dismissal of the theory that sexual attraction is *the* basis of primate society should open the way for a more careful study of the multiple functions of sexual behavior. The great differences among the primate species should provide data to prove or disprove new theories. In passing it might be noted that the human mating system without estrous cycles in the female and without marked seasonal variations is unique.

Systems of Mating

Mating systems, like the presence or absence of seasonality in breeding and the frequency of copulation, are extremely variable in monkeys and apes. Eventually the relation of these variations to species adaptations will be understandable; at present it is most important to note that monkeys do not necessarily live either in harems or in promiscuous hordes as was once assumed. Restrictive mating patterns such as the stable and exclusive pairbond formed between adult gibbons and the harem system of the Hamadryas baboon are comparatively rare. The most common mating pattern of monkeys and apes is promiscuity more or less influenced by dominance relationships. In species in which dominance relations are not constantly at issue, such as langurs, chimpanzees, or bonnet macaques, matings appear to be relatively promiscuous and are often based on the personal inclination of the estrous female. When dominance relationships are constantly at issue, as in baboons, Japanese macaques, and rhesus macaques, sex often becomes one of the prerogatives of dominant rank. In such species dominant males tend to do a larger share of the mating than do more subordinate animals, but it is only in unusual situations that subordinate animals are barred from the mating system altogether. Mating systems probably support the general adaptation of the species to its environment. In most baboons and macaques the tendency for a few males to do much of the mating may be partly a by-product of natural selection for a hierarchy of adult males which dominates the troop so that in a dangerous terrestrial habitat external dangers will be met in an orderly way. Selection is not only for a male which can impregnate many females but it may also have favored a dominance-oriented social organization in which sexual activity has become one of the expressions of that dominance.

Dominance Relationships

Long-term field studies of monkeys and apes in their natural habitats have emphasized that social relationships within a group are patterned and organized in very complex ways. There is no single "monkey pattern" or "ape pattern"; rather, there is great variability, both among different species and among different populations of the same species, in the organization and expression of social relationships. A difference in the relative dominance of individuals is one of the most common modes of social organization in monkey and ape societies. Dominance is not synonymous with aggression, and the way dominance is expressed varies greatly between species. In the gorilla, for example, dominance is most often expressed by extremely attenuated gestures and signals; a gentle nudge from the dominant male is more than enough to elicit a submissive response from a subordinate, whereas, in baboons, chases, fights, and biting can be daily occurrences. In many primates there is a tendency for the major age-sex classes to be ranked in a dominance order; for example, in baboons, macaques, and gorillas, adult males as a class are usually dominant over adult females, and females are dominant over young. This may not always be true, for in several species of macaques some females may outrank some adult males, although groups dominated by a female (such as the Minoo-B troop of Japanese macaques) are extremely rare. Dominance relationships may be quite unstructured, as in the chimpanzee, where dominance is expressed in interactions between individuals but where these relationships are not organized into any sort of hierarchy. A much more common situation is one in which dominance relations, among males at least, are organized into linear hierarchies that are quite stable over time, as in baboons, langurs, and macaques. Sometimes these dominance hierarchies are complicated by alliances among several males who back each other up very effectively or even by an alliance between a male and a female. Although dominance varies widely among monkeys and apes both in its form and function, it is certainly one of the most important axes of social organization to be found in primate societies.

Genealogical Relationships

Recognition of individual animals and repeated studies of the same groups have opened the way to the appreciation of other long-continuing social relationships in monkeys and apes which cannot be interpreted in terms of dominance alone. Long-term studies of free-ranging animals have been made on only two species of nonhuman primates, Japanese macaques, which have been studied since 1950 by members of the Japan Monkey Center, and Indian rhesus macaques living free on Cayo Santiago, Puerto Rico, the island colony established by Carpenter in 1938. In these studies, when the genealogy of the animals has been known, it has been obvious that genetic relationships play a major role in determining the course and nature of social interactions. It becomes clear that bonds between mother and infant may persist into adult life to form a nucleus from which many other social bonds ramify. When the genealogy of individual animals is known, members of commonly observed subgroupings, such as a cluster of four or five animals grooming or resting together, are likely to be uterine kin. For example, members of a subgroup composed of several adult animals, both male and female, as well as juveniles and infants, may all be offspring of the same female. The relations continue to be very important in adult life not only in relaxed affectional relationships but also in dominance interactions. Sade saw a female rhesus monkey divert the attack of a dominant male from her adult son and saw another adult female protect her juvenile half-sisters (paternity is not determinable in most monkey societies). There is a very high frequency of grooming between related animals, and many animals never seek grooming partners outside of their own genealogies.

It should be stressed that there is no information leading us to believe that these animals are either recognizing genetic relationships or responding to any sort of abstract concept of family. Rather these social relationships are determined by the necessarily close association of mother with newborn infant, which is extended through time and generations and which ramifies into close associations among siblings. We believe that this pattern of enduring social relations between a mother and her offspring will be found in other species of primates. Because of their dramatic character, the importance of dominance and aggression has been greatly exaggerated compared to that of continuing, positive, affectional relations between related animals as expressed by their sitting or feeding together, touching, and grooming. Much of this behavior can be observed easily in the field, but the extent to which it is in fact an expression of social genealogies has been demonstrated only in the studies cited above.

Positive, affectional relations are not limited to relatives. Male Japanese macaques may take care of young by forming special protective relationships with particular infants, but whether these males have any special relationship to the infants as either father or brother is uncertain, and the mating system is such that paternity cannot be known either to the observer or to the monkeys. MacRoberts has recorded a very high frequency of care of infants by males in the Gibraltar macaque. In addition, he has demonstrated that these positive protective relations are very beneficial to the juvenile. Two juveniles which had no such close relationship were forced to be peripheral, were at a great disadvantage in feeding, and were groomed much less than other juveniles in the group.

The status of the adult can be conferred on closely associated young (frequently an offspring when the adult is female), and for this reason the young of dominant animals are more likely to be dominant. This inheritance of rank has been discussed by Imanishi for the Japanese macaque and by Koford for the rhesus. Sons of very dominant females seem to have a great advantage over other males both because their mothers are able to back them up successfully in social interactions and because they stay with their mothers near the other dominant animals at the center of the group. They may never go through the stage of being socially and physically peripheral to the group which is typical for young males of these species. A male cannot simply "inherit" high rank; he must also win this position through his own abilities, but his chances of so doing are greatly increased if he has had these early experiences of associating with and being supported by very dominant animals.

There could hardly be a greater contrast than that between the emerging picture of an orderly society, based heavily on affectionate or cooperative social actions and structured by stable dominance relationships, and the old notion of an unruly horde of monkeys dominated by a tyrant. The 19th-century social evolutionists attributed less order to the societies of primitive man than is now known to exist in the societies of monkeys and apes living today.

Communication

Research on the communication systems of monkeys and apes through 1962 has been most ably summarized and interpreted by Marler. Most of the data represent work by field observers who were primarily interested in social structure, and the signals, and their meanings, used to implement and facilitate social interactions were more or less taken for granted. Only in the last year or so have communication systems themselves been the object of careful study and analysis. Marler has emphasized both the extraordinary complexity of the communication systems of primates and the heavy dependence of these systems on composite signals. Most frequently it is not a single signal that passes between two animals but a signal complex composed of auditory, visual, tactile, and, more rarely, olfactory signals.

Communication in some monkey species is based on a system of intergrading signals, whereas in others much more use is made of highly discrete signals. For example, most sounds of the vervet monkey are of the discrete type, there being some 36 different sounds that are comparatively distinct both to the human ear and when analyzed by a sound spectrograph. In contrast, Rowell and Hinde have analyzed the sounds of the rhesus monkey and found that of 13 harsh noises, 9 belonged to a single intergrading subsystem expressing agonistic emotions.

As more and more study is done on primates it will probably be shown that their communication systems tend to be of mixed form in that both graded and discrete signals are used depending on the relative efficiency of one or the other form in serving a specific function. In concert this use of both discrete and intergrading signals and of composites from several sensory modes produces a rich potential for the expression of very slight but significant changes in the intensity and nature of mood in the signaling animal. Marler has emphasized that, except for calls warning of danger, the communication system is little applied to events outside the group. Communication systems in monkeys and apes are highly evolved in their capacity to express motivation of individuals and to facilitate social relationships. Without this ability to express mood, monkeys and apes would not be able to engage in the subtle and complicated social interactions that are a major feature of their adaptations.

Social Learning

Harlow and Harlow's experiments show the importance of learning in the development of social life; however, monkeys and apes are so constituted that, except in the laboratory, social learning is inevitable. They adapt by their social life, and the group provides the context of affection, protection, and stability in which learning occurs. No one factor can explain the importance of social behavior, because society is a major adaptive mechanism with many functions, but one of the most important of these functions is the provision of a rich and protected social context in which young mature. Field observations, although mainly observations of the results of learning rather than of the process itself, provide necessary clues as to the nature of the integration of relevant developmental and social factors. These factors can then be estimated and defined for subsequent intensive controlled research in a laboratory or colony.

It has become clear that, although learning has great importance in the normal development of nearly all phases of primate behavior, it is not a generalized ability; animals are able to learn some things with great ease and other things only with the greatest difficulty. Learning is part of the adaptive pattern of a species and can be understood only when it is seen as the process of acquiring skills and attitudes that are of evolutionary significance to a species when living in the environment to which it is adapted.

There are important biological limitations which vary from species to species and which do not reflect differences in intelligence so much as differences in specializations. For example, Goodall has observed young chimpanzees learning to fish for termites both by their observation of older chimpanzees and by practice. It takes time for the chimpanzee to become proficient with these tools, and many mistakes are made. Chimpanzees are not the only primates that like termites, and Goodall has observed baboons sitting near chimpanzees watching and waiting while the latter are getting termites. The baboons are just as eager as the chimpanzees to eat termites but are unable to learn how to fish for termites for themselves.

It is likely that there are important variables among groups of a single species that make it possible for the acquisition of new patterns of behavior or the expression of basic learned species patterns to vary from group to group and from one habitat to another. For example, the nature of the integration and operation of a social unit vary in the extent to which it depends on the personalities of individuals in the group—this is another dimension of our understanding of how social behavior may affect species survival. Particularly aggressive adult males can make the behavior of their groups relative to that of adjacent groups with less assertive males substantially different. For example, a group with very aggressive males can control a larger geographic area than is occupied by a group with much less aggressive males. The tenor of life within a group may be tenser or more relaxed depending on personalities of adults in the group.

Imprinting has traditionally been distinguished from other learning processes by the fact that in imprinting the young animal will learn to follow, to be social, without an external or immediate reward. However, among monkeys and apes, simply being with other animals is a reward, and learning is reinforced by the affectional, attentive, supportive social context of the group. Butler was the first to use the sight of another monkey as a reward in psychological experiments. The field worker sees sick and practically disabled animals making great efforts to stay with their group. Among ground-living forms, animals that have lost or broken limbs or are so sick that they collapse as soon as the group stops moving, all walk along as the troop moves. Instances of wounded rhesus macaques' moving into langur groups after the rhesus have left or been forced out of their own group have been recorded. Clearly, it is essential for the young monkey or ape to mature in a social setting in which it learns appropriate skills and relationships during early years and in which it continues to learn during adulthood. "Where the individual primate is, in temporary isolation, learning a task without reference to any other member of its species, the learning is not normal."

Future Primate Studies

At present many long-term studies are in process and major films are being edited (Goodall on chimpanzee and DeVore on baboon). There will be about twice as many major accounts available in 2 years as there are now. Since it is now clear that detailed descriptive studies of undisturbed free-ranging primates can be made, and since available data show that there are substantial differences in the behavior of the different species, more species should be investigated. So far studies have concentrated for the most part on the larger ground-living forms which are easier to study. There is no study of *Cercocebus*, little on *Colobus*, and nothing on the numerous langurs (*Presbytis*) of southeast Asia. New World monkeys have been investigated very little, and there are numerous genera that have not been the subjects of a major field study. Also, since local variation is important, forms such as the chimpanzee and gorilla should be studied in more and contrasting localities.

Once the general characteristics of the behaviors of several species are known, then interest can shift to topics such as detailed ecology, birth, infant behavior, peer groups, affectionate behaviors, sex, or dominance, to mention only a few. The behavior of a whole species is a large problem, and description has to be at a very general level when the goal is a first general statement. A problem-oriented study permits choice of species and elaboration of techniques. A further advantage of the problem-oriented approach is that it allows the close coordination of the field work with experimental work in the laboratory. Fortunately, no division has developed between those doing the field work and those involved in the experimental analysis of behavior. Many scientists have done both controlled experiments and field studies. The interplay between naturalistic observation and controlled experiment is the essential key to the understanding of behavior. The character of the natural adaptation of the species and the dimensions of the society can be determined only in the field. Many topics, such as geographic range, food, predation, group size, aggression, and the like, can be seen only under field conditions. But the mechanisms of the observed behavior can be determined only in the laboratory, and this is the more complicated task. The relation of a field study to scientific understanding is like the relation of the observation that a man walks or runs to the whole analysis of locomotion. The field worker lists what the animals eat, but this gives no understanding of nutrition. The kinds of interactions may be charted in the field, but their interpretation requires the laboratory. Field workers saw hours devoted to play, but it was Harlow's experiments that showed how essential this activity was to the development of behavior. As the field studies develop it is to be hoped that they will maintain a close relation to controlled experiment. It is most fortunate that the present studies are being carried on by anthropologists, psychologists, and zoologists. An understanding of behavior is most likely to come from the bringing together of the methods and interests of many sciences, and we hope that the field studies remain a part of general behavioral science and do not become independent as workers and problems become more and more numerous.

Even now, in their preliminary state, the field studies can offer some conclusions that might be pondered by students in the multiplicity of departments now dividing up the study of human behavior. Behavior is profoundly influenced by the biology of the species, and problems of perception, emotion, aggression, and many others cannot be divorced from the biology of the actors in the social system. Early learning is important, and an understanding of the preschool years is essential to an understanding of behavior. Play is tremendously important, and a species that wastes the emotions and energies of its young by divorcing play from education has forfeited its evolutionary heritage—the biological motivation of learning. Social behavior is relatively simple compared to the biological mechanisms that make the behavior possible. Ultimately a science of human behavior must include both biological and social factors, and there is no more reason to separate the study of human behavior into many compartments than there would be to separate the field studies from the intellectual enrichment coming from the laboratory.

21 The New Physical Anthropology

Sherwood L. Washburn

HOW OLD CAN SOMETHING NEW BE? THE SELECTION THAT FOLLOWS WAS *first published when many readers of this book were still in the nursery, and some may not yet have been born. It is an excellent piece and retains its edge because it addresses itself to concepts of problem and to methods of research and analysis that remain fresh and current. Even when it deals with bones, it does not render them dry, but treats them in the context of the living situations in which they developed and were exercised. The anthropology described here readily includes the goals set by Holloway (No. I:14); though years have passed, it remains the "new physical anthropology."*

Recently, evolutionary studies have been revitalized and revolutionized by an infusion of genetics into paleontology and systematics. The change is fundamentally one of point of view, which is made possible by an understanding of the way the genetic constitution of populations changes. The new systematics is concerned primarily with process and with the mechanism of evolutionary change, whereas the older point of view was chiefly concerned with sorting the results of evolution. Physical anthropology is now undergoing the same sort of change. Population genetics presents the anthropologist with a clearly formulated, experimentally verified, conceptual scheme. The application of this theory to the primates is the immediate task of physical anthropology.

In the past, physical anthropology has been considered primarily as a technique. Training consisted in learning to take carefully defined measurements and in computing indices and statistics. The methods of ob-

SOURCE: *Transactions of the New York Academy of Sciences*, Series II, Vol. 13 (1951), pp. 298–304. Reprinted with the permission of the author and publisher.
For biographical data on the author, see selection 20.

servation, measurement, and comparison were essentially the same, whether the object of the study was the description of evolution, races, growth, criminals, constitutional types, or army personnel. Measurements were adjusted for various purposes, but measurement of the outside of the body, classification, and correlation, remained the anthropologist's primary tools. The techniques of physical anthropology were applied to a limited group of problems and any definition or statement of traditional anthropology must include both the metrical methods and the problems for which the methods were used. Further, anthropology was characterized by theories, or rather by a group of attitudes and assumptions.

There has been almost no development of theory in physical anthropology itself, but the dominant attitude may be described as static, with emphasis on classification based on types. Any such characterization is oversimplified, and is intended only to give an indication of the dominant techniques, interests, and attitudes of the physical anthropologist. Except for emphasis on particular animals, physical anthropology shared much with the zoology of the times when it developed. Much of the method was developed before the acceptance of the idea of evolution, and all of it before the science of genetics.

Physical anthropology should change, just as systematic zoology has changed. The difficulties which accompany the necessary modifications can be greatly reduced if their nature is clearly understood. Naturally, in a time of rapid flux there will be numerous doubts and disagreements as to what should be done. This is natural, and what I have to offer is a tentative outline to indicate how parts of the new physical anthropology may differ from the old.

The old physical anthropology was primarily a technique. The common core of the science was measurement of external form with calipers. The new physical anthropology is primarily an area of interest, the desire to understand the process of primate evolution and human variation by the most efficient techniques available.

The process of evolution, as understood by the geneticist, is the same for all mammals. The genetic composition of a population may be described in terms of gene frequencies. The modification of these frequencies results in evolution which is caused by *selection*, mutations, drift, and migrations. Mutations and migrations introduce new genetic elements into the population. But selection on the phenotype, adapting animals to their environment, is the primary cause of alteration in gene frequencies.

This is essentially a return to Darwinism, but with this important difference: Darwin wrote in a pregenetic era. Therefore, he did not understand the mechanism which makes possible the production of variation and the possibility of selection. Since Darwin's ideas could not be proved in detail by the techniques available in his time, the concept of selection did not become fully effective. Therefore, some pre-evolutionary ideas continued in full force. More Linnaean species were described from types after Darwin than before. The idea of evolution created interest in species, but the species were described in pre-evolutionary terms. Further, it is possible for people to hold a variety of theories in place of, or in addition to, Darwin's. For example, Lamarckian ideas have continued right down to today. Orthogenesis has been widely believed and irreversibility has been regarded as a law.

It has been claimed that evolution should be described in terms of nonadaptive traits, yet this is impossible if evolution is largely due to selection. The first great achievement of the synthesis of genetics, paleontology, and systematics is in clearing away a mass of antiquated theories and attitudes which permeate the writings of the older students of evolution. Further, the new evolutionary theory shows which aspects of past work are worth using, extending, and strengthening. This is possible because much of the mechanism of evolutionary change is now understood, clearly formulated, and *experimentally verified*. The logic of Darwin's great theory could only become fully effective when techniques had been developed to prove that selection was right and that other ideas of evolution were wrong. A change in theory, no matter how popular, is not enough. The new ideas must be implemented by effective techniques.

If a new physical anthropology is to differ effectively from the old, it must be more than the adoption of a little genetic terminology. It must change its ways of doing things to conform with the implications of modern evolutionary theory. For example, races must be based on the study of populations. There is no way to justify the division of a breeding population into a series of racial types. It is not enough to state that races should be based on genetic traits; races which can not be reconciled with genetics should be removed from consideration. If we consider the causes of changes in gene frequency as outlined above, and if we are concerned with the process of evolution, the task of the anthropologist becomes clear. He has nothing to offer on mutation, but can make contributions with regard to migration, drift, and selection.

The migrations of man made possible by culture have vastly confused the genetic picture. Before selection can be investigated, it is necessary to know how long a people has been in an area and under what conditions they have been living. For example, the spread of European people, of Bantu speakers, or of Eskimo, all have changed the distribution of the blood groups. The interpretation of the genetic situation demands an understanding of history. Whether people became adapted to cold by selection or by change in their way of life completely alters the interpretation of the distribution of physical traits. This has been widely recognized by anthropologists, and the solution of this difficulty requires the active collaboration of archeologists, ethnologists, linguists, and students of the physical man.

Drift is related to population size, and this depends on the way of life. Again, as in the case of migration, the situation in which drift may have taken place cannot be specified by the physical anthropologist alone, but requires the active collaboration of many specialists. The adoption of modern evolutionary theory will force a far closer and more realistic collaboration between the branches of anthropology than ever before.

Although much of the present distribution of races may be explained by migration and although drift probably accounts for some differences, selection must be the explanation of long term evolutionary trends and of many patterned variations as well. Anthropologists have always stressed the importance of adaptation in accounting for the differences between apes and men, and sometimes have used the idea in interpreting racial divergences. But suggestions of adaptations are not enough. It is easy to guess that a form is adaptive, but the real problem is to determine the precise nature of a particular adaptation. The work I have been interested in is designed to demonstrate the relation of form to function. My feeling has been that it is impossible to do more than guess about this matter using traditional anthropological measurements, and that the literature is already too full of uncontrolled speculations. Therefore, I would like to take this opportunity to present an outline, a beginning, of an analysis of the human body into complexes which may vary independently.

In this work, the guiding principle has been that the major force in evolution is selection of functional complexes. A variety of methods has been used to demonstrate the adaptive complexes. The four major methods for factoring complexes out of the body are: (1) comparison and evolution; (2) development; (3) variability; and (4) experiment. All these have been used by numerous investigators, but, to the best of my knowledge, they have not been combined into a working system. All must be used to gain an understanding of the human body.

Figure 1 shows the body divided into the major regions, which seem to have had remarkable independence in recent evolutionary history. The complex to attain its present pattern first is that of the arms and thorax. This complex is associated with arm swinging in the trees, the way of life called "brachiation." It is association with a reduction in the deep back muscles and in the number of lumbar vertebrae and consequent shortening of the trunk and elongation of all parts of the upper extremity, adaptation of the joints and muscles to greater pronation, supination in the forearm, and flexion and abduction at the shoulder. Many changes in the positions of viscera are associated with the shorter trunk. We share this complex with the living gibbons and apes. The bipedal complex was the next to develop and seems to have been fundamentally human in the

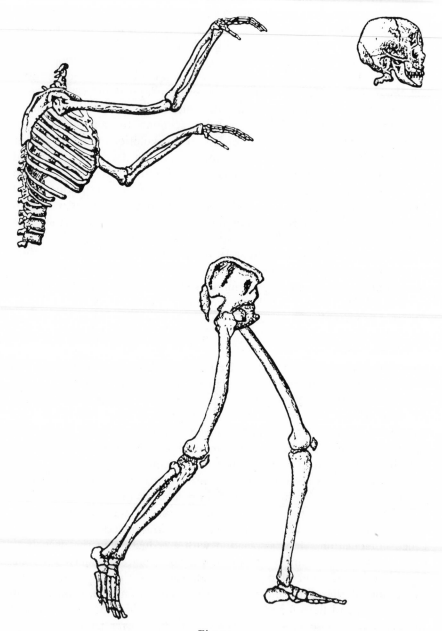

Figure 1

South African man-apes. The major changes are in the ilium and in the gluteal muscles. Just as in the arm, the change is in a bone-muscle complex, which makes a different way of life possible. The head seems to have attained essentially its present form during the fourth glacial advance, perhaps 50,000 years ago. The brain continued to enlarge until the end of the last interglacial period, and the face decreased in size for some time after that. The great increase in the size of the brain and decrease in the face was after the use of tools.

Evolution, in a sense, has dissected the body for us, and has shown that great changes may occur in arms and trunk, pelvis and legs, and brain case, or face, accompanied by little change in the rest of the body. The

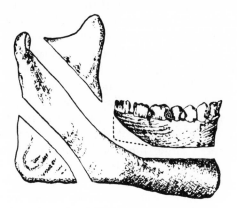

Figure 2

first two complexes to change are related to brachiation and bipedal locomotion. The final changes in the head may well be related to changed selection after the use of tools.

To carry the analysis further, it is necessary to deal with one of the areas suggested by this preliminary dividing of the body. Let us consider the face, and especially the lower jaw. Figure 2 shows a lower jaw divided into regions which can be shown to vary independently by all the methods of analysis suggested before. The coronoid process varies with the temporal muscle. The angle of the jaw varies with the masseter and internal pterygoid muscle. The tooth-supporting area varies with the teeth. The main core of the jaw is affected by hormones which do not affect the other parts, as shown in acromegaly. Alizarin dye, which stains the growing bone, reveals the pattern of growth. The split-line technique (Benninghoff) shows the mechanical arrangement.

After making an analysis of this kind, comparisons of a different sort are possible. The simple statement, that a trait is or is not there, is replaced by the attempt to understand under what conditions it might be present. For example, if the simian shelf is developed in monkeys and apes when the jaws are long and the anterior teeth large, then the South African man-apes and other fossil men would not be expected to have such a shelf. The dental characters necessary to bring out the expression of the shelf are absent in all. It can be argued that we have the potential for a simian shelf but that we do not have the necessary tooth and jaw size to make it evident. Trying to understand the process which produces a trait leads to very different evaluations than does a listing of presence or absence.

In the light of this sort of information, let us look at the skull of an Eocene Lemur, *Notharctus*. The jaw is long, in conformity with the length of the teeth. It is low, and there is a large angular region. This region has been described as lemuroid. If this angle has remained there for 50 million years, however, over countless generations of lemurs, it must have more of a function than to mark the jaw as primitive or to help us in identifying lemur jaws. If the mandible of a remarkably similar modern leum (genus *Lemur*) is examined, it is found that the internal pterygoid muscle inserts at the end of the angle, but that the masseter muscle inserts only on the lateral side of the ascending ramus, leaving the angle bare of muscle. An internal pterygoid muscle inserting in this position is a protruder of the jaw. The function of the angle of the lemur jaw is to provide insertion for a large, functionally important muscle. The dependence of the angular process on the internal pterygoid and the exact function of the internal pterygoid need to be experimentally verified.

The only point to be stressed now is that the theory that such a process is of adaptive significance, and that it is maintained by selection, leads one to look for a functional complex. If such a process is regarded simply as a taxonomic aid, or as non-functional, no guide is available for research or future understanding.

The post-orbital bar of this same lemur again illustrates the advantage of assuming, until it is proved otherwise, that a part is functionally important. Originally, the complete bony ring around the orbit may have been for protection or for some other unknown function. Once the ring is established, however, the skeletal framework for radical modification of the skull is present. The change from the lemur skull, with a wide interorbital region, to the monkey skull, with reduced olfactory mechanism and reduced interorbital space, is mechanically possible because pressure, tension, and buttressing of the sides of the face is provided by the complete rings of bone around the orbits. Structures which probably develop as part of a protective mechanism were pre-adaptive for a reorganization of the face.

Classic Neanderthal man differs from other fossil men in that the angle of the lower jaw is poorly developed, the part of the malar bone associated with the origin of the largest part of the masseter muscle is small, and the lateral part of the brow-ridge is less sharply demarcated.

All these differences may be related, and certainly the association of the small angle and malar suggest that the masseter muscle was small compared to the temporal muscle. Differences of this sort should be described in terms of the variation in the groups being compared. Since similar differences may be found in living men, the development of appropriate quantitative, descriptive methods is merely a matter of time and technique. The procedure is: (1) diagnose the complex; (2) develop methods appropriate to describe variations in it; and (3) try to discover the genetic background of these variations.

So far, we are still engaged in finding the complexes, but even at this level it is possible to make suggestions about fossil men. Probably some Mongoloid groups will have the highest frequency of the big masseter complex, and some of the Negro groups the lowest. This is merely stating some traditional physical anthropology in a somewhat different way by relating statements about the face to those on the lower jaw and relating both to a large and important muscle. It differs from the traditional in the technique of analysis and avoids speculation of the sort which says that the characteristics of the Mongoloid face are due to adaptation to cold.

In this preliminary analysis of the lower jaw, the attempt has been made to divide a single bone into relatively independent systems and to show that the differences make sense in terms of differing adaptations. Eventually, it may be possible to understand the genetic mechanisms involved. If this type of analysis is at all correct, it is theoretically impossible to make any progress in genetic understanding by taking the traditional measurements on the mandible. They are all complex resultants of the interrelation of two or more of the variables. The measurements average the anatomy in such a way that it is as futile to look for the mode of inheritance of the length of the jaw as it is to look for the genes of the cephalic index.

The implications for anthropology of this type of analysis may be made clearer by some comparisons of the skulls of monkeys. If the skulls of adult male and adult female vervets are compared, many differences may be seen. The male skull is larger in all dimensions, particularly those of the face. If, however, an adult female is compared to a juvenile male with the same cranial capacity and the same weight of temporal muscle, all the differences disappear, except that in the size of the canine tooth. What would appear to be a very large number of unrelated differences, if traditional methods were used, are only aspects of one fundamental difference in the size of the face. If a large-faced monkey is compared with a small-faced one, both of the genus *Cercopithecus*, there appear to be many differences. Yet again, if animals of the same cranial capacity and the same temporal muscle size are compared, almost all the measurements are the same. The species difference is in quantity of face, although this appears in many different forms. If these two skulls were fossil men, differing in the same way, and if they were treated by the usual anthropological methods, they would be found to differ in numerous observations, measurements, and indices. Yet one may be transformed into the other by a simple reduction in mass of face (including teeth, bones, muscles). Perhaps many fossils are far less different than we have supposed. The methods used created the number of differences, just as a metrical treatment of these monkeys would make the adults appear very distinct.

The purpose of this paper has been to call attention to the changes which are taking place in physical anthropology. Under the influence of modern genetic theory, the field is changing from the form it assumed in the latter part of the nineteenth century into a part of modern science. The change is essentially one of emphasis. If traditional physical anthropology was 80 per cent measurement and 20 per cent concerned with heredity, process, and anatomy, in the new physical anthropology the proportions may be approximately reversed. I have stressed the impact of genetics on anthropology, but the process need not be all one way. If the form of the human face can be thoroughly analyzed, this will open the way to the understanding of its development and the interpretation of abnormalities and malocclusion, and may lead to advances in genetics, anatomy, and medicine. Although evolution is fascinating in itself, the understanding of the functional anatomy which may be gained from it is of more than philosophical importance. The kind of systemic anatomy in which bones, muscles, ligaments, *etc.* are treated separately became obsolete with the publication of the "Origin of Species" in 1859. The anatomy of life, of integrated function, does not know the artificial boundaries which still govern the dissection of a corpse. The new physical anthropology has much to offer to anyone interested in the structure or evolution of man, but this is only a beginning. To build it, we must collaborate with social scientists, geneticists, anatomists, and paleontologists. We need new ideas, new methods, new workers. There is nothing we do today which will not be done better tomorrow.

22 Medical Anthropology and the Study of Biological and Cultural Adaptation

Alexander Alland, Jr.

THERE WAS A TIME, NOT TOO LONG AGO, WHEN ONLY A HANDFUL OF THE BEST *graduate students were attracted to physical anthropology. Then physical anthropology, under stimuli such as comprise the subject of the previous selection, began to change. As the vitality of the subject grew, so did its attractiveness, but at the same time there was a noticeable breaching of the barriers that had separated physical from cultural anthropology. Some years ago, it seemed that "four-field" anthropology would certainly die for lack of substantial cross-cutting interests. Now there are many scholars pursuing studies that incorporate without stress or condescension the methods, data, and conclusions of more than one field.*

The concept of a "medical anthropology" is not a novelty, but its realization is. This is a field bursting with problems and challenges, and its excitement is the product of the practical and desirable benefits to world health promised by its conclusions, and the knowledge of its researchers that they are in the vanguard of science, combining some of the best elements in diverse fields.

In the present article, an anthropologist who has devoted much of his time to developments in this new field reviews some of its accomplishments and future goals.

SOURCE: *American Anthropologist*, Vol. 68, 1 (1966), pp. 40–50. Reprinted with permission of author and publisher.

The author (b. 1931) is Assistant Professor of Anthropology at Columbia University. His fieldwork was done in West Africa. His two books presently in press are *Genetics, Evolution and Human Behavior* and *A Reader in Medical Anthropology*.

In its short history medical anthropology has served primarily as an adjunct to applied anthropology and public health. While there are obvious and good reasons for combined research in these subjects it seems to me that there is a vast area for medically oriented research within the main stream of anthropological theory. In fact it shall be my contention in this paper that medical anthropology may serve as a major link between physical and cultural anthropology, particularly in the areas of biological and cultural evolution.

A good deal of recent research has shown that the evolution of man's sapient form has been an interactive process between cultural and physical development. Simpson has suggested that culture itself is an adaptive process of biological evolution. While most physical anthropologists accept the role of culture in physical development many of those interested in cultural evolution have tended to bypass the biological aspect of cultural development.[1] They have concentrated instead on the cumulative aspect of the evolutionary process. No one can deny that biological evolution is cumulative in the two senses that there has been a proliferation of species through time and that greater complexity of the nervous system has been a constant of phylogenetic development. Nor can one deny that functional interrelationships exist between specific ecological niches and different levels of cultural complexity. Primary focus on these, however, has led researchers away from the main tenets of Darwin, variation and selection, the latter reflected in selective fertility and selective mortality. In fact Leslie White has stated that the theory of cultural evolution owes more to Spencer than to Darwin.

Sahlins and Service have applied an analogue model of the Darwinian theory to problems of culture, but in their system there are no measurable biological variables and no generalizations may be made from established biological laws.

Even the multilineal evolutionists, virtuous in their attention to environmental factors, have tended to overcategorize their material in premature attempts to show orderly levels of development within particular ecological niches. But while the development of complexity may well be a long term effect of evolution, it is not itself a determinant in the process, and the study of complexity is not particularly germane to an understanding of process.

I think that everyone would agree with the proposition that the extension of Darwin's theory to cultural phenomena is good science in that it would add to the generalizing power of that theory and place more

[1] V. G. Childe is the one major exception since he attempted to use population growth as a measure of evolution. Other cultural anthropologists who have considered the relationships between biology and the development of culture have not been associated with any school of cultural evolution. I refer here particularly to Geertz, Hallowell, and Wallace.

material on human development within the mainstream of biology. The question that must be raised is: Can the Darwinian model of evolution be applied to cultural evolution and if so, to what extent and how? Before an attempt can be made to answer these questions, certain theoretical points associated with the organization and analysis of data must be clarified.

First of all it must be emphasized that the unit of such studies is a human population characterized by a configuration of biological and cultural traits and occupying a specific ecological space. The term culture shall be reserved to denote traits which are shared by a significant number of individuals and which are transmitted through the learning process. This should help us to avoid the tendency toward typological thinking which too often accompanies the use of the term culture to describe human societies and facilitate the study of cultural and biological variables as interacting factors in the adaptive process.

Second, it must be understood that what is to be studied is neither a teleological nor a unidirectional process. Traits which have adaptive value do not necessarily arise as a response to need. Thus there is no question of causality in the analysis. This is in keeping with the theory of evolution which provides functional explanations for the fixation or loss of random events (mutations) within a defined system (a population). Factors responsible for mutation may be investigated independently, just as factors responsible for the origin of particular cultural traits may be investigated independently, but these are not our major concern.

Traits which have survival value may be sorted out in a process which may well be, though it need not be, independent of the individuals involved. This is not to say that all cultural traits are adaptive, but the proposition that many of them are is not a new one. What is new is the proposed investigation of the biological adaptability of such traits within a given environment.

Lastly I must emphasize that medically oriented studies are only one means of pursuing research in the field of human evolution. Adaptive environmental exploitation and adaptive forms of social structure are, of course, of extreme if not major importance, but I think that medical studies will provide units of analysis which are more directly measurable and which may reveal more readily the relationships between biological and cultural variables.

It is often pointed out that the major difficulty in applying Darwinian evolution to so-called cultural adaptation is the fact that culture traits are extrasomatic and therefore not bound to genetic mechanisms. Hence it is said, quite correctly, that different rules govern their transmission. They are not only passed from generation to generation through a learning process, but may easily transgress societal boundaries without concomitant interbreeding. But how important is this difference? As I have pointed out above, adaptation is the major concern here, not the origin of traits nor the mechanism of their transmission. The relationships between traits and environments have the same effect on adaptation whether the traits are biological or cultural, and adaptation in human groups is bound to be the result of combined biological and cultural forces.

As far as methodological orientation is concerned, most biologists accept the fact that careful studies on the microevolutionary level are essential to an understanding of the mechanisms of evolution. If we accept the principle that microevolutionary studies are a necessary prerequisite for this type of research, then it becomes possible to discuss specific lines of attack on those areas which are subject to biological measurement. Generally speaking these measurements are fertility and fecundity, morbidity and mortality. The material to be examined falls into two groups. First, those relationships between culture and biological variables which affect the distribution and frequency of genes, and second, those relationships between culture and biological variables which directly affect disease frequency, disease outcome, and fertility. The first group reflects primarily the effects of culture on physical development, but changes in genes may well feed back to culture. The second group is concerned specifically with cultural development as it is affected by biological variables. Where genes are concerned we have the added measure of gene frequency.

Before presenting a general outline for research in medical anthropology, I should like to cite a series of articles which reflect the major theme of this paper. Although I have reservations about some of the ideas presented, they are not offered here for critical review, but rather as a series of studies which, taken together, help form the basis and direction for further investigation.

Frank Livingstone's brilliant paper on sickle cell anemia has opened a vast field of research into the relationships among genes, disease, and cultural practices. In this paper Livingstone has correlated the distribution of the vector in West Africa for Falciparum malaria with the introduction of agriculture to this area. The increase in vector population is related to an increase in disease incidence and the increase of disease incidence to the development of an adaptive polymorphism based on the resistance of heterozygotes for the sickle cell trait to a highly fatal form of malaria.

It is unfortunate that further research of this type has not been pursued, although there is data in the literature on the genetics of disease resistance and susceptibility. Cultural factors which act to increase the frequency of disease organisms in particular ecological areas or which act to reduce or increase resistance will have an effect on the genetic constitution of populations.

A recent paper by F. L. Lambrecht on the evolution and ecology of the tsetse fly and trypanosomiasis provides much material of anthropological interest. While Lambrecht does not investigate the genetics of disease resistance to trypanosomiasis in present human populations, he does relate the distribution of various species of carrier and disease organism to both environmental and cultural factors. This paper is interesting also because the author raises the question of relationships between primate and hominid evolution and the incidence of disease. To quote his summary paragraph: "Exposure to and invasion by parasitic organisms may play an important part among many other intrinsic factors that guide the evolution of animal forms. Trypanosomes, two species of which cause African sleeping sickness today, are blood parasites of great antiquity. Their presence in Africa at the time of the first stages of human evolution may have been of great consequences, at first acting as a discriminating agent between resistant and nonresistant types of hominids, and later also in shaping migration routes and settlement patterns. As a possible clue as to why man arose in Africa, the author postulates that trypanosomes may have precluded the development of certain ground-dwelling faunas, allowing certain more resistant primates to fill the empty ecological niches."

The suggestion that disease has been a factor in primate evolution has also been made by A. H. Schultz. "I feel that this question could be answered by a geneticist (is there a relaxation of Natural Selection in variable species?) together with some pathologist, since disease is the most potent selective factor in anthropoids."

It is interesting to note in this respect that macaques will drive sick animals away from their territory and thus protect the group from an increased frequency of disease organisms. Thus disease may well have played a selective role in the evolution of certain primate behavioral traits as well.

A phenomenon observed in chickens and rabbits that may have implications for certain human populations is the existence of variance in the thermoregulatory processes which has been related to disease resistance and the function of phagocytes. To quote F. B. Hutt:

"Evidence of a similar relationship in a mammal between superior control of thermoregulatory processes and resistance to infection was found by Locke who studied resistance of rabbits to virulent pneumonococci. He could not measure the degree of control over body temperature as easily or as nicely as we could *(using chickens)*. He measured it by what he called the warming time, i.e., the number of minutes needed for rabbits to get the body temperature back to normal after they had been chilled by immersion in cold water. Those with short warming time proved more resistant than others."

Now if this relationship exists or existed in man we should expect to find it in groups with primitive technology inhabiting areas which have cold periods either seasonably or diurnally, or in populations which for subsistence reasons have prolonged body contact with cold water. At least two population groups for which these conditions exist and for which there is evidence of thermoregulatory processes may be found. These are the Indians of Tierra del Fuego and the Australian aborigines. Although there are indications that the Alacaluf and Yahgan suffered disastrous consequences from diseases introduced by Europeans, the possibility remains that these populations and populations like them are resistant to certain diseases, particularly those caused by bacteria and which are attacked by phagocytes. The Tierra del Fuegans were wiped out primarily by virus infections.

If the relationship which obtains in lower animals applies to these groups, it would certainly suggest that such an adaptive mechanism may once have been widespread in human populations and that cultural advances served to relax selection pressure. Furthermore it is very possible that variation in thermoregulation may exist as a polymorphic trait in more highly developed cultures, including our own, and that disease remains the selective mechanism. The frequency of the adaptive trait may be related to cultural factors influencing the incidence of specific diseases.

A hypothesis relating culture traits to biological adaptation has been offered by Whiting who suggests that long post partum sexual taboos and consequent late weaning may be related to the incidence of kwashiorkor in certain areas of the world. Late weaning is often associated with long post partum sexual taboos and late weaning is adaptive in the face of kwashiorkor which is assumed to be a form of protein malnutrition. Even under extreme protein deficiency mother's milk is believed to remain at a relatively constant protein level and of major importance in baby diets in protein deficient areas. Whiting has correlated a host of other traits with post partum sex taboos. Many of these may be non-adaptive, at least as far as disease is concerned, but the hypothesis states that a biologically adaptive culture trait lies at the base of the entire sequence.

There have been few adequate field studies of fertility, but Nag in his cross cultural analysis points out that venereal disease is a major factor in both sterility and fertility. Gonorrhea and granuloma venereum cause tubal obstruction in women and syphilis is known as a cause of congenital abnormalities and miscarriages. Social patterns associated with marriage and sexual license are important cultural factors in the distribution of disease organisms. Rosman (personal communication) has informed me that among the Kanuri of Northern Nigeria upper class men tend to marry virgins, while lower class individuals rarely do. Thus rich men and their wives are less likely to be infected by venereal organisms (the commonest is syphilis) and their fertility is significantly higher than other social groups within the culture.

The role of sexual selection in groups with genetic deformity and/ or high incidence of chronic diseases such as leprosy and tuberculosis may well affect the reproductive potential of such victims of disease and insulate at least part of the population from frequent contact with particular disease organisms or debilitating genetic traits. Intermarriage within sub-groups showing a high frequency of a recessive trait will increase the expression of such a trait within such groups by raising the coefficient of inbreeding, but it will also tend to restrict the distribution of the train in the population at large and weed out the higher frequency of homozygous individuals. There is no mention of such breeding patterns in the literature, but the possibility that they exist should certainly be investigated.

Laughlin presents an interesting hypothesis regarding the effect of longevity on cultural complexity. He suggests that in pre-literate societies where longevity is high for a significant portion of the population the "faculty-student ratio" is increased, leading to an increase in accumulated knowledge. This is an interesting idea, although the process must be somewhat circular, i.e., other things being equal, cultures with a greater accumulation of knowledge may have higher longevity due to better nutrition as well as more effective medical practice. Still, the circularity of the process does not negate the possibility that disease has played an indirect but non-genetic role in slowing down the process of cultural evolution in isolated populations in adverse environments. The entire question of longevity and culture is one which may be studied both in the field and archeologically, and I hope that the field of medical anthropology will stimulate more skeletal analysis of age at death as well as paleopathology, particularly for those cultures whose members thoughtfully provided the archeologist with graveyards and thus good sample populations.

Another little understood area of possible direct relationship between disease and cultures is stress, particularly overcrowding. In a delightful article on the cause of lemming migrations Deevey suggests a connection between overcrowding, stress and hypoglycemia. Deevey quotes J. J. Christian from the August 1950 issue of the Journal of Mammalogy:

"We now have a working hypothesis for the die off terminating a cycle. Exhaustion of the adreno-pituitary system resulting from increased stress inherent in a high population, especially in winter plus the late winter demands of the reproductive system, due to increased light or other factors, precipitates population-wide death with the symptoms of adrenal insufficiency and hypoglycemic convulsions."

Stress, no doubt, has bearing upon morbidity in terms of lowered resistance to infective agents as well as its possible effects on fertility. Factors which tend to expose or protect individuals from stress conditions are certainly important in the general investigation of cultural epidemiology. The negative effect of stress may well act as an adjustive mechanism to decrease population when a level of adaptive saturation is achieved. One of the major problems in stress research is the lack of good definitions and measuring devices. Such problems should be the concern of the anthropologist as well as the physiologist.

Analysis of the direct relationship between culture and specific diseases presents a fertile field for research of the type suggested above. In these studies the adaptive value of traits may be measured against comparative mortality and morbidity rates for specific diseases in the same or similar ecological zones.

General Problems for Research in Medical Anthropology

Although there are obvious difficulties it may be possible to measure the overall adaptation of a population group in terms of size and general measurements of fertility, morbidity, and mortality. Studies of this type may be controlled for economic and other factors as well as for environmental variables. A society transacted by caste differences would be an ideal laboratory for such research. Each caste would be treated as a subunit of society to be investigated independently for relationships between disease and culture. The combined ecological picture presented by the caste village as a single unit would also have to be included in such a study.

It would also be interesting to investigate those situations in which a society appears to be expanding at the expense of neighboring peoples. This is not to suggest that health levels and ecological adjustments to disease will be the only or even the major factor in such expansions, but they may well play some part in the vitality of the dominant culture. Relationships between disease and culture should be examined along with technology and social structure as possible determinants of adaptation.

In my field study in West Africa the dominant group in the area, the Abron of the Ivory Coast, were strikingly superior to their subject peoples in relation to political organization and health as measured by morbidity statistics. The health factor was related to superior hygiene practices.

Population size, density, and total distribution are probably the best measures of evolution (these reflect reproductive success and the widening of environmental niches) but there are situations in which expanding population would be non-adaptive. Insular populations must certainly require some measure of control for optimum adjustment. In crowded areas one would expect various functional disorders and lowered vitality to occur in high frequency as a result of stress and factors related to the ecology of disease organisms. In such situations there may be some sort of self-regulating mechanism which acts to keep population at an optimum level, although we may have recently outsmarted ourselves with the invention of the germ theory.

In most cases an expanding population must eventually increase its living space. The expansion of a group across certain ecological boundaries may be inhibited, however, by an inability to cope with new health problems. European expansion into parts of Africa was partially limited by a combination of low genetic resistance to many of the prevalent diseases such as yellow fever and malaria and by cultural practices which made adjustment difficult.

The framework within which disease and culture traits are related is extremely complex, and many factors must be taken into account. Among these are:

1. The mutual adjustment between host and parasite.

    The introduction of a new parasite of high virulence into a population creates a genetic sieve through which non-resistant individuals are rapidly selected out. At the same time natural selection will tend to operate on the parasite population to produce a strain of lowered virulence since a parasite benefits most by living in accommodation with its host. The death of an infected individual creates the problem of transfer for the disease organism, and while natural selection also works to refine the mechanisms associated with viable transfer, low grade infection is usually advantageous to the parasite population.

2. Cultural practices which indirectly affect health and fertility levels.

    a) Long term adjustments. Practically all behavior patterns will affect disease incidence in some way. Not all of these will be adaptive epidemiologically since adjustment to disease is only one of several problems faced by a population. It is likely that minimax situations develop through time such that benefits are matched, at least crudely, against harmful situations. The use or non-use of human excrement as a fertilizer may be an example of just such an adjustment. The practice increases soil fertility, but also increases contact with, and spread of, disease organisms. In areas where land is plentiful the practice has little to recommend it, but in over-populated areas it becomes almost an economic necessity. The distribution of this trait throughout the world reflects such a situation.

    It is my conclusion from a hasty perusal of the literature that the eating of carrion resulting from the natural death of domestic animals is restricted to areas in which animal husbandry is a difficult pursuit and where live cattle are rarely slaughtered. This is certainly true for the area of West Africa in which I did field work. People living in an environment well-suited for cattle raising will not eat diseased animals, while those living in more marginal areas will. The eating of carrion is, of course, a somewhat risky business as far as disease is concerned, but carrion is also a source of protein.

While the examples given are cases of adoption or non-adoption of a trait, there must be situations in which strategies based on compromise between profit and loss develop. Any study of ecological adaptation as systematic adjustment should, I would think, view the process in terms of such accommodations. The type of game theory analysis offered by Davenport may shed light on this aspect of ecology, although problems of quantification are obviously severe.

b) The introduction of new technology. Almost any technological change is bound to upset the ecological adjustment which developed in times of relative stability. In addition to creating problems in the economic order which may themselves be reflected in disease incidence due to increased stress, technological innovations may change the environment sufficiently to create new and advantageous opportunities for disease organisms or their carriers. Livingstone's example of agricultural development in West Africa is one example, the development of irrigation systems and the spread of schistosomiasis is another.

3. Ethnomedicine.

a) Drugs. All societies have means of treating disease. Many of these treatments involve the use of effective drugs. The result of effective medicinal knowledge feeds back to the prevalence of disease organisms and the incidence of disease.

b) The cognitive system as it relates to disease theory. The way in which disease is viewed by members of a society affects what individuals do about it, and this of course feeds back to the total ecological situation. Symptom categories may increase or decrease the effectiveness of treatment. The general attitude towards disease may orient therapy in the direction of symptoms, cause, or a total condition, and affect the success or failure of therapy in relation to specific disorders.

c) The medical practitioner. The role of treatment sources in a society and the methods they employ must also be considered. Strategies which are based on the analysis of the patient's complaint, for example, should be more effective than those which ignore the patient and make appeal to supernatural revelation.

4. Introduction of new diseases through contact.

Genetic and cultural adjustments are both upset with the introduction of new disease organisms. The general level of resistance in the population may be affected so that other diseases which have been brought under control may once again become a problem. Like any other change in environmental conditions the introduction of new disease organisms upsets the existing ecological relationships.

5. Acculturation.

A change in significant cultural practices by even a few members of the community may provide new avenues for the invasion of disease organisms. Social breakdown as a result of acculturation may affect only a minority of individuals and still create new situations for disease organisms to invade the entire population. The loyalty of conservative members of the community to traditional norms may break down as they themselves become victims of disease even though they refuse initially to change their traditional behavior.

Summary: Methods, Techniques and Problems for Study

At the beginning of this paper I asked the question: Can the Darwinian model of evolution be applied to cultural evolution and, if so, to what extent and how? I have attempted to answer the first part of this question in the affirmative by relating evolutionary studies to disease ecology and by suggesting areas for further research. What we should study is not biological or cultural evolution but evolution as a total process. Human evolution as a process is based on the interaction of cultural and physical variables. Medical anthropology clearly offers us an opportunity to study existing populations in terms of these factors and, as such, is a valuable area for research. But what are the limitations of such an approach, particularly in those situations in which genetic change is not a variable? I have no doubt that increasingly sophisticated environmental exploitation and innovation in social organization are major factors in the increase and spread of human populations and that except under special conditions disease is a somewhat less pervasive factor. But I am also convinced that any good theory of evolution must be Darwinian with biological variables as major factors in process and with population as the constant measuring device. If this is indeed the case, then medical anthropology has its place in such studies. The basic method is ecological with the focus on cultural and biological parameters. The theoretical basis of such research is the biological theory of evolution with the assumption that there are areas of culture which are open to investigation on the biological level. Reductionism in this sense is not to be feared. Specific studies may be carried out on a variety of levels but should include the following:

1. Studies of culture traits associated with presence or relative absence of specific diseases (functional, genetic, nutritional, and infectious).

2. Studies of population size in relation to fertility, and health levels as measured by mortality and morbidity in specific ecological niches.

3. Historical and paleopathological studies of disease distribution and its effects on population size and distribution.

4. Comparative studies of populations and behavioral systems in culture areas located in epidemic and endemic centers of disease.

5. Studies of the relation between types of stress and disease as well as fertility.

6. Studies of disease ecology in situations of culture change.

All studies of medical ecology require careful attention to demographic details. Population size, age pyramids, and sex ratios are all important sources of data. In addition to these, overall death rates, mortality, morbidity, fertility, and fecundity statistics are essential with breakdowns for each related to specific disorders. Problems related to genetics, of course, require adequate genealogical material as well as the appropriate biological techniques associated with the gathering of physiological samples. In addition to these techniques specific problems may require training in paleopathology and historical epidemiology. These in turn require training in ethnohistorical methods and biology. Where vectors are part of a disease cycle an entomological survey may be a prerequisite.

A basic understanding of ethnographic techniques and biological ecology is essential for all research in the areas described. This calls for training which goes beyond the traditional fields of anthropology, although it includes them. Teamwork is one way of dealing with the requirement of specialized knowledge but it is desirable and, I would hope, not impossible to train medical anthropologists to work with a minimum of aid. The major area of necessary cooperation is between anthropology and medicine, but in the long run the anthropological overview will be necessary to derive generalizations from data.

Linguistics

LINGUISTICS IS THE study or science of language. It is an independent discipline and, in the eyes of some of its foremost students, has no more necessary involvement with cultural anthropology than with history or philosophy. Yet the anthropologist has a different view. His subject is culture and culture rests upon the capacity to symbolize. Language is the most fundamental means of symboling, *ergo*, the anthropologist has a vital interest in linguistics. Indeed, so significant is the study of language for anthropology that it has its own linguistic specialists.

The division between general and anthropological linguistics is neither sharp nor consistent. To some extent it had significance when general linguists devoted themselves almost exclusively to Eurasian languages, particularly those of the Indoeuropean stock. Then the anthropologist who recorded or analyzed American Indian or African languages could work, for better or worse, in virtual independence. But, this state of affairs has been in the process of change for some time. Many able scholars trained as linguists have turned their attention to language families which once would have been considered exotic. Meanwhile, anthropological specialists in linguistics have increased their familiarity with the content and theory of general linguistics. Sharing problems and methods, the distinction between general and anthropological linguists is now often merely academic.

Just as physical anthropology embraces many different kinds of study, so linguistics has its special fields. For our purposes, these may be reduced to three: descriptive linguistics, historical linguistics and a more recent and controversial field known as meta- or psycholinguistics. Some of the content and methodology of each of these is discussed in the selections which follow. The first article, however, is devoted to the "symbol," the revolutionary element that simultaneously underlies both language and culture.

23 The Origin and Nature of Speech

Leslie A. White

MAN IS NOT THE ONLY ANIMAL THAT LEARNS. BEHAVIORAL PSYCHOLOGISTS *tell us that learning is an aspect of life, that it is found, to some degree, in all creatures, even the simplest. Man continues to learn in the fashion of his animal ancestors—through situational conditioning—but man has added a new dimension to the medium of learning and has thereby been transformed. The essence of the change lies in the concept of symbols and symboling. By means of symbols, man becomes free of situations and events in his learning process. Put otherwise, this means that it is not necessary to experience something in order to learn about it. Symbols— language—can convey the experiences of others to the innocent and naive. By an extension of this process the learning of one generation passes to the next. This is culture.*

The position maintained in the following selection, that symbols are associated only with man, is not beyond doubt. The attitude of Charles Darwin, though criticized by White, is still entertained by responsible scholars—who do so in terms not covered by White's suggestions. Furthermore, many linguists do not use the words "symbol" and "sign" in quite the same way as does White. At any rate, while the ability of certain nonhuman animals to create and use symbols is open to argument, and though a completely standardized vocabulary has yet to emerge in this field, the salient point of the following selection is basic to the an-

SOURCE: William S. Knickerbocker (ed.), *Twentieth Century English* (New York: Philosophical Library, 1940), pp. 93-103. Reprinted with the permission of the author and publisher.

For biographical data on the author, see I:3.

thropological understanding of human behavior. Only man, on this planet, engages in massive, systematic and continuous symboling. Only man has culture.

We can distinguish three stages in the development of vocal communication. In the first and most primitive stage the meanings of the vocal utterances are inherent in the sounds and the sounds are produced by instinct. In the second stage, meanings become attached to sounds, and are dependent, therefore, upon the situation rather than upon germ plasm. In the third stage, which is found only in the human species, meanings are determined and bestowed upon sounds by man himself. Let us examine each type in turn.

Vocal communication among some of the lower animals may properly be called instinctive. By this we mean that the utterances they make are direct, unlearned expressions of their organisms which indicate a state or condition of the organism. And, just as the production of these sounds is instinctive, so also is their appreciation by members of the species; the animal hearing them understands them (i.e., responds appropriately) by virtue of his own inborn neuro-sensory equipment. Thus, vocal communication of this type is simple, elemental, wholly instinctive. The production of sounds and the responses thereto are determined by the inherent properties of the organism. The meanings of the utterances are inherent in the sounds, which means that they are inherent in the organisms themselves.

In the second type of communication the meanings of the sounds are not inherent in the organisms of the animals concerned but are acquired by them. Thus, a certain sound might come to mean "Here is food" to a pig. We teach dogs, horses, and other animals to respond appropriately to vocal commands. The sounds "roll over" are originally meaningless to a dog. In time, however, by means of the mechanism known as *conditioned reflex*, the dog learns to roll over at the proper command. The sounds have acquired a meaning for the dog. In contrast with Type I, this meaning has come to the dog from the external world, not from his own organism. To be sure, the dog must have a certain type of nervous system to be able to acquire new meanings in this way; not every animal can do this. But the point here is that the meaning of the instrument of communication, the vocal command, is determined by external circumstance, not by the dog's neuro-sensory constitution. The meaning is not inherent in the sound but is acquired by it through experience.

In the third type of communication, meanings are bestowed upon sounds by those who use them. Thus the sound combination *po* may be given the meaning "fried rabbit," "come quickly," or "unfortunate." *Po*, which is quite meaningless in itself, had acquired a meaning and a significance. But is this not like the sounds "roll over" that acquire meaning for the dog? In neither instance is meaning inherent in the sounds. In both cases it is acquired through experience, the dog learning the meaning of the sounds as we learn the meaning of *po* or of *chien, hund,* or *syzygy*.

The two cases are indeed so much alike that the great Darwin argued in *The Descent of Man* that there is no fundamental difference between the mind of man and that of lower animals, but merely a difference of degree. "The lower animals differ from man solely in his almost infinitely larger power of associating together the most diversified sounds and ideas," he argues. Many psychologists, sociologists and anthropologists today still think as Darwin did decades ago, and maintain that man merely has more extensive mental powers than his sub-human relatives but none that is unique.

We are obliged, however, to disagree with Darwin and with present-day scholars who share his view. The difference between the mind of man and that of the lower animals *is* fundamental and is one of kind rather than merely of degree. An analysis of this difference leads us into the heart of the problem of speech.

Man is able to use symbols; no other creature possesses this ability. A symbol is a thing whose meaning is determined by those who use it as a means of communication. A symbol may have any perceptible form: a gesture, a sound, a shape, color, taste or odor. The most important form of symbolic expression is, however, articulate speech. Sounds—or, in writing, marks—are endowed with meaning by human beings who are thereby enabled to communicate ideas with them. Thus, "see," "cat," "sweet," "faint," etc., are made significant by arbitrary assignment of value to them and by mutual agreement to recognize these values. But are we not back again to the dog who has learned to sit up and bark at the command "Beg!"? Does not the dog learn the meaning of "words and sentences," to use Darwin's phrase, as we do? Yes, he does indeed, but this is not the whole story. The dog can acquire new meanings but he cannot originate them. The dog can learn the meanings of words, but he cannot determine what those meanings may be. Herein lies the difference between the mind of man and that of other living creatures, even the highest. Man can originate and bestow meaning and value upon things as he chooses. We can let *x* equal anything we please, a ton of coal, ten parsecs, or the honor of a king; red can stand for danger, courage, or a subversive political movement. In the realm of symbols, man can do as he pleases; he can assign any meaning to anything. No other creature can do this. Upon this unique faculty the whole of *human* existence depends and rests. It is the exercise of this ability that has created all civilizations of mankind. Before surveying the consequences of the symbolic faculty, however, let us analyze the difference between man and dog a bit further.

The dog understands words and phrases, as we know. He lies down, begs, and rolls over at the proper commands. But what he is doing is responding to a class of stimuli which we call *signs*. A *sign*, as we shall use the term, is something which indicates something else. We see smoke and infer fire; we see a red light and avoid danger. The meaning, the significance, of the sign may inhere in the physical properties of the sign itself and in its relation to the thing indicated, as in the case of smoke indicating the presence of fire. Or, the sign's meaning may be merely associated with its physical form, identified with it through the mechanism of the conditioned reflex, as in the case of the red light signifying danger. In either case, however, once the meaning of the sign has become identified with its physical form through association or conditioning, it functions as if it really were inherent in it. Let us now return to words.

Words function both as symbols and as signs. In other words, they are sometimes employed in *symbol* contexts, sometimes in *sign* contexts. The meaning of symbols cannot be perceived with the senses. One cannot tell, for example, what the sound compound *dola* means merely by hearing it. When the Spaniards first entered Mexico they could hear the Aztec word *calli* distinctly enough, but they had no way of telling from the sound alone whether it meant "house," or "tired." Neither could the Aztecs tell what *santo* means in Spanish merely by listening to its sound. The meanings of symbols can be grasped, and hence communicated, only by means of a neural structure for which we have no better name than "symbolic mechanism." Similarly with symbols in other forms. We cannot tell merely by looking at a color whether it stands for sorrow, courage, or leprosy. Symbolic gestures do not betray their significance to the senses. We can discover the meaning of symbols only by means of symbolic communication itself, by the exercise of our neurological symbolic faculty.

To say that we cannot perceive the values of symbols is, of course, but another way of saying that their meanings are not inherent in them but are derived from another source. We can discover the saline value of salt, or the saccharine value of sugar, with our senses because these properties are an integral part of their atomic and molecular structure. But we cannot tell, by any amount of sensory inquiry, or by physical and chemical examination, whether these articles will sell for two cents a pound or six. Their commercial value is a symbolic value, bestowed upon them by society just as meanings are assigned to hat-tipping and green lights. The realm of symbols is, therefore, a supra-sensory world, so to speak, a region in which values live and function but they cannot be grasped and measured with our senses. To be sure, symbols must have physical forms, and these forms are perceptible, otherwise they could not enter our experience at all. But the physical form of a symbol is one thing; its meaning quite another. Symbols are, therefore, imperceptible values lodged in physical forms. The only way in which symbolic meanings can be communicated is by the same means which brings them into being in the first instance: the neurological "symbolic faculty." Animals who lack this faculty can never experience values which can exist only in symbolic form. This is why no other creature can ever enter the world of man, the human being.

Symbols are created by bestowing a meaning or value upon some physical form. But after one has encountered the meaning in its physical form a few times they become so fused in experience that the physical form itself is able to express and to communicate the meaning. Thus we can coin a word, *bota*, give it the meaning "close your eyes." After a few experiences the meaning becomes so identified with the sounds that we can respond immediately and appropriately upon hearing them. We can also distinguish *bota* from *boka* which might mean "shake your head." We see, then, that after the meaning has become identified with the physical form through the process of conditioning, we behave as if the meaning were inherent in the sounds, for we now perceive the meanings with our senses. But the words are no longer functioning in the *symbol* context; they are now functioning as *signs*. In human behavior, therefore, words originate as symbols, but after we have learned their meaning they function as signs. Let us return now to our dog who "understands words and sentences" and see what the situation is there.

We can invent a word, *pado*, give it a meaning, "sit down," and teach the dog to react appropriately to the command; we say "Pado!" and the dog sits down. But suppose a human being were our subject instead of a dog. Would the two experiments differ in any significant respect? Not at all. The human being might learn more quickly or he might not, but so far as the *kind* of behavior involved is concerned, the two experiments would not differ at all. In each case, sounds acquire a meaning, the subject of the experiment learns it, and reacts accordingly. How, then, do dogs differ from men in word behavior? Simply in this: words can only be *signs* to a dog; they are *symbols* as well as *signs* to man.

Here is what the dog cannot do: He cannot bestow meanings upon things. He can acquire new meanings but he cannot originate them. He can learn what meaning has been given to *pado*, but he cannot take any part in the determination of that meaning. Moreover, the range of meanings which he can acquire is limited by the range of his senses; he cannot ever receive symbolic meanings because they lie beyond the boundaries of mere perception. Thus a dog could be taught to respond in a specific manner to the word *sin* or *holy*. He could distinguish between *sin* and *pin*, or *skin*, as we do, and react to each in a definitely prescribed manner. But he could never have any conception of what *sin* means to us, because this word, like all other words, has also a symbolic significance as well as a sign significance and that can be grasped only by the special neural mechanism which man alone possesses.

Here we have, then, the difference between the mind of a dog, or any other of the lower animals, and the mind of man. Man can originate and bestow meaning upon anything he chooses. He can communicate these meanings to others of his kind in the vehicle of physical forms. The dogs, apes, rats, etc., can only acquire meanings which have become identified in their experience with certain forms. They can have no part in determining these meanings. And they cannot rise above the level of sense perception in their grasp of meaning. The significance of this difference is, of course, tremendous; it is the difference between a human being and a mere brute. But before examining this difference in detail, let us inquire into its origin.

A man sees with his eyes, hears with his ears, and smells with his nose. But what what does he "symbol" with? Since the most conspicuous and important forms of symbolic expression is articulate speech, some have thought that this peculiarly human faculty lies in the organs of speech. But there are no "organs of speech," properly speaking. There are, of course, organs of vocal utterance, but speech is more than mere sound. Some birds are able to reproduce the sounds of words, but this is not speech. Apes have the anatomical and muscular mechanisms requisite for speech so far as jaws, tongue, lips, larynx, etc., are concerned, yet they are incapable of speech. On the other hand, the communication of ideas by symbolic means does not require articulate vocal utterance, as we know. We can do this with writing or with other gestures. Given the ability to use symbols, to assign meanings to physical forms, we could devise a system of communication in which we did no more than move a single finger or toe in a system of dots and dashes. We could even symbol with our ears if we could move them. In short, we could communicate symbolically with any part of our body which we can move at will and which can be observed by someone else. To be sure, these non-vocal means of symbolic communication would be more cumbersome and less efficient than spoken words, but they are no less possible. The human species uses vocal utterance as its principal means of symbolic communication not because it is the only possible one, for there are many other possibilities, but because it is the easiest, the most efficient and economical.

If the "organs of speech" are not the seat of symbolic communication, what then is? The fact of the matter is that we know very little about the basis of this faculty. We have no doubt but that it resides in the nervous system, especially in the forebrain. But it is easy to jump to unwarranted conclusions here. The ape's brain is very much like man's, yet the ape is without symbols. Man's brain is larger than the ape's, both absolutely and relatively in proportion to body size, and is more highly convoluted. But man has no kind of brain cells or brain connections that the ape does not have; both brains are composed of the same kind of material and are constructed on essentially the same plan. How is it, then, that man is capable of symboling whereas the ape is not?

The only answer at the present time appears to be: more brain. Sometimes differences in quantity produce differences in quality; additions of degree eventuate in differences in kind. Thus additional quantities of heat will transform water into a different kind of structure: vapor. When development within the egg reaches a certain point, the bird hatches and embarks upon a new kind of life. In somewhat the same way, we reason, when the primate brain had reached a certain stage of development a new kind of function became possible. This is a reasonable and valid assumption, but it does not tell us much. The fact is, we know almost nothing about the neurology of symboling.

We are not to assume, of course, that the transition from the subsymbolic level to the symbolic in primate evolution took place suddenly. The ability to use symbols does not mature overnight in the child, but requires considerable time to become habitual and effective. In the same way, we may assume, it took time, perhaps thousands of years, for the evolving symbolic faculty among anthropoids to become sufficiently developed to receive overt expression, and still longer for it to become an habitual and effective instrument in the conduct of life.

But the fact that the transition from non-symbolic to symbolic behavior in the species and in the individual is gradual rather than sudden in no way invalidates our contention that the difference is one of kind rather than of degree. An animal is either able to symbol or it is not; there are no half-way stages. All attempts to teach apes, our nearest non-human relatives, to talk have failed. It is not that such efforts have met with little success; they have had *no success at all.*

Let us turn now to the consequences of the use of symbols. We have said earlier that everything that is peculiarly human, everything that separates man from the lower animals, all civilizations, depend upon the symbolic faculty. We shall now see how this can be true. Anatomically, man is much like the anthropoid apes. Temperamentally, too, man closely resembles his simian relatives, much more so, for example, than he does the ungulates, rodents, or carnivores. Physiologically, in the dynamics of the living processes, man is fundamentally like, not only the other primates, not only other mammals, but other vertebrates, including the fishes. But in one respect man is different, and this difference sets him off from all other creatures and makes him unique on earth: symbols. It was a sound intuition that led earlier peoples to declare "In the beginning was the word." Sound, too, was their appreciation of the creative power of words, for it was words that transformed an ape into a man, and the crude culture of a savage into the civilization of today.

It used to be customary to define man as the tool-using animal. But apes use tools with versatility and skill. Not only that, they can even invent and make tools. But the use of tools among apes is a discontinuous process, subjectively as well as objectively. Being discontinuous it is neither cumulative nor progressive. One generation of apes begins its career of tool-using where the preceding generation began. With man it is different. To man a tool is not merely an object, an instrument with which to cut or pound. It is also an idea, a concept which is expressed in symbolic form. Thus the actual tool may often lie outside the range of his sensory experience. But the idea-tool is with him always. So vivid and real is the tool-idea that man comes to regard it as primary, as the ideal of which real tools are only imperfect and ephemeral copies. In this way, the tool process in the human species becomes a continuous process; and, being continuous, it can become cumulative and progressive. It was the symbolic faculty which transformed the occasional and discrete tool experiences of the ape into the continuous, cumulative, progressive process that has produced our civilizations in their material aspects.

The social and intellectual superstructures of all civilizations must, of course, rest upon a material, mechanical basis that has been wrought with tools. Without a civilized technology there could be no civilized society or philosophy. Contrariwise, a primitive technology must mean a primitive type of social life and thought. The Tool is the measure of civilizations.

But if the tool is both basis and measure, the symbol is always the means, for without symbols social and intellectual life above the anthropoid level would be impossible.

Without articulate speech we would have no rules of social life other than those arising from desire, directed by whim and validated by brute force. We could have rules neither of monogamy nor of polygamy, for how could these concepts be communicated and agreed upon without symbolic communication? How could one know that he might have two mates, providing he possessed them one at a time but not both at once, without speech? How could one know that he could marry a cousin of the second degree but not of the first, without language? Indeed, how could we have any classification of relatives at all were it not for words to distinguish one from another?

How could one know right from wrong without symbols? How could there *be* a right or a wrong? How could one know that the kid should not be seethed in the mother's milk if he were not told? Or, that he should not mar the corners of his beard? How could he know how many souls he had (the number varies, of course, in the beliefs of man), which god to worship, which spirit to exorcise, and how to dispose of the dead, if it were not possible to symbol?

Examples are endless. From one end of human behavior (behavior, that is, which is peculiar to the species man) to the other, from the simplest thing in civilization to a World State, a Universal Church, or the Philosophy of Science, the symbol is the *sine qua non* of existence.

We can now see even more clearly the uniqueness of symbolic experience in the human species. It is impossible to bring any dog, rat or ape, no matter how intelligent, to any appreciation of the significance of such concepts as *cousin, Tuesday, 3, kosher, money,* etc. The most gifted ape can never know the difference between a Buddhist and a Baptist, that it might be wrong for him to eat bananas on Wotan's day, or that he may not marry his cousin. We could teach a dog to react in a certain way to the stimulus $\sqrt{-1}$, Santa Maria, or " 'twas brillig and the slithy toves," but we could never bring him to an appreciation of the meanings they have for us. Our life is a thing apart. Our world, with its heavens and its gods, its institutions and its laws, its morals and rituals, its arts, philosophies and science, is a house built with symbols and in it we live alone. We may, as fellow animals, play with dogs or labor with camels and oxen. But our brute friends can never cross the threshold of our house and share our symbols with us. This is our own, our private world.

24 The Human Revolution

Charles F. Hockett and Robert Ascher

THE EDITOR'S PROBLEM WITH THIS SELECTION WAS WHERE TO PUT IT. NO *apologies would have been necessary if it had been placed in the section on human evolution; indeed, it may have been assigned to you in precisely that context. Yet at the heart of the human revolution is the evolution of what we assume to have been an ancient ancestral dependence upon a limited call system into an ability to communicate through the complexities*

SOURCE: *American Scientist*, Vol. 52 (1964), pp. 70–92. Reprinted with the permission of the authors and publisher. This paper will be found also in *Current Anthropology*, 5, 1964, where the text is accompanied by extensive critical apparatus and bibliography, and is followed by comments from some twenty-five specialists. Since the function of the authors has been largely that of compilers of data gathered and hypotheses formulated by others, the reader who is led to refer to the present paper in any formal context is earnestly requested to consult the fuller version, that he may give credit where credit is due.

The authors dedicate this essay to the memory of Paul Fejos, whose encouragement, over a number of years, played an important part in bringing the work to fruition.

Charles F. Hockett (b. 1916) is Professor of Linguistics and Anthropology at Cornell University, where he also teaches Chinese. His interests range over the general field of linguistics with special reference to problems of the relations between language and culture. Among his works are *A Manual of Phonology* (1955) and *A Course in Modern Linguistics* (1958). He is co-author with Chao-ying Fang of *Spoken Chinese* (1945) and the author of a recent article of specific interest to readers of this volume, "Animal 'Languages' and Human Language," *Human Biology*, Vol. 31, i (1959).

Robert Ascher (b. 1931) is Professor of Anthropology at Cornell University. He has done fieldwork in classical archaeology and ethnology (Seri Indians of Lower California) and is currently Associate Editor of *American Anthropologist*. His major research interests are the origins of man and method and theory in archaeology; one of his recent articles deals with computer-analyzed archaeology.

of language. The beauty of the selection that follows is its treatment of this development within the larger context of an informed view of general human evolution. It is worth noting that this article represents a prime example of the easy fusion of the four major disciplinary orientations of anthropology. Obviously, all work will not fuse the fields, but the value of doing so when in the realm of general statements about our evolution bodes well for the continued unity of anthropology as a whole.

This essay attempts to set forth the story of the emergence of the first humans from their prehuman ancestors. A special feature is that we have tried to incorporate the various steps and stages of the evolution of language into the total picture.

The term "revolution" in our title is not intended to be flamboyant. A revolution is a relatively sudden set of changes that yield a state of affairs from which a return to the situation just before the revolution is virtually impossible. This seems to be the sense of the word intended by V. Gordon Childe when he speaks of the "Neolithic Revolution" and of the "Urban Revolution." But these two revolutions were experienced by our fully human ancestors. The second could not have occurred had it not been for the first. The first could not have taken place had it not been for an even earlier extremely drastic set of changes that turned non-humans into humans. These drastic changes, as we shall see, may have required a good many millions of years; yet they can validly be regarded as "sudden" in view of the tens of millions of years of mammalian history that preceded them.

For the reconstruction of human evolution we have evidence of two sorts, plus certain firm and many tentative principles of interpretation.

One kind of evidence is the archeological, fossil, and geological record. The fossil record of our own ancestry is still disappointingly sparse for the bulk of the Miocene and Pliocene. Doubtless the record will never be as complete as we might wish. But techniques of interpretation improve, and we suspect that the archeological record, in particular, holds an as yet unrealized potential.

The second kind of evidence is the directly observable physical structure and ways of life of ourselves and of our nearest nonhuman cousins, the other hominoids of today. Chimpanzees, gorillas, orang-utans, gibbons, siamangs, and humans have ultimately a common ancestry not shared with any other living species. We shall refer to their most recent common ancestors as the *proto-hominoids*. Since all the hominoids of today constitute continuations of the proto-hominoids, we can attempt to reconstruct something of the physical structure and of the lifeways of the common ancestors by comparing those of the descendants. Such an effort at reconstruction must at the same time propose realistic courses of development from the ancestral group down to each of the directly observable descendant groups, and must make proper provision for those strains known only through fossils or archeological remains.

The method is very much like the comparative method of historical linguistics—and, as a matter of fact, it was first devised in the latter context, only subsequently transferred to the domain of biological evolution. The term "comparative" appears also in "comparative morphology" (or "comparative anatomy"); we must therefore emphasize that the method of which we are speaking applies not only to gross anatomy but also to the fine-scale phenomena dealt with in biochemistry, and not only to structure but also to behavior.

In any domain of application, a comparative method shares with all other historical methods the fact that it can yield reliable results only insofar as one can be sure of certain key *irreversible* processes. Given information about stages *A* and *B* in the history of a single system, we can posit that stage *A* preceded stage *B* if and only if the change from *A* to *B* is the sort that happens, while a change from *B* to *A* is impossible or highly improbable. In historical linguistics, the requisite irreversibility is afforded by sound change. The philologists of the late nineteenth century were correct when they characterized sound change as slow, constant, inexorable, and beyond conscious control; for, as we shall see later, it is a necessary by-product of a crucial design feature of all human language, and could not be eliminated save by altering language into something unrecognizable. Whenever sound change leads to the repatterning of the phonological system of a language—and this has happened about one hundred times in English between King Alfred's day and our own—the consequences ramify through every part of the language; soon the results are so scattered, so subtle, and from the point of view of effectiveness of communication so *trivial*, that a return to the state of affairs before the repatterning has, in effect, probability zero.

The situation in biological evolution is more complicated, with no simple analog for sound change. Is a particular organ in a particular species (living or fossil) vestigial or incipient? Is the swimming bladder of current teleosts a former lung, or is the lung of lungfishes a one-time swimming bladder? Evolutionists are plagued by such questions. The answers are often obtainable, but not through any simple formula. A new fossil does not automatically resolve the dispute, since one's opinions as to lines and directions of development will affect one's notions as to how the new fossil is to be fitted into the picture.

For the *mechanisms* of change we are in less trouble. We have now a good understanding of genetics, and also of the traditional transmission of lifeways. The latter was once believed to be exclusively human, but this is not so. At least for land mammals and for birds, genetics and tradition work in a constant dialectic complementation, neither being wholly responsible for anything. We are also clearer about a point that used to be quite obscure: the domain (so to speak) within which these two mechanisms operate is not primarily the individual but the community, which has a gene pool, a distribution of phenotypes, and a repository of lifeways, and which, as a functioning unit, faces the problems of survival.

The greatest pitfall in evolutionary thinking stems from the keenness of hindsight. For example, we know that long ago, over a long period of time, our own ancestors abandoned the trees for the ground and developed effective machinery for bipedal locomotion. This seems beyond dispute, because the prehominoid primates were arboreal and we ourselves are bipedal ground walkers. But when we ask *why* this change, we must remember that our ancestors of the time were not striving to become human. They were doing what all animals do: trying to stay alive.

Thus, in searching for causes of the change we must look to conditions pertaining at the time. There are only two possibilities. The conditions at that time may have been such that minor variations in gait and posture had no bearing on survival. We should then class the change that actually did take place as fortuitous. Or, the conditions of life at the time may have positively favored selection for bipedal locomotion and upright posture. If this is what happened, then the change was adaptive. By definition, a change that was neither adaptive nor fortuitous would lead to the extinction of the strain that underwent it, and in the present instance we know that that did not happen.

The most powerful antidote for the improper use of keen hindsight is a principle that we shall call "Romer's Rule," after the paleontologist A. S. Romer who has applied it so effectively—without giving it any name—in his own work. We phrase this Rule as follows:

The initial survival value of a favorable innovation is conservative, in that it renders possible the maintenance of a traditional way of life in the face of changed circumstances.

Later on, of course, the innovation may allow the exploration of some ecological niche not available to the species before the change; but this is a consequence, not a cause.

One of Romer's examples concerns the evolution of Devonian lungfishes into the earliest amphibians. The invasion of the land was feasible only with strong fins (which in due time became legs). But strong fins were not developed "in order to" invade the land. The climate of the epoch was tempestuous; the water level of the pools in which the lungfishes lived was subject to sudden recessions. There was thus selection for those strains of lungfishes which, when stranded by such a recession, had strong enough fins to *get back to the water*. Only much later did some of their descendants come to stay ashore most of the time.

It is worthy of note that Romer's Rule is not anti-teleological. We are permitted to speak in terms of purposeful behavior whenever we are dealing with a system that incorporates negative feedback. Individual organisms, and certain groupings of organisms (the kind we call "communities"), are such systems. There is nothing wrong in asserting that a stranded Devonian lungfish tried his best to get back to the water. We are forced, however, to distinguish carefully between purposes and *consequences*, and we are not allowed to ascribe "purposefulness" to any such vague and long-continuing process as "evolution."

No principle, no matter how universal, answers all questions. Romer's Rule cuts as keenly as any razor ever devised by Occam to expose, excise, and discard unworkable pseudo-explanations. Yet it is applicable, in a sense, only after the fact. For example, in this paper we follow majority opinion and trace man's ancestry back to a point of separation from the ancestors of the great apes, the gibbons, and the siamangs. Having assumed this, we elaborate one of Romer's own suggestions as to how some of the early developments may have come about. Suppose, however, that new fossil finds should convince us that man is actually more closely related to some other group of surviving primates. We should then be confronted by a different set of putative historical facts requiring explanation; but we should evoke the same Rule as we sought that explanation. The Rule does not tell us which line of descent to postulate.

The Proto-Hominoids

From the location, date, and morphology of the fossil dryopithecine *Proconsul* we infer that the proto-hominoids lived in East Africa in the Middle or Lower Miocene or, at the earliest, in the Upper Oligocene. This does not mean that *Proconsul* himself—in any of the strains or species so far identified—was a proto-hominoid; indeed, he is not a good candidate as an ancestor of the gibbons and siamangs, to whom, by definition, the proto-hominoids were ancestral. But *Proconsul* was clearly an *early* hominoid, and at the moment he is the best fossil evidence available for the data and provenience we seek.

The proto-hominoids inherited certain crucial capacities from their totally tree-dwelling ancestors. It is the arboreal pattern that developed the keen accommodative vision characteristic of the higher primates, deemphasized the sense of smell, turned forelimbs into freely movable arms with manipulative hands, and built brains somewhat larger than the average for land mammals.

The balance of the characterization we are about to give derives mainly from the comparative method applied to what we know of the hominoids of today. We shall not give all the evidence in detail. Furthermore, for the sake of vividness we shall allow some interpolations of a degree of precision that may be unwarranted. The proportion of guesswork in each statement will, we think, be obvious.

Like most of their descendants, the proto-hominoids were hairy. Like all of them, they were tailless. They were smaller than we are, though not so small as present-day gibbons, whose size has decreased as an adaptation to brachiation. They had mobile facial muscles; they had neither mental eminence nor simian shelf (nor mastoid processes); they had large interlocking canines, and could chew only up and down; their tooth pattern was $\frac{2:1:2:3}{2:1:2:3}$. It seems likely that there was little sexual dimorphism, although on this the comparative evidence is conflicting. The chromosome count was somewhere in the forties.

They lived in bands of from ten to thirty, consisting typically of one or a very few adult males plus females and offspring. They had a roughly defined nucleated territoriality: that is, the territory within which the members of a band moved about had only roughly demarcated boundaries, but centered on the specific arboreal sites in which they built their nests. The total population was probably never very great, nor very dense, from the proto-hominoids all the way down to the first true humans.

They were expert climbers and spent much of their lives in the trees of the tropical or subtropical forests which were their habitat, certainly building their nests in the trees and sleeping there. Like rodents, they climbed up a tree head first; unlike rodents, they climbed down stern first. They slept at night, from dusk to dawn, which in the tropics means nearer to one-half of each twenty-four-hour period than to the one-third characteristic of ourselves in recent times. They were active during the day. Some activities, particularly the constant search for food, led them not only among the trees—in which they may have brachiated, but with no great expertness—but also quite regularly to the ground below. On the ground, they could stand with a semiupright posture (erect enough to raise their heads above shoulder-high grass to look about), and they could sit with arms free for manipulative motions; they could walk on all fours and could run on their feet, but bipedal walking was infrequent and awkward.

Occasionally they would pick up a stick or stone and use it as a tool. Judging from modern chimpanzees, they may have reshaped such tools slightly, using nothing but their hands and teeth to do so, and may have carried a tool for a short distance for immediate use, thereafter discarding it. They carried other things too, in mouth or hands or both, in connection with nest-building; and at least the females, perhaps on occasion the males, carried infants.

Their diet was largely vegetarian, supplemented by worms and grubs, and sometimes by small mammals or birds that were injured or sick and thus unable to escape. They scavenged the remains of the kills of carnivores whenever they could. Unlike all other mammals except the

Dalmation coach hound, their bodies produced no uricase; hence uric acid was not converted into allantoin before secretion in the urine, and had a chance to accumulate in the bloodstream. The structural formula of uric acid is something like that of caffein and, like the latter, it seems to be a mild brain stimulant. Since this type of purine metabolism is shared by all the hominoids, it can hardly explain our own unusual brilliance; but it may help to account for the generally high level of hominoid intelligence as compared with that of other primates and other mammals.

The males had the pendulous penis typical of the primates. Copulation was effected exclusively with the dorsal approach common to land mammals in general. Gestation required about thirty weeks. The uterus was single-chambered, and twinning was as rare as it is for us today. The placenta was of the single-disc type. The young required and received maternal care for many months. Mammary glands were pectoral; nursing females held infants to the breast in their arms, though doubtless the infant clung to the mother's fur also. The eruption of permanent teeth began perhaps at two and one-half or three. Menarche was at eight or nine years; general growth stopped for both sexes at nine or ten. The females showed a year-round menstrual cycle rather than a rutting season. Inbreeding within the band was the rule. The life-span was potentially about thirty years, but death was largely from accident, disease, or predation, or a combination of these, rather than old age. Corpses were abandoned, as were members of the band too sick, injured, or feeble to keep up with the rest, and were disposed of by predators or scavengers. Adult males were sexually interested in females and "paternally" interested in infants, but without any permanent family bond, and without any jealousy when they were themselves sexually satisfied.

Relations with adjacent bands were normally hostile to neutral, rarely if ever friendly; yet there was surely enough contact to provide for some exchange of genes. Social differentiation within the band turned largely on age and sex, secondarily on physical strength. In case of conflict of interest within the band, the huskiest adult males normally got their way. Collective activities required intragroup coordination, effected by various forms of communication—patterns of body motion, pushing and prodding, changes of body odor, and vocal signals. The conventions of these forms of communication were transmitted in part genetically, but in some part by tradition, acquired by the young through guided participation in the ways of the group. This implies also a certain capacity to learn from experience, and to pass on any new skills thus acquired to other members of the band by teaching and learning, rather than merely by slow genetic selection. But we may assume that usually there was very little new in any one lifetime thus to be learned or passed on.

A kind of activity called *play* is widespread among land mammals, and obviously intensified among primates; we can be sure that the proto-hominoids indulged in it, at least before maturity. It is very hard to characterize play precisely, beyond saying that it resembles one or another serious activity without being serious. Play at fighting, observable for example among dogs, goes through much the same gross motions as true fighting but the participants receive no injury. Sexual play has the general contours of courtship, but ends short of coitus or with mock coitus. We suspect that play is *fun*, for any species that manifests it, and that that is the immediate motive for indulging in it. But play is also genuinely pedagogical, in that the young thereby get needed practice in certain patterns of behavior that are biologically important for adult life.

The proto-hominoids did not have the power of speech. The most that we can validly ascribe to them in this respect is a call system similar to that of modern gibbons. Even this ascription may be stretching the comparative evidence somewhat. It is not hard to assume that a line of continuity from the proto-hominoids to the gibbons should have maintained such a call system essentially unchanged. It is also quite reasonable, as we shall see, to explain the evolution of a call system into language among our ancestors. The difficulty is to account for the apparently less highly developed vocal-auditory signaling of the great apes. Our hypothesis for the proto-hominoids suggests that the communicative behavior of the great apes may be somewhat more subtle and complex than has yet been realized. Be this as it may, we posit a call system for the proto-hominoids because we know no other way to proceed.

The essential design features of a call system are simple. There is a repertory of a half-dozen or so distinct signals, each the appropriate vocal response—or the vocal segment of a more inclusive response—to a recurrent and biologically important type of situation. Among gibbons, one such situation is the discovery of food; another is the detection of danger; a third is friendly interest and the desire for company. A fourth gibbon call apparently does nothing but indicate the whereabouts of the gibbon that emits it: this call keeps the band from spreading out too thin as it moves through the trees. One can guess at other possible situations appropriate for a special call: sexual interest; need for maternal care; pain. Band-to-band differences in calls may help to distinguish friend from alien.

A single call may be varied in intensity, duration, or number of repetitions, to correlate with and give information about the strength of the stimulus which is eliciting it. However, the signals of a call system are *mutually exclusive* in the following sense: the animal, finding himself in a situation, can only respond by one or another of the calls or by silence. He cannot, in principle, emit a signal that has some of the features of one call and some of another. If, for example, he encounters food and danger at the same time, one of these will take precedence: he is constrained to emit either the food call or the danger call, not some mixture of the two.

The technical description of this mutual exclusiveness is to say that the system is *closed*. Language, in sharp contrast, is *open* or *productive:* we freely emit utterances that we have never said nor heard before, and are usually understood, neither speaker nor hearer being aware of the novelty.

A call system differs from language in two other ways, and perhaps in a third. (1) Gibbons do not emit, say, the food call unless they have found food (or, perhaps, are responding to the food call from another gibbon, as they approach for their share). Furthermore, the gibbon that finds food does not go back to headquarters and report; he stays by the food as he emits the call. A call system does not have *displacement*. Language does: we speak freely of things that are out of sight or are in the past or future—or even nonexistent. (2) The utterances of a language consist wholly of arrangements of elementary signaling units called *phonemes* (or *phonological components*, to be exact), which in themselves have no meanings but merely serve to keep meaningful utterances apart. Thus, an utterance has both a structure in terms of these meaningless but differentiating elements, and also a structure in terms of the minimum meaningful elements. This design feature is *duality of patterning*. A call system lacks it, the differences between any two calls being global. (3) Finally, the detailed conventions of any one language are transmitted wholly by the traditional mechanism, though, of course, the capacity to learn a language, and probably the drive to do so, are genetic. On this score we are still in ignorance about the gibbons. Regional differences in gibbon calls have been noted, but various balances between tradition and genetics can yield that. We believe it safer to assume that proto-hominoid call systems were passed down from generation to generation largely through the genes, tradition playing a minor role. This assumption is the conservative one—it gives us more to try to explain in later developments than would any alternative.

This completes our characterization of the proto-hominoids, which can now serve as point of departure for the story of our own evolution.

Out of the Trees

Some of the descendants of the proto-hominoids moved out of the trees and became erect ground-walking bipeds. Romer's description of how this may have begun affords another example of the application of the Rule we ascribe to him.

Geological evidence suggests that at one or more times during the East African Miocene a climatic change gradually thinned out the vegetation, converting continuous tropical forest into open savannah with scattered clumps of trees. As the trees retreated, some bands of hominoids retreated with them, never abandoning their classical arboreal existence;

their descendants of today are the gibbons and siamangs. Other bands were caught in isolated groves of slowly diminishing extent. In due time, those bands whose physique made it possible for their members to traverse open country to another grove survived; those that could not do this became extinct. Thus, for those bands, the survival value of the perquisites for safe ground travel was not at all that they could therefore begin a new way of life out of the trees, but that, when necessary, they could make their way to a place where the traditional arboreal way of life could be continued. The hominoids that were successful at this included those ancestral to the great apes and to ourselves.

Sometimes the band forced to try to emigrate from a grove would be the total population of that grove. More typically, we suspect, population pressure within a diminishing grove would force bands into competition over its resources, and the less powerful bands would be displaced. Also, when a migrating band managed to reach another grove, it would often happen that the new grove was already occupied, and once again there would be competition. Thus, in the long run, the trees would be held by the more powerful, while the less powerful would repeatedly have to get along as best they could in the fringes of the forest or in open country. Here is a double selective process. The trees went to the more powerful, provided only that they maintained a minimum ability to traverse open country when necessary: some of these successful ones were ancestral to the great apes of today. Our own ancestors were the failures. We did not abandon the trees because we wanted to, but because we were pushed out.

We are speaking here of displacements and movements of whole bands, not of individual animals. There is one thing that surely accompanied any band whenever it moved: the essential geometry of its territoriality. At any halt, no matter how temporary, whether in the trees, under the trees, or in open country, some specific site became, for the nonce, "home base"—a GHQ, a center, a focus, relative to which each member of the band oriented himself as he moved about. Headquarters was the safest place to be, if for no other reason than the safety of numbers. In a later epoch—though doubtless earlier than will ever be directly attested by archeology—headquarters among our own ancestors came to be crudely fortified, as perhaps by a piled ring of stones; it became the place where things were kept or stored; in due time it became house, village, fort, city. But earliest of all it was *home*. The tradition for this sort of territoriality is much older than the proto-hominoids, and has continued unbroken to the present day.

It is at this point in our story that we must stop referring to our ancestors as "hominoids" and start calling them "hominids." Of course, all hominids are hominoids; but we have now seen the sorting-out of the pre-apes from the pre-humans, and when we wish to speak exclusively of the later the appropriate term is "hominid."

This is also the appropriate point for a warning. Because it does not take very long to describe a series of putative evolutionary events (such as the recession of the forest and its impact on the hominoids), it is all too easy to visualize those events as a fierce, intense, tooth-and-nail struggle. That is assuredly wrong. The typical pace of evolution is extremely leisurely. To observe that pace, we need only look about us today.

Carrying

It is no joke to be thrown out of one's ancestral home. If the next grove is only a few miles away, in sight, then one has something to aim for; but sooner or later movements must have taken place without any such visible target. Treeless country holds discomforts and dangers. There may not be much food, at least not of a familiar sort. There may be little available water, for the trees tend to cluster where the water is more abundant. And there are fleet four-footed predators, as well as herbivorous quadrupeds big and strong enough to be dangerous at close quarters. One cannot avoid these other animals altogether, since their presence often signals the location of water, or of food fit also for hominid consumption. The quest for food must be carried on constantly, no matter how pressing may be the drive to find a new grove of trees in which to settle. It is a wonder that any of the waifs of the Miocene savannah survived at all. Enormous numbers of them must have died out.

The trick that made survival possible for some of them was the trick of *carrying*. The proto-hominoids, as we have seen, probably carried twigs and brush to make nests, and certainly carried infants. Also, they had fine arms and hands usable for carrying as well as for climbing, grasping, and manipulating; and the comparative evidence suggests that they occasionally picked up sticks or stones to use as tools. These are the raw-materials for the kind of carrying to which we now refer. But it takes something else to blend them into the new pattern. In the trees, hands are largely occupied with climbing. The infant-in-arms grabs onto the mother when the latter needs her hands for locomotion. The twig being taken to the nest is transferred to the mouth when the hand cannot at the same time hold it and grasp a tree branch. One puts down one's ad hoc tool when one has to move.

The conditions for carrying are no better on the ground than in the trees if the hand must revert to the status of a foot. But if bipedal locomotion is at all possible, then the hand is freed for carrying; and the survival value of carrying certain things in turn serves to promote a physical structure adapted to bipedal locomotion.

Two sorts of ground carrying in the hands may have been extremely early; there seems to be no way of determining which came first. One is the carrying of crude weapons; the other is the transportation of scavenged food.

The earliest ground carrying of weapons may well have been a sort of accident. Imagine an early hominid—perhaps even a prehominid hominoid—sitting on the ground and pounding something (a nut, say) with a handy stone. A predator approaches. Our hero jumps up and runs away as best he can on two legs—there are no trees nearby into which to escape—but keeps his grasp on the stone for no better reason than that he does not need his hand for anything else. Cornered, he turns, and either strikes out at the predator with the hand that holds the stone, or else throws it. The predator falls or runs off, and whatever in our hero's genes or life experience, or both, has contributed to his behavior stands a chance of being passed on to others.

The first carrying of scavenged food back to headquarters (instead of consuming it on the spot) may also have been a sort of accident. A scavenging hominoid is eating the remains of a predator's kill where he has found it, and is surprised by the predator who is coming back to make another meal from the same kill. The hominoid runs off towards headquarters, still holding a piece of meat in his hand. In due time, he or his successors developed the habit of carrying the spoils off without waiting for the predator to turn up.

As described, these two early kinds of hand-carrying involve movements of a single animal *within* the band's territory. The carrying-along of things as the whole band moves is another matter, and probably a later development. Surely the earliest carrying of this latter sort was of unshaped weapons of defense. Yet other things might have been taken along. Extra food would be a great rarity, but if some were taken along because no one happened to be hungry as a movement began, it would be important if the band reached a particularly barren region. Water-carrying would have been extremely valuable—primates in general have to drink at least once a day, in contrast to some mammalian species which can store up several days' supply. Short hauls of small quantities of water cupped in the large leaves of tropical plants may have been quite early; large-scale water transport as a whole band moves must have been a great deal later, since it requires technologically advanced containers.

The side-effects of carrying things in the hands are of incalculable importance. We have already seen that its immediate practical value helped to promote bipedal walking, which in turn selected both for carrying and for an upright posture that renders bipedal walking mechanically more efficient. A less obvious consequence is that carrying made for a kind of behavior that has all the outward earmarks of what we call "memory" and "foresight": one lugs around a heavy stick or stone despite the absence of any immediate need for it, as though one were remembering past experiences in which having it available was important and were planning for possible future encounters of the same kind. Taking scavenged meat back to headquarters without waiting for the predator to return to his kill also looks like foresight. We do not mean to deny the validity of the terms "memory" and "foresight." The point is that the outward earmarks surely came first, and only over a long period of time *produced* the psychological characteristics to which these terms refer.

A third consequence of carrying and of wandering was a change in dietary balance. The first tools to be carried were defensive weapons. Often enough, no doubt, the use of these weapons against a predator, even if successful, would only scare him off. But sometimes the predator would be killed. Why waste the meat? We can also suppose that the wandering Miocene or Pliocene hominids occasionally found themselves in open country where no suitable plant food was available. Herbivorous animals could eat the grass; quadruped predators could eat the grazers; and the hominids, if they were lucky, could eat the grazers or the predators, or else starve. Thus the hunted became the hunters, and weapons of defense became weapons of offense.

The gradual increase of meat in the diet had important consequences of its own, to which we will turn after noting one further direct consequence of hand-carrying.

The use of the hands for carrying implied that the mouth and teeth, classically used for this by land mammals, birds, and even reptiles, were freed for other activities. It can quite safely be asserted that if primate and hominid evolution had not transferred from mouth to hand first the grasping and manipulating function and then the carrying function, human language as we know it would never have evolved. What were the hominids to do with their mouths, rendered thus relatively idle except when they were eating? The answer is: they chattered.

Remember that the proto-hominoids are assumed in this account to have had a call system, and that that system would not have been lost by the stage we have now reached in our story. The hunting of dangerous animals is a challenge even with advanced weapons. With primitive weapons there is a great advantage if it can be done collaboratively. But this calls for coordination of the acts of the participants. Their hands hold weapons and are thus unavailable for any complicated semaphore. Their visual attention must be divided between the motions of the quarry and those of the other participants. All this favors an increase in flexibility of vocal-auditory communication.

Other factors also favor such an increase. Meat is a highly efficient and compactly packaged food, as compared with uncultivated plants. A small kill may not go very far, but with collective hunting larger quarry were sought. After such a large kill, there is often more food than can be consumed even by all the direct participants in the hunt. Sharing the food among all the members of the band comes about almost automatically, in that when the hunters themselves are sated they no longer care if the rest take the leavings. Thus the sharing of meat makes for the survival of the whole band. Collective hunting, general food-sharing, and the carrying of an increasing variety of things all press towards a more complex social organization, which is only possible with more flexible communication. These same factors also promote what we vaguely call the "socialization" of the members of the band.

Another development bearing on the quality, if not the degree, of hominid socialization must have taken place during this same period. At some point during the slow morphological shift to efficient upright posture, the frontal approach for copulation must have first become anatomically possible, and it was doubtless immediately exploited. It may even be imagined that, for certain strains of the hominids at certain times, the expansion of the gluteus maximus rendered the dorsal approach so awkward that the invention of the frontal approach had the conservative value required by Romer's Rule. Humans have never shown much tendency to confine themselves to this position for intercourse, but it does seem to be universally known, and is almost exclusively human, recurring apparently only for the pygmy chimpanzee, the porcupine, the hamster, and the two-toed sloth. Just how this change may have affected hominid lifeways is not clear. Our guess is that it changed, for the adult female, the relative roles of the adult male and of the infant, since after the innovation there is a much closer similarity for her between her reception of an infant and of a lover. This may have helped to spread the "tender emotions" of mammalian mother-infant relations to other interpersonal relationships within the band, ultimately with such further consequences as the Oedipus complex.

Opening of the Call System

We have seen a changing pattern of life that would be well served by a vocal-auditory communicative system of greater complexity and subtlety. Now a call system can become more flexible, within limits, through the development of totally new calls to fit additional types of recurrent situation. But it cannot take the first step towards language as we know it unless something else happens: through a process about to be described, the closed system becomes open.

Let us illustrate the way in which this can come about by describing what may occasionally happen among the gibbons of today—though, to be sure, such an occurrence has never been observed. Suppose a gibbon finds himself in a situation characterized by both the presence of food and the imminence of danger. The factors are closely balanced. Instead of emitting either the clear food call or the unmistakable danger call, he utters a cry that has some of the characteristics of each. Among gibbons such an event is doubtless so rare and unusual that the other members of the band have no way of interpreting it; thus, the consequences are negligible. But if we suppose that the early weapon-carrying hominids had a somewhat richer call system (though still closed), functioning in a somewhat more complex social order, then we may also assume that this type of event happened occasionally, and that sooner or later the other members of a band responded appropriately, therefore handling an unusually complex situation more efficiently than otherwise. Thus reinforced, the habit of *blending* two old calls to produce a new one would gain ground.

Indeed, we really have to believe that this is what happened, because the phenomenon of blending is the only logically possible way in which a closed system can develop towards an open one. (This is not quite true: we omit a possible line of development that would yield a continuous open system structurally comparable to bee-dancing and hence, except for openness, very unlike language.) Let us represent the acoustic contours of one inherited call arbitrarily with the sequence of letters *ABCD* and those of another with *EFGH*. All we mean by either of these representations is that each call possesses two or more acoustic properties on which primate ears could focus attention; it does not matter just how many such acoustic properties are involved nor just what they are. Suppose that *ABCD* means "food here," while *EFGH* means "danger coming." Finding both food and danger, the hominid comes out with *ABGH*. If this new call becomes established, then the two old calls and the one new one are all henceforth *composite*, instead of unanalyzable unitary signals. For, in *ABCD*, the part *AB* now means "food" and the part CD means "no danger"; in *EFGH*, *EF* now means "no food" and *GH* means "danger"; while *ABGH* means "food and danger" because *AB* and *GH* have acquired the meanings just mentioned. One might eventually even get *EFCD*, obviously meaning "no food and no danger."

It must be asked whether this mechanism of blending can really turn a closed system into an open one. The answer is that it can start the transformation (while no other known mechanism can), but that further developments must follow. Consider the matter for a moment in a purely abstract way. Suppose the initial closed system has exactly ten calls, and that each is blended with each of the others. After the blending, there are exactly 100 calls. From one point of view a repertory of 100 calls—or of 1000, or of ten million—is just as closed as is a system of ten calls. A second point of view is more important. Each of the hundred possible calls now consists of two parts, and each part recurs in other whole calls. One has the basis for the habit of *building* composite signals out of meaningful parts, whether or not those parts occur alone as whole signals. It is this habit that lies at the center of the openness of human languages. English allows only a finite (though quite large) number of sentences only two words long. But it allows an unlimited number of different sentences because there is no fixed limit on how long a sentence may be.

Surely the opening-up of the closed call system of our ancestors required literally thousand of years, just as all the other developments on which we have touched came about at an extremely leisurely pace. It is irrelevant that the production of a single blend, or the momentary accidental carrying of a stick or stone in the hand, is a brief episode. A potentially crucial type of event can recur numberless times with no visible effect, or with effect on a band that later becomes extinct for unrelated reasons, for every one occurrence that has minuscule but viable consequences. When the opening-up of the formerly closed call system was finally achieved, the revolutionary impact on subsequent developments was as great as that of hand-carrying.

For one thing, the detailed conventions of an open system cannot be transmitted wholly through genes. The young may emit some of the calls instinctively. But they are also exposed to various more or less complex composite calls from their elders, and are obliged to infer the meanings of the parts, and the patterns by which the parts are put together to form the whole signals, from the acoustic resemblances among the calls they hear and from the behavioral contexts in which they are uttered. (To this day, that is how human infants learn their native language.) Thus, the development of an open system puts a premium on any capacity for learning and teaching that a species may have, and selects for an increase in the genetic basis for that capacity.

If the conventions of a system have largely to be learned before the system can be efficiently used, then much of that learning will eventually be carried on away from the contexts in which the utterances being practiced would be immediately relevant. We recall the general mammalian phenomenon of play. The development of an open, largely traditionally transmitted, vocal-auditory communicative system means that *verbal play* is added to play at fighting, sexual play, and any other older categories. But this, in turn, means that situations are being talked about when they do not exist—that is, it means the addition of displacement to the design features already at hand. Speaking of things which are out of sight or in the past or future is very much like carrying a weapon when there is no immediate need for it. Each of these habits thus reinforces the other.

What was formerly a closed call system has now evolved into an open system, with details transmitted largely by tradition rather than through the genes, and with the property of displacement. Let us call such a system *pre-language*. It was still not true language, because it lacked the duality of patterning of true language. Nothing like pre-language is known for sure in the world today. This does not mean that none exists—there are vast numbers of unexamined animal communicative systems, and one logically like pre-language may yet be discovered. However, any *hominid* strain that developed its vocal-auditory communication only to this stage has become extinct. If we could hear the pre-language of our forerunners, it would probably not sound like human speech. It would sound much more like animal calls, and only very careful analysis would reveal its language-like properties.

The development of openness, with the various consequences already mentioned, either accompanied or paved the way for some radical developments in tool habits. We imagine that tool *manufacture*—as over against the using and carrying of tools—received its single greatest impetus from this source. If carrying a weapon selects for foresight, shaping a rough weapon into a better one indicates even greater foresight. The manufacturing of a generalized tool—one designed to be carried around for a variety of possible uses—and the development of tools specialized for use in the making of other tools, certainly followed the inception of pre-language. Weapon-making and tool-shaping are further activities at which the young can play, as they learn their communicative system and other adult ways by playing with them.

We must suppose that the detailed conventions of pre-language underwent changes, and became differentiated from one band to another, much more rapidly than had the earlier call system from which it sprang (though perhaps much more slowly than languages change today). Both of these points are implied by the increased relative role of tradition as over against genetics. New blends were not uncommon. They introduced new patterns for combining elements into whole signals, and old patterns became obsolete. Any such innovation of detail spread naturally to all members of the band in which it occurred, but not readily, if at all, from one band to another. If a band fissioned into two bands—this must have happened repeatedly throughout hominoid and hominid history—the "daughter" bands started their independent existence with a single inherited pre-language, but innovations thereafter were independent, so that in course of time the two daughter bands came to have two "mutually unintelligible" pre-languages. This is exactly—except for rate of change—what has happened to true human languages in recent millennia; we must assume that the phenomena of change and of divergence are as old as the emergence of pre-language.

The Inception of Duality

Something else had been happening during prehominid and hominid evolution up to this point. In apes, the glottis lies very close to the velum, and articulatory motions anything like those involved in human language are structurally awkward. The development of upright posture, with the completion of the migration of the face from the end to the ventral side of the head, turns the axis of the oral cavity to a position approximately at right angles to the pharynx, and introduces a marked separation of glottis from velum. Hundreds of generations of chattering, first in a call system and then in pre-language, increase the innervation of the vocal tract and enrich the cortical representation of that region. The stage is set for the development of the kinds of articulatory motions familiar today.

Now, neither of these changes leads directly and inevitably to duality of patterning. Indeed, the first change is in no sense logically required if duality is to develop; in a way, it was fortuitous, since it was a by-product of changes taking place for a totally different set of selective reasons. In another species with a different earlier history, duality might use some other apparatus. If early primate history had for some reason promoted precision of control of the sphincter, and of the accumulation and discharge of intestinal gas, speech sounds today might be anal spirants. Everything else about the logical design of human language could be exactly as it actually is.

However, the two changes described above did set the stage in a certain way. The hominids were in a state in which, if duality did develop, the machinery used for it was in all probability going to be the kind of articulatory motions we still use.

We can envisage the development of duality as follows. Pre-language became increasingly complex and flexible, among the successful strains of hominids, because of its many advantages for survival. The constant rubbing-together of whole utterances (by the blending mechanism described earlier) generated an increasingly large stock of minimum meaningful signal elements—the "pre-morphemes" of pre-language. Lacking duality, however, these pre-morphemes had to be holistically different from one another in their acoustic contours. But the available articulatory-acoustic space became more and more densely packed; some premorphemes became so similar to others that keeping them apart, either in production or in detection, was too great a challenge for hominid mouths, ears, and brains. Something had to happen, or the system would collapse of its own weight. Doubtless many overloaded systems did collapse, their users thereafter becoming extinct. In at least one case, there was a brilliantly successful "mutation": pre-morphemes began to be listened to and identified not in terms of their acoustic gestalts but in terms of smaller features of sound that occurred in them in varying arrangements. In pace with this shift in the technique of detection, articulatory motions came to be directed not towards the generation of a suitable acoustic gestalt but towards the sufficiently precise production of the relevant smaller features of sound that identified one pre-morpheme as over against others.

With this change, pre-morphemes became true morphemes, the features of sound involved became phonological components, and pre-language had become true language.

Although brilliant and crucial, this innovation need not have been either as sudden or as difficult as our description may seem to imply. With openness, but as yet without duality, the hearer is already required to pay attention to acoustic detail, rather than merely to one or another convenient symptom of a whole acoustic gestalt, if he is to recognize the constituent pre-morphemes of a composite call and thus react appropriately to the whole call. In a pure call system, the beginning of a call may be distinctive enough to identify the whole call; the rest does not have to be heard. In pre-language, one cannot predict from the beginning of a call how it will continue and end. This clearly paves the way for duality. It is then, in one sense, but a small step to stop regarding acoustic details as *constituting* morphemes and start interpreting them as *identifying* or *representing morphemes*.

Here, as for all the other developments we have mentioned, we must remember Romer's Rule. The ultimate consequences of the inception of duality have been enormous. But the immediate value of the innovation was conservative. It rendered possible the continued use of a thoroughly familiar type of communicative system in a thoroughly familiar way, in the face of a gradual but potentially embarrassing increase in the complexity of the system.

The emergence of true language from a closed call system, by the steps and stages we have described, should properly be thought of not as a replacement of one sort of communicative system by another, but rather as the growth of a new system within the matrix of the old one. Certain features of the proto-hominoid call system are still found in human vocal-auditory behavior, but as accompaniments to the use of language rather than as part of language. The proto-hominoids could vary the intensity, the pitch, and the duration of a single call. We still do this as we speak sentences in a language: we speak sometimes more loudly, some times more softly, sometimes in a higher register and sometimes in a lower, and so on. Also, we use certain grunts and cries (*uh-huh, huh-uh, ow!*) that are not words or morphemes and not part of language. These various *paralinguistic* phenomena, as they have come to be called, have been reworked and modified in many ways by the conditions of life of speaking humans, but their pedigree, like that of communicative body motion, is older than that of language itself.

The phenomenon of sound change, mentioned briefly at the outset of this paper, began immediately upon the transition from pre-language to true language, continues now, and will continue in the future unless our vocal-auditory communication crosses some currently unforeseeable Rubicon. The phonological system of a language has almost as its sole function that of keeping meaningful utterances apart. But a phonological system is a delicately balanced affair, constantly being thrown into slight disbalance by careless articulation or channel noise and constantly re-patterning itself in a slightly altered way. It is perfectly possible, in the course of time, for two phonemes to fall together—that is, for the articulatory-acoustic difference between them to disappear. Obviously, this changes the machinery with which morphemes and utterances are distinguished. The interest this holds for us is that it affords an example of the workings of Romer's Rule in a purely cultural context instead of a largely genetic one.

What happens seems to be about as follows. A particular phonemic difference is slowly eaten away by sound change, to the point that it is no longer reliable as a way of keeping utterances apart. This is the "changed circumstances" of Romer's Rule. The speakers of the language develop, by analogy, a way of paraphrasing any utterance that would be poten-tially ambiguous if uttered in the traditional way. The paraphrase is the "innovation" of the Rule. The value of the paraphrase is that the speakers can thereby continue to speak in largely the same way they learned from their predecessors. The innovation is minor and trivial, but effective in that if the phonemic contrast disappears entirely, ease of communication is in no way impaired. The inevitable and continuous process of sound change never reduces the machinery of a language to zero. A compensa-tion of some sort is developed for every loss of contrast.

Chronology

We have now outlined a plausible evolutionary sequence leading from the proto-hominoids to our earliest truly human ancestors. For we assert that as soon as the hominids had achieved upright posture, bipedal gait, the use of hands for manipulating, for carrying, and for manufactur-ing generalized tools, and language, they had become men. The human revolution was over. Two important questions remain. How long did the changes take? How long ago were they completed?

It is certain that the changes we have talked about did not begin before the time of the proto-hominoids. But at present we have no way of knowing how much later than that was their inception. Conceivably the hominids of the Middle or Upper Pliocene, though already separated from the pongids, were very little more like modern man than were the proto-hominoids.

On the other hand, we are convinced that all the crucial develop-ments of which we have spoken had been achieved by about one million years ago—that is, by the beginning of the Pleistocene.

The most important evidence for the date just presented is the *subsequent* growth of the brain, attested by the fossil record. The brain of *Australopithecus* is scarcely larger than that of a gorilla. But from about three-quarters of a million years ago to about forty thousand years ago, the brain grew steadily. Part of this increase reflects an over-all increase in body size. Allowing for this, there is still some *relative* growth to be explained. Was the increase in relative size fortuitous or adaptive?

It is utterly out of the question that the growth was fortuitous. A large brain is biologically too expensive. It demands a high percentage of the blood supply—twelve per cent in modern man, though the brain accounts for only about two per cent of the body's volume—and all that blood, in an upright biped, must be pumped uphill. It requires an enlarged skull, which makes for difficulty during parturition, particularly since the development of upright posture resculptures the pelvis very badly for childbirth. This cost cannot be borne unless there are compensations.

We must therefore assume that if a species has actually developed a bigger and more convoluted brain, there was survival value in the change. For our ancestors of a million years ago the survival value of bigger brains is obvious if and only if they had *already* achieved the essence of language and culture. Continued growth would then be advantageous up to a certain maximum, but thereafter unprofitable because it made for excessive difficulties in other respects but yielded no further usable gain in brain power.

The archeological and fossil record supports our date, or even suggests that we have been too conservative. Until recently, the earliest obviously shaped tools that had been dug up were not quite so ancient, but they implied an earlier period of development that was not directly attested. Now, however, we have the direct evidence of at least crudely shaped stone tools in association with hominid fossils from Bed I at Olduvai, for which a maximum date of one and thee-quarters million years ago is seriously proposed. What is more, the Australopithecines show the typically human reduction in the size of the canine teeth, formerly used for cutting and tearing; and this reduction could not have been tolerated had the hominids not developed tools with which to perform such operations.

It might be suggested that, although all other crucial innovations of the human revolution were as early as we have proposed, the inception of duality may have been later. There are two reasons why we think that duality is just as old as the rest.

One side-effect of brain growth is that the top of the head is pushed forward to form a forehead. We do not see why this should in itself entail a recession of the lower part of the face, to yield the essentially flat perpendicular human physiognomy which, with minor variations, now prevails. In terms of the balancing of the head above an upright body, perhaps the recession of the snout and the decrease in its massiveness are useful. If cooking is a sufficiently old art, then perhaps this external predigestion of food at least rendered possible the reduction in size of teeth and jaws. But it seems to us that these factors still leave room for a further influence: that of the habit of talking, in a true language that uses the kinds of articulatory motions that are now universal, requiring precise motions of lips, jaw, tongue, velum, glottis, and pulmonary musculature. If true language can be assumed for our ancestors of a million years ago, then it is old enough to have played a role in the genetically monitored evolutionary changes in what we now call the "organs of speech." And if this is correct, then "organs of speech" is no metaphor but a biologically correct description.

Our other reason for believing that duality of patterning, and the modern type of sound-producing articulatory motions, are very old, turns on time, space, and degrees of uniformity and diversity. The fossil record shows that the human diaspora from East Africa cannot be much more recent than the Middle Pleistocene. This means that several hundred thousand years have been available for a genetic adaptation to a wide variety of climates and topographies. Yet man shows an amazingly small amount of racial diversity—far less, for example, than that of dogs, which has come about in a much shorter span of time. (Of course, the difference in generation span between men and dogs must be taken into account; but when one allows liberally for this the comparison, though less striking, still seems valid.)

There is this same striking lack of diversity in certain features of language. Though we can have no fossils, our observations of the languages of today, and of those few attested by written records during the past few millennia, have some relevance. Almost every type of articulation known to function in any language anywhere recurs in various other languages, with no significant pattern of geographical distribution. Phonological systems—as over against individual speech sounds—show much less variety than could easily be invented by any linguist working with pencil and paper. This uniformity precludes the independent invention of duality of patterning, and of modern articulatory motions, in two or more parts of the world. The crucial developments must have taken place once, and then spread. The innovations could have been either recent or ancient, except for an additional fact: in every language, the phonological raw materials are used with remarkable efficiency. This speaks for great antiquity, since we cannot imagine that such efficiency was an instant result of the appearance of the first trace of duality.

True diversity is found in more superficial aspects of language, and in all those other phases of human life where tradition, rather than genetics, is clearly the major mechanism of change and of adaptation. We are thus led to a familiar conclusion. The human revolution, completed before the diaspora, established a state of affairs in which further change and adaptation could be effected, within broad limits, by tradition rather than genetics. That is why human racial diversity is so slight, and it is why the languages and cultures of all communities, no matter how diverse, are elaborations of a single inherited "common denominator."

Additional Pleistocene Changes

The further consequences of the human revolution include, in the end, everything that we have done since. Only a few of the more striking (and earlier) of these subsequent developments need to be mentioned here.

Language and culture, as we have seen, selected for bigger brains. Bigger brains mean bigger heads. Bigger heads mean greater difficulty in parturition. Even today, the head is the chief troublemaker in childbirth. This difficulty can be combatted to some extent by expelling the fetus relatively earlier in its development. There was therefore a selection for such earlier expulsion. But this, in turn, makes for a longer period of helpless infancy—which is, at the same time, a period of maximum plasticity, during which the child can acquire the complex extra-genetic heritage of its community. The helplessness of infants demands longer and more elaborate child care, and it becomes highly convenient for the adult males to help the mothers. Some of the skills that the young males must learn can only be learned from the adult males. All this makes for the domestication of fathers. This, together with the habit of paying attention to past experiences and future contingencies (which we have seen arising in the context of play, of tool-carrying, of the displacement of pre-language, and of tool-making), promotes male jealousy. The seeds of this may have been earlier, but it now becomes eminently reasonable for a male to reserve a female, even when he is not sexually hungry, that she may be available when the need arises.

In the developments just outlined we can also see contributing sources for the complex restrictions with which human sexual relations are hedged about. These include not only all the rules of exogamy and endogamy and the varying principles controlling premarital and extramarital relations, but also the whole matter of taste—some individuals of the opposite sex are attractive, others unattractive, according to criteria learned from one's community. Any male past puberty, and any female between nubility and menopause, can, in a matter of seconds, stand a good chance of launching a new human. But child care requires time and energy thereby unavailable for other important activities. From this stem such varied modern institutions as celibate orders and beauty contests.

Among the proto-hominoids the band leaders were the strongest adult males. Language, in particular, changes this. The oldest members of the band, strong or feeble, are valued because they have had time to learn more. They are repositories of information on which the community can call as it is needed. This use of the elderly as encyclopedias perhaps helps to select for a greater life span, though the pedomorphism discussed earlier may also have played a part in bringing about this result. Certainly the increased social utility of the elderly promotes a protection of the old and feeble by the young and strong; it may contribute to doing something positive about the disposal of the dead.

As soon as the hominids had achieved a reasonably effective bipedal *walking* gait—not running, which is useful for fast coverage of short distances—they had the basic wherewithal for migrating slowly throughout all the continental territory to which they could adapt their lifeways. For the invasion of some climatic zones, protection against the cold is necessary. There are various physiological ways of doing this, but hominids developed an additional device: clothing.

The Chinese variety of *Pithecanthropus* used fire for warmth. By his epoch, then, the hominid invasion of cold climates had begun. But we suspect that clothing was a much earlier invention, already available when it was first needed for warmth.

Clothing serves roughly three functions: protection, as against the cold; modesty and vanity; and *carrying*. The last of these functions was, we suggest, the one of earliest relevance. If one's way of life rests on hand-carrying, and if the number and variety of things to be carried is increasing to the point of awkwardness, then the invention of a device that helps one carry things has the conservative survival value required by Romer's Rule. The first clothing-as-harness may have been nothing more than a piece of vine pulled from the trees and draped over the shoulder or around the waist. Later, when the hominids were regularly killing small animals, the hides—useless as food—might have been put to this use. A hide cannot be eaten, but if one is hungry enough there is some nourishment to be obtained by chewing at it. Almost as early as the first use of hides as harness, it may have been discovered that a hide that has been chewed is more flexible and comfortable to wear than one that has not. This way of processing hides was still widespread only yesterday.

It is unlikely that any direct archeological evidence of these posited early clothing developments will ever turn up. But if clothing of sorts is actually that ancient, then it was already available, with only minor modifications, when it was first needed to help explore ecological niches characterized by cold. It may even be old enough to have played a part in permitting the development of the relative hairlessness characteristic of all strains of *Homo sapiens* today.

25 The Science of Linguistics

Joseph H. Greenberg

LINGUISTICS IS ONE OF THOSE FIELDS OF SCIENCE IN WHICH MAJOR CHANGES *are occurring so rapidly that it is difficult to find general statements about its contents, methods, and directions of development that will not be somewhat obsolete by the time they are printed. Yet another difficulty arises when rapid change is the environment. The synthesizer is often tempted to seize and emphasize the new while neglecting or completely rejecting what is not novel. To yield to such temptation may kindle excitement in some students, but does a disservice to basic education. The problem is somewhat exacerbated in the present case, since the goals of anthropological linguistics are not completely identical with those of general linguistics; and the differences, though small, tend to make anthropological linguistics somewhat conservative in terms of the most contemporary developments in general linguistics. (Curiously, for the same reason, anthropological linguistics was the vanguard ground breaker in past decades, and could resume that position again in some future realignment.)*

Against this background of scholarly conflict, we are fortunate that Joseph Greenberg, a distinguished anthropological linguist, feels a deep commitment to the presentation of pedagogically sound surveys of the

SOURCE: "Linguistics," in Robert A. Lystad (ed.), *The African World: A Survey of Social Research* (New York: Frederick A. Praeger, 1965), Chap. 15, pp. 415–428. Revised and reprinted with the permission of the author and the publisher.

The author (b. 1915) is Professor of Anthropology and Linguistics at Stanford University. He is best known for his reclassification of the languages of Africa and articles on linguistic theory, but he has done ethnographic work in Africa, particularly among the Hausa. Among his publications are *The Influence of Islam on a Sudanese Religion* (1946), *Studies in African Linguistic Classification* (1955), and *The Languages of Africa* (1963). A new book, *Language and Culture*, is in press in the Random House Studies in Anthropology.

field as a whole. He has therefore undertaken, on our behalf, to exten-sively revise such a survey that he published only two years ago; this revision was completed in January, 1967.

Introduction

All the sciences and humanities deal in some manner with data which are linguistic; to cite but a few examples, the documents of the historian, the informant statements of the ethnologists, the very materials of folk-lorist and literary studies are linguistic in form. Even the physical sciences share at least one linguistic preoccupation with disciplines concerned with human and therefore largely verbal behaviour: namely, a concern with the language of science itself. However, all these other areas of study deal with language as a means to an end. Only linguistics studies languages as an end in itself. The distinction between the linguistic system as such, de-scribable by a set of rules, and the system in actual use has been variously phrased as *langue versus parole,* code versus message or competence versus performance (transformational approach). However stated, it serves to delimit in a general way the province of linguistics as against the linguistic aspects of all other fields of study.

Linguistics is a social science. The very notion of language pre-supposes a social group which employs it as a means of communication. Linguistics, therefore, deals with the speech of an individual as repre-sentative of that of a social group, often called the speech community. Further, language as a highly complex body of learned behaviour forms a part of the cultural heritage of the community which uses it. Indeed it has a central role as the fundamental vehicle of transmission of other cultural traits within and across social groups. From this point of view, linguistics may be considered a specialized branch of cultural anthropology.

The primary interest of the linguist is in spoken language. Writing and similar systems are viewed by virtually all linguists as derivative phenomena. Speech has priority over writing in the life history both of the individual and the race. Writing always implies some spoken form, but the converse does not hold. A further reason for assigning priority to the study of spoken language has to do with the study of language change. Writing systems are highly stable whereas spoken languages constantly change. Hence the changes in a writing system can be under-stood by reference to the spoken language but not vice versa. The effect of writing on speech in the form of spelling pronunciations is a real but relatively insignificant factor. Although his attention is thus centered on the spoken language, the linguist cannot but be concerned with the rela-tion between spoken and written forms. Almost all our knowledge of past languages comes from texts which must be subject to linguistic interpre-tation in terms of a primary written source. In setting forth the results of descriptive analysis, moreover, the linguist himself employs a written description. He may also become involved in the practical problem of devising orthographies.

Linguistics is divided into two main branches: descriptive and historical—or, as they are sometimes called, synchronic and diachronic. Linguistics in its recognisably modern form arose in the first decades of the nineteenth century as a basically historical discipline chiefly concerned with the specific problem of the reconstruction of the ancestral Indo-European language. Interest tended to shift to problems of language description with the rise of various 'structural' schools from approximately 1920 onwards. The relation between these two main fields of study is complementary, not hostile. The degree of success of historical enquiry is in the final analysis dependent on the reliability and completeness of descriptive data. On the other hand, while a language can be described without reference to its own past, and this has been an ideal of the structuralist approach with its strict separation of the synchronic and diachronic aspects of language, it is now becoming apparent that the very description of a language is more revealing if it incorporates dynamic statements which parallel the historical processes which gave rise to it. Moreover, the historical mode of explanation inherited from the earlier linguistics of the nineteenth century still plays a fundamental rôle in the understanding of synchronic phenomena.

The aim of a scientific language description is to state as accurately, completely and economically as possible the structure of a language at a particular time. There are a number of differing theoretic approaches to the problem of language description characteristic of various 'schools' of linguistics. In spite of these differences the descriptions are largely convertible from one framework to another.

In view of these differences of approach, any attempt to describe linguist theory for the specialist must steer between the Scylla of all-inclusiveness, going far beyond the purpose and scope of the present exposition, and the Charybdis of a biased presentation based on a single theory. The orientation will be towards problems rather than specific solutions. The overall purpose will be to sharpen the non-linguist reader's awareness regarding some of the fundamental issues debated by linguists and to acquaint him with some frequently encountered linguistic terms and concepts.

Descriptive Linguistics

There are three main aspects of any language description, and it would seem that, on any showing, they have a certain irreducible distinctiveness which cannot be eliminated theoretically and in practice lead to quite different sets of problems. These are *phonology* (the study of sound systems), *grammar* (the study of rules governing the arrangement of meaningful elements), and *semantics* (the study of meaning). There are, of course, interconnections. There is the aspect of language called morphophonemics which has as its subject matter the variations in the phonological and representations of meaningful units. In English, for example, the rules regarding the occurrence of the three phonologically different forms of the -s plural: [s] as in 'hats', [z] as in 'bags' and [əz] as in 'roses' belong to morphophonemics which thus has relations both to phonology and to grammar. Again, semantics is concerned not merely with dictionary or 'lexical' meanings of individual items but with the wider task of sentence interpretation, a process which involves the grammatical structure of the sentence as well as specific lexical meanings. The structuralist approach in American linguistics has tended to treat each of the three main aspects of language as autonomously as possible and to view semantics, since it necessarily involves extra-linguistic considerations, as external to, or even not to be included in, linguistics. The transformational approach to be discussed later does not shrink from "mixing levels" and seeks to integrate the three basic aspects of linguistics into a single integrated pattern of description.

PHONOLOGY

All contemporary schools distinguish in some manner between a level of description based on sounds (phonetics) and a more abstract level of description in terms of functioning units of the language structure (phonological level).

The basis of any description of this aspect of language is an accurate description of the sounds of the language. An indispensable tool for accomplishing this is training in the theory and practice of articulatory phonetics. The theoretical framework of this phonetics developed in its essentials in the course of the nineteenth century. In effect, this system provides a set of co-ordinates, almost all stated in terms of articulatory processes, that is, positions and movements of the speech organs, by means of which all possible speech sounds may be defined. Thus the English *b* sound in this system would be described (in an oversimplified fashion for purposes of illustration) as a bilabial voiced stop, each of these three terms referring to features of articulation, contact of the lips (bilabial), vibration of the vocal chords (voiced) and completeness of the closure (stop). A very few features are, however, *faute de mieux*, described in terms of acoustic impression rather than articulations. Thus pitch or fundamental frequency depends in its articulation upon the frequency of vibration of the vocal cords; this cannot be measured by noninstrumental methods. Hence pitch, in traditional phonetics, is described on the basis of acoustic impression as high, low, falling, etc.

The training of the practical phonetician includes the understanding of the theoretical framework of this system and the ability to place any sound accurately within it. The technique is largely one of mimicking and introspective analysis of the matching sound thus produced. Visual observation, e.g., of the lip movements, plays a definite but minor role. The tape recorder, by providing a virtually permanent, indefinitely repeatable, record of speech sounds, has been of great practical importance in the more accurate application of such methods. Finally, the practical phonetician must learn to apply a standard method of transcription in order to codify his results and make them understandable to others.

A second set of fundamental methods is that of laboratory phonetics. To a certain degree, these methods simply provide more objective data about articulation. By the use, for example, of the palatogram—essentially an artificial palate covered with a removable substance—it is possible to discover what part of the palate has been subject to contact in a specific articulation. In particular, recent developments in X-ray photography promise much in the area of the objective observation of speech articulations. The heart of laboratory phonetics, however, is acoustic analysis of the sound wave itself as employed in speech: a source of information obviously not available without instrumental means. Fundamental advances have occurred during the last two decades through the invention of the sound spectograph. From a sound input this instrument produced a spectogram in which the relative power within each of a number of frequency bands is indicated by the darkness of the impression on the paper. The subsequent invention of a speech synthesiser, by which the process is reversed so that hand-painted spectograms are utilized as inputs with synthetic sound as output, provides another basic tool in acoustic research.

Such laboratory methods are obviously of considerable relevance to the linguist-phonetician involved in the description of specific languages. However, if only for practical reasons of time, expense and the absence of servicing facilities under field conditions, such instrumental methods cannot as yet replace the traditional methods of practical phonetics. No one has yet been able to analyse the sounds of a language by purely instrumental means, although individual points of doubt in the analysis can often be clarified by such methods. Outside of any such practical help in linguistic analysis, it is clear that research into the acoustic nature of speech is of fundamental importance to linguistics and communication in studies.

A method very different from those already described is required in those cases where the only evidence regarding a language is in the form of written texts from a past period. The methods employed consist of highly complex inferences based on comparative linguistic methods, transcriptions of loan words into and borrowings from other languages, and the contemporary phonetic facts when study is being made of an earlier stage of a language still spoken. The results are necessarily both more uncertain and less detailed than when direct observation is possible.

The fundamental unit of phonological structure has usually been the phoneme, the basic principle of which is foreshadowed in the pre-scientific invention of alphabet writing. It might be thought that single principle would suffice: namely, the consistent assignment to each individual sound of a symbol. In this case the phonologic unit would correspond in a simple one-to-one fashion to the phonetic notion of a distinct sound as defined by the co-ordinates of phonetics as described earlier. In fact, however, there is often a multiplicity of sounds, consistently distinguishable by a trained phonetician but intuitively regarded as the same sound unit by the average speaker. For example, the average speaker of English, untrained in phonetics, is unlikely ever to have noticed that the sound spelled *t* in 'stop' (unaspirated) is distinct from the *t* in 'top' (aspirated). It is not enough to say that the difference is small, for this precise difference of aspiration or lack of aspiration of *t* and other stops is evidently phonetic in Hindi, Chinese and many other languages.

If the approach to a foreign language is naïve, a response will be made only to those sound differences which are structurally relevant in the investigator's language. He will thus ignore relevant differences in the foreign language where he is not accustomed to respond to them and will sometimes erroneously assume that the differences are relevant when they coincide with differences familiar to him from his own language. Thus an untrained observer will tend to arrive at essentially the same sound system for any language he describes and two untrained observers with different first languages will describe the same foreign language in different ways.

The concentration on those differences which are functionally relevant in each language has significant theoretic byproducts. It becomes evident that the sound system of every language is in a quite precise sense an organized whole. For example, the significance of aspiration in the Hindi *t* sound and its lack of significance in English is not an isolated phenomenon in either language. In Hindi it extends to a whole series of sounds which are paired as aspirate versus non-aspirate while in English there are no such pairs. The example of aspiration in Hindi will serve to illustrate another essential point about phonologic structures, namely, that what is involved is not so much the property of aspiration but a significant opposition, aspiration versus non-aspiration, which functions as part of the system of Hindi but not as part of English. In fact, it turns out that all sound units (phonemes) can be defined in terms of the recurrent oppositions in which they participate. This procedure is known as distinctive feature analysis.

Since, as in the instance of aspiration versus non-aspiration, such distinctive principles of contrast are binary, that is, consist of two terms, the attempt has been made to reduce all oppositions to binary ones. This approach which was pioneered by Jacobson is at present quite influential. It further seeks to reduce the total number of such binary oppositions to a relatively small number, commonly twelve, which are considered to be sufficient to account for all the sound contrast of the languages of the world. This is in part accomplished by exploiting recent advances in acoustic theory in order to use acoustic criteria of similarity alongside of the mainly articulatory rubrics of traditional phonetics.

The following is an example of this approach. A single binary opposition flat versus non-flat encompasses several contrasts which differ from the articulatory point of view. For example, the contrasts velarized versus non-velarized and pharyngealized versus non-pharyngealized are included under the opposition flat versus non-flat. In spite of their articulatory differences, they have in common acoustic characteristics. Moreover, it is found that no language employs a contrast between them. Thus we may say that in two different languages the same feature flat versus non-flat exists but that it is implemented as velarization in one language and pharyngealization in another.

Even in the present brief presentation, it is necessary to point out that an analysis which seeks to account for all structurally relevant differences in sound sequences must reckon with additional entities beyond the phoneme. Along with the succession of discrete sound units are various elements characteristic of the syllable, word, phrase or sentence which are, as it were, superimposed on this underlying sequence and can only arbitrarily be assigned a position within it. In American structural linguistics, such units have been called prosodic features, in contrast to the segmental units or phonemes proper. In England, the 'prosodic' school of J. R. Firth has emphasized such phenomena and tended to reduce the role of segmental entities, called 'phonematic units' in their terminology. Because sentence, phrase and words are grammatical units, we have here once again a linguistic phenomenon involving the relation of two fundamental aspects, the phonological and grammatical.

GRAMMAR

The basic strategy of phonological analysis has been described as the attempt to develop a method which exhibits the functionally relevant feature of the sound system as an organised whole. It might be maintained that the most significant advances of grammatical theory have been along the same lines. The aim has been to develop techniques through which the functional categories of each language emerge in place of an *a priori* set derived from traditional models of Latin grammar as applied to Western languages. It was, indeed, the challenge of "exotic languages" differing drastically in type from European languages, which exposed the inadequacies of traditional methods of grammatical analysis. At the same time, by representing each language as a unique structure, there is the danger that the basic similarities among languages may be overlooked. As with distinctive feature analysis in phonology, it is possible in this more objective and non-ethnocentric framework to isolate general characteristics of grammatical structure common to all languages. There has in recent years, therefore, been a revival of interest in such universal properties of language.

The basic problem of grammatical theory as it relates to the structure of individual languages may be characterized as the generation of an infinity of grammatically possible sentences based on a necessarily finite set of given utterances and by means of a necessarily finite set of rules.

If the number of grammatical sentences in a language were finite, they could be ordered in degree of length, and there would be some one or more finite number of sentences of maximum length. But from a sentence of any length a still longer sentence can always be formed by the addition of co-ordinate clauses, additional modifiers, e.g. adjectives, and by still other methods. Although each sentence is itself of finite length, the number of sentences in any language forms what mathematicians call a countable infinity. Grammars, therefore, cannot take the form of a simple finite enumeration of sentences. This is confirmed by everyday experiences in that speakers constantly understand and make up sentences which they have never encountered in their previous experience.

The possibility of a grammar which generates an infinity of sentences arises through the existence of constructions in which the same finite class of words can occur repeatedly without limit (e.g. adjectives modifying a single noun), as well as by more complex indefinitely repeatable processes (e.g. coordination of clauses). It follows, then, that in one guise or other, at least some grammatical statements must be in terms of such classes of finite membership. Traditional grammar has made us familiar with the most inclusive of such classes, the so-called parts of speech. The most common variant of traditional grammar, based on a fixed set of parts of speech and even on a fixed order of treatment among them, has furnished the ground plan of innumerable grammars.

Such a grammar consists of two kinds of statements. The first, or morphological, concerns variations in form, that is, constituent sounds, particularly those connected with the functioning of the same part of speech in different constructions (inflection). Here then belong the tables of conjugation and declension. The second type of statement has to do with the use rather than the form of parts of speech. In fact, it becomes a statement regarding the meanings of inflectional categories. The two types of statement define a dichotomy between form (morphology) and use (syntax). Thus, in a traditional Latin grammar a morphological section states, say, that the ablative singular of *vir* ('man') is *viro* while the syntactic section includes a description of the uses of the ablative under such rubrics as 'the ablative of separation', 'the ablative of instrument', etc.

The heart of this doctrine is obviously the notion of parts of speech. It presupposes a universally valid set of categories (noun, verb, etc.) believed to be present in all languages because they are necessary to human thinking. The definition is thus necessarily semantic.

The reaction against this scheme largely developed in terms of a rejection of universal *a priori* semantically based definitions for isolating the classes of elements to be employed in grammatical description. In consequence a formal (i.e. non-semantic) approach to the definition of grammatical categories arose. Such classes were defined in terms of morphological behavior; for example, by their occurrence in certain inflectional categories as marked by afformatives of specified phonemic shapes, or by their occurrence in the same or similar environments. To say that elements occur in the same environment is tantamount to saying that one can substitute for another. Hence the definition of classes by substitution became a key operation in structural linguistics, particularly in its American version. These techniques often led to the isolation of classes of meaningful elements which departed widely from the traditional model, even for familiar languages, e.g. English.

Still other procedures of structuralism undermined even more decisively the very concept of parts of speech which constitutes the core of the traditional scheme. It is obvious that traditional analysis requires that the basic unit of grammatical description be the 'word'. Morphology is the study of the formal (phonologic) internal structure of the word, and syntax has reference to its use in the sentence. It should be noted that in this usage some term such as paradigm is perhaps more appropriate than word. Thus in the traditional view *man, man's, men* and *men's* are all variants (accidents or inflectional forms) of the same underlying word. But the search for a minimal unit corresponding to the phoneme in phonology led to the postulation of a unit smaller than the word as a basis for grammatical theory. This unit, first introduced by Bloomfield, was the morpheme, defined by him as the minimum meaningful unit. Thus, a word such as 'farmers' would consist of three morphemes: *farm-*, *-er-* and *-s*. In this way, inflectional elements likewise become morphemes, so that the above-mentioned paradigm of *man* is dissolved into morpheme combinations.

A consistent attempt was made to develop an overall theory of linguistic description based on the phoneme and morpheme as the two basic units and with a good deal of parallelism in the analytic procedures involved in both. This finds its classic expression in a paper by Z. Harris, in which, by repeated substitution procedures on higher and higher levels, there is a *gradus ad Parnassum* from the morpheme to the sentence. The word level appears here only tacitly, so that for all practical purposes, the old morphology-syntax division disappears. Form variations formerly handled in declensional and conjugational tables with words as units are treated as allomorphs (i.e., variants) of the same morphemic unit, e.g., *-en* is an allomorph of the plural morpheme in the environment . . . *ox-*. . . .

The morphophonemics of the language is then comprised in a set of statements describing all such varying shapes of morphemes and constitutes, in this scheme, a distinctive compartment of the grammar. The connection with phonology is via what Hockett called the principle of accountability, according to which, as far as possible, every phoneme is assigned to one and only one allomorph in a specific context.

The model sketched is, basically, one of several distinct levels, each with minimal units and with rules which describe the variants of each unit and the combinations in which it occurs with units on the same level. This general model which has numerous variations in theory and practice has been widely influential and many grammars have been written in accordance with it. In particular the type known as tagmemic and developed chiefly by K. Pike has been employed by linguistic workers affiliated with the missionary-oriented Summer Institute of Linguistics in the description of many languages throughout the world.

A fundamentally different model, commonly known as the transformational, first attracted attention in 1957 with the publication of N. Chomsky's *Syntactic Structures* and, at the time of writing, had clearly assumed a dominant position within American linguistics. During the first ten years of existence it has itself undergone considerable changes and it seems clear that its development is by no means closed. Hence any discussion of its basic outlines at the present time is subject to the promise that this model is quite likely to undergo further drastic changes in the future.

A transformational grammar is a subclass of the generative type of grammar. In general, the notion of a generative grammar requires use at the start of a set of primitive symbols, normally a single one, symbolized S (= sentence). For any particular language, by various rewritings and further manipulations in accordance with the given rules, a succession of strings, each consisting of a sequence of symbols, is generated. As constituted at present, such a grammar consists of base rules, a lexicon, a transformational component, and sets of phonological and semantic interpretation rules. The base consists of the base rules and the lexicon. It produces the abstract underlying structure of the sentence, the so-called deep structure. In principle, this is sufficient for semantic interpretation of the sentence since it contains all the relevant grammatical and lexical information required for sentence interpretation. The transformational component, whose form of rules is different from that of the base, produces a "surface structure" from the deep structure of any sentence. This in turn undergoes the phonological rules to produce a sequence of symbols subject to phonetic interpretation. As currently practiced, binary feature analysis is employed in phonological representations and semantic feature analysis in the lexicon and in the semantic interpretation. Semantic features will be briefly described in a subsequent section.

This scheme has not yet been applied in its entirety to any language but a fair number of partial descriptions have been produced in accordance with the earlier forms of the transformational model. In general, this approach differs from the phoneme-morpheme model in a number of ways. In the former, there are units which are supposed to be discoverable by procedures applied, ideally at least, in a mechanical way from a given body of actual utterances. Hence sentences in their overt forms as sound sequences are ultimately described and classified in terms of such units and their combinations. In the generative approach, there is rather a sequence of abstract structures which do not assume the form of the actual sentence until the operation of semantic and phonological interpretation. The adequacy of particular alternative formulations is judged in relation to the overall structure of rules for the entire language with the aim of incorporating to the maximum extent the possibilities of generalization within the description. The ultimate aim is the justification of such choices in terms of their applicability in principle to all linguistic descriptions, i.e., their universality.

Levels are distinguished not in terms of the nature of the units which occur in them but on the logical form of the rules of which they consist. By incorporating semantic interpretation rules as well as phonological rules, this model seeks an overall integrated theory of linguistic description. The grammatical aspect, here generally called the syntactic, has, as can be seen, the central position in that it generates the underlying structures subject to semantic and phonological interpretation.

SEMANTICS

A central problem in semantics, traditionally *the* basic problem, is the statement of meanings in terms of definitions, whether the language is the same (periphrasis) or different from (translation) the object language. This has been primarily the task of the lexicographer or dictionary-maker. The division between the written productions commonly called grammars and dictionaries, however, does not completely coincide with the division of the subject into grammar and semantics. Certain kinds of meanings, e.g. those of inflections, are treated in grammars, at least in traditional ones, and are almost never found in dictionaries. On the other hand, the assignment of words to paradigm classes, e.g. the gender of nouns in French and irregularities of morphological formation, particularly the former, are regularly included in dictionaries. Thus, a grammar of French will describe the phenomenon of grammatical gender and give rules relating to agreement in gender, but it will not normally list all masculine and feminine nouns.

Lexicography is still very much an art learned by apprenticeship or unguided imitation of existing dictionaries with relatively little in the way of codified principles or theoretical elaboration. It is significant to note that the lexicographic aspects of hitherto unwritten languages or of those with a minimal written literature are quite different from those of established or standardized literary languages. Oral information from informants rather than published texts provide the basis for entries. Moreover, the languages are frequently parts of non-Western cultures with which the dictionary-maker or the non-indigenous user may not be familiar. The lexicographer, in these instances, finds his task extraordinarily close to that of the ethnographic fieldworker. Indeed, a really firstrate dictionary cannot be compiled under these circumstances without coincident investigation of non-linguistic culture and is itself an ethnographic document of first-rate importance.

There is, then, an absence of an organized theoretical framework in the actual practice of the dictionary-maker. Nevertheless, there have been important developments in recent semantic theory, none of these as yet incorporated in full-fledged dictionaries, which bid fair ultimately to alter this situation. The most important development here has been a notable gain in the precision of methods based on the semantic analysis by features, which was inherited from the earlier theoretical literature of semantics. These methods have been employed with particular success in the area of kinship terminologies and the basic principles have been adopted into the program for semantics being developed by transformational theorists as noted earlier.

Some of the basic notions of semantic feature analysis can be illustrated from the set of kinship terms in the English language. Each particular term, e.g. 'brother', 'aunt', can be defined by reference to a set of features which recur elsewhere in the system. Most of these features are, as in phonology, binary. A simple and not entirely adequate model which will, however, illustrate these principles is the following. We have a set of the following features: sex of the person referred to, lineal versus collateral, consanguineal versus affinal, generation. All except the last of these is binary. The term 'uncle' is then defined as male, collateral, consanguineal, first-ascending generation. Just as in phonology, there is a restricted universal set of features and every language utilizes only some of them. For example, English does not use the feature 'sex of the speaker' but for some Bantu languages, this category appears in the existence of distinct terms of reference for a male sibling in relation to a male sibling as against a female sibling in relation to a male sibling. On the other hand, many systems, unlike English, do not distinguish lineal from collateral relatives.

Comparative Linguistics

Great as is the value of descriptions of the thousands of the world's languages from both the practical and the theoretic point of view, it can be argued that description is but the initial task of linguistic science. Only by comparisons of languages can either law-like generalizations or specific historical conclusions be derived from linguistic study.

HISTORICAL METHOD

One basic type of comparison is that of two or more historical stages of the same language. This, the direct historical method, depends on the existence of documentation for the earlier periods of the language. Historical depth can also be attained by the comparative method, which involves the systematic comparison of related languages in order to reconstruct the ancestral language from which they have sprung. A specialised aspect of the comparative historical method is the intensive study of dialect variation within a single language, for such inter-dialectal relationship can be considered the limiting case of closest relationship. This field, which has a highly developed set of techniques, is called dialect geography. Its characteristic production is the dialect atlas, in which the geographical distribution of linguistic features within the total language area is mapped. In principle, social stratification of linguistic forms on class and occupational lines is likewise an aspect of linguistic variability within the bounds of a single language, but this area of study is still in its infancy.

The concept of genetic relationship of languages, the bases of comparative historical linguistics, is an extension of the notion of dialectic divergence over a longer time span. The dialects of one period become the separate but related languages of a later time. Language is always changing, and no language spoken over an extensive area can maintain full and equal communication within the entire speech community. A further factor in language change is migration, which may result in a community of speakers who are permanently removed from frequent and easy communication with the home community, i.e., Dutch in South Africa which evolved into a separate language, Afrikaans. Under the conditions just outlined, linguistic innovations, which may occur in all aspects of language, tend not to diffuse over the communication barriers; the results are local differentiation or dialects, as they are called. As the process continues, the dialects shift further apart beyond the point of mutual intelligibility. Each of the new languages which arises in this way may itself once more undergo the same splitting process.

The recovery of this sequence of events leads to the postulation of a family tree or genetic classification of languages. Hypotheses of this kind are based on shared resemblances which are retentions, though often in a modified form, from the original period of linguistic unity. The systematic comparison of such related languages leads to the reconstruction, as far as may be possible, of the traits of the ancestral language and the processes of change in the languages during the intervening period. A fundamental part of this method is the technique of determining sound correspondences. Sound change is regular in that a phoneme in a particular language changes to another phoneme virtually without exception under stated conditions, these conditions themselves being phonetic. Sometimes all instances of a phoneme change under all conditions (so-called unconditioned sound change). An example of a conditioned change is the shift from earlier *t* in German to *s* (written *ss*) in non-initial position and to *ts* (written *z*) in initial position. Since in English *t* did not change under these circumstances, there have resulted two sets of correspondences between English and German. Initially, German *ts* = English *T*, as in *zwei: two; Zunge: tongue*, etc.; non-initially, German *s* = English *t*, as in *beissen: bite; schiessen: shoot*, etc. An example of an unconditioned change is the shift of Anglo-Saxon *ā* to modern English *o*, e.g. *hām: home; stān: stone*, etc.

An understanding of regular sound changes and a number of other processes of change permits, by a kind of triangulation, the determination of features of the parent language. Such comparative study is most advanced in the case of the Indo-European languages, but it has been applied successfully to closely related groups of languages in many parts of the world, even in the absence of earlier written records. An incidental but important by-product is the sorting out of resemblances among both related and non-related languages which result from borrowing rather than descent with modification from a form in the ancestral language.

It is evident that the most important contributions of linguistics to historical research lie in this area. Until recently, conclusions of this kind have lacked the all-important aspect of absolute chronology. Since about 1950, however, Swadesh and others have developed a method called glottochronology, which attempts to fill this gap. The fundamental assumption of glottochronology is that the rate of change by replacement within a standard vocabulary list is reasonably constant for all languages. The absolute value is calculated from a number of documented cases from earlier and later stages of the same languages in Europe and the Near East. If it is hypothesized that attrition in related languages is occurring independently at this rate, then there will be an expected number of common retentions, the so-called cognate forms. From the percentage of cognates in such cases it is possible to derive an estimate of the chronological date at which divergence within the original unified speech community began. Recently both the empirical and mathematical bases of the theory have come under sharp attack.

TYPOLOGIC METHOD

Another type of comparison has come into renewed prominence in recent years. This is typologic comparison and classification in which the criteria employed refer to similarities which may arise without any necessary implication of historical connection through either contact or common origin. Languages can have noun case systems, for example, which considerably resemble each other in the semantic categories but which do not have corresponding similarities in the sound sequences which express these categories. Thus certain Australian, Caucasian, Indo-European, Amerind, and other languages in all probability have independently developed systems of case inflection in the nouns. To cite but a few instances of a widespread phenomenon in phonology: Ewe in West Africa, Chinese in Eastern Asia, and Zapotecan in Mexico, make use of pitch distinctions in their phonemic systems although the languages have had no historic connection.

Non-historical comparison using such criteria leads to classification of languages into types. The complete absence of certain logically possible types and the significantly different frequencies of others evidently lead to generalizations about human language as a whole. In the past there has been a tendency to confuse typological and genetic criteria for resemblances, but the growing clarification of this problem has tended to elucidate the legitimate role of typological comparison in the development of both synchronic law-like generalizations and diachronic regularities governing the change of type.

Other Linguistic Disciplines

In addition to the two core fields of descriptive and comparative linguistics just outlined, a number of more or less peripheral, though definitely related, topics possess the common characteristic of having fairly direct relevance to other disciplines. In certain instances the area of common interest is sufficiently extensive to have given rise to nascent subdisciplines, notably psycholinguistics and ethnolinguistics. In the present context the emphasis is on common ground with other social sciences, and no consideration need be given to such fields as semantic analysis, an important joint interest of linguistics with logic.

Because language is a part of culture, and linguistics, from this point of view, may be considered a branch of cultural anthropology, the relationship between language and other aspects of culture has naturally become a concern of anthropological linguistics. This rather vague area of knowledge is often called *ethnolinguistics*. Among its basic problems is the determination of the rôle of language in the transmission of culture from one generation to another (enculturation) and from one culture to another (acculturation). Studies have been made, for example, of the changes induced in one language by contact with another in the context of the general culture-contact situation, including its non-linguistic aspects. Another set of problems has to do with possible correlations between language, particularly in its semantic aspect of classification of concepts, and non-linguistic cultural behaviour. The by now classic anthropological topic of the relation between kinship terminology and patterned kinship behaviour is an example of this. But the sharpest issues in this area have been raised through the largely posthumous interest in the writings of Benjamin Whorf. The Whorfian thesis or 'linguistic Weltanschauung hypothesis', as it has been called, in its most extreme interpretation would assert that the general 'world view' of its speakers is determined by, or at least mirrored in, the categories of the language which they speak. This thesis has aroused wide interest and has been the stimulus both for analytic discussion and for cross-cultural psychological experimentation.

Like ethnolinguistics, the merging subdiscipline of *psycholinguistics* does not as yet have a clearly delineated set of problems or techniques. In order to give a general notion of its contents, a number of topics generally considered relevant may be mentioned here. These include the psychological processes in language-learning, whether of first or subsequent languages, and in language-loss in the pathological condition known as aphasia; the study of sound perceptions in speech; and the psychological aspects of meaning interpreted as the reaction of subjects to words operating as stimulus objects. This last type of interest has given rise to the semantic differential as an instrument to measure meaning as response along a set of dimensions.

Even more recent is the interest in what has come to be called *sociolinguistics*, including such topics as: the relation of language differences to social class; the differential social roles of different languages coexisting in the same society; the development and spread of lingua francas as auxiliary languages in multilingual situations; the factors involved in the differential prestige ratings of languages; the rôle of language as a sign of ethnic identification; language in relation to nationalism; and problems of language policy, e.g., in education. This area has become a focus of interest largely because of problems arising in developing areas.

Still another aspect of language, namely, its employment as a *medium of aesthetic expression*, must also be considered. There is a purely linguistic side to the characterization of individual and folk style in written and unwritten literature. Linguistic considerations also enter into the description and analysis of differences between prose and various poetic types of language. One particular poetic device, metre, cannot be analysed without reference to strictly linguistic factors. The use of language in song, for example, the relation between linguistic and musical pitch patterns in tone languages, raises at least partly linguistic considerations. Departing somewhat from the strictly aesthetic aspect, one may also consider the ritual use of language, secret languages, the linguistic aspect of drum and other communication based on language and the playful modification of language involved in tongue-twisters, dog-Latin and similar devices.

26 Underlying and Superficial Linguistic Structure

Paul M. Postal

THE 1950'S PRODUCED A NEAR EXPLOSION IN THE QUIET FIELD OF LINGUISTICS, *and the echoes have not yet died down. Out of the expanded needs of language teachers and experiments in mechanical or machine translation and out of theoretical linkings of approaches drawn from linguistics, mathematics, philosophy (logical analysis in particular) and, to a lesser degree, psychology came a movement sometimes known as the school of generative or transformational grammar. The breakthrough, as its partisans might term it, came in 1957 with the publication of the book* Syntactic Structures *by Noam Chomsky and the long and laudatory review of that book published shortly thereafter in* Language. *As is the case with most scientific events, generative grammar was not invented out of the blue but had an interesting developmental history in which many prominent linguists figured, including Zellig Harris, Chomsky's teacher.*

The science of linguistics will never be the same as it was before the advent of transformational grammar. Nonetheless, the approach has a number of highly controversial aspects. Ideally, its central problem is to provide "a mechanical procedure for discovering the correct grammar of any given language," to use the words of Robert B. Lees. Since there are several reasons why this is not a feasible task, a more modest goal is set, and the school of generative grammar concentrates on constructing

SOURCE: *Harvard Educational Review,* Vol. 34, 2 (Spring, 1964), pp. 246–66. Reprinted with the permission of the author and publisher.

The author (b. 1936) is Professor of Linguistics at Queens College, New York City. Professor Postal's field research was done on Mohawk syntax; his book on general phonology is in press.

364

methods of differentiating between alternative models of grammatical systems and attempts to state exactly why one of these models is better than the others. This objective can be phrased in terms of the description of the grammatical rules which govern the formation of "well formed sentences."

There are many reasons for the scholarly antagonisms raised by the school of generational grammar, a school which one linguist, Martin Joos, has identified as a "heresy" within the main tradition of American linguistics rather than a competitor to it. One criticism is of special interest since it extends well beyond the technical field of linguistics and pertains instead to fundamental epistemological questions of ethnography. This is a matter that appears in Volume II of these readings. At its crux is the problem of "emics," "etics," and the "new ethnography." The problem is raised in linguistics when a contrast is made between the study of how people are actually observed to use language patterns and the Chomskyan view of linguistics which sets the task as describing " 'linguistic rules that the speaker has in his possession,' separating these from 'his misapplications of them, his memory and perceptual limitations, fluctuations in his psychological state, etc.,' " as Robert Dixon has put it.

The selection below flows directly from the school of generative grammar but touches only implicitly on the issue mentioned above. Essentially it is devoted to sketching some of the problems involved in constructing a generative grammar with special reference to English. If the subject is found difficult, the student should be reassured there is no simple way into these problems.

The following remarks based on examples from English are a rather informal discussion of some of the kinds of results and implications of linguistic research being done in the conceptual framework which has come to be called 'generative grammar.' [1]

A linguistic description of some natural language is designed to provide a specification of the knowledge which speakers of that language have which differentiates them from non-speakers. This knowledge is evidently enormous in extent and varied in nature. It includes, among other things, the ability to distinguish those noises which are sentences of the language (*well-formed* or *grammatical*) from those which are not; to recognize similarities between utterances and their parts; to recognize identities of various sorts from full rhyme on the phonological level to identity of meaning or paraphrase on the semantic level, etc. Since each speaker is a finite organism, this knowledge must be finite in character, i.e. learnable. Yet a moment's thought is sufficient to show that someone who has learned a natural language is in fact in possession of full information

---

[1] The following abbreviations are used throughout the article: NP—Noun Phrase; S—Sentence; VP—Verb Phrase; *—non-sentence.

about an infinite set of linguistic objects, namely the sentences. This follows because there is no longest sentence. Given any sentence we can always find a longer one by replacing some noun with a noun and following modifier, or by replacing some verbal phrase with a conjunction of two verbal phrases, etc. Of course, the finite and in fact rather small bound on human memory will prevent actual speech behavior from making use of more than a small finite subclass of all possible sentences. But this in no way affects the psychologically and linguistically fundamental fact that knowledge of a natural language provides a speaker in principle with knowledge of an infinite set of linguistic objects. Only this assumption, for example, makes it possible to explain why, as the limits on memory are weakened, as with the use of pencil and paper, speaker's abilities to use and understand sentences are extended to those of greater length. It is no accident that traditionally, for example, written German involves lengthy and complex constructions not normally found in the spoken language. The analogy with arithmetic is appropriate here. One who has learned the rules of arithmetic is clearly capable in principle of determining the result of multiplying any two of the infinite set of whole numbers. Yet obviously no one ever has or ever could compute more than a small finite number of such multiples.

In principle knowledge by a finite organism of an infinite set of linguistic facts is neither paradox nor contradiction, but results from the fact that there are kinds of finite entities which specify infinite sets of objects. In mathematics these are often referred to by the term 'recursive.' For example, consider the set of rules:

(1) $A \rightarrow X$

(2) $X \rightarrow X + X$

where the arrow is to be interpreted as the instruction to rewrite the left symbol as the righthand string of symbols. It is evident that continued application of these rules will specify an endless, unbounded, i.e. strictly infinite set of strings of the form X, XX, XXX, XXXX, etc. And a person who learned these two rules plus the finite set of instructions for applying them would, in a precise sense, have learned the infinite set of possible outputs.

It is in exactly this sense that we must postulate that a speaker has learned the infinite set of sentences of his language, by learning some finite set of rules which can enumerate, list, specify, or, as it is usually said, *generate* these sentences. Such a set of rules can be called a *grammar* or *syntax*.

A *language* in these terms is then just the set of strings of symbols (the 'X's in the above trivial example) enumerated by the grammar. We shall see below that this conception of language must be greatly enriched. Having come to the point of seeing each sentence as a string of symbols of some type, it is natural to ask about the nature of these symbols in actual natural languages like English, Chinese, etc. It is traditional to think of these as *words*, i.e. roughly as minimum units of pronunciation, those elements which may be uttered independently. Modern linguistics has greatly emphasized, however, that words are themselves in fact composed of or analyzable into syntactically significant parts, usually referred to as *morphemes*. For example, it would be pointed out that the word:

(3)   uninterrupted

is composed of at least three morphemes *un = interrupt = ed*, the first of which is also found in (4), the second of which is also found in (5), and the third of which is also found in (6):

(4)   unhappy
(5)   interruptable
(6)   destroyed

It thus follows that the syntactic structure of each sentence must be represented as a string of words with morpheme boundaries also indicated.

However, all linguists are in effect agreed that sentence structure is not exhausted by division into words and morphemes. Most crucially, the words and morphemes must be considered as grouped into significant sequences; in other words to be *parsed*, or *hierarchically bracketed*. Thus in the sentence:

(7)   Harry liked the nice girl

most linguists would probably agree that the elements must be bracketed something like:

Harry	liked		the	nice	girl
	liked		the	nice	girl
	like	ed	the	nice	girl
				nice	girl

Such a bracketing indicates that the sentence is first made up of two basic parts, *Harry* and everything else; that everything else is made up of two primary parts *liked* and the remainder, etc. However, it would further be agreed that such bracketing representations are inadequate if not accompanied by an associated *labelling* of the segments obtained by the bracketing. It has become common to represent such labelled bracketings in the form of rooted trees like Diagram 1 but such are perfectly equivalent to (labelled) box diagrams like that above or labelled parenthesizations, or any other suitable diagrammatic equivalent. Such a labelled bracketing provides far more explanatory insight into the structure of a sentence than the mere bracketing alone. It accounts for similarities between various sequences, i.e. for example our knowledge that *Harry* and *the nice girl* are in some sense similar kinds of elements as against *liked*, or *the*. I shall refer to the kind of linguistic structure represented by labelled bracketings in any of their various forms as *phrase markers*. Such structures describe for each sentence (string of minimal syntactic symbols) what parts make it up, how these are grouped together into significant sequences, and what type of grouping each is.

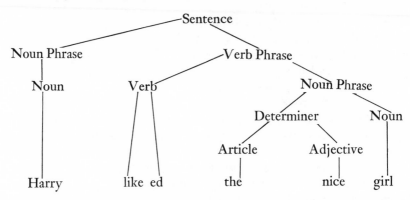

Linguists are rather well agreed on the fact that each sentence of a natural language is correctly represented by at least one phrase marker of some kind. This agreement is, of course, accompanied by many disagreements of various types, both substantive and terminological, which need not concern us here. Since each speaker knows an unbounded set of sentences, and since it is agreed that each sentence has one phrase marker, it follows that each speaker must learn a finite set of rules which can enumerate not only strings of symbols (words or morphemes) but rather an infinite set of correct phrase markers. It follows then that a linguistic description of a language must contain just this finite set of rules. A crucial problem for linguistic theory is then the specification of the character or form of such rules, the way they associate phrase markers with an infinite output of strings of symbols, etc.

Underlying Grammatical Structure

However, in stopping at the point, in effect widely agreed upon, that the syntactic structure of a sentence is given by a single phrase marker, we will have seemed to embrace a position which we cannot in fact accept. There is overwhelming evidence showing that the syntactic structure of the sentences of natural languages is by no means adequately representable by single phrase markers, regardless of how elaborated. Although each sentence certainly has one phrase marker which provides a labelled bracketing of the actual string of morphemes and words which are directly related to its phonetic manifestation, this is only the most superficial aspect of syntactic structure. There is a whole other domain of required structure which is crucial for describing both the formal syntactic properties of sentences and the way they are understood, i.e. their semantic properties.[2] The superficial phrase marker of each sentence is chiefly relevant only to the way sentences are pronounced. To determine what sentences mean, one must attend to the far more abstract underlying structure.

Consider the following English sentences:

(8) drink the milk
(9) go home
(10) don't bother me.

These are normally referred to as *imperative sentences*. And in terms of their superficial phrase markers it is evident that they consist of an uninflected verb plus other elements of the Verb Phrase but no preceding 'subject' Noun Phrase of the kind found in declaratives like:

(11) he drank the milk
(12) I went home
(13) John didn't bother me.

English also contains so-called *reflexive pronouns* like the italicized 'objects' in such sentences as:

(14) the man cut *himself*
(15) John admired *himself* in the mirror
(16) you overestimate *yourself*

If one now inquires into the rules which govern the occurrence of this kind of reflexive form in English, one finds, among other things, that there are sentences of the form $NP_1 + Verb + reflexive\ pronoun + Y$ just in case one can also find sentences of the form $NP_2 + Verb + NP_1 + Y$. That is, those verbs which take reflexive pronoun 'objects' are just those which can elsewhere occur with 'objects' identical to the 'subjects' of the reflexive sentences. Hence one finds:

(14)–(16) and:
(17) John cut the man
(18) I admired John in the mirror
(19) she overestimates you

but we do not find:

(20) *Harry demands himself
(21) *you concede yourself
(22) *Mary completes herself

and accordingly there are also no English sentences:

(23) *I demand Harry
(24) *John concedes you
(25) *you complete Mary

[2] This conclusion is in effect implied by the whole literature which argues that adequate grammatical description involves transformational rules.

although one can find:

    (26)   I demand the answer
    (27)   John concedes the game
    (28)   you complete the task

    These facts show that the rule for forming reflexives of the type being considered is in effect based on *a possible equivalence* of 'subject' and 'object' Noun Phrase and suggests that reflexive sentences be described by rules which in some some sense 'derive' reflexive sentences from structures in which there are equivalent 'subjects' and 'objects'. Hence (14)–(15) would be derived from abstract structures something like the following schematically indicated *phrase markers:*

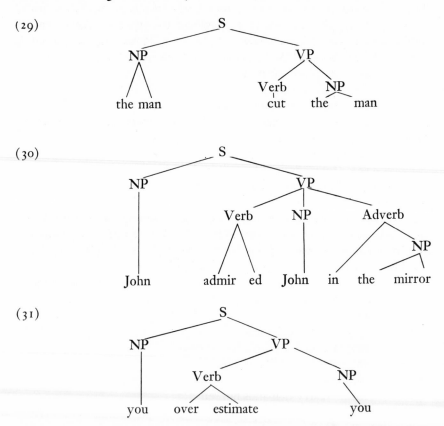

(29)

(30)

(31)

Notice that the rules which associate 'subjects' and 'objects' with verbs, these rules being part of the set which enumerate phrase markers like (29)–(31), will be *simpler* if they are allowed to produce such structures as (29)–(31) than if not, since, as we have seen, all the possible 'subjects' and 'objects' of (29)–(31) must be allowed with their respective verbs in any event. Hence to prevent derivation of structures like (29)–(31) and their analogues would require adding special restrictions to the grammar prohibiting identical 'subjects' and 'objects' with a single verb.

But now if structures like (29)–(31) are enumerated they provide a simple means for describing correctly reflexive sentences if one simply adds the rule that the second Noun Phrase in a structure $NP_1 + Verb + NP_2 + X$ is replaced by the appropriate reflexive pronoun when $NP_1 = NP_2$. This correctly derives just those reflexive strings which meet the equivalence condition stated before and permits retention of the non-complicated verb-'object' and 'subject'-verb selection rules by eliminating the need for special restrictions to prevent the enumeration of the analogues of (29)–(31). This follows because this new reflexive rule converts (29)–(31) and all similar phrase markers into the superficial phrase markers which must represent the occurring reflexive sentences like (14)–(16) and these must be described anyway.

But this analysis of reflexives provides an immediate explanation of why an English speaker *understands* reflexive sentences to refer to 'objects' identical to their 'subjects,' *if* we insist that the understanding of a sentence refers to abstract structures like (29)–(31) rather than to the superficial phrase markers of actual sentences like (14)–(16) in which the 'subject'-'object' equivalences cannot possibly be marked.

This very natural and explanatorily powerful description of reflexive sentences requires, however, a radical shift in one's notion of grammatical structure. It requires that the grammatical structure of a sentence be taken to consist, not of a *single phrase marker*, but at least of a *set of phrase markers*, these being related by the kind of rules illustrated by our description of the reflexive. This leads to a picture of syntax in which there is a basic division into two components, one containing rules which derive very abstract *underlying phrase markers* like those represented by (29)–(31); the other containing rules like the reflexive above. These latter rules apply to whole phrase markers and derive new phrase markers. The last such phrase marker derived by the final rule of this second component is called a *final derived phrase marker* and represents the superficial labelled bracketing of the actual string of words of the sentence. Rules which derive phrase markers from phrase markers have been called *transformations*. The rules which enumerate underlying phrase markers are simpler in character. It was assumed at first that these were roughly variants of rules like (1) and (2) above, i.e. rules which operated exclusively on strings of symbols by replacing single symbols by certain distinct strings of other symbols. These were called *phrase structure* or *constituent structure* rules. Such phrase structure rules as the following have been proposed:

(32)   Sentence → NP + VP
(33)   NP → Determiner + Noun

It has become increasingly apparent, however, that underlying phrase markers cannot in fact be correctly described exclusively with rules of this type. It appears that such rules must be supplemented by more powerful devices to help account for so-called 'selectional restrictions' such as the fact that certain verbs occur only with animate 'subjects' and inanimate 'objects,' others with inanimate 'subjects' and animate 'objects,' others with animate 'subjects' and animate 'objects,' etc. It appears that the sub-component of syntactic rules which enumerates underlying phrase markers is itself divided into two elements, one containing phrase structure rules and the other containing a *lexicon* or *dictionary* of highly structured morpheme entries which are inserted into the structures enumerated by the phrase structure rules. Although quite new and too complicated to say more about here, research into this area of syntactic structure promises to yield great insights into many areas of traditional interest, including characterizations of such notions as *word, inflection, derivation, Noun,* and *Verb,* as well as resolving the original difficulties with selectional restrictions.

We can provide more motivation for an extension of the notion of grammatical structure to include a whole set of phrase markers for each sentence, including most crucially abstract underlying phrase markers, by returning to imperative sentences which superficially have no 'subjects.' These may also contain reflexives:

(34) wash yourself
(35) don't kill yourself

However, there is a crucial restriction on the reflexive pronouns which can occur in imperative sentences, namely only *yourself* is permitted. Hence there are no sentences like:

(36) *wash himself
(37) *wash themselves
(38) *don't kill myself
(39) *don't kill herself

But we recall the fact that reflexives are based on an equivalence of 'subject' and 'object.' This means that if we are to embed imperative reflexives into the simple description of reflexives given earlier, imperatives must be derived from underlying phrase markers which contain *you* 'subjects.'

As support for this, consider so-called 'tag' questions like:

(40) Mary will come, won't she
(41) John can run, can't he
(42) I have won, haven't I

It is evident that the part of such questions which follows the intonation break (represented by the comma) involves a repetition of the Auxiliary [3] and 'subject' of the first pre-comma part, with the proviso that the

---

[3] That is, the constituent which in underlying phrase markers represents such elements as the Tense morphemes, as well as *will, may, be, can, have,* etc.

order must be changed, the negative added, and the 'subject' pronominalized.[4] But there are tag sentences in which the first part is *imperative* in
form:

    (43)   eat the meat, will you

    (44)   go home, won't you

And there is a constraint here that the pronoun form after the commas
can only be *you*. Hence we find no English sentences like:

    (45)   *eat the meat, will $\left\{\begin{array}{l} \text{she} \\ \text{he} \\ \text{they} \end{array}\right\}$

    (46)   *go home, will $\left\{\begin{array}{l} \text{I} \\ \text{we} \end{array}\right\}$

But this can be readily explained in terms of the fact that the second
Noun Phrase is a repeated pronominalized form of the 'subject' Noun
Phrase before the comma, if it is assumed that imperatives have in their
underlying phrase markers a *you* 'subject' Noun Phrase in front of the
verb. We see then that the evidence of reflexives and tag sentences
converges on the conclusion that the underlying structure of imperatives
contains a second person 'subject.' But now this can immediately provide
an explanation of the fact that every English speaker understands an
imperative to refer to the second person if, as before, we assume that the
structures relevant to understanding are the underlying phrase markers.

    Here as before we must posit a transformational rule which will
derive the superficial structure of imperatives from the underlying phrase
markers. Notice that the Auxiliary repetition of tag questions shows that
the underlying phrase markers of imperatives must contain the modal *will*
(*will + contracted not = won't*) since this is the form found in imperative tags and in fact is the only permitted Auxiliary form:

    (47)   *eat the meat, did he

    (48)   *eat the meat, can he

But this provides an explanation of why we understand that imperative
sentences refer to the future. The transformational rule which derives the
superficial forms of imperative sentences will delete the *will* (and preceding tense morpheme) and optionally delete the 'subject'. Optionally only
because we find imperatives with explicit *you*:

    (49)   you eat your meat

    (50)   you go home (or I'll tell your mother)

These also have a *non* imperative declarative semantic interpretation but
this need not concern us here.

    We have suggested that in order to provide an account of both the
formal properties of sentences and the way in which they are understood
it is necessary to extend the notion of grammatical structure in such a
way that each sentence is represented by a whole set of phrase markers,

[4] When the initial element is itself negative, then the part after the comma must
be non-negative.

including crucially quite abstract underlying ones. This conclusion is greatly strengthened if we consider so-called grammatical relations like *subject-verb*, or *verb-object*. To understand a sentence it is obviously quite crucial to know which parts bear which relations to which other parts. For example, despite the fact that the following sentences contain identical elements we understand them differently:

(51)   Mary loves John
(52)   John loves Mary

In (51)) we understand that it is Mary who does the loving and John who receives the affection; in (52) conversely. The fact that these differences are associated with a distinct order of elements might suggest that the various relations involved can be precisely characterized in terms of *order*. We can say that in a phrase marker the first Noun Phrase bears the *subject* relation to the Verb, the Noun Phrase following the Verb bears the *object* relation to this element, etc. However, attractive as this proposal is, it obviously fails for *superficial* phrase markers because of the enormous number of cases like:

(53)   John was loved by Mary
(54)   Mary was loved by John
(55)   John is anxious to please Mary
(56)   John is easy for Mary to please

In (53) the relations between *John* and *Mary* and the Verb are the same as in (51), while in (54) they are the same as in (52). Yet the order of constituents in (53) is like that in (52) and the order in (54) is like that in (51). Similarly in (55) we recognize that *John* is the 'subject' of *please* while in (56) it is the 'object' of this Verb. Yet its relative order is the same. In short we see that in the actual superficial forms of sentences the crucial grammatical relations are not associated with any unique configurations of constituents.

It seems, however, that in underlying phrase markers this is the case. That is, in underlying phrase markers grammatical relations are uniquely and uniformly definable in terms of constituents and their order. Hence the underlying structures of (52) and (54) are quite similar to those of (51) and (52) respectively and the actual order to elements in (53) and (54) is derived by the so-called *passive transformation* which, among other things, inverts 'subject', and 'object' Noun Phrases. This solution is formally motivated *inter alia* by the fact that for a fixed Verb type those Noun Phrase elements which can occur in the initial position of passive sentences are just those which can occur in the 'object' position of declaratives. Hence one finds:

(57)   John admires Harry
(58)   John admires truth

but not:

(59)   *truth admires John

and similarly:

(60)   Harry is admired by John

(61)   truth is admired by John

but not:

(62)   *John is admired by truth

and:

(63)   John demands a raise

(64)   John believes Harry

but not:

(65)   *John demands Harry

(66)   *John believes love

and similarly:

(67)   a raise is demanded by John

(68)   Harry is believed by John

but not:

(69)   *Harry is demanded by John

(70)   *love is believed by John

If passive sentences are not derived from underlying structures in which the 'subject' and 'object' elements are in the same order as in active sentences, all these selectional facts must be stated twice. Thus again we find formal motivation for abstract underlying phrase markers which contain structures of just the type needed to explain the way the occurring sentences are understood.

Consider finally (55) and (56). These sentences are in a sense fundamentally different from any considered before because their underlying structure must be taken to include a *pair* of underlying phrase markers which are combined to produce the occurring sentences. The transformations which perform such combining operations have been called *generalized transformations*. Sentences like (55) in which the initial Noun Phrase (NP) is understood as the 'subject' of the verb in the infinitive phrase must be derived from a pair of structures of roughly the form $NP_1 + is + Adjective + Complement$, $NP_1 + Verb + NP_2$. That is, the two phrase markers which are combined must have identical 'subject' Noun Phrases. This restriction is necessary to account for the fact that those verbs which can occur in the infinitives of sentences like (55) are just those which can take as 'subject' the initial Noun Phrase. Hence one does not find:

(71)   *truth is anxious to see Mary

(72)   *love is anxious to marry Mary

because there is no:

(73)   *truth sees Mary

(74)   *love marries Mary

etc. But these formal reasons force us to derive sentences like (55) from underlying structures in which *John* is the 'subject' of the verb *please* in terms of the uniform configurational account of grammatical relations roughly sketched earlier.

In (56) the situation is analogous although reversed. Here the sentences must be derived from a pair of underlying strucutres with the forms:

$$NP_1 + is + Adjective + Complement, NP_2 + Verb + NP_1$$

In this case the equivalence of Noun Phrases is between the 'object' Noun Phrase of the second underlying phrase marker and the 'subject' of the predicative type phrase marker. This is necessary because those verbs which can occur in the *for* phrases of sentences like (56) are just those which can occur with the sentence initial Noun Phrase as 'object.' Hence one does not find:

(75)   *truth is easy for Mary to please

(76)   *meat is easy for Mary to prove

because one cannot find:

(77)   *Mary pleases truth

(78)   *Mary proves meat

But this means that one is forced by these formal facts to derive sentences like (56) from underlying structures in which *John* is indeed the 'object' (by the uniform characterization given above) of *please*. So that again the independently motivated underlying structures provide a correct account of the way sentences are understood with respect to grammatical relations.

Linguistic Summary

We have briefly considered a few of the enormous number of cases which support the view that the grammatical structure of sentences can only be adequately represented by structural descriptions which include highly abstract underlying phrase markers. We see then that a linguistic description must minimally include rules to generate the correct set of underlying phrase markers, rules to combine underlying phrase markers in the case of sentences which are complex [like (55) and (56)], and finally rules to derive the correct superficial phrase markers of sentences from their abstract structures. A full account of the nature of all such rules has yet to be given, although tremendous progress has been made in recent years and the outlines of correct solutions appear to be relatively clear. The crucial point is that any adequate theory of grammar must provide an account of such rules for only in this way can such a theory provide the theoretical apparatus which individual linguistic descriptions must draw on in order to explain the finite mechanism a speaker has learned which yields his knowledge of the underlying and superficial structures of the endless class of well formed utterances.

We have been speaking essentially only of syntactic structure. It is obvious that a full linguistic description must contain other aspects. First, it must contain a *phonological component* whose rules specify the phonetic character of each structure generated by the syntactic rules. It appears that the phonological component operates exclusively on the *final derived phrase markers* of the syntax and associates a phonetic representation with each. The phonetic rules must also, quite crucially, characterize the notion of 'phonetically possible morpheme.' That is, it is these rules which will state that in English, although neither *ftorts* or *geyk* is an actual morpheme, the latter but not the former is a possible morpheme, and might be introduced tomorrow as the name of a new soap, or a new concept. Much progress has also been made recently in our knowledge of the form and character of phonological rules but this will not concern us further.

Most important, however, is the fact that a full linguistic description must contain a *semantic component* whose task is to assign each sentence a *meaning*. We have shown that the syntactic structure relevant to this task is present in underlying but not superficial grammatical structure. But nothing has been said precisely about how semantic interpretations are assigned to the structures which the syntactic rules generate. Obviously, however, a full linguistic description must specify this information, since it is evident that speakers know the meanings of the sentences of their language as well as their grammatical structure and pronunciation features.

Although fundamental insights into this question have recently been achieved, this topic is too complex and too new for extended treatment here. The problem for a semantic description is to specify how the speaker who learns the meanings of a finite number of *lexical items*, morphemes, multimorpheme idioms, plus the rules which characterize the grammatical structure of the sentences which contain these lexical items, determines the meanings of sentences. This can be formulated as a purely formal problem of specifying rules which operate on the grammatical structure (the underlying phrase markers) and the meanings of lexical items, if the notion *meaning of a lexical item* can be formally characterized. This can be done by postulating abstract atomic elements, *semantic markers*, which represent the conceptual content of lexical items. For example, we can postulate a semantic marker (male) which will be associated with the lexical items, *man, boy, father,* or *uncle,* to represent part of the conceptual similarity between these (as opposed for example, to *car, truth, mother, girl*). Besides a dictionary which associates sequences of such semantic markers *(readings)* with lexical items, the semantic component of a lingustic description will also contain a set of *projection rules* which will combine the readings of lexical items in order to obtain derived semantic characterizations for higher order constituents, on up to the constituent Sentence itself. These rules will operate on the readings of lexical items plus the grammatical relations which hold between these items, these relations being indicated in the underlying phrase markers in the manner suggested earlier.

The output of the semantic component will be a formal semantic characterization of each constituent of each sentence. These characterizations will provide an explanation of such semantic properties as *ambiguity, paraphrase, synonymy,* or *anomaly.*[5] It should be emphasized that this kind of semantic theory leaves its primary descriptive objects, the semantic markers, uninterpreted. That is, it does not specify the relation of these elements to the nonlinguistic world. (This means that such notions as *reference,* and *truth,* are not characterized.) This task is left as a fundamental (and fantastically difficult) psychological problem independent of the problem of formulating linguistic descriptions and the theory underlying them. Interpretation of the system of markers is seen as part of the fundamental problems of concept formation, categorization of experience, etc.

It appears then that the linguistic knowledge whose possession characterizes a speaker of a language has the form of an abstract lingusitic object containing three major components of rules. The basic element is a generative syntactic component whose rules generate highly complex structures including a set of phrase markers for each derived string of words. There are then two subsidiary *interpretive* components. The phonological component provides each sentence with a phonetic interpretation and accounts for the speaker's knowledge of the facts of pronunciation. The semantic component provides each sentence with a semantic interpretation in the form of a set of readings and accounts for the speaker's knowledge of the facts of meaning.

It seems that the two interpretative components are each based on a fixed, universal vocabulary of primitive conceptual elements with universally specified relations to the non-linguisitic world. In the case of the phonological component, this vocabulary consists of the set of phonetic features with which sentences are described (Voicing, Stress, and Nasality). That is, there is a fixed universal phonetic alphabet which provides all the relevant phonetic information about each sentence. In the case of the semantic component, the vocabulary consists of the set of semantic markers, about which, however, much less is known. The universality of the set of semantic markers is plausible but much work on a wide variety of languages will be needed before it can be verified to anything like the extent to which the universality of the phonetic features has been

---

[5] These properties are respectively illustrated by:
a. I observed the ball
b. John is a farmer; John is someone who farms
c. not living; dead
d. John married a potato pancake

confirmed. In claiming that the atomic elements of both interpretive components are universal, one is saying that the child who learns a language based on them need not learn these elements or their relations to the non-linguistic world. That is, for example, someone who learns English need not learn what the semantic marker (Male) denotes or what properties of vocal utterances the phonetic feature (Nasal) refers to. He only need determine *if* these elements play a role in English sentences, and if so, how, that is, what rules describe them, what other elements they are related to, etc.

It is unquestionable that the form of the rules in each of the components is a linguistic universal, to be characterized in general linguistic theory. It is also quite likely, I believe, that some of the content of the various components is universal. That is, there are very probably universal rules, and many of the elements which occur in linguistic rules may be universally specified. In particular, there is much hope that the goal of traditional universal grammar, namely, the cross-linguistic characterization of notions like *Noun, Verb, Adjective,* and *Modifier,* can be given in general linguistic theory by limiting the specification to highly abstract underlying phrase markers rather than by attempting to give it in terms of superficial phrase markers wherein all previous attempts have failed.

Implications

In the above sections we have given a quite informal discussion of some of the properties which must be attributed to adequate linguistic descriptions and the theory of language which underlies them. Unfortunately, there has been much confusion about the nature of the subject matter or domain which a linguistic description describes, and the relation between the output of such generative devices and actual speech behavior. This then requires brief discussion.

It must be emphasized that in no sense is a linguistic description an account of actual 'verbal behavior.' Even the grosser aspects of the descriptions of sentences provided by a linguistic description, the phonetic outputs of the phonological component, cannot be identified with real utterances of speakers. Any real utterance will, for example, contain features which provide information about the speaker's age, sex, health, emotional state, etc. And these features have obviously nothing to do with the *language* which the linguistic description characterizes. It is just these 'nonlinguistic' features which differentiate different speakers of the same language and different 'verbal performances' by the same speaker. But it is of course impossible to observe any actual utterances which do not contain such features. It is thus necessary to posit a relation of *representation* which holds between real utterances and the output of linguistic descriptions. The output for any sentence S_1 must be assumed to specify a set of phonetic conditions which any utterance must meet if it is to be an *instance* of S_1.

However, the relation between actual speech behavior and the output of linguistic descriptions is by no means exhaustively described in the above way. It is evident that actual verbal performances contain an enormous number of utterances which do not in the strict sense represent any sentences at all. These are nonetheless perfectly adequate for communication and often more appropriate to the occasion than utterances which do represent full sentences. For example, in answer to questions such as (79)–(81):

(79)   where is the car
(80)   is John inside
(81)   who did it

one can hear such answers as: *inside, yes, Bill*. It is evident that these utterances are understandable because in the context of the previous question they are understood as *versions* of the full sentences:

(82)   the car is inside
(83)   yes John is inside
(84)   Bill did it

It is only the full sentences that should be generated by the linguistic description proper which must draw the line between full sentences and fragments which can represent full sentences in particular environments. Part of the differentia of these two classes of utterances, utterances which directly represent full sentences, and those which do not but are still understandable, is that the former have a *fixed* finite set of semantic interpretations independently of all context, and their interpretation in any one context is simply a selection from among this fixed set. For fragments, however, occurrence in isolation permits no interpretation at all. And their interpretation in context is directly determined by, and does not involve an elimination of fixed interpretations inappropriate to, the context. Thus the fragments given above can as well be answers to

(85)–87) as to (79)–81):

(85)   where did you leave your coat
(86)   can Hitler really be dead
(87)   who was clawed by the tiger

And in these cases the fragments must be understood as versions of:

(88)   I left my coat inside
(89)   yes Hitler really can be dead
(90)   Bill was clawed by the tiger

In short we see that sentence fragments of the type being discussed have no finitely fixed number of interpretations at all and in this way are radically distinct from utterances which directly represent full sentences. The utterances *inside, yes, Bill* have an infinite number of possible interpretations and can hence not be described *as such* by a finite linguistic description. To account for the understanding of fragments and many other kinds of utterances, suitable for communication in various contexts but distinct from full sentences, it is then evident that linguistic theory must provide a means for extending the description of full sentences to a class of *semi-sentences*. We can say little about this here besides noting that (1) it would be surprising if the apparatus for extension to semi-sentences was not an inherent property of human beings, hence cross-linguistic, and (2) it is obviously impossible to carry out research on the topic of semi-sentences independently of extensive knowledge of the properties of full sentences. And it is just this knowledge which the study of linguistic descriptions in the narrow sense is designed to yield. We conclude then that a linguistic description does not describe actual speech behavior but rather an indefinite class of highly structured (in three distinct though interrelated ways, syntactic, semantic, phonological) abstract objects, *sentences,* which define the *language* which in various ways underlies all speech behavior. A linguistic description is, in other words, a partial account of linguistic *competence.* To extend the characterization of this to an account of linguistic *performance* then requires a number of studies of various types of the way in which this underlying knowledge of linguistic rules is put to use.

The distinction between *competence* and *performance* or *language* and *speech* is quite crucial for understanding at least three goals related to linguistic descriptions proper, goals whose pursuit is crucial if a full account of the domain of language study is to be given. First, there is the task of constructing a *model of speech recognition,* that is, a model of the way speakers use their linguistic knowledge (language) to understand noises that they hear. In terms of the above outline of linguistic structure, this task is the task of determining what sentence the noise represents and then determining the underlying structure of that sentence in order to determine its possible range of semantic interpretations.

When the above tasks have been carried out successfully, the context of the utterance must be applied in some way to pick the interpretation which was 'intended.' Almost nothing can be seriously said at the moment about this problem of contextual *disambiguation* of utterances beyond the obvious point that the problem cannot be seriously posed without understanding of the nature of language or linguistic structure. It appears that every piece of possible human knowledge about the world is relevant to the disambiguation of some sentence and thus to its understanding in context. This has rather obvious implications of two sorts. On the one hand it shows that theoretically there can be no *general* theory of the way contexts serve to permit choice of one of several possible interpretations for some sentence, and on the other, it shows that practical attempts to utilize linguistic research for the mechanical replacement of human performers (as in so-called 'machine translation') are doomed to failure.

A third goal which is involved in a full linguistic account is the problem of formulating a *model for the speaker*. This must involve specification of how a desired *message* is given as input to the linguistic description to yield as output a phonetic representation which is the input to the speaker's speech apparatus, the output of this being the actual utterances.[6] It appears that the inputs to the linguisitic description must be taken to be *semantic objects*, i.e. *readings* in the sense of our earlier brief discussion. But just as linguistic theory as such does not specify the relation of semantic markers to the non-linguistic world, so also it cannot deal with the relations between a speaker's experiences, verbal or otherwise, and the utterances he produces. That is, it cannot deal with the fantastically complicated question of the *causation* of verbal behavior, although this is a task which modern pyschology has too prematurely tried to deal with. Too prematurely, because it is obviously impossible to even *formulate* the problem of causation prior to an understanding of the character of speech behavior. And this, as we have seen, requires prior knowledge of the abstract *language* which underlies such behavior. Hence study of the causation of verbal behavior is two steps removed from reasonable possibility if attempted independently of the kind of studies discussed earlier.

It should be obvious at this point that a linguistic description as such which *generates* sentences, i.e. highly abstract triples of syntactic, semantic, and phonological properties, is neither a model of the speaker nor of the hearer although it is often confused with these. *Generation* is not *production* or *recognition*. A linguistic description simply characterizes the objects which a model of recognition must recover from verbal noise and which a model of production must encode into such noise. The study of linguistic descriptions per se is hence logically prior to the study of questions of recognition, contextual determination, production, and causation since it defines the objects in terms of which the problems with which these latter studies deal must be formulated.

Finally, the kind of conclusions reached above have obvious and important implications for any study of the problem of language learning. If, as we have argued, the structure of the sentences of natural languages

---

[6] It is because this output is determined by other factors besides the phonetic representations which are the most superficial aspects of linguistic structure generated by the linguistic description that the latter can not be said to generate any actual utterances. That is, given a fixed phonetic or pronunciation code as input to the speech apparatus, the output is also determined by such factors as the presence or absence of food in the oral cavity, the speaker's age, sex, state of health (cleft palate or not, etc.), degree of wakefulness or intoxication, etc. Facts like these are sufficient in themselves to demonstrate the futility of any view of language which cannot go beyond the gross observations of utterances to the abstract structures which underlie them, i.e., the futility of any view of language which identifies the significant linguistic objects with what can be obtained from tape recorders.

involves an extremely complex and highly abstract set of entities related to actual utterances only by an extensive set of highly structured rules, it follows that the problem of language learning must be phrased in quite specific terms. That is, it is necessary to study the question of how an organism, equipped with a quite complex and *highly specific* characterization of the possible nature of a natural language, determines from various kinds of linguistic data, heard sentences, contexts, corrections, the particular manifestation of this abstract theory used in the community into which he was born. Again the primary constraint on the study of language learning is the logically prior knowledge of the character of the linguistic system which must be learned. And the more specific and detailed this knowledge can be made, that is, the more closely one can describe the general theory of linguistic descriptions which amounts to a hypothesis about the innate genetic knowledge which the human child brings to language learning, the greater is the possibility of being able to formulate the techniques or strategies which the child uses to apply this inherent knowledge of possible linguistic structure to induce the details of a particular language from his linguistic experience. From what was said earlier about the abstract character of linguistic structure, underlying phrase markers, and the like, it is clear that enough is already known about the nature of language to show that views of language learning which restrict attention to the gross phonetic properties of utterances, either by adherence to psychological theories which do not countenance concepts more abstract and specific than 'stimulus,' 'generalization,' 'chaining,' 'response,' etc., or linguisitic theories which do not countenance more than the kind of linguistic structure representable by final derived phrase markers, cannot teach us very much about the fantastic feat by which a child with almost no direct instruction learns that enormously extensive and complicated system which is a natural language, a system which has thus far defied the efforts of the best students to describe it in anything like a complete or adequate way.

I hope that the too brief and inadequate remarks of this final section will nonetheless have shown that the study of any aspect of language or linguistic behavior cannot hope to progress beyond superficialities if it is not based on firm knowledge of the character of the highly complex, abstract, finitely specifiable though infinite linguistic system which underlies all observable linguistic performances. In short, I hope to have shown that the results of generative linguistics are not an obscure oddity, of interest only to the specialist in linguistics, but rather provide the kind of knowledge which is prerequisite to the understanding of the domains of the entire range of language studies.

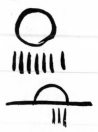

27 Glottochronology

Morris Swadesh

GLOTTOCHRONOLOGY IS DEFINED AS "THE STUDY OF RATE OF CHANGE IN LAN-
*guage . . . especially for the estimation of time depths . . . to provide a
pattern of internal relationships within a family." In other words, glottochronology is a linguistic technique that takes two or more related languages and by examining their similarities and divergencies seeks to establish the length of time that has elapsed since they parted company. An
important definitional aspect of glottochronology that has been pointed
out by Trager, Hymes and others is that it is tied to a specific and relatively brief list of words assumed to be a "basic vocabulary."*

*Glottochronology has been attacked at various points. The concept of
basic vocabulary has been criticized, as has the notion of its inclusion of
words of relative "non-cultural" nature, that is, of words implicating
meanings so basic to daily life as to have little dependence upon the content of a specific culture. Criticisms have also been directed at specific
techniques of making estimates of duration and other technical linguistic
matters. Although the literature now abounds in statements and applications of glottochronological theory more up to date and refined than the
article which follows, our selection is by the linguist who more than anyone else may be said to have invented glottochronology.*

SOURCE: "Diffusional Cumulation and Archaic Residue as Historical Explanation,"
Southwestern Journal of Anthropology, Vol. 7 (1951), pp. 1-21. Reprinted with the
permission of the author and the publisher.

The author (1909–1967) was a member of the Instituto de Historia, Professor of
Anthropology at the Escuela Nacional de Antropologia e Historia of Mexico, and
Professor of Linguistics, University of Alberta, Edmonton, Canada. Closely associated
with Edward Sapir, he extended the ethnographic work his teacher, Sapir, did among
the Nootka of Vancouver. Swadesh was a pioneer in glottochronology and continued
to work in the vanguard of this approach. He published papers on the Nootka, a
primer of Chinese called *Chinese in Your Pocket* (1948), *Russian Before You Know
It* (1945), and numerous scholarly papers on linguistic topics. Among his last publications was a dictionary of the Yana Indian Language (1960) with Edward Sapir
(posthumous).

If two cultures have traits in common to an extent that cannot be explained by sheer coincidence, a historic basis must be assumed. There are two principal possibilities. The sum of common traits may be the cumulative results of a long series of separate borrowings, or they may be all that is left of a once extensive complex anciently shared by fore-runners of the two cultures. The problem of distinguishing between the two types of cases is important for every aspect of culture history but for certain reasons is most clear-cut with reference to language, where it has been formulated as the question of diffusion versus common origin. The classic controversy on this subject between Franz Boas and Edward Sapir resulted in considerable clarification of the main problem, even though there was a limited area in which these two scholars never agreed. The present paper attempts to resolve or to narrow the moot point, and to develop the general theoretical implications of the problem. This is done by reëxamining the main arguments of Boas and Sapir and by experiment-ing with the use of objective tests for distinguishing diffusional cumula-tion from archaic residue. We discuss linguistic phenomena primarily, but attempt to see them in the perspective of the general cultural prob-lem.

1

Language is a cultural complex. It has its special characteristics, of course, but it is nonetheless a body of customary forms transmitted from generation to generation and from society to society in the same way as other cultural forms. Both Boas and Sapir recognized this, as shown, for instance, in the following quotations.

Speech is a human activity that varies without assignable limit as we pass from social group to social group, because it is a purely historical heritage of the group, the product of a long-continued social usage. (Sapir)

Thus it appears that language has behaved in the same way as all other cultural traits. . . . (Boas)

Now, since language behaves in the same general way as other as-pects of culture, it is interesting that the problem of common origin versus diffusion has been raised only in connection with language. There seem to be two reasons for this. First, the special characteristics of lan-guage make the problem more apparent. And second, the question has been inaccurately formulated in such a way as to obscure its general ap-plication.

The crucial fact that distinguishes language among cultural forms is suggested by Sapir in the following words:

Language is probably the most self-contained, the most massively resistant of all social phenomena. It is easier to kill it off than to disintegrate its individual form.

As these remarks indicate, language is different in degree, not in kind, with reference to a quality which Sapir describes as being "self-contained" and which results in strong resistance to structural change. Societies have been known under special circumstances to drop the use of traditional languages and to adopt new languages. Examples are the tribes of Gaul and Iberia which took over Latin, or the American Indian groups which now use English, Spanish, or Portuguese. In this process, it sometimes happens that the new language is modified in the direction of the old language. However, more often than not the effect of the old language on pronunciation, vocabulary, and phraseology is eventually ironed out.

Why is language so self-contained? For one thing, languages are large highly organized systems, involving hundreds or thousands of conventional symbols (words or morphemes) which are combined in conventional sequences (sentences, phrases, complex or compound words). Secondly, language is an archaic human invention probably developed concomitantly with the earliest definitely human society. As far back as history and prehistoric reconstruction permit us to penetrate, we find fully developed languages comparable with those existing today. Thirdly, the communicative function of language is possible only on the basis of a body of conventions that is preponderantly stable. By its nature, elemental communication is largely neutral to social upheaval. An advanced technology, a new economic system, or a more complex social organization will generally be reflected in a changed and enlarged vocabulary but without necessary changes in the phonetics or structure of the language or in the basic vocabulary.

These are the facts that make languages more resistant to radical changes than other social phenomena. However, it must be emphasized that the difference is not an absolute one. Other complex patterned social forms also admit superficial modifications more readily than fundamental change.

2

A general examination of the main processes of culture history will prove helpful in clarifying our problem.

Diffusion is the spread of culture traits or complexes from one group to another. A contrasting process is tradition, whereby culture is handed down from generation to generation.

The life of every cultural feature is accompanied by fluctuation and change, which sometimes proceed so slowly as to be imperceptible but in principle are constantly going on. Changes are especially apt to take place in the process of diffusion. The borrowing culture often sluffs off or replaces traits in a borrrowed complex. Frequently the borrowing culture takes over single traits, incorporating them into native complexes. A society, usually over a period of generations, may take on a new language and let its original language fall into disuse. Or it may incorporate into the native speech one or more individual vocabulary elements or even a phonetic or morphological feature from a neighboring language. In general separate traits are borrowed more readily than complexes; subordinate patterns within a larger complex are more readily diffused in inverse proportion to their complexity. Of the component traits, some are bound into the entire system in particularly intimate fashion and are consequently less likely to pass from one culture to another independent of the complex.

While diffusion carries culture from one society to another, societies themselves experience considerable flux, marked by growth or diminution of population and by splitting up or coalescence with other groups. The growth of a group may involve territorial changes, either in the form of gradual expansion or contraction of the area or by relatively abrupt migrations of portions of the group to new areas. As long as conditions of close internal communication prevail in the society, the culture tends to remain uniform throughout; changes appearing in one part of the area either spread quickly through the whole territory or are dropped because of the cultural influence of the bulk of the society. Where the size of the territory or other circumstances prevent the fullest internal contact of the group, there is a tendency to develop local variations of the culture which may eventually amount to major differences.

The processes of gradual change and regional differentiation and the interweaving effect of migration and diffusion can be clearly observed in connection with language. For example, Latin, having spread through Italy, Iberia, Gaul, and Dacia, developed local dialects which eventually differentiated into Italian, Spanish, French, Rumanian, and other Romanic languages. These tongues are of common origin because they all started out as variations of a single original language. Their development involved the full gamut of historical processes: migration, development of regional differences, diffusion of the whole complex to new populations, diffusional borrowing of separate elements from different neighboring languages.

The processes shown here affecting language operate in essentially the same way with regard to other culture complexes. While Latin was spreading and differentiating, many features of Roman industry, ceremonialism, art, government, and economy were carried by migration and diffusion and went through local changes comparable to what took place in language. In this way, non-linguistic culture patterns now found in France, Spain, Italy, and Rumania are of common origin. However, the other complexes did not necessarily show the same limits of diffusion as the Latin language; they generally went much farther. Wine culture, military organization, and the alphabet are especially good examples of Mediterranean culture features that traveled much farther than the Latin language. Many individual features of the language, particularly vocabulary, also went much farther.

It is clear that diffusion and common origin are not opposites. Instead, the former refers to the process of conveyance and the latter to the source. Duffusion along with migration accounts for the occurrence in different places of complexes having a single origin. In a strict sense, therefore, there is no such thing as a problem of diffusion versus common origin either in language or in any other aspect of culture. The question which occupied Boas and Sapir was actually not diffusion versus common origin but diffusional cumulation versus archaic residue.

3

The theoretical differences between Boas and Sapir on the subject of language history were not as great as is sometimes supposed. It is not by any means that the one believed in diffusion and the other did not. On the contrary both were keen students of diffusion both as a general cultural phenomenon and in its application to language. Nor must one imagine that Boas did not accept the concept of a common origin of groups of languages. The question rather turned on the extent to which science can trace groups of languages back to such prototypes. Boas' notion is simply that deceptive cases can arise as a cumulative result of the diffusion process, so that in some instances he considered it impossible to be certain that a group of languages has or has not a common origin. Sapir, on the other hand, is convinced that a careful examination of the evidence will definitely establish the prehistory of the supposedly ambiguous cases.

Here is Boas' statement of the problem:

. . . the whole theory of an "Ursprache" for every group of modern languages, must be held in abeyance until we can prove that these languages go back to a single stock and that they have not originated, to a large extent, by the process of acculturation.

From this point of view I should not be inclined to claim, for instance, that Tlingit and Athabascan are members of the same linguistic family. There is not the slightest doubt that the morphology of the two groups shows the most far-reaching similarities. Since, furthermore, the two languages are contiguous, the inference is inevitable that these similarities must be due to historical causes. It is, however, another question whether we are to infer immediately that these differences [read *similarities*] are due to the fact that in very early times the two groups had a common "Ursprache." The vocabularies of Tlingit and Athabascan are fundamentally distinct, and it does not seem to me that Dr. Sapir has proved his case of relationship between the two languages by the comparison of a limited number of words that show slight phonetic similarities. The question would remain to be answered, why there should be such fundamental dissimilarities between by far the greater number of words, and the question should still be asked how these dissimilarities are to be explained.

Sapir's answer is as follows:

. . . The theory of "borrowing" seems totally inadequate to explain those fundamental features of structure, hidden away in the very core of the linguistic complex, that have been pointed out as common, say, to Semitic and Hamitic, to the various Soudanese languages, to Malayo-Polynesian and Mon-Khmer and Munda, to Athabascan and Tlingit and Haida.

. . . certain languages have, in all probability, taken on structural features owing to the influence of neighboring languages. An examination of such cases, however, almost invariably reveals the significant fact that they are but superficial additions on the morphological kernel of the language. So long as such direct historical testimony as we have gives us no really convincing examples of profound morphological influence by diffusion, we shall do well not to put too much reliance in diffusion theories. On the whole, therefore, we shall ascribe the major concordances and divergences in linguistic form—phonetic pattern and morphology—to the autonomous drift of language, not to the complicating effect of single, diffused features that cluster now this way, now that.

Boas years later, in 1939, restates his position in very reserved fashion:

It follows from all this that for many distantly related languages the history of which are unknown, a categorical answer in regard to their genetic relationship cannot be given. In many cases historical relation must be assumed, but whether we are dealing with mixture of languages or with divergent branches of an ancient stock will remain doubtful.

Thus, Boas limits the problem to certain cases of "distantly related languages," and insists that in some of these cases one cannot know with certainty whether one is dealing with a residue of similarities from a single earlier language or an accumulation of common features through borrowing of single traits. Sapir maintains the possibility of distinguishing the "morphological kernel" of a language from "superficial additions." Basing himself on documented cases ("direct historical testimony") he holds that no accumulation of features of the kind that may be diffused singly is likely to add up to the appearance of an essential core of morphological features.

Stated in this fashion, it is easy to see that the problem of accumulation versus residue in language is not unlike familiar problems in other branches of culture. For example, myths belonging to two cultures are compared. It is found that myth A of one culture has a number of points in common with myth X in the other culture. Are we dealing with the same original myth which has diverged in two directions until only the given number of common details remain, or have these details recently been incorporated into originally distinct myths? Normally such a problem can be easily solved on the basis of internal evidence. Do ambiguous cases occur? Folklorists may attempt to answer this question on the basis of their experience. In the present paper we attempt a definitive answer with reference to language. We do not know to what extent the answer holds for industrial complexes, ceremonial forms, art, social organization, and so forth, but we are satisfied that the general facts have a great deal in common with language. Perhaps, also, our approach to the problem may suggest something of interest for the other aspects of culture.

4

Sapir singles out morphology as the most fundamental component of language and among morphological features he points out that some are relatively superficial while others enter into the "morphological kernel" of the language. This gives the key to the problem of accumulation and residue. The inference is that the sharing of superficial features may reflect single-trait borrowing while the sharing of fundamental features, particularly if a number of them go together, demonstrates common origin. The validity of this criterion can be tested by examining various controlled cases, where we have a relatively complete developmental record of known end-products. Such knowledge may come from written samples of the languages from a succession of periods or from a detailed reconstruction made by systematic comparison of several related languages.

A convenient as well as very adequate test for our purposes is provided in the two-fold relation existing between English and French, which involves both ancient common origin and long recent contact. Systematic comparison and detailed reconstruction have demonstrated beyond doubt that a whole series of languages of the ancient world, including Latin and Teutonic, were divergent developments from an earlier single language, known as primitive Indo-European. The period of common Indo-European—when its divergent forms presumably did not constitute more than local dialects—may have been about 5000 years ago. Present-day French is a modern continuation of Latin. English as we know it today is the modern form of Anglo-Saxon, belonging to the Teutonic group. Thus French and English are the end-products of two lines of divergent development from a common origin and have had perhaps 5000 years in which to develop their present divergent characteristics. In the last 2000 years these two historical streams have been in contact under conditions very favorable for diffusion. A striking measure of the close contact of the two languages is the fact that about half of the English vocabulary corresponds with French on the basis of recent borrowings. This includes loans from French at different stages of its history, from Latin down to the modern speech; elements possessed in common with French because the latter has borrowed from English or from older forms of Teutonic; and words which both languages have from some source, including classical written Latin and Greek, and a miscellaneous variety of modern languages (Italian, Arabic, American Indian, African, etc.). However, it may not be assumed that structural borrowings have been as extensive as those in the vocabulary, and it is the structural relationships we must now examine.

The historic data of the recent centuries shows progressive gradual loss of residual common features of morphology. For example, in the earliest records both historic lines, that is Latin and Anglo-Saxon, have nouns inflected for case by means of suffixes; there are analogies in the usage of the cases and even a few similarities of endings. In recent centuries French has lost its case endings entirely and English preserves only the genitive. Noun plural formations are maintained in English but are vestigial in French, occurring only in phrase "liaison." French preserves the person distinctions in the verbal endings of the plural while English has lost them in the plural. Thus we see in process the slow changes which have been reducing the inventory of residual common features. On the other hand we find some new common features acquired by diffusional influence. We can therefore pose the test question: How does the inventory of common residual features compare with the present accumulation of traits acquired by diffusion? We present for consideration lists of typical features in each category. As will be recognized, the lists are intended to be representative rather than complete.

Features of modern English and French which go back to their ancient common form, that is Indo-European, include such traits as the following:

1. Separate noun and verb inflection. Verb-stems in some instances identical with noun-stems.

2. Inflectional categories of singular and plural number; past and present tenses (perhaps based on an original aspect system); past and present participles. Inflection shown by endings. The actual formatives show phonetic similarities in some instances.

3. Substantival rather than verbal-type adjectives. This contrasts with Chinese and many other languages, even though it is not exclusively Indo-European.

4. Adjectival forms of pronouns, e. g., *we-our, nous-nôtre.*

5. Inflectional irregularities including the first person pronoun (*I-me, je-moi*) and the use of two stems in the predicative verb (*is-be, est-fus*), though the places where each stem is used agree only in part.

6. Relational and local prepositions. The same elements also used in association with verbs in directional or derived senses, e. g., *in-come, entendre.*

Common structural features of French and English which reflect diffusional influences of recent centuries include:

1. Use of definite and indefinite articles developed in Teutonic and Romanic languages out of demonstratives and the unitary numeral; the articles are preposed in most languages of both groups but are postposed in Scandinavian and Rumanian. Historic evidence suggests that Latin may have led the way in this development, with Teutonic influenced by it, even though the actual forms are developed out of native elements in each language group.

2. Genitive relation shown by preposition (English *of*, French, *de*), universal in Romanic, restricted in English.

3. A few freely used affixes in English, including *re-* as in *re-do*, *ex* as in *ex-fighter*, *-able* as in *lovable*. Borrowed from French.

4. Bound prefixes used only with stems of Latin origin, as in *extract-retract-subtract-contract-distract protract*. English has adopted these elements in their characteristic combinations partly from French but mainly from the learned use of Latin.

5. Formative suffixes added, with consonant changes, to non-independent stem-forms in such series as *electric-electricity-electrify-electrification* or *delicate-delicious-delicacy*. In French this process belongs partly, in English largely, to the field of learned late borrowings from classic Italian and Greek.

6. Limited instances of untypical word order with modifier second in such names of *Cafe Boston* instead of *Boston Cafe*) in English or with modifier first in French as in the newspaper name *Paris Express* (instead of *Express de Paris*).

If nothing were known of the history of two languages and they were found to have in common only such features as are given in our second list, would one have any doubts as to whether these were residual or cumulative similarities? Obviously not. The similarities in word order are very limited and obviously represent exotic rather than normal usage. The bound prefixes and suffixes are mostly used with learned or refined vocabulary, and generally exist side by side with more everyday elements; for example, *ex-* in *extract* serves the same function as *out* in *to pull out* and the latter is the simple every-day equivalent of the former; similarly *shiny is* the down-to-earth equivalent of *lustrous*. The prepositional genitive in English shares the function of the *suffixal* form, and the latter corresponds to the irregularly made pronominal forms (*his*, *her*, *my*, *our*, *your*). Of the two genitives, therefore, the prepositional is the less archaic; only if the suffixal genitive went entirely out of use might the resemblance to French be suspected of being residual. The freely used affixes (*re-*, *ex-*, *-able*) cannot be taken for residual correspondences with French because their forms coincide too closely with the latter; if they were residual after a long period of separate development their phonetic forms would have diverged considerably more. Only one feature, the use of articles, could possibly be regarded as pointing toward common origin. But, standing alone, it would have no force. It is not the kind of feature that might be expected to persist longer than any other over a period of time sufficient to remove all other vestiges. Moreover, it is a simple enough trait to be taken over under diffusional influence.

We have seen that residual common traits after some 5000 years still constitute an impressive array. The number is not so great, but their relation to the languages is intimate. And they involve formational irregularities that could hardly come over with borrowed words. But what would happen after a much longer time? Suppose twelve or twenty-four thousand years had elapsed since the common history of the two languages. Would not the structural similarities become less and less in number and more and more attenuated in form until they are reduced to perhaps only one recognizable but very vague similarity? In this case, would the situation be indistinguishable from one in which a single trait had been taken over by borrowing? Not necessarily. If the last vestigial similarity involved a deep-seated coincidence in formation, such as that between English *I-me* and French *je-moi*, then even one common feature would be strongly suggestive of common origin rather than borrowing. If the common feature were more superficial, say like the use of preposed articles, it could just as easily be a borrowed feature. However, it could also constitute a chance coincidence with no necessary historical relationship at all. It therefore can be concluded that in any instance where morphological similarities between two languages force the conclusion that they have some kind of historical connection, there should be no difficulty in determining whether that connection is residual from a common origin or cumulative from a series of borrowings.

We can test this conclusion on the case which Boas regarded as probably unresolvable, the relationship between Tlingit and Athabaskan. To do so we list the structural similarities as noted by Sapir:

1. Frequent stem from CV (C), that is consonant followed by vowel and perhaps by another consonant. Tlingit also has CVCC. Comparison with Haida seems to indicate that the initial consonant is in some instances reduced from a consonant cluster, particularly groups beginning in *s* and *ł*.

2. Absence of reduplication. A negative feature but a striking one among languages of the Northwest Coast, where reduplication is typical.

3. Noun and verb distinct, but some stems function as both.

4. Very little affixing on nouns. Possessive prefixes, largely identical with object prefixes of the verb. Suffixes include plural of humans and a diminutive.

5. Noun plus noun compounds, with a qualifying element first.

6. Verb complex involves a single verb stem, at or near the end. Pre-

fixes for pronominal object and subject, mode, adverbial elements of instrument, direction, place. Adverbial prefixes often identical with or related to nouns.

7. A few temporal-modal and aspectival suffixes used with verbs.

8. Postpositions used with pronominal prefixes and with nouns in the manner of second-position elements in compounds. Postpositions often identical with nouns, e. g., Tlingit *wan* meaning "edge" or "around," Athabaskan *man* meaning "edge" or "close to." Some postpositions also used with verbs.

9. Use of relative suffix (Tlingit *-yi*, Athabaskan *-ye*) with verbs. Identical element also added to nouns when used with pronominal prefix in possessive usage, except for relationship terms and most body parts.

The foregoing list of common structural features bears out Boas' statements that "There is not the slightest doubt that the morphology of the two groups shows the most far-reaching similarities" and further that "the inference is inevitable that these similarities must be due to historical causes." However, in the light of our control case, we no longer need have any doubts as to the kind of historical causes which gave rise to this array of structural similarities. It is clearly of the same general order as that shown by the residual similarities of English and French. In fact, Tlingit and Athabaskan show a distinctly closer structural affinity than English and French. With this as a basis of comparison we see that it would be fantastic to imagine such a body of fundamental structural affinities coming about by a series of borrowings.

Similar to our use of a control case is Truman Michelson's pointed observation:

Thus Athapascan, so far as we know, has been in just as intimate contact for a very long period with Salishan and Esquimauan as with Tlingit; but there is not the slightest resemblance structurally between Athapascan, Salishan and Esquimauan.

Salishan and Eskimo thus confirm Sapir's thesis, even though we know little about their past history. The relation of French and English is both well documented and convenient for the purposes of illustration. However, several other control cases might have been taken, such as the influence of Chinese on Japanese, of Arabic on Persian, of Indic on Burmese or Malay, of Latin on Albanian, of Greek on Russian, etc. Any of these cases would give essentially the same general results as those we have seen.

5

In his treatment of "How languages influence each other," Sapir discusses the borrowing of words at some length but does not mention the possibility of using vocabulary as a criterion of residual and cumulative relationships. However, as is reflected in Sapir's discussion and as is well known, there is a gamut of probability in word borrowings. And this fact can be very effectively used in studying relationships. Properly handled, vocabulary becomes a highly reliable criterion, just as reliable in fact as morphology, and it has the special advantage that it can be converted into percentages with consequent advantages in objectivity. The chief significance of employing vocabulary as a measure of relationship is that it affords an additional separate test, capable of verifying the results of the morphological criterion.

The use of vocabulary in historical studies is based on the same general principle as that used in morphology, namely that some elements are more fundamental and therefore more stable than others. The stability of words is related not only to the structure of the language but also to their place in the life of the people using the language. Culture words are borrowed readily, basic words much more rarely. Though this fact is generally recognized, the degree of difference objectively measured may prove surprising. We can take the same control languages we used for morphology.

There are few languages that have borrowed so liberally as has English. The bulk of the borrowings has been from Romanic, both through spoken Latin and French and through learned borrowings from the written tradition of Latin. English has also taken vocabulary from classical Greek, from Arabic, American Indian, African, and many other languages. On the other hand, the Romanic languages have received many vocabulary influences from Teutonic in the old days and from English in modern times. And they have shared in cultural terms (e.g., *café*, coffee) which English has from exotic tongues. As a result of these factors, about half of the general English vocabulary coincides with French on the level of borrowing, either of one language from the other or of both from a common source. Against this large percentage of borrowings in the general vocabulary, loans in the basic vocabulary are all but negligible.

In order to obtain an index of diffusional influence on the basic vocabulary, we have used a list consisting of 215 items empirically chosen for their relatively stable character. The test list, designed as a general measure of affinity between related languages, is not fully satisfactory in its selection of stable items, but will serve our purposes. The procedure in using any such technique has to be standardized so that one may always get approximately the same results from the same material. We have operated as follows. Each item is expressed in English and a series of notes narrows the meaning in the event of ambiguity; for example, "know" is understood to refer to facts rather than persons, so that the French equivalent is *savoir* not *connaître*. For each item we enter the most common simple form used in the given language, avoiding the complication of having to deal with a choice of words. After the lists are filled in for two languages, one compares them for correspondences and non-correspondences. For the present study, the correspondences are marked either residual or borrowed as the case may be. A correspondence is an instance in which the compared elements derive, in whole or in part, from a common prototype; affixes and composite elements are disregarded, e.g., French *avoir peur* is considered to correspond with English *to fear* despite the difference of formation. Phonetic changes have to be taken into account in terms of the regular developments known to have taken place, based on historically recorded facts or the best available reconstructions. We confine ourselves to the words entered for each item, disregarding correspondences which do not fit the meaning; for example, French *uns* and English *some* must be counted a non-correspondence even though another English word, *ones*, related to the French word.

The results of the test are dramatic. As against perhaps 50 percent of borrowed correspondences between English and French in the general vocabulary, we find just 6 percent in the basic vocabulary. Residual correspondence are found to be 27 percent. Thus the archaic residuum after 5000 years turns out to be five times greater than 2000 years of accumulated borrowings. Similar results are found between German and French, except that the borrowings are only 3 percent. The residual relations between German and English, with only about 2000 years of independent development, are much closer than those between French and English. Here are the comparative figures:

	Borrowed	Residual	Unrelated
English and German	2%	60%	38%
English and French	6%	27%	67%
French and German	3%	29%	68%

If suitable dictionaries were available it would be a simple matter to measure basic vocabulary correspondences among the Nadene languages in order to compare the results with English-German-French. In the absence of adequate dictionaries we can make shift with the comparative vocabulary which Pliny Earle Goddard gives in his attempt to disprove the relationship of Tlingit and Athabaskan. Goddard includes all the items for which he had available both a Tlingit form and an Athabaskan form, taken from Hupa, Kato, Chasta Costa, Chipewyan, Jicarilla, or Navaho. Since his list is intended to be as complete as he could make it, giving whatever forms it was "possible to match," and was not chosen to exaggerate the similarities of Tlingit and Athabaskan, we take it to be representative and unbiased for our purposes. From his comparisons we take all items which coincide with our test list, amounting to 82. Of these, 36 show phonetic correspondence suggestive of common origin. This amounts to 44 percent. Even allowing a liberal margin for errors in determining the correspondences and for chance resemblances, this figure is far too high to be explained by accumulation of borrowings. More than that, it is clearly within the range of residual corespondences found in our examination of German, English, and French, exceeding the 27–29 percent residuum found persisting after 5000 years, but less than the 60 percent persisting between English and German after 2000 years of separate development. The inference is that Tlingit and Athabaskan have diverged from a single language, and that they separated more than 2000 and less than 5000 years ago. This conclusion corroborates what is indicated by the morphological criterion.

6

Diffusional cumulation of basic vocabulary is counteracted by the universal trend of gradual vocabulary displacement. That is, once foreign words are brought into the basic vocabulary of a language they are subject to being subsequently displaced in the same way as all other vocabulary elements. As a result only a small fraction of the basic vocabulary can ever be loanwords. It is possible to calculate the approximate size of this fraction.

The study of basic vocabulary change as a phenomenon of culture history has barely begun, but there are already indications that the rate of change is not indefinitely variable. Since the test vocabulary has not yet been perfected and some problems of statistical technique have not been standardized, there is little point in presenting a detailed report of the results to date. Instead we note that the figures we have cited for English, German and French are fairly typical of other languages with reference to the rate of basic vocabulary change they indicate. For present purposes we may operate simply with these figures.

The percentage of change in successive time periods applies to the vocabulary at the beginning of each period, not to the original common vocabulary. Our comparison of English and German shows that 40 percent of the original common basic vocabulary has been displaced in one or the other or both languages in 2000 years. If the same percentage of the original vocabulary were affected in subsequent time periods, then in 5000 years two diverging forms of an original language would no longer have any common basic vocabulary. But this does not happen. If 60 percent of the original basic vocabulary is still held in common after 2000 years, then after a second like period there remains 60 percent of those 60 percent, that is 36 percent. To obtain the percentage after an additional 1000 years, making 5000 in all, one must multiply 36 percent by the square root of 60 percent. The calculated percentage is then 28 percent. Since the actual percentage for English-French is 27 percent and for

German-French 29 percent after approximately 5000 years, we have here a corroboration of the general correctness of this approach.

Applying this rate of retention to the maximum rate of borrowing, we can determine the maximum percentage of diffusional cumulation in the basic vocabulary. There is small likelihood in culture history that conditions favoring maximum borrowing of vocabulary will persist indefinitely over thousands and thousands of years. Nevertheless, for the purpose of calculating a statistical limit, let us proceed on the assumption that in successive periods of 2000 years 6 percent loan correspondences appear between two languages. During the second such period, while 6 percent of new borrowed correspondences are accumulating, the first 6 percent reduces to 60 percent of itself or 3.6 percent. This gives a total of 9.6 percent at the end of the second 2000 year period. For the third period we take 60 percent of 9.6 percent and add 6 percent. Continuing thus, the total would reach 15 percent in 12,000 years, after which the total would increase no further, because the rate of loss would just equal the maximum rate of cumulation.

To accumulate 44 percent of common elements through borrowing is thus utterly out of the question. Even reaching 15 percent of borrowed correspondence is so remote a possibility as to be negligible, since it could come about only if the same two languages continue to exist side by side under the most favorable kind of culture contact for a tremendous span of time. It would assume that no migrations separate the two languages, that neither of them displaces the other in all this time and that neither gives way to a third language.

By recognizing the diagnostic significance of basic vocabulary, we reduce almost to the vanishing point the uncertainty which Boas saw in the problem of diffusional cumulation versus archaic residue. Tlingit-Athabaskan, which he felt epitomized the problem, is found to be completely removed from the category of doubtful cases. It is conceivable that the area of uncertainty reappears at a much greater time-depth, but even this possibility must not be taken for granted. We must look into it further. However, it is worthwhile to first examine some questions of stable vocabulary and of phonetic change.

7

A few points regarding stable vocabulary need to be clarified.

We have presented a mathematical test of the common origin of languages based upon the use of an empiric basic vocabulary. But we do not claim that only this particular list may be used for such a purpose, nor can we hold that the proof has to be narrowly statistical. Normally any substantial array of correspondences among stable vocabulary elements constitutes adequate proof of genetic relationship. By this token, Sapir's demonstration of the Nadene stock was fully successful. He listed ninety-eighty comparisons of structural morphemes and basic vocabulary in at least two of the three branches of the new stock—Tlingit, Athabaskan, and Haida. Not more than one or two of his comparisons can be considered to be of doubtful stability. Therefore, Harry Hoijer gives undue weight to illusory counterarguments when he says:

> The complete evidence for this classification is not yet available. It has, however, been attacked by Boas and Goddard, who point out that the similarities listed by Sapir as evidence of genetic relationship may have resulted from borrowing.

Hoijer's reservations are unjustified because, as we have seen, it would be impossible for such a substantial number of correspondences among stable vocabulary items to accumulate through borrowing.

It is understood that stability, whether of basic vocabulary or of formative elements, means relative and not absolute stability. Pronouns, for example, can and do change. English and German pronouns do not agree at all points. English and French have only their first-person singular in common. Tlingit and Athabaskan show less correspondence than English and German but more than English and French. Athabaskan and Haida are almost completely unrelated in their pronouns. However, Mattole *ya-* "third person plural prefix, meaning 'all' " may be residually related to Haida *ga* "they (indef.)" and other relationships may appear when the phonology of the Nadene languages is better known. In any event, the small number of personal pronoun elements demonstrably comparable between Haida and Athabaskan may prove that Haida is more distantly connected than Tlingit but does not destroy the case for including Haida in the Nadene stock.

In the Indo-European languages, the numerals from one to ten show remarkable stability. From this, we may conclude that counting had developed into a very fixed form in common Indo-European. But we cannot conclude that all stocks must show the same stability in their numbers. Many tongues have only five primary numbers, with the remainder built on these. Some have only four, and the word for "four" may be built on the word for "two." This seems to be the case in Tlingit and Haida. The word for "five" in all three branches seems to be related to "hand," even though the actual forms are not the same in all three (Athabaskan *dla*, Tlingit *-djin*, Haida *tli'l*). There seem to be two numerals that correspond among the Nadene languages, "one" and "four," and this should be regarded as postive evidence.

Boas lays a great deal of emphasis on divergent vocabulary, declaring that "The question would remain to be answered, why there should be such fundamental dissimilarities between by far the greater number of words, and the question should still be asked how these dissimilarities are to be explained." However, our examination of control cases has already provided the explanation. We have seen that divergences accumulate approximately in proportion to the lapse of time. The only explanation that is needed to account for 60 percent divergent basic vocabulary in Tlingit-Athabaskan is a separate development of about 4000 years.

8

To study cultural correspondences, one needs to understand and allow for minor changes of form and function, which affect all traits in the course of their cultural life. In linguistics this means giving attention to changes in the phonetics and meanings of elements. Since it is known that phonetic changes tend to operate with complete consistency, so that all like sounds in like phonetic surroundings are uniformly affected, these are the easiest of all cultural changes to study. By painstaking comparison of divergent modern forms, it is possible to reconstruct the ancient prehistoric forms of words with a high degree of accuracy.

Cultural comparison which fails to take the factor of change into account is bound to fall wide of the mark. By failing to consider phonetic and semantic change, particularly the former, Goddard was able to let pass through his hands a large body of overwhelming evidence of the genetic unity of Tlingit and Athabaskan and yet come away with the belief that only a handful of words showed any appreciable similarity. Here is his conclusion:

Morphologically, Tlingit is very similar to Athapascan. . . . With this striking likeness in morphology, one would expect lexical similarity leading to the definite conclusion that the languages were originally one, or sprang from the same source. The comparisons made of the lexical content, however, do not justify this conclusion. The similarities are few, forming but a slight percentage of the whole. They might be attributed to accident were there not at hand a more acceptable solution. The few nouns that are common are probably due to borrowing. It would be a remarkable thing if fully the number noted had not been borrowed in the course of the generations that Tlingit and Athapascan peoples have been neighbors.

Goddard's whole discussion shows that he does not consider elements comparable unless they are identical or nearly so in form and meaning. For example he belittles Sapir's comparison of Tlingit *s'axw* "hat" with Chipewyan *c'ah* on the ground that the Athabaskan word refers to "dance hat." Thus, he fails to take into account the shifting that takes place in the meaning-association of linguistic elements in the course of time. By such an approach, one might reject the comparison of German *hund* with English *hound*, since the former refers to dog in general while the latter refers to a given type of dog. But Goddard's phonetic rigidity is an even more serious drawback to meaningful comparative work. His approach applied to French and English might mistakenly conclude that French *feu* and English *fire* are related, even though correct reconstructive method would show this to be impossible because the sounds, though similar, are inconsistent with other known correspondences; the actual historic fact is that the French word is derived from Latin *fokus* "hearth" and has developed a purely secondary and accidental similarity to the English word. On the other hand, Goddard's standard would miss a considerable number of superficially obscured relationships, like English *tooth*, French *dent*, which could be proved by comparative linguistic methods to be of common origin even if we did not possess documental intermediary forms, like Greek *dont-*, Gothic *tunth-*.

In general the process of reconstruction consists of positing and testing for each of the related languages a series of prehistoric phonetic changes by which the contemporary forms may be derived from reconstructed original prototypes. The procedure involves making hypotheses on the basis of one or more instances and then looking for further examples to confirm or contradict the hypothesis. In other words it is a matter of guided guesses followed by a rigid check-up as to the correctness of each guess.

In his comparison of Tlingit, Athabaskan, and Haida, Sapir assembled a large number of elements of similar form and meaning in the three languages. Of these he published only about one hundred in his article, intended as a preliminary report. Among the compared forms he showed consistent relationships of sounds, in some instances involving identity, in some instances consistent divergence. For example, several compared elements show *n* in each of the languages. In another set of comparisons, *y* of the Athabaskan and Tlingit was found to coincide with *g* of Haida. The fact that the same relationship obtains in a fair number of examples tends to substantiate and to demonstrate historic linguistic processes as against chance similarity. The present author has carried Sapir's exploration a bit farther and continues to find more and more corroboration of the genetic relation indicated by Sapir. However, even the limited data contained in Sapir's published material is fully convincing.

9

Phonology, besides being a necessary concomitant of any effective study of vocabulary correspondences, constitutes an additional criterion for the differentiation of residual and cumulative similarities. If the phonologies of compared languages are such as to admit their being derived by realistic regular formulas of change from a realistic reconstructed prototype language, one cannot doubt the fact of common origin and residual relation. The interwoven fabric of a reconstructed speech-sound pattern is too complex to be pulled together out of thin air.

While a few words can be forced to fit a reconstruction, and while a few historically unjustified correspondences may creep into any reconstructive effort, there are no tricks of the trade that could give a realistic explanation for any large number of forms unless the languages are actually related in the way assumed by the general theory.

Foreign words taken into a language at a given time tend to follow a consistent pattern of phonologic adjustment to the borrowing language. Once these words become part of the language, they share all the phonologic changes that may affect the whole system from that time forward. In consequence it is possible to discover strata of diffusion differentiating elements that came in early from those which were adopted more recently. For example, English *village* is marked by its accent and sounds to be an earlier borrowing from French than the word *garage*.

This consideration removes the last possibility of confusing diffusional overlay with residual relationship. Suppose two languages show correspondences in, say, 15 percent of their basic vocabularies as measured by the standardized list which we have used. As we have seen, it is conceivable though not likely that such a figure might accumulate over a period of many thousands of years, but it is impossible for such a large portion of the basic vocabulary to be adopted in a few generations or even a few centuries. Therefore, in reconstructing the earlier phonetic forms of accumulated borrowings, it is impossible to treat them all on the same level. Some are only slightly divergent, others profoundly different. The reconstructions and the assumed shifts necessary for one group of correspondences do not work out with the next. The material thus falls into a series of strata, and one thereby detects that there has been an accumulation of borrowing over a long time span. Only if a substantial percentage of common elements of stable type can be reconstructed by a unified theory of sound changes may one conclude common origin of the compared languages.

If two languages have, say, 5 percent of basic vocabulary in common, this could be due either to relatively recent borrowing or to very ancient original identity. These two cases can easily be distinguished through phonologic criteria. If it is a recent diffusional relationship, the elements in the two languages will be phonetically fairly close. In fact the main distinction is likely to be due to the lack of given sounds in one of the languages, necessitating substitution of the next closest sounds. On the other hand the reduction of an orginally identical basic vocabulary to only 5 percent in common through gradual divergence would require something like 12,000 years. During such a time span no language can escape suffering a whole series of phonologic shifts. The cognate words in the two languages would therefore be phonologically very divergent. Indeed, unless there were several languages that could be brought into the comparison, it might prove impossible to demonstrate historical relationship at all.

10

By way of conclusion, we may then say that in the structure of complex cultural features, some component traits are relatively fundamental and others relatively superficial. This fact makes possible dependable inferences as to prehistoric relationships whenever divergent forms of the same original traits are found in two or more cultures. If a number of similarities are found in the corresponding complexes of two cultures, the criterion of essentiality enables the culture historian to determine whether the similarities are residual from an originally identical complex or cumulative from continued borrowing of individual traits.

Languages, constituting extensive self-contained complexes operating to a considerable extent on a non-conscious level, lend themselves particularly well to historical study. Highly dependable separate tests can be developed in the three areas of structure, basic vocabulary, and phonology. These three criteria, moreover, are mutually confirmatory.

The effectiveness of this method is shown by applying it to Tlingit-Athabaskan, a case which Boas regarded as impenetrable by comparative linguistics. We are able to demonstrate by qualitative and statistical evidence far beyond the minimum requirements, that these languages are of common origin on an ancient level. Their common period may go back as much as 4000 years. However, the possibility of establishing archaic against diffusional relationship exists even when the time period is far greater than this.

28 The Sapir-Whorf Hypothesis

Harry Hoijer

IT IS NOW SOME YEARS SINCE ANTHROPOLOGICAL LINGUISTICS SERIOUSLY *turned its attention toward problems of the relationship between language and culture with special reference to language as a controlling frame for individual cognitive processes within a given cultural setting. Pushing beyond language as a vehicle for thought and commentator on activity, anthropological linguists raised questions about language as a mold of both thought and activity. Ethnolinguistics is also known as psycholinguistics and is sometimes classified with sociolinguistics (the sociology of language) as a study lying just outside the formal boundaries of the field, hence in "metalinguistics."*

The basic problems of this subfield have to do with questions of both epistemology, as we seek to understand the nature of knowledge and our means of obtaining it, and ontology, as we struggle to define reality. It is not simply a question of asking whether what is most important is the situation or what we think the situation to be, but the ancient question of whether what we think the situation to be actually constitutes a significant determiner of the situation. In terms of simple polarities, those who have favored the latter view have usually been identified as philosophical

SOURCE: Harry Hoijer (ed.), *Language in Culture*, American Anthropological Association, Memoir No. 79 (1954), pp. 92–104. Reprinted with the permission of the author and Professor Robert Redfield, the copyright owner.

The author (b. 1904) is Professor of Anthropology at the University of California, Los Angeles, and a former President of the American Anthropological Association. An ethnographer as well as a linguist, he is an authority on several American Indian cultures. He is the co-author (with Ralph Beals) of a text, *An Introduction to Anthropology* (1953; rev. 1963), and has contributed extensively to the field of American Indian linguistics, as in the volume *Studies in the Athapascan Language* (1963), which he assembled with other linguists.

idealists, while those who stress the independent determining character of reality have been called materialists. In many of the selections that follow in this volume, and practically all the selections in Volume II, the distinction between these two views will be significant, although usually implicit rather than openly discussed by the authors.

In this selection we are introduced to some of the major assumptions of psycholinguistics by an anthropological linguist who is basically sympathetic to most of the underlying hypotheses of psycholinguistics, although capable of critically evaluating them.

The Sapir-Whorf hypothesis appears to have had its initial formulation in the following two paragraphs, taken from an article of Sapir's, first published in 1929.

Language is a guide to "social reality." Though language is not ordinarily thought of as of essential interest to the students of social science, it powerfully conditions all our thinking about social problems and processes. Human beings do not live in the objective world alone, nor alone in the world of social activity as ordinarily understood, but are very much at the mercy of the particular language which has become the medium of expression for their society. It is quite an illusion to imagine that one adjusts to reality essentially without the use of language and that language is merely an incidental means of solving specific problems of communication or reflection. The fact of the matter is that the "real world" is to a large extent unconsciously built up on the language habits of the group. No two languages are ever sufficiently similar to be considered as representing the same social reality. The worlds in which different societies live are distinct worlds, not merely the same world with different labels attached.

The understanding of a simple poem, for instance, involves not merely an understanding of the single words in their average significance, but a full comprehension of the whole life of the community as it is mirrored in the words, or as it is suggested by their overtones. Even comparatively simple acts of perception are very much more at the mercy of the social patterns called words than we might suppose. If one draws some dozen lines, for instance, of different shapes, one perceives them as divisible into such categories as "straight," "crooked," "curved," "zigzag" because of the classificatory suggestiveness of the linguistic terms themselves. We see and hear and otherwise experience very largely as we do because the language habits of our community predispose certain choices of interpretation.

The notion of language as a "guide to social reality" is not entirely original with Sapir. Somewhat similar ideas, though far less adequately stated, may be found in Boas' writings, at least as early as 1911. Thus we find in Boas' introduction to the *Handbook of American Indian Languages* a number of provocative passages on this theme, to wit:

It seems, however, that a theoretical study of Indian languages is not less important than a practical knowledge of them; that the purely linguistic inquiry is part and parcel of a thorough investigation of the psychology of the peoples of the world.

. . . language seems to be one of the most instructive fields of inquiry in an investigation of the formation of the fundamental ethnic ideas. The great advantage that linguistics offer in this respect is the fact that, on the whole, the categories which are formed always remain unconscious, and that for this reason the processes which lead to their formation can be followed without the misleading and disturbing factors of secondary explanation, which are so common in ethnology, so much so that they generally obscure the real history of the development of ideas entirely.

As Greenberg points out in a paper contained in this volume, approaches somewhat similar to the Sapir-Whorf hypothesis may be found among European writers, and are "particularly strong in the German-speaking world," where they can be "traced back at least as far as Herder in the latter part of the eighteenth century." Alexander von Humboldt is mentioned as having a profound influence in this development, together with more modern scholars like Ernst Cassirer, Johann Leo Weisgerber, and Jost Trier. To these we should probably add Charles Bally, Marcel Granet, Claude Lévi-Strauss, Jean Piaget, Alf Sommerfelt, and L. Wittgenstein.

The Sapir-Whorf hypothesis, however, gains especial significance by virtue of the fact that both these scholars had a major interest in American Indian languages, idioms far removed from any in the Indo-European family and so ideally suited to contrastive studies. It is in the attempt properly to interpret the grammatical categories of an American Indian language, Hopi, that Whorf best illustrates his principle of linguistic relativity, the notion that "users of markedly different grammars are pointed by their grammars toward different types of observations and different evaluations of externally similar acts of observation, and hence are not equivalent as observers but must arrive at somewhat different views of the world."

The purpose of this paper is threefold: (1) to review and clarify the Sapir-Whorf hypothesis, (2) to illustrate and perhaps add to it by reference to my own work on the Navaho language, and (3) to propose a series of studies intended to test and further develop the hypothesis.

The central idea of the Sapir-Whorf hypothesis is that language functions, not simply as a device for reporting experience, but also, and more significantly, as a way of defining experience for its speakers. Sapir says, for example:

Language is not merely a more or less systematic inventory of the various items of experience which seem relevant to the individual, as is so often naïvely assumed, but is also a self-contained, creative symbolic organization, which not only refers to experience largely acquired without its help but actually defines experience for us by reason of its formal completeness and because of our unconscious projection of its implicit expectations into the field of experience. In this respect language is very much like a mathematical system which, also, records experience in the truest sense of the word, only in its crudest beginnings, but, as time goes on, becomes elaborated into a self-contained conceptual system which previsages all possible experience in accordance with certain accepted formal limitations. . . . [Meanings are] not so much discovered in experience as imposed upon it, because of the tyrannical hold that linguistic form has upon our orientation in the world.

Whorf develops the same thesis when he says:

. . . that the linguistic system (in other words, the grammar) of each language is not merely a reproducing instrument for voicing ideas but rather is itself the shaper of ideas, the program and guide for the individual's mental activity, for his analysis of impressions, for his synthesis of his mental stock in trade. . . . We dissect nature along lines laid down by our native languages. The categories and types that we isolate from the world of phenomena we do not find there because they stare every observer in the face; on the contrary, the world is presented in a kaleidoscopic flux of impressions which has to be organized by our minds—and this means largely by the linguistic systems in our minds.

It is evident from these statements, if they are valid, that language plays a large and significant role in the totality of culture. Far from being simply a technique of communication, it is itself a way of directing the perceptions of its speakers and it provides for them habitual modes of analyzing experience into significant categories. And to the extent that languages differ markedly from each other, so should we expect to find significant and formidable barriers to cross-cultural communication and understanding. These barriers take on even greater importance when it is realized that "the phenomena of a language are to its own speakers largely of a background character and so are outside the critical consciousness and control of the speaker."

It is, however, easy to exaggerate linguistic differences of this nature and the consequent barriers to intercultural understanding. No culture is wholly isolated, self-contained, and unique. There are important resemblances between all known cultures—resemblances that stem in part from diffusion (itself an evidence of successful intercultural communication) and in part from the fact that all cultures are built around biological, psychological, and social characteristics common to all mankind. The languages of human beings do not so much determine the perceptual and other faculties of their speakers vis-à-vis experience as they influence and direct these faculties into prescribed channels. Intercultural communication, however wide the difference between cultures may be, is not impossible. It is simply more or less difficult, depending on the degree of difference between the cultures concerned.

Some measure of these difficulties is encountered in the process of

translating from one language into another that is divergent and unrelated. Each language has its own peculiar and favorite devices, lexical
and grammatical, which are employed in the reporting, analysis, and categorizing of experience. To translate from English into Navaho, or vice
versa, frequently involves much circumlocution, since what is easy to express in one language, by virtue of its lexical and grammatical techniques,
is often difficult to phrase in the other. Simple illustration is found when
we try to translate the English phrases *his horse* and *his horses* into
Navaho, which not only lacks a plural category for nouns (Navaho ł̜·?
translates equally English *horse* and *horses*) but lacks as well the English
distinction between *his, her, its,* and *their* (Navaho bilį́·? may be translated, according to context, *his horse* or *horses, her horse* or *horses, its*
horse or *horses,* and *their horse* or *horses*). These Navaho forms ł̜·?,
bilį́·? make difficulties in English also because Navaho makes a distinction between a third person (the bì- in bìlį́·?) psychologically close to
the speaker (e.g., *his* [that is, a Navaho's] *horse*) as opposed to a third
person (the hà- of hàlį́?) psychologically remote (e.g., *his* [that is, a non-
Navaho's] *horse*).

Differences of this order, which reflect a people's habitual and
favorite modes of reporting, analyzing, and categorizing experience,
form the essential data of the Sapir-Whorf hypothesis. According to
Whorf, it is in these "constant ways of arranging data and its most
ordinary everyday analysis of phenomena that we need to recognize the
influence . . . [language] has on other activities, cultural and personal."

The Sapir-Whorf hypothesis, it is evident, includes in language both
its structural and its semantic aspects. These are held to be inseparable,
though it is obvious that we can and do study each more or less independently of the other. The structural aspect of language, which is that most
easily analyzed and described, includes its phonology, morphology, and
syntax, the numerous but limited frames into which utterances are cast.
The semantic aspect consists of a self-contained system of meanings,
inextricably bound to the structure but much more difficult to analyze
and describe. Meanings, to reiterate, are not in actual fact separable from
structure, nor are they, as some have maintained (notably Voegelin), to
be equated to the nonlinguistic culture. Our interest lies, not in questions
such as "What does this form, or form class, mean?" but, instead, in the
question, "In what manner does a language organize, through its structural semantic system, the world of experience in which its speakers
live?" The advantage of this approach to the problem of meaning is clear.
As Bloomfield long ago pointed out, it appears quite impossible, short of
omniscience, to determine precisely the meaning of any single form or
form class in a language. But it should be possible to determine the limits
of any self-contained structural-semantic system and the ways in which it
previsages the experiences of its users.

To illustrate this procedure in brief, let us turn again to Navaho and one of the ways in which it differs from English. The Navaho color vocabularly includes, among others, five terms: łìgàì, dìłxìł, łìžìn, łìčí·?, and dò·λ'ìž, to be taken as one way of categorizing certain color impressions. łìgàì is roughly equivalent to English *white*, dìłxìł and łìžìn to English *black*, łìčí·? to English *red*, and dò·λ'ìž to English *blue* or *green*. Clearly, then, the Navaho five-point system is not the same as English white-black-red-blue-green, which also has five categories. English *black* is divided into two categories in Navaho (dìłxìł and łìžìn), while Navaho has but one category (dò·λ'ìž) for the English *blue* and *green*. We do not, it should be noted, claim either that English speakers cannot perceive the difference between the two "blacks" of Navaho, or that Navaho speakers are unable to differentiate "blue" and "green." The difference between the two systems lies simply in the color categories recognized in ordinary speech, that is, in the ordinary everyday ways in which speakers of English and Navaho analyze color phenomena.

Every language is made up of a large number of such structural-semantic patterns, some of which pertain to lexical sets, as in the case of the Navaho and English color terms, and others of which pertain to sets of grammatical categories, such as the distinction between the singular and plural noun in English. A monolingual speaker, if his reports are to be understood by others in his speech community, is bound to use this apparatus, with all its implications for the analysis and categorization of experience, though he may of course quite often select from a number of alternative expressions in making his report. To quote Sapir again:

> . . . as our scientific experience grows we must learn to fight the implications of language. "The grass waves in the wind" is shown by its linguistic form to be a member of the same relational class of experiences as "The man works in the house." As an interim solution of the problem of expressing the experience referred to in this sentence it is clear that the language has proved useful, for it has made significant use of certain symbols of conceptual relation, such as agency and location. If we feel the sentence to be poetic or metaphorical, it is largely because other more complex types of experience with their appropriate symbolisms of reference enable us to reinterpret the situation and to say, for instance, "The grass is waved by the wind" or "The wind causes the grass to wave." The point is that no matter how sophisticated our modes of interpretation become, we never really get beyond the projection and continuous transfer of relations suggested by the forms of our speech. . . . Language is at one and the same time helping and retarding us in our exploration of experience, and the details of these processes of help and hindrance are deposited in the subtler meanings of different cultures.

It does not necessarily follow that all the structural-semantic patterns of a language are equally important to its speakers in their observation, analysis, and categorizing of experience. In describing a language, we seek to uncover all its structural-semantic patterns, even though many of these exist more as potentialities of the system than in actual usage. For ethnolinguistic analysis we need to know, not only that a particular linguistic pattern exists, but also how frequently it occurs in everyday speech. We also need to know something of the degree of complexity of the pattern of expression. There are numerous patterns of speech, particularly among peoples who have well-developed arts of oratory and writing, that are little used by any except specialists in these pursuits. The patterns of speech significant to ethnolinguistic research fall clearly into the category of habitual, frequently used, and relatively simple structural-semantic devices; those, in short, which are common to the adult speech community as a whole, and are used by its members with the greatest ease.

Not all the structural patterns of the common speech have the same degree of semantic importance. In English, for example, it is not difficult to ascertain the semantic correlates of the structural distinction between singular and plural nouns; in most cases this is simply a division into the categories "one" versus "more than one." Similarly, the gender distinction of the English third-person singular pronouns, as between "he," "she," and "it," correlates fairly frequently with the recognition of personality and sex.

In contrast to these, there are structural patterns like that which, in many Indo-European languages, divides nouns into three great classes: masculine, feminine, and neuter. This structural pattern has no discernible semantic correlate; we do not confuse the grammatical terms "masculine," "feminine," and "neuter" with the biological distinctions among male, female, and neuter. Whatever the semantic implications of this structural pattern may have been in origin, and this remains undetermined, it is now quite apparent that the pattern survives only as a grammatical device, important in that function but lacking in semantic value. And it is perhaps significant that the pattern is an old one, going back to the earliest history of the Indo-European languages and moreover, that it has disappeared almost completely in some of the modern languages of this family, notably, of course, in English.

In ethnolinguistic research, then, it is necessary to concentrate on those structural patterns of a language which have definable semantic correlates, and to omit those, like the Indo-European gender system, which survive only in a purely grammatical function. The assumption behind this procedure is as follows: every language includes a number of active structural-semantic categories, lexical and grammatical, which by virtue of their active status serve a function in the everyday (non-scientific) analysis and categorizing of experience. It is the study of these categories, distinctive when taken as a whole for each language, that yields, or may yield, significant information concerning the thought world of the speakers of the language.

One further point requires emphasis. Neither Sapir nor Whorf attempted to draw inferences as to the thought world of a people simply from the fact of the presence or absence of specific grammatical categories (e.g., tense, gender, number) in a given language. To quote Whorf on this point: the concepts of time and matter which he reports for the Hopi

do not depend so much upon any one system (e.g., tense, or nouns) within the grammar as upon the ways of analyzing and reporting experience which have become fixed in the language as integrated "fashions of speaking" and which cut across the typical grammatical classifications, so that such a "fashion" may include lexical, morphological, syntactic, and otherwise systematically diverse means coordinated in a certain frame of consistency.

To summarize, ethnolinguistic research requires the investigator to perform, it seems to me, the following steps:

1. To determine the structural patterns of a language (that is, its grammar) as completely as possible. Such determination should include not only a statement of the modes of utterance but as well a careful indication of the frequency of occurrence of these modes, lexical and grammatical, in the common speech.

2. To determine, as accurately as possible, the semantic patterns, if any, that attach to structural patterns. This is a task neglected by most structural linguists who, as is repeatedly mentioned in the discussions that follow, are frequently content simply to label rather than to define both lexical units and grammatical categories. In this connection it is important to emphasize that the analyst must not be taken in by his own labels; he is to discover, where possible, just how the form, or form class, or grammatical category functions in the utterances available to him.

3. To distinguish between structural categories that are active in the language, and therefore have definable semantic correlates, and those which are not. It goes without saying that such distinction requires a profound knowledge of the language, and possibly even the ability to speak and understand it well. Mark Twain's amusing translation of a German folktale into English, where he regularly translates the gender of German nouns by the English forms "he," "she," and "it," illustrates, though in caricature, the pitfalls of labeling the grammatical categories of one language (in this case, German gender) by terms belonging to an active structural-semantic pattern in another.

4. To examine and compare the active structural-semantic patterns of the language and draw from them the fashions of speaking there evidenced. As in Whorf's analysis of Hopi, while clues to a fashion of speak-

ing may be discovered in a particular grammatical category or set of lexical items, its validity and importance cannot be determined until its range and scope within the language as a whole is also known. Whorf's conclusions as to the nature of the concept of time among speakers of English rest not alone on the tense distinctions of the English verb (mixed as these are with many other and diverse distinctions of voice, mode, and aspect) but as well on techniques of numeration, the treatment of nouns denoting physical quantity and phases of cycles, and a host of other terms and locutions relating to time. He says:

The three-tense system of SAE [Standard American English] verbs colors all our thinking about time. This system is amalgamated with that larger scheme of objectification of the subjective experience of duration already noted in other patterns—in the binomial formula applicable to nouns in general, in temporal nouns, in plurality and numeration.

5. Taken together, the fashions of speaking found in a language comprise a partial description of the thought world of its speakers. But by the term "thought world" Whorf means

more than simple language, i.e., than the linguistic patterns themselves. [He includes] . . . all the analogical and suggestive value of the patterns . . . and all the give-and-take between language and the culture as a whole, wherein is a vast amount that is not linguistic yet shows the shaping influence of language. In brief, this "thought world" is the microcosm that each man carries about within himself, by which he measures and understands what he can of the macrocosm.

It follows then that the thought world, as derived from ethnolinguistic studies, is found reflected as well, though perhaps not as fully, in other aspects of the culture. It is here that we may search for connections between language and the rest of culture. These connections are not direct; we see, instead, in certain patterns of nonlinguistic behavior the same meaningful fashions that are evidenced in the patterns of the language. Whorf summarizes this facet of his researches in a discussion of "Habitual Behavior Features of Hopi Culture and Some Impresses of Linguistic Habit in Western Civilization."

It may be helpful to outline briefly some aspects of Navaho culture, including the language, as illustration of the Sapir-Whorf hypothesis. In particular, I shall describe first some of the basic postulates of Navaho religious behavior and attempt to show how these fit in a frame of consistency with certain fashions of speaking evidenced primarily in the morphological patterns of the Navaho verb.

A review of Navaho religious practices, as described by Washington Matthews, Father Berard Haile, and many others, reveals that the Navaho conceive of themselves as in a particular relationship with the environment—physical, social, and supernatural—in which they live. Navaho man lives in a universe of eternal and unchanging forces with which he attempts to maintain an equilibrium, a kind of balancing of powers. The mere fact of living is, however, likely to disturb this balance and throw it out of gear. Any such disturbance, which may result from failure to observe a set rule of behavior or ritual or from the accidental or deliberate committal of some other fault in ritual or the conduct of daily activities, will, the Navaho believe, be revealed in the illness or unexplained death of an individual, in some other personal misfortune or bad luck to an enterprise, or in some community disaster such as a food shortage or an epidemic. Whereupon, a diviner must be consulted, who determines by ritual means the cause of the disturbance and prescribes, in accordance with this knowledge, the appropriate counteracting religious ceremony or ritual.

The underlying purpose of the curing ceremony is to put the maladjusted individual or the community as a whole back into harmony with the universe. Significantly, this is done, not by the shaman or priest acting upon the individual and changing him, nor by any action, by shaman or priest, designed to alter the forces of the universe. It is done by re-enacting one of a complex series of religious dramas which represent, in highly abstract terms, the events, far back in Navaho history, whereby the culture heroes first established harmony between man and nature and so made the world fit for human occupation. By re-enacting these events, or some portion of them, the present disturbance, by a kind of sympathetic magic, is compensated and harmony between man and universe restored. The ill person then gets well, or the community disaster is alleviated, since these misfortunes were but symptoms of a disturbed relation to nature.

From these numerous and very important patterns of Navaho religious behavior, it seems to me we can abstract a dominant motif belonging to the Navaho thought world. The motif has been well put by Kluckhohn and Leighton, who also illustrate it in many other aspects of Navaho culture. They call it, "Nature is more powerful than man," and amplify this in part by the Navaho premise "that nature will take care of them if they behave as they should and do as she directs." In short, to the Navaho, the way to the good life lies not in modifying nature to man's needs or in changing man's nature but rather in discovering the proper relation of nature to man and in maintaining that relationship intact.

Turning now to the Navaho language, let us look at some aspects of the verb structure, illustrated in the following two forms:

> nìńtį́ *you have lain down.*
> nìšíńłtį́ *you have put, laid me down.*

Both these verbs are in the second person of the perfective mode; the ń- marks this inflection. Both also have a prefix nì-, not the same but subtly different in meaning. The nì- of the first means [*movement*] *terminating in a position of rest*, that of the second [*movement*] *ending at a given point*. The second form has the causative prefix ł- and incorporates the first person object, expressed in this form by ši-. The stem -tį́, common to both forms, is defined *one animate being moves*.

The theme of the first verb, composed in nì- . . . -tį́, means *one animate being moves to a position of rest*, that is, *one animate being lies down*. In the second verb the meaning of the theme, nì- . . . -ł-tį́, is *cause movement of one animate being to end at a given point* and so, by extension, *put an animate being down* or *lay an animate being down*.

Note now that the first theme includes in its meaning what in English we should call both the actor and the action; these are not, in Navaho, expressed by separate morphemes. The subject pronoun prefix ń- serves them simply to identify a particular being with the class of possible beings already delimited by the theme. It functions, in short, to individuate one belonging to the class *animate being in motion to a position of rest*. The theme of the second verb, by reason of the causative ł-, includes in its meaning what in English would be called action and goal. Again the pronoun ši-, as a consequence, simply identifies or individuates one of a class of possible beings defined already in the theme itself. It should be emphasized that the forms used here as illustration are in no sense unusual; this is the regular pattern of the Navaho verb, repeated over and over again in my data.

We are now ready to isolate, from this necessarily brief analysis, a possible fashion of speaking peculiar to Navaho. The Navaho speaks of "actors" and "goals" (the terms are inappropriate to Navaho), not as performers of actions or as ones upon whom actions are performed, as in English, but as entities linked to actions already defined in part as pertaining especially to classes of beings. The form which is glossed *you have lain down* is better understood *you* [*belong to, equal one of*]*a class of animate beings which has moved to rest*. Similarly the second form, glossed *you have put, laid me down* should read *you, as agent, have set a class of animate beings, to which I belong, in motion to a given point*.

This fashion of speaking, it seems to me, is wholly consistent with the dominant motif we saw in Navaho religious practices. Just as in his religious-curing activities the Navaho sees himself as adjusting to a universe that is given, so in his habits of speaking does he link individuals to actions and movements distinguished, not only as actions and movements, but as well in terms of the entities in action or movement. This division of nature into classes of entity in action or movement is the universe that is given; the behavior of human beings or of any being individuated from the mass is customarily reported by assignment to one or other of these given divisions.

Analyses such as this one, though admittedly incomplete, point up the potential value of the Sapir-Whorf hypothesis in cross-cultural under-standing. Further work is obviously needed, on languages and cultures as diverse as can be found, to develop the hypothesis. To this end, I venture to suggest the following study, arising mainly from my own experience, and designed to examine the question: If the thought world implies, as we have said, the existence of significant connections between language and the rest of culture, how are we to account for the fact that peoples very similar in the rest of their culture speak languages that are wholly un-related, and that closely related languages are frequently spoken by peoples very different in the rest of their culture?

The data for a project centering about this question are already in large part collected; they require only to be completed and analyzed in terms of the Sapir-Whorf hypothesis. The project involves researches on the following cultures, chosen for their similarities and differences in culture area and linguistic affiliations.

1. The Navaho, who share a number of nonlinguistic culture pat-terns with their Hopi neighbors, speak a language (of the Athapaskan stock) that is not in the least related to Hopi (of the Shoshonean stock). There is already a great deal of linguistic and other cultural data on both these groups, though much is as yet unpublished. A Navaho grammar is now in preparation, and studies of Navaho nonlinguistic culture, pub-lished and in preparation, are numerous and detailed. For Hopi there is perhaps less published linguistic material but a considerable amount of data on the rest of the culture. A beginning has also been made on the characterization of the Hopi thought world; Whorf's Hopi studies are the most complete in his works.

Preliminary comparisons indicate that the Hopi and Navaho thought worlds are very different, despite the similarities between the two groups in certain overt cultural patterns. It should be kept in mind, however, that the likeness of Navaho to Hopi culture has probably been exaggerated; most of the similarities that led Wissler and others to put them into the same culture area are indeed superficial.

2. The Hopi and the Hopi-Tewa (the pueblo of Hano) offer a far better contrast. Here we find two peoples who, already sharing a general Puebloan culture, have lived in close association on First Mesa since about 1700. Their languages, however, are very divergent; the language of Hano is of the Tewan family and has its closest affiliations to the Rio Grande pueblos farther east. Data on Hano nonlinguistic culture have recently been collected by E. P. Dozier, who is now preparing them for publication. Unfortunately, there is as yet little work on the Tewan languages, though a beginning has been made on the Santa Clara dialect. It is interesting that the differences between Santa Clara Tewa, spoken in the Rio Grande region, and the Tewa of Hano are minor.

A study of one or more of the Rio Grande Tewa-speaking pueblos should be included in this project. In this comparison between Hopi, Hano, and the Tewa speakers of the Rio Grande, there are unusual possibilities. Some of the questions that now appear important are: How wide are the differences between the Hopi culture of First Mesa, that of the Hano, and that of the Rio Grande Tewa? To what extent have the Hano been acculturated to the Hopi? Is there a greater similarity between the Hopi and the Hano thought worlds than between those of the Hano and the Rio Grande Tewa? Since the move of the Hano people to First Mesa can be dated with some precision, it is possible in this project to gain some indication of the extent to which a thought world may change relative to changes in the rest of the culture.

3. The Hupa should be studied and contrasted with the Navaho. Here is an instance where two languages are indubitably and closely related; both Hupa and Navaho are of the Athapaskan stock. The non-linguistic cultures, however, are widely divergent. Hupa has a northern California culture, very different from that of the Southwestern Navaho. Field data on the Hupa language are complete; the material is now being prepared for publication. Much material on Hupa nonlinguistic culture is already published and more is in preparation.

4. A final phase of this project might involve a contrast of the Hopi with the Southern Paiute. The languages are related (both belong to the Shoshonean stock), but the nonlinguistic cultures offer the same order of difference as exists between the Navaho and the Hupa. There is much useful data on the Southern Paiute language, published by Sapir some years ago, and some published material on their nonlinguistic culture. It is probable, however, that more data may be needed.

It may be useful, in conclusion, to speculate a bit on the possible results of the project outlined above. The following quotation is relevant.

If language and culture have been regarded by some as distinct variables . . . it is perhaps because (1) they define language too narrowly and (2) they limit culture (especially in establishing culture areas) to its more formal and explicit features, those which are most subject to borrowing and change.

It is quite possible that the features of a language (largely phonemic) by means of which we link it to others in a stock or family are among the least important when we seek to connect it to the rest of culture. The fashions of speaking that Whorf finds so important to habitual behavior and thought are, after all, derived from the lexical, morphological, and syntactic patterns of a language, and these, in turn, are arrangements of phonemic materials. Two or more languages, then, may well have their phonemic materials from the same historical source and yet develop, under the stimulus of diverse microcosms, quite different fashions of speech. In short, the fact that languages belong to a common stock does not prove that they have the same fashions of speaking; such proof, if it is forthcoming at all, must be demonstrated empirically.

The cultures included in the same culture areas, on the other hand, tend to resemble each other only in discrete cultural features, those which are easily diffused, and not necessarily in the ways in which these features are combined into fashions of behaving or in the basic premises to which such fashions of behaving may point.

29 Language and
Evolutionary Theory

Joseph H. Greenberg

IF THERE IS SOMETHING IN THE CONCEPT OF ANTHROPOLOGY AS A DISCIPLINE *uniting such diverse strands as biology, language and culture, it requires more than a central focus on "man" to achieve unity. The most powerful tool yet developed for accomplishing a truly broad unifying view is a competent theory of evolution. With particular reference to language, we have already been exposed to some aspects of evolutionary theory in the article by Hockett and Ascher (No. 24). We know, then, that the languages associated with primitive cultures are not necessarily simple in terms of phonology, grammar, or their capacity for synthesizing or accumulating vocabulary. Furthermore, we know that languages are always in the process of change and that such changes may go as readily from complexity to simplicity as the reverse. We need, therefore, to attempt to go beyond what this volume has already offered on this subject, and we raise in the broadest sense the question of how language fits into the evolutionary process. We turn again to Joseph H. Greenberg for an interesting overview of the problem.*

In the present chapter, only one of the many ways in which the science of language is related to other sciences dealing with cultural behavior will be systematically considered. The group of problems selected may be described as the interpretation and evaluation of various theories of culture in the light of the data provided by language. This particular facet of what may be broadly termed "ethnolinguistics" has apparently been little

SOURCE: *Essays in Linguistics* (New York: Wenner-Gren Foundation for Anthropological Research Monograph No. 24, 1957), Chap. 5, pp. 56–65. Reprinted with the permission of the author and the publisher.
For biographical data on the author, see I:25.

considered up to now. It is a generally accepted thesis that language is a part of the cultural behavior of peoples. Linguistics is thus logically a branch of cultural anthropology, the general science which is concerned with such behavior. However, linguistics has existed in addition to this affiliation and continues to flourish outside anthropology in the general academic division of labor and is the heir of concepts and theories independently derived and often antedating those of anthropology as a whole. The inevitable result of such historically conditioned disparity is that the applicaton of cultural theories, usually conceived without any, or with only minor, reference to language, requires as a preliminary the interpretation of such terminology into the traditional frame of reference employed in linguistics. This in itself has an intrinsic value as a step toward the unification of terminology within anthropology. More important, it allows us to employ linguistic data as a test of theories of culture. One putative advantage to be gained from the analysis of language often adduced by anthropologists is its transparency. But granting the truth of this observation, the transparency of the data will be of no avail if the terminology in which it is traditionally described is such as to mask its relevance for cultural theory. The present essays do not claim to be more than a modest beginning of this complex and frequently difficult task.

The concept of evolution is one of wide significance, as is evident from its central role in certain philosophical systems and from the breadth of its applications in a variety of disciplines ranging from the natural and biological sciences (cosmic, terrestrial, and animal evolution) to the social sciences and humanities, particularly cultural anthropology and history. A concept of such far-flung uses necessarily differs much in individual instances, so much so that at times it seems difficult to discover the common elements underlying the diversity of applications. Several prevalent uses of the term "evolution" may be eliminated at the outset as inappropriate. One instance is the use of the term to mean orderly change in general. In this sense the existence of evolutionary phenomena is simply an affirmation of the basic scientific faith that the universe is ordered and coherent and therefore susceptible to the explanatory methods of science. If this is what is indicated by "evolution," no scientist, at least, is likely to disagree. It is evident, however, that something at once more distinctive and more controversial is usually indicated by the term.

Another meaning, which may be rejected, on the contrary ground of overspecificity, is that of "gradual" as opposed to "revolutionary" or sudden change. This usage is pretty much confined to sociology and political science. In these realms the existence of both types of social change is admitted as a fact. By some stretching of terminology, perhap the term "revolutionary" might also be extended to the catastrophic changes in geology assumed by the advocates of the early Neptunian and Vulcanian theories. The concept of gradual, as opposed to violent, change seems too narrow to constitute the basis of a general concept of evolution. Still, both coherence and gradualness do play a certain role in the more generally applicable formulations of evolutionary theory to be outlined here.

Perhaps we may come closer to the essential ideas underlying all evolutionary approaches by considering that in every case we have to do with the explanation of how a variety of forms, whether biological species, languages, or cultural systems, came to be. Two general types of explanation exist which we may call the "creationist" and the "transformist." The former, with sporadic exceptions, held the field until the turn of the nineteenth century. In its purest version it assumes that all kinds are unchangeable, except for more or less haphazard modifications within the bounds of the type, and have existed in their present form since they came into being by a single act of creation. Such was the generally accepted view regarding biological species before Darwin, and such likewise was the traditional Tower of Babel explanation of the origin of language diversity.

The opposite view is that all existing forms are historically connected by a dynamic process of growth. On this view, the greater the similarity among existing forms, the more recent the common ancestry. But, whether less remotely or more remotely, all forms are ultimately connected by descent. As a further consequence, common ancestors are forms different from any existing today and are conceived to be such as to give rise to present forms by differential independent development. Such growth is viewed as, in general, gradual and coherent, allowing for minor leaps, such as those induced by mutations in biology. Were changes sudden and capricious, anything might issue from anything at a not too distant remove, and the observed natural groupings of species would not occur. The employment of the term "evolution" exclusively for gradual change or coherence in change mentioned earlier is implied by these considerations.

In fact, creationism and transformism in their pure forms are polar concepts between which gradations are possible. On an extreme transformist view, all forms are related by ultimate common origin. There must therefore be some single primeval form from which all others developed. Monogenesis is therefore logically required. It would be possible to maintain a more moderate transformism in which each existing form is connected with at least some others but not with all, as a consequence of several distinct creations. Biologists who postulate connecting forms among some of the phyla for which plausible common ancestry cannot at present be found are espousing the monogenist version of transformism. It is clearly possible to assume, with polygenists, several creations where links cannot be found and still deny that species are fixed types. Another intermediate view is that adopted by most geologists for a time in the nineteenth century to account for fossils. The belief was rejected that existing species are the unchanged continuations of the species created at the beginning while the fixity of species was maintained. From time to time all species were supposed to have been destroyed and new ones created without affiliation by descent from the forms of the previous era. In this fashion the basic notion of fixity of kinds could be maintained. This approach may be termed "catastrophism." There are thus four basic types of explanation of specific diversity: the evolutionary monogenetic, the evolutionary polygenetic, the creationist, and the catastrophic. The first and third assume single creations, the second and fourth, multiple creations; the first and second, transformation of species, the third and fourth, fixity of species.

In the sense of transformism, whether monogenetic or polygenetic, evolution was an accepted theory in linguistics earlier than in biology, though not under that name. The recognition that the resemblance of certain languages to one another is to be explained by common descent is the fundamental hypothesis underlying the concept of genetic relationship among languages. In Semitic studies for one, such theories were already held in the eighteenth century. The recognition of the Indo-European family at the turn of the nineteenth century is the single event which marks most clearly the birth of modern linguistic science. The evidence at that time led, as it still leads, to a polygenetic theory, since not all languages can be demonstrated to have a common origin. But, as in biology, the assumption of a similar process of differentiation for an earlier period and the absence of any proof of spontaneous generation in historic times lend plausibility to the speculation of monogenesis. Some day the problem may well be solved by the indirect evidence of anthropology, psychology, and general linguistic science.

The essential likeness between genetic theories in language and the evolutionary hypothesis in biology was explicitly recognized by Schleicher, a leading linguist of the nineteenth century. In his work *Die Darwinsche Theorie und die Sprachwissenschaft,* he treats evolutionary theory in biology as, in principle, the equivalent of the genetic model of linguistic relationship. In this, the transformationist sense, then, language may be said to evolve, and the recognition of the fact in linguistic science preceded its general acceptance in biology.

But a further idea seems to be required by the term "evolution" in its most generally accepted sense. A theory, for example, which regarded all species as interconnected but which posited some mammalian form as the primeval ancestral type, whence descended in one line all the other vertebrates, in another the ancestor of all non-vertebrate phyla, with Protozoa first appearing in a very recent period, would not be adjudged a representative evolutionary theory. In addition to the notion of transformation, another—that of progress or advance of some kind—is evidently required. Before examining further this idea of progress, its logical distinctness from transformism should be noted. For example, a holder of the catastrophic theory may well believe that each successive creation represents progress over previous ones. In fact, geologists in general accepted progress while denying transformation of species for a considerable period during the nineteenth century. It is well at the outset also to distinguish the fact of evolutionary advance, if it should turn out to be possible to characterize it in some objective fashion, from the ethical judgment that this advance is good which often accompanies it and tends to be the motivation for accepting its validity. The judgment that evolutionary advance exists and is good I shall call "progress." The fact itself I shall call "advance" or "evolutionary advance." The belief in evolutionary advance is compounded of the belief in some scale on which species or kinds can be rated as more or less advanced and the belief that, on the whole, less advanced forms have preceded more advanced forms in time.

In what way, for example, can man be said to be more advanced than an amoeba (N.B., not better)? The classic definition of Spencer states this difference in terms of heterogeneity and complexity as characteristic of advanced forms. But it is not heterogeneity or complexity as such which constitutes advance on the usual view. For example, the simplification of the toes of the horse to form the hoof, which resulted in more efficient running, would be considered evolutionary advance. The single comprehensive law of Newton is an advance over Kepler's three laws of motion. In general, in the words of Herrick, it is "change in the direction of and increase in the range and variety of adjustments to environment" which is involved. Among developments that may be considered as advance, there are, on the perceptual side, ability to respond to finer discriminations of stimuli, to stimuli from a greater distance, and to new ranges of stimuli, e.g., a new sense. On the motor or effector side the ability to live in a greater range of temperature, moisture, or other physical conditions of environment, speed of movement, and the ability to make finer manipulatory adjustments of objects in the environment may be cited as examples. In the intervening activity between perception and response comes the coordination of responses and the lesser or greater appropriateness of responses to stimuli, e.g., the development of a central nervous system, of social co-operation, and of intelligence in general.

This gives us many facets of comparison. Most, or perhaps even all, are, in principle, subject to objective comparative, even quantitative, evaluation. For example, we can measure speed of muscular response by reaction time, speed of locomotion in feet per minute, etc. Still, judgments on these varied scales may well show that, of two species, one is more advanced in some respect, one in another. This is what leads some biologists to say that each species is a perfect adaptation in its own way. Yet undoubtedly, on an over-all basis, man is more advanced than the amoeba; many similar judgments can be made. Moreover, it is a reasonable expectation, borne out by the paleontological record, that, *on the whole*, less advanced have preceded more advanced species. This might well be expected, for fineness of perceptual discrimination, the development of new organs of sense, the genesis and expansion of a central nervous system, the differentiation of specialized motor organs, all require time. Some correlation with the afore-mentioned criteria of Spencer— heterogeneity and complexity—may therefore be expected. For enhanced discrimination in perception and response, it can be argued, requires increased specialization of parts and increased complexity of organization of the whole and of each of the constituent organs. Still, complexity is merely an incidental, however frequent, accompaniment of some aspect of efficiency.

If we now turn to language with these considerations in mind, we note that the typical nineteenth-century evolutionary theory of language which established the framework of all subsequent discussion was one which assumed complexity as the sole criterion of evolutionary advance in language, and only one aspect of complexity—morphological complexity—at that. For the nineteenth-century theory, in the standard formulation of Schleicher, set up three stages: isolating, agglutinative, and inflective, each of which was defined basically in terms of the morphological structure of the word. In contemporary terminology an isolating language is one in which each word consists of a single morpheme. In the agglutinative stage words are multimorphemic, but there are, ideally, no irregular morphophonemic alternations. With inflecting languages, there are irregular alternations such that, in principle, the assignment of certain phonemes to one or the other of two morphemes is arbitrary. This is sometimes called "fusion." The line of evolutionary advance, then, is from isolating languages, characterized by the simplest word structure, through the agglutinative to the inflectional stage, marked by the most complex types of formation. This was alternatively characterized as an advance from analytic to synthetic forms of thought or from formless to true form languages.

The ethnocentrism, lack of rigor, and absence of correspondence of these stages with those derivable from non-linguistic culture all led to the general abandonment of the theory. As examples of non-correlation with general cultural evolution, we may note that the isolating, or most primitive, stage had as its most typical representative Chinese; that various American Indian languages turned out to have a more complex word structure than the Indo-European languages; and that in historic times Indo-European languages seemed to be changing from a synthetic to a more analytic or isolating type, a retrograde movement from the viewpoint of the standard theory.

In subsequent discussion it has usually been held that language does not evolve, since there is no correlation between morphological complexity and economic or other criteria of evolutionary advances. This position is assumed even by writers with a predominantly evolutionary approach. A few writers, notably Jespersen, reverse the classical theory. The more primitive a language, the more complex according to their view, and evolutionary advances are marked by increasing simplification. Jespersen has, practically alone, considered seriously the problem of efficiency in language. He believes that the greater morphological simplicity of modern European languages, as compared to older forms in the same area, is an advantage and that the general movement of language is in the direction of such simplification. The weakness of Jespersen's treatment is that he has practically confined his interest to Indo-European languages. What is probably an internally conditioned drift toward morphological simplification has therefore been mistaken for a universal linguistic trend. An objective survey fails to disclose any decisive correlation between morphological complexity and the usual criteria of cultural evolution.

From this discussion it is evident that the subject of evolution of language has been treated almost solely in the context of morphological simplicity and complexity. But morphology is only one of the aspects of language. Simplicity in morphology might, for example, be accompanied by great semantic complexity, the presence, as in English, of numerous phrase idioms, of homonyms, and of multiple meanings of the same morpheme (ambiguity). The significance of morphological simplicity or complexity in the over-all picture of language in relation to the work it performs has certainly been overrated. Irregular alternations are, by definition, functionless. The variation between *go* and *wen-* is useless, since the difference in meaning is already expressed by the *-t* of the past. A past *go-ed* would perform the same work and without the burden of learning the alternation, which constitutes a real, if hardly noticed, difficulty for the native speaker and a more conspicuous one for an individual who learns English as a second language. That this is a point of linguistic inefficiency is evidenced by the universal tendency toward analogic change, which typically cancels such functionless alternations. In this matter Jespersen is correct, and the nineteenth-century theorists in error. Morphological simplicity is therefore at least a minor aspect of efficiency, and no discernible advantage accrues to the irregularities which many linguists have tended to glorify. However, as critics of Jespersen have pointed out, while such changes in the direction of morphological efficiency do take place, the process of conditional sound change produces new alternations, so that no over-all movement in the direction of morphological simplicity is discernible.

Recapitulating in the light of our earlier consideration of evolutionary advance, we see that it is not complexity as such that is significant, it is rather the over-all degree of efficiency. But efficiency is meaningful only in terms of some function to be performed. A hoof is more efficient than toes only in relation to speed of locomotion as a function. In the function of manipulation of objects it is less efficient. Hence evolutionary advance can be determined only by reference to function or functions to be performed. The traditional criterion of morphological complexity is here of only minor significance. The basic function of language is communication. This leads us to place language in the total frame of the evolution of means of communication. The question of the evolution of language refers to the place of language among other means of communication and whether, in this wider context, a line of evolutionary advance can be discovered. To ask the question regarding language alone is like discussing the evolution of the bow without regard to its position among other weapons.

Means of communication from the standpoint of cosmic evolution can be divided into three stages: prelanguage, language, and postlanguage. Language presumably first appears with hominids. In fact, some would probably want to define hominid in terms of the possession of spoken language. Prelanguage communication is, in the terminology of the first chapter of this work, not a sign system, since there are no combinations of elements subject to grammatical rules. There are signs and even perhaps symbols in the usual acceptation of the terms, but they form no system because there are no constructions involving the combination of elements. Prelanguage signs continue to function even in human societies as gesture and otherwise.

The advantage brought by grammar is chiefly the ability to specify separate aspects of a situation and their relations to one another. Moreover, rules of grammar allow us to combine in constructions aspects not found together in actuality. It becomes possible to state lies, hypotheses, and past and future states of affairs. In the phraseology of semanticists, it is grammar which makes man the time-binding animal.

Natural spoken language is, by general consent, the earliest sign system to appear. In accordance with the normal usage of linguistics, by "language" I shall mean natural spoken language. In addition to the values inherent in any grammatical system, certain advantages of sound as a medium help to explain why language was the first such system to appear. The use of the vocal organs, an overlaid function, did not require the development, through the slow mechanism of genetic change, of a new specialized organ. The voice is always available, involves little physical exertion, and does not interfere with any other activity, except, to a minor degree, eating. Above all, it allows the hands to be free for manipulatory activity. It may be utilized by day as well as night, and it is perceptible in all directions.

Despite all these advantages, language in its physical aspect lacks, above all, permanence and range. Moreover, while the fact that it is not confined to a single channel is, in general, an advantage, under certain circumstances, such as the desire for secrecy or the irrelevance of the message for many within range, separate channels are more useful.

The first advance in the direction of greater physical efficiency is the invention of writing, which gives permanence to speech. The effects of this invention are so great that the difference between civilized and so-called primitive peoples is most frequently defined in terms of it. Recent inventions, such as telegraphy, radio, and teletype, are all designed to give greater range and the possibility of channelized communication.

All these developments have in common that they are isomorphic with language and with one another, at least on the sentence level. Hence any inefficiencies which adhere to the semantic and grammatical systems of language continue unaffected.

In its semantic aspect certain disadvantages of language arise from its method of definition, which is implicit and the result of historic tradition. Dictionaries, which attempt to codify these traditional meanings, exercise a minor influence in the direction of standardization. But the meanings, even when so codified and standardized, commonly suffer from two important defects: ambiguity and vagueness. By "ambiguity" is meant the existence of alternative and different meanings for the same linguistic form, i.e., homonymy. "Vagueness" is the lack of agreement in regard to the instances to be included under a given term. Bertrand Russell gives a striking example. Imagine that speakers of English are confronted with a man without a single hair on his head. Presumably they will agree in the statement that the man in question is bald. Now take a man with a full head of hair and remove the hairs one by one. There will be lack of agreement among speakers of English as to the point at which the statement "the man is bald" is true.

Terms in everyday discourse usually have ambiguous alternative meanings, each of which is, in turn, vague. Ambiguity, in principle, can be eliminated simply by assigning a new and separate term for each ambiguous meaning. Actually, much ambiguity is quite harmless and even a useful conservation of vocabulary resources. For example, the use of the term "case" both in grammatical discourse and in the law courts will presumably mislead no one. Far more insidious than obvious homonyms are the closely similar, but distinct, meanings disclosed only by analysis and tending to persist even in scientific discourse, e.g., the various meanings of "function" in the social and biological sciences and in mathematics.

Vagueness probably cannot be eliminated, for empirical terms at least, but its area can be reduced and its limits specified. For example, we can define a bald man as one who has less than ten active hair follicles. It then remains to define "active hair follicle."

The needs of philosophical and scientific discourse cannot always, in the long run, be satisfied by the use of traditional implicit definition. The first step, which involves a departure from the procedures of traditional language definition, is the use of definition by postulation but within the grammatical and semantic framework of natural language. The physicist defines "force" for his own purposes by explicit agreement, taking as his point of departure its meaning in everyday language, with the understanding that it will have this new meaning in the context of physical discourse.

But sometimes half-measures prove inadequate and, as in the case of mathematics and symbolic logic, an entire sign system is created by postulation or fiat. The form of the symbols, their meaning, and grammatical rules of combination are then all postulated.

A third line of development is the invention of various international languages. These do not, in principle, alter the physical nature of the language sign vehicle. The meanings, though all created by fiat of the inventor, are along traditional language lines and probably are as vague and ambiguous as those of natural language. The one structural advantage of such languages is the practical absence of the dysfunctional morphological complexities of natural languages. Even this advantage accrues almost to the same degree to pidgin languages.

The development of forms isomorphic to language, with the advantages described previously for the physical aspect of communication and the appearance of postulated sign systems which overcome in good part the semantic and grammatical inefficiencies of language, does not mean the supersession of language. It may rather be interpreted as a process of differentiation and specialization within the communication process, whereby each communication need becomes more efficiently served by an instrument which more adequately fulfils some specific function.

In the course of this development language comes more and more to fulfil the functions for which it is most appropriate. The constant availability and flexibility of language suggest that it will not be replaced in person-to-person interaction in the foreseeable future, if ever. Moreover, the abolition of vagueness and ambiguity, whatever its advantages for the purely informational aspects of communication, would result in the probable elimination of humor (certainly of punning, which stems from ambiguity) and of poetry, which flourishes on vagueness. Finally, language plays a unique role in communication, which, aside from all other considerations, doubtless assures its future. If we wish to explain a symbol or a meaning, we do it in a sign system. If the term is still not understood, it must be explained in terms of a sign system of lower level, and so on. But at some point this process must reach an end. Either understanding is achieved, as evidenced by appropriate reaction, or we must resort to the co-ordination of an element or elements of a sign system with that which is not a sign, namely, a set of events. Such a system provides the level of ultimate explanation. Language serves this function, hence its generality as compared with the limited subject matter of other systems or of individual signs. Thus what is sometimes called "art symbolism" is, in a sense, secondary symbolism operating through the symbolism of language. If, for example, I "explain" a Navaho symbolic use of red as referring to the north, I am explaining it in terms of a linguistic symbol "north" which I assume to be understood. So, too, mathematical symbols are ultimately defined in terms of ordinary language.

Ontogenetically, too, we normally learn such symbolisms or post-language sign systems after language and in terms of language. Even when, as is possible in the case of gestures, we may learn them before language and independently of language, we may later explain them in terms of language, but never vice versa.

Finally, two other aspects of the evolution of communication may be pointed out which involve the social dimension, that is, the distribution of sign systems with respect to populations. In general, the greater the economic productivity, density of population, and facilities for transportation of persons and goods, the less likely that speech communities will differentiate into many local communities speaking mutually intelligible languages and the more the felt needs of wider communication will result in the development of standard languages and lingua francas, eventuating in extensive monolingual communities. Likewise, the greater differentiation within a group is reflected in specialization within the realm of communication. Before the advent of mass communication, all individuals were of roughly comparable status as senders and receivers of messages, with leadership marked, no doubt, by some degree of superiority in effectiveness, if not of volume of communication. In industrial societies, specialized senders, such as editorial writers, broadcasters, and writers of books, send to far more people than those from whom they receive.

Our general conclusion, then, is that it is not language as such which evolves but rather communication in general. Within this process language does have a central and key position as the source of all postlanguage developments and the general instrument which fulfils the function of the ultimate level of explanation. While it may seem somewhat rash to prejudge the case, it appears that natural languages are all very much on the same level as far as efficiency is concerned. A comparative measure of efficiency which includes all relevant phonological, grammatical, and semantic aspects has never been worked out, and, in view of the complexity of each aspect and the disparity among them, it does not appear very likely that one can be developed. Traditional theories of language evolution have usually taken but one of these aspects, the morphological, and have further assumed a correlation between complexity and advance which is unjustified. Indeed, as we have seen, just the opposite seems more likely to be the case, so that in this limited aspect the despised pidgin languages are more advanced than such cherished forms of speech as classical Sanskrit. Certainly, then, the evolution of language as such has never been demonstrated, and the inherent equality of all languages must be maintained on present evidence. Yet in the broader sense some correlation between communication and the evolution of culture can be discerned, and language evolves by begetting that which is not language but transcends it, even while it is dependent upon it.

Archeology

BY HIS DIGGING you shall know him. Whether he uses a shovel or directs a squad of excavators, or works with a trowel or a spoon to remove the soil from a delicate specimen long buried, the job of an archeologist is to uncover the evidences of cultures of some by-gone day. But this is by no means the only task of archeology, nor is it the most difficult. The archeologists whose work is characterized by the selections which follow are anthropologists as well and this has far-ranging significance in determining what they do.

Archeology has many personalities. There is the archeology carried out by people whose interests lie in what is called the classical world. These specialists are concerned with ancient Egypt and Mesopotamia, with classical Greece and Rome. They are historians, connoisseurs of art, and delvers into the origins of contemporary religions. While these specialists have fed anthropology and sometimes been nourished in return, the connections are generally weak and tenuous, though in recent years certain centers of learning, such as the Oriental Institute of the University of Chicago, have managed to achieve genuine cooperation and common effort.

Anthropological archeology is concerned with the study of culture, and its investigations of specific sites are comparable to the studies of cultural anthropologists in specific tribes or communities. Where some cultural anthropologists, however, can immerse themselves in the present to such a degree as to exclude history, archeologists are haunted by time and its processes and almost inevitably think in terms of change and development.

Archeologists work in any culture-bearing stratum. They may be aesthetes, but as professionals they seek any and all evidences of the past—broken pieces of pottery, discarded tools, evidences of shelters and hearths, and the remains of the people themselves. Indeed, graves and garbage dumps are among the likeliest of archeological hunting grounds. Anthropological archeologists have dug amost everywhere, though so little in most places that an enormous amount of work remains. Professional archeologists with anthropological orientation will be found digging in Tahiti, Patagonia, Mongolia, Kenya, Egypt, Australia, Sarawak, Easter Island, Long Island, Montana, Mexico, Peru, Siberia, Hungary, China, Iraq, and anywhere else they can get permission and funds to start their excavations.

For every moment in the field, the archeologist spends hours, even days, in the laboratory or museum analyzing his find and its meaning. The objects he recovers are of great importance but equally crucial is their precise location in the ground. Amateur archeologists who dig for relics as if they were treasures, ripping them from the earth without considering their spatial relationships to the site as a whole or its other contents—these are the bane of the profession.

The evidence from the past is invariably fragmentary and discontinuous. How shall it be reconstructed, interpreted, or related to other materials? Unfortunately in the past archeologists quite generally committed a serious error of method that also plagues other kinds of anthropologists. Archetyping is a generalizing procedure whereby a concept of the standard or the normal is achieved at the cost of surpressing deviation. We have already seen something of this concept at work reducing the living complications of racial heterogeneity to a myth of distinctiveness and separation through time. In archeology a similar effect is produced when we think of a culture as depending totally on one kind of tool or, more usually, on one set of procedures for making tools. We think, in brief, of people who make "core tools" or "chopper-chopping tools" and then it is but a step to thinking of the makers of such tools as irrevocably distinct, never the twain shall meet.

Actually, there is something of a "new archeology," and its main discriminating tenet is dependence upon the statistical analysis of the contents of a site or of an archaeological culture, rather than a stereotyping or archetyping. Such analyses are much more in harmony with scientific anthropological theory in other parts of the discipline and have, as their consequence, much more to offer to our understanding of the evolution of culture in general, as well as a more accurate appreciation of the development of particular cultures. Because the writings that rely on statistical rather than archetypal profiles tend to be intensely technical, none has been reprinted in this volume. You will find some samples of ecologically informed work that has grown in conjunction with and benefitted from the antiarchetypal approach. We begin, however, by considering some of the very general theoretical principles underlying archeological work and analyses.

30 Archeological Theory and Method: Some Suggestions from the Old World

Christopher Hawkes

REFLECTION ON THE THEORETICAL UNDERPINNINGS OF ARCHEOLOGY IS NOT *confined to the Americas. At a specially arranged conference at Harvard in 1953, a distinguished English archeologist discussed some of the major theoretical problems of his field, particularly those which concerned the contributions of archeology to the general science of culture. Specific aspects of the problem raised questions such as the degree to which ideological aspects of culture could be surmised from the physical remains which, all too frequently, are all that is left to the archeologist. The selection which appears below is not the original draft of the paper read at that conference but a revision incorporating some of the fruits of the discussion.*

In this rewriting of the theme which I prepared, in October 1953, for the conference recorded above, I have been greatly helped both by the

SOURCE: *American Anthropologist*, Vol. 56 (1954), pp. 155–168. Reprinted by permission of the author and publisher.

Charles Francis Christopher Hawkes (b. 1905) is Professor of Archaeology and Director of the Institute of Archaeology at the University of Oxford. He has specialized in European archeology. Among his works are *The Prehistoric Foundations of Europe to the Mycenean Age* (1940) and, with Jacquetta Hawkes, *Prehistoric Britain* (1953).

434

comments made on it by the participants, and by much else that I have heard and read on theory and method in archeology during my four-month stay in the United States. The New World's interest in the subject should certainly have an Old World counterpart. And I hope that my attempts to think toward one have profited from American thinking in the New World field of study, although, naturally, they themselves belong properly to the Old World field, with which alone I can claim adequate acquaintance. At any rate my starting point will be familiar to American readers, namely, Walter W. Taylor's book *A Study of Archeology*, which is concerned mainly with New World archeology. As an Old World archeologist, I am of course not competent to assess or criticize Taylor's detailed contentions in this book. But all readers will know the general objection that he raised in it against New World archeology, for having limited itself to what he called "mere chronicle" —an almost exclusive preoccupation with charting the connections, in space and time, of the types of archeological material obtained from sites. He insisted that such things as these connections cannot have entered directly into the way of life of the ancient peoples concerned: they are outside it. The significance of the types inside the people's way of life will have been something immediate and local, something cultural in the functional sense of the term, which this sort of archeology was missing.

Now, if I understand Taylor aright, he did not object to "where and when" archeology in itself. Exhaustive statements of that kind of evidence are obviously necessary, if we are to obtain thorough knowledge of the geography and history of the types; the fact that the people who made and used the types need not have known their geography and history is no reason for our not getting to know them. What Taylor objected to was limitation of archeology to this "where and when" chronicle, and refusal to carry inquiry further into the way of life of the people being studied, and into the significance of this or that type to that way of life. To correct such shortcomings, he recommended a fresh approach, which he called "conjunctive." Analysis or assessment of this "conjunctive" program as a whole, from me, would be superfluous. But I should like to concentrate attention on one point, namely, Taylor's claim that if archeology limits itself to a mere external chronicling of material culture traits, it will be stopping short of its proper anthropological objective, and will be simply compiling statistics when it ought to be revealing culture. For to this point there is surely a corollary: that in order to reveal culture, the approach required will be not just a material-analytic one, but one which, whatever the details of the program, can still more rightly be called "conjunctive" because the material-analytic in it will be conjoined with other, and more deeply penetrating, lines of thought and operation.

In my submission, both Taylor's point and my corollary are in their essence just. "When and where" archeology should be a means to a further end. But the question remains, how to get to that? And here, I suggest, the answers may be found to differ, in practice if not in theory, with differing archeological fields. At the least, we cannot predicate one uniform set of answers, valid for all archeological fields, unless we have first examined several of these fields, and see what answers appear to be valid for each one. Then, by comparing the various answers, we can see what they have in common, and so abstract the general element in them from the particular.

I will therefore now move on from Taylor and his New World program, and take the call for a "conjunctive approach" with me over to the Old World, or to such a segment as I can claim to be well acquainted with. What echoes will it arouse when relayed over there?

In the Old World, the sort of archeology most obviously comparable to that examined for the New by Taylor normally proclaims itself Prehistoric, and has been at pains to declare its independence of the written texts of history and the merely antiquarian study of historical monuments and artworks. Its pride has been to be "text-free," and not "text-aided." The proof of the geological antiquity of man, and of his Paleolithic cultures, has given a long and scientifically chartered background, at once for man's material culture and his biological evolution, behind recorded ancient history. The adoption of Thomsen's system of classifying prehistoric archeological remains by material, into three Ages, placed those of Bronze and Iron in succession next behind the historic record, and the Stone Age behind them again, divided presently into Paleolithic and Neolithic, the former geologically Pleistocene and the latter Recent. This prehistoric archeology, which held its first International Congress in 1866, has always reckoned itself a branch of anthropology, concerned to apply scientific treatment to a natural history of man. It has applied it by way of evolutionary theory verified by stratigraphic fact, and has extended it by classification of archeological material into types, arrived at by sorting collections of specimens into groups and series wherein types could be recognized, each one uniform because expressing a consistent purpose on the part of its ancient makers, and each normally followed by another in a kind of evolution, toward an ever more efficient realization of such purpose. And by "efficient" has in general been meant efficient for the successful survival of the human group, in its physical environment at whatever period.

Now of course, in our day, the modes of formulation of this "text-free" prehistoric archeology, and of its theory of knowledge, must be admitted to have undergone great changes. Yet the underlying axioms inevitably remain; and these amount to declaring that the human activity which it can apprehend conforms to a series of norms, which can be aggregated under the name of cultures, definable in terms of time and space and recognizable each by its standard range of material products. In the standard range, however delicately the bounds of classification are adapted to the variability, the notion of types must be comported. And change, from one norm to another, is to be followed in the changing of the types, and of the standard ranges of the products whence the norms can be inferred. The notion of norms seems fundamental, since without it there could be no firm claim of comparability between the phenomena given by the material; and there must be this claim, since only by comparison can those be got to make any collective sense. It is from the comparison of archeological phenomena that one's reasoning must proceed, inductively, to the human activity that has produced them. This is what I conceive to be the process of pure archeological inference. However much scientific apparatus and intellectual refinement it employs, it has to go that way, and it has to rest on the notion of norms in man's activity, which is an anthropological generalization, based on the extreme degree of conservatism shown by primitive man in his technological traditions. Without this notion, as Movius, following Bordes, has lately been reminding us, the whole subject would crumple up.

Compared with the "text-free" mode of archeology, the other mode, which I call "text-aided," is not hard to grasp, and has been familiar longer. Its basis lies in antiquities or archeological phenomena that are known or knowable historically, from consideration of which it proceeds with the aid—direct or at least indirect—of the relevant historical texts to conclusions about the past human activity thus indicated. Some of these antiquities, to begin with, are things that have never been forgotten, so that the activity that has produced them has always remained in some sort known, and needs only investigation by archeology to be fairly fully known. That the Romans came to Britain, and built a wall, or walls, across the north of it to keep out the barbarians, has never been forgotten in Britain. Moreover, things that have been forgotten can be rediscovered; their mere rediscovery and description may be no more than antiquarianism, but their systematic study, comparison, and classification are undeniably archeology. The object will be their correct attribution to a known historical context, using either readable inscriptions found among or on them, or the identification of their localities with localities described in a reliable historic record. From such historically guaranteed examples, this mode of archeology can then determine types, as of Greek temples or Celtic coins or Roman camps, of which it can go on to recognize further examples, previously unrecognized and no matter where occurring, by comparison. This comparison will not rest on its practitioner's own theory, as in the "text-free" archeology just now considered; it rests on textual statements guaranteeing that there were such types, standardized and varying only in detail, in the historic cultures concerned. But with such guaranteed cases as starting points, one can build these, and then other types as well, into series, the successive members of which are seen as related to each other in processes of development or degeneration. This, of course, is just like the typology of the "text-free" mode of reasoning and, like it, is based on the idea of norms in the human activity responsible—starting from cases perceived with the aid of texts, and then recognizing others by comparison and analysis. The same proceeding can be undertaken, too, with styles of ancient art; for a style is a norm, and essentially the same canons of comparison and analysis apply. But all these series must, at some of their points, be pegged to points in textually documented history. No new discovery or theory can upset the known dates of the Roman campaigns in Britain that left the camps and walls there. To that extent the "text-free" mode of archeology, with its dependence on experimental classification, is the more exacting of the two: it must supply its guarantees for itself. Where the "text-aided" mode is the more exacting is in its dependence on its documentary aids: once get too far away from these, and its logical force becomes too weak to be compulsive. And in practice, of course, we are most often making use of both modes, combining text-aided and text-free reasoning together, in varying degrees according to the circumstances.

In many Old World fields, indeed, we are so familiar with this combination that we frequently use it without reminding ourselves what it is. Yet it is a conjunction of two really different logical approaches; and when we add, as in modern practice we inevitably do, approaches from natural-scientific study of environment, techniques, and raw materials, and where possible from relevant modern folk-life too, and conjoin all these approaches as far as practicable into one, I conceive that this is in some sort a "conjunctive" approach, like that we have seen advocated for New World archeology. Perhaps, then, it is worth examining a little further.

In my Presidential Address to the Prehistoric Society, given in London in February 1951 and published in the Society's *Proceedings* for that year, I tried an installment of such examining, and an airing of some new suggestions in terminology, which should help to make the scene somewhat clearer. I pointed out that what Englishmen largely and loosely call "prehistory," namely, everything that happened in their country or in countries similarly placed on the periphery of ancient civilization before the establishment there of Imperial Roman rule, could only be rightly so called in a conversational and generalized sense. Roman Britain itself, indeed, is in good part historic; but there is much in it that is historic only dimly and embryonically, and much in the centuries after Rome's withdrawal that in historic status is more rudimentary still. The best word for these stretches of incompletely historic time, I suggested, is "Protohistory." Our cognition of them, that is to say, is based on the beginnings or rudiments, the protoplasm if you like, of textual-historical evidence, but no more. Just the same will be true, then, of the latter end of our "prehistoric" time, directly before Rome's coming: it is already "protohistoric," for there are already some texts and also some inscribed coins. And because we have protohistoric cognition of it accordingly, we can know things about it which we cannot expect to know so readily about our earlier phases. Within the resources of this protohistoric cognition, too, we can reckon the native Celtic sources, written down in Britain and Ireland indeed only considerably later, but telling sometimes of events and of institutions in both islands that take us back right through our protohistoric times.

However, this protohistory cannot very well be taken back, in its own right, before the 1st century B.C. For the few centuries before that, with British archeology illumined by comparison with a Continental Europe that was, in its own right, partly then already protohistoric or historic, I suggested in 1951 that our cognition could be called "penehistoric," because it was almost historic but not quite. I have not found this terms in practice very useful, and I intend to drop it: it is not very important anyway, because the period connoted could never be more than short. What I believe much more important is that our cognition of all the better known parts of prehistoric Europe before Protohistory and History begin there, and in spite of their not having yet begun there, is not simply "prehistoric" in the sense in which our cognition of the Old Stone Age is prehistoric, but is conditioned by the fact that somewhere alongside of these barbarian regions, or at the worst somewhere a long way from them but not too far to have significance for them, there is already a history, beginning to be explicit in written texts from before 3000 B.C., in the civilized central regions of the ancient world: the Near and Middle East.

This means that wherever, between that time and the coming of our own protohistory and history, we can see cultures in Europe that have relation, in any degree, to those of the Near or Middle East, our awareness of that relation enters necessarily into our cognition of them, and conditions our archeological interpretation of them. And I distinguish two modes of cognition here, according to the distinctness and proximity of the civilized history, based on texts, to which there is relation. Where it is distinct because contacts with it are well attested, I call the mode of cognition "parahistoric," from the Greek *para,* "alongside." From the 16th century B.C., when the New Kingdom was set up in Egypt and Late Minoan and Late Helladic or Mycenean culture in Crete and Greece, the cultures of barbarian Europe are set alongside those historic or protohistoric ones, and thus, though of course prehistoric in the loose sense of the word, are parahistoric when one speaks more strictly. Go back before that time, or to regions outside that range of relations to the historic, and you find your cognition is still to some extent conditioned by knowledge based on textual history, but the history is indistinct and a long way off. The cultures of the mature Neolithic and earliest Metal Ages in Europe are as intelligible to us as they are because they carry elements diffused to them from—ultimately—the ancient East, which was already historic or at the very least protohistoric in their day. But the diffusion was a long-distance and often tenuous affair, so that the history is remote. I therefore call our mode of cognition of these and all similar cultures "telehistoric," from the Greek *tēle*, "far off," the same word as in telephone or telepathy.

I believe this conception to be important both for the theory of our archeology, and for its method. As soon as we have telehistoric or para-historic cognition—and still more obviously when we have protohistoric cognition—we are no longer interpreting our archeological evidence simply and solely by ideas of anthropological "process," or of ecological determination. In rural economy, burial rites, technology, sociology, or what not, there is always, somewhere or other, a point of reference within the historic order. We can interpret as we do because we are dealing with the outer parts of a diffusion-sphere, or of more than one diffusion-sphere, which we know to have history, and ultimately textual history, at its center. Our "conjunctive" approach to them therefore will always have something of the historical about it.

This has its effect both on the framework of the "prehistory" thus constructed—that is, its chronology—and also on its cultural content; I take the latter first. Let us recall Taylor's complaint that the statistical assembling of many archeological data still can leave one outside the cultural reality of the life of the people one is studying. A historical element among one's resources for interpretation, conjoined with those of technology and of natural history, can surely—at least sometimes—answer that complaint. The fertility symbols so prevalent in the archeological material of Neolithic and Early Metal Age Europe stand to be interpreted with the help of what is historically known about the fertility cults of the ancient East whence the diffusions to the Europe of those Ages started. The interpretation will be by reasoning in the telehistoric mode. The social organization of much European culture of the Late Neolithic, Bronze, and Iron Ages, with its little kinship groups, each headed by a father bred to bearing arms, which is displayed by the single-graves, tumuli, or barrows so frequent in these periods' sepulchral archeology, and by its settlement sites too if well enough explored, stands to be interpreted by what is historically known of the social organization of the Indo-European peoples, and reflected in their epic literature—Homer, Beowulf, the Germanic and Celtic sagas—running from the historic and protohistoric back through the parahistoric to the telehistoric mode. Written accounts of Germanic and Celtic religion find some archeological echoes anyhow as far back as the parahistoric Late Bronze Age.

Medieval laws and land-books, in certain cases, can help to interpret the ancient field systems, of that age and later, if not earlier, which air photography is revealing extensively in Britain and elsewhere in northwest Europe. Such examples will show, in general, what I mean.

But once get right away from any such historical basis in your cognition, and you will immediately find interpretation much more difficult. You will find it by no means easy to get inside your people's cultural life from their mere material remains. You will find that the "conjunctive" approach cannot always take you far enough. You can, and of course must, conjoin your archeology with natural history, in the analysis of raw materials, the investigation of techniques, and the study of environment and of your people's response to it, by every one of the natural sciences that can be brought to serve. All these things—and the study of modern folk-life too, if there is any relevant—are obligatory. But when you have done your utmost with them, how much will you have learned? Remember, you are now completely in the "text-free" mode of reasoning; you are right out of touch with history based even remotely upon texts; and if you want a name for your cognition it could well be "ante-historic," for you are in a world wholly anterior to textual-historical evidence. And from anthropology you have in the last resort only "process"—notions of a quite general sort about the social life and activities of primitive man, and the generalization about his conservatism which I mentioned some while back. Otherwise, you have got to use inductive reasoning, to take you from comparison and analysis of observed phenomena to the human activity that once produced them. How easy will you find it? I have a fourfold answer to this question.

1. To infer from the archeological phenomena to the *techniques* producing them I take to be relatively easy. The modes of research required are themselves no doubt difficult, and in detail often tedious. But the reasoning employed, I maintain, is basically simple.

2. To infer to the *subsistence-economics* of the human groups concerned is fairly easy. Operationally, of course, it is laborious. Not only must their material remains be closely studied, and the economic purposes implied by them carefully nosed out; their physical environment also must be investigated and its potentialities assessed: this will mean bringing in natural scientists and weighing the human significance of their expert testimonies. Yet, in the end, the reasoning one must use is not so hard. The impressive book lately published by my Cambridge colleague, Grahame Clark, *Prehistoric Europe: The Economic Basis* (Cambridge, 1953), is a fine example of this sort of work, and a wonderful compendium of knowledge. But its logic is simple, and need never be anything but straightforward.

3. To infer to the *social/political institutions* of the groups, however, is considerably harder. If you excavate a settlement in which one hut is

bigger than all the others, is it a chief's hut, so that you can infer chief-tainship, or is it really a medicine lodge or a meeting hut for initiates, or a temple? Richly furnished graves may help you, but what if the graves are all poorly furnished? Or if the more richly furnished graves are women's, does that mean female social predominance, or male predominance using the adornment of its subjected womenfolk for its own advertisement? How much could the archeologist of the future infer, from his archeol-ogy alone, of the Melanesian institutions studied by Malinowski? No, rea-soning of this kind surely cannot all be easy.

4. To infer to the *religious institutions and spiritual life* may seem superficially, perhaps, to be easier, and for the first few steps it may some-times be so. Paleolithic art clearly has much to do with institutions of hunting-magic and, in the case of the so-called "Venuses," with expres-sions of desire for human fertility. Grave goods, again, indicate a belief that the dead need material supplies or equipment, as though still alive. But how much further can one go than that? Besides the animal and human portrayals in Stone Age art, are there not very many abstract signs whose meaning most often is just unknowable? What part were the dead, furnished with grave goods, supposed to play in the life of the com-munity still living? You can use ethnological data obtained from modern primitives to stimulate your imagination by suggesting the sort of reli-gious institutions and spiritual life your prehistoric people may or could have had, but you cannot this way demonstrate what they did have, and you know you cannot even hope to unless you can show some real con-nection between *this* modern and *that* prehistoric. I have heard the thing attempted, indeed, from the side of the modern South African Bushmen and the significance of their paintings, back to prehistoric African, and then maybe European, Stone Age paintings and their significance. But it is a very long shot, and even the possibility of it, in the Old World, is something very rare. In general, I believe, unaided inference from mate-rial remains to spiritual life is the hardest inference of all.

And now there is worse to come. If material techniques are easy to infer to, subsistence-economics fairly easy, communal organization harder, and spiritual life hardest of all, you have there a climax of four degrees of difficulty in reasoning. What is this climax? It is a climax lead-ing up from the more generically animal in man to the more specifically human. Human techniques, logically speaking, differ from animal only in the use of extracorporeal limbs, namely tools, instead of corporeal ones only; human subsistence-economics differ from animal more obviously, but only (again logically speaking) in the amount and degree of fore-thought which they involve; human communal institutions next transcend the animal level very considerably; and human spiritual life transcends it altogether. So the result appears to be that the more specifically human are men's activities, the harder they are to infer by this sort of archeology. What it seems to offer us is positively an anticlimax: the more human, the less intelligible.

And the critical factor, standing between fair intelligibility and stark unintelligibility, is surely ecology, the study of the physical environment. So long as you can depend on that, as you can for the material aspects of man's life, his technology and his economic existence, your exercise of this sort of archeology is rewarding. How rewarding, a book like Clark's well shows. But now transcend that, and your returns diminish sharply. There is nothing in North American ecology, by itself, to compel either Iroquois institutions, say, or the Constitution of the United States. I do not say that you are left in the end with nothing that you can apprehend. But I do say that there cannot be much, and that we should ask ourselves just what there can be.

I must now come back to the other, or text-aided, mode of archeological reasoning. I mentioned above its helpfulness to the making of a framework for prehistory—the framework of measured time. Time is an essential category of all archeological thought. It is the time dimension, which archeology as an extension of history alone can give, that entitles it to a unique and indispensable place among the anthropological disciplines. The studies in cultural or social anthropology today which are limited to the "social present" (of the three generations normally alive at once) are depriving themselves, for purely practical reasons, of something that anthropology should never wish to be without. The practical reasons are of course perfectly sensible on a short-term reckoning of advantages. They include a very proper refusal to fill the place of a history not immediately knowable by an imaginary one fabricated by the anthropologist himself. But for social anthropologists to forget that they are practical reasons only, and to slip into the habit of ignoring the time dimension altogether, is surely exceedingly unwise. Indeed, I should call it scientifically indefensible. To restrict anthropological field work to peoples whose real history does appear at present more or less unknown is a convenient, and sometimes popular, way of running away from the time dimension. But were it to become a universal habit, anthropology would be quickly ruined. It is a vital function of archeology to stand with history in reminding anthropologists that time really does exist, and cannot ultimately be run away from if truth is to be served. All the more, then, does it behoove archeology to be very careful about its own treatment of the time dimension, and to see that it is intelligently managed.

There is to my mind no inherent difficulty in this, provided that one does not let oneself get muddled. Unfortunately, people in the past, sometimes very influential, have in fact been muddled in their chronological thinking. It was due to the 19th-century climate of thought in which they grew up. When pre-history was supposed to be a single, simple, tale of human progress, through Pleistocene into geologically Recent times, it was given a simple division into periods on a geological basis. The Neo-lithic was Recent, the Paleolithic was Pleistocene and divided into Lower, Middle, and Upper because it should lie stratigraphically that way. But for a long while no need was felt to distinguish, terminologically, between periods and cultures; and presently, when later ages were likewise subdivided, the same confusion was re-enacted. Montelius established four periods for the Neolithic of northern Europe, and six for its Bronze Age, and all the material remains assigned to any one period were labeled by that period's serial number. Reinecke did something similar for the Bronze and Iron Ages of south Germany, only using serial letters instead of numbers. All that was then needful was to give each period its absolute date in years B.C. And nobody saw that there was a confusion of thinking here at all, until it began to appear that different groups of people within the same period had left different kinds of material remains—in other words, that several cultures could exist within the same broad region simultaneously. Now that that has been realized, things have become apt to look very complicated, because the descriptive terminology will not fit what it is supposed to be describing. Thus, the notion of periods of time that are automatically also units of culture history has proved to be a serious nuisance in European prehistory and we have to rid ourselves of the muddles it has caused. The way to do so, of course, is to distinguish fundamentally between periods and cultures, and construct the former as a fixed framework of time units, into which the cultures are then stuffed, in their sequences and juxtapositions according to the evidence, and given names of their own, distinct from the names or numbers of the periods.

The absolute dating of the periods, of course, will still have to be found. This, where any historical system of dates is available, as are those of the Near East for Europe from about 3000 B.C. as above explained, has to be done by establishing synchronisms between points in the scheme of periods and points in the system of dates. Such synchronisms can be given by proving a reciprocal exchange of material products, or adopting or copying of some specific type or design or symbol or style of art or ornament—a "horizon style"—or borrowing of some technique, from the region already dated into the region requiring to be dated. Some of these synchronisms of ours are good and tight, others are more dubious and may wobble over a margin of error which has to be allowed for. When there is doubt of that kind, some chronological weighting may be brought in from the quantitative bulk, and the degree of typological uniformity, of the material representing the cultures which the period or periods must contain. Thus in one way and another, and with many varying degrees of precision, can be constructed a chronological framework for the 3000 years B.C. in prehistoric Europe: most precise where our cognition is protohistoric, less so where it is parahistoric, and least so where it is telehistoric.

Natural science, however, can also furnish us with dates. Records of eclipses, comets, etc., astronomically datable exactly, have a distinct part to play in framing the historical date-systems of the Near East, as of course have the dated recurrences of the heliacal rising of Sirius for Egypt. But natural scientific dating can be taken right outside the historical sphere by the now well known carbon 14 method; there is of course also dendrochronology, and the probably less reliable varve-analysis of sedimentary geology; and finally, transcending all these in the huge lengths of time which it seeks to embrace, the astronomical chronology of Milankovic for the climate phases of the Pleistocene, based on the periodicity of solar radiation. The trouble about all these methods, however, is that either the time-lengths they give are so large that many human events which we should like to have chronologically separated can have occurred within any one of them, or else, as with carbon 14, the number of determinations required to establish cultural duration, as opposed to pin-pointing single local episodes, is rather large. Thus the theoretical possibility that by all or any of these means the ante-historic stretches of prehistory may come to be as closely charted chronologically as the para- or tele-historic, is probably still rather far from being realized.

In any case, it is on the whole clear enough that archeology's claim to a distinctive place among the anthropological disciplines depends to a great extent on the accuracy of the chronology for events and cultures that it can offer. And this is particularly clear when we come to consider the phenomena of diffusion.

That elements of aggregations of culture have been diffused, by one means or another, from certain centers over wide areas of the inhabited world, has been repeatedly demonstrated, most often with the help of archeology. But the demonstration, to be fully acceptable, ought to prove not only the fact, and the correct setting in chronology, but the means whereby it has been accomplished. It seems to me that these means may be broadly divided into two. Actual folk movements or migrations of peoples, or human groups of whatever size or character, give what I call a *primary diffusion.* Influences, transmitted from one group or people to another without actual group migration, give what I call a *secondary diffusion.* In assessing the question whether a newly claimed diffusion is really that or not (the alternatives being independent invention, or convergent development, of the things advanced in evidence), it is important to have clear ideas on which of the comparable known diffusions in one's field of study are primary and which secondary. For, in the newly claimed case, the one might be possible, the other not; and in any event, the loose and vague use of words such as influence, transmission of elements, etc., ought wherever feasible to be replaced by more precise expressions, if only for the sake of tidy thinking.

It is also important not to forget the diffusions, whether primary or secondary, that are known historically. For these include movements that on archeological evidence alone would be got quite wrong. The Hellenization of the Orient, in the three centuries before the Roman Empire, for example, would never archeologically be supposed the sequel to a single military expedition headed by the Macedonian Alexander. It is more often the secondary diffusions resulting from such primary movements that loom large in archeology, and the archeological elusiveness of primary diffusive movements is a thing that prehistorians should carefully remember. For a large part of their business is the inferring of diffusions from archeological evidence alone, and the determination of their true character. And this is a delicate and exacting task, for which they should neglect no comparative resources that may be helpful.

There is here one specific point, to which I cannot forbear to call attention. Where natural life-forms, or rock or mineral products, have been moved about the world by human agency, there is a great deal to be learned by correctly attributing them to their proper original habitat or location. That the first domesticated cattle and sheep, wheat and barley, attested in prehistoric Europe were not native there, but introduced from the southeast by Neolithic man, is a fact of the highest importance contributed to human by natural history. A much higher degree of precision can be obtained by similar work on transported stone and minerals, as by the British Committee for the Petrological Identification of Stone Axes which has been working for a number of years and issues its periodic reports in the *Proceedings of the Prehistoric Society*. Other examples could easily be given, and many will be found in the book by Clark already cited, drawn from all over Europe.

But it remains for me to point out that far less such work has yet been done on transported mineral products other than stone, and above all on metal ones. The metals or metal alloys of which prehistoric artifacts were made can frequently, like the stone of the stone axes but of course in a more complex manner, be assigned by analysis to their original mineral deposits. It is easy to see the importance for Bronze Age archeology of an application of this method on a wide scale. Yet what has been done hitherto has been restricted by the techniques available. An apparatus has lately been devised and constructed in the Clarendon Laboratory at Oxford, with the encouragement of Lord Cherwell, whereby quantitative analyses of archeological metal objects can be obtained, without damaging them in any way, by X-ray spectrometry. It is now being employed experimentally with a view to the further development of the method. There seems no doubt that if laboratory research of this kind were employed systematically to localize the sources of the metals, and also to discern the metallurgical techniques employed in products transported over such large areas of distribution in the ancient world, the

extension of knowledge would be very great, and questions of diffusion
and long-range commerce, and of comparative technology, at present
often handled with too little recourse to factual evidence, could receive
methodically documented answers.

We need, then, both precise and sensibly expressed chronology, and
accurate determinations of our raw materials. According as we are well
or less well equipped with these, and competent or less competent in our
techniques, we shall be able to undertake the task of getting from our
people's external archeology to the internal content of their cultures, and
to the interrelation of these in the pattern created by diffusions. I have
explained that in the conjunctive approach that is necessary to this end, I
believe a historical, text-aided element to be required for any full success.

One day, the conjunction of all our other resources together with
natural-scientific chronology may enable us to transcend the limitations
under which we now labor when we have left such aid behind. But I
think that day is still distant, and there is much for us to do meanwhile:
above all, I would suggest, in the fields like my European one where an
element of such historical aid is present for some thousands of years in
varying degrees, amenable to what I have called protohistoric, parahistoric, or telehistoric cognition.

I have often been embarrassed by the formal necessity of beginning
the prehistoric narrative at its beginning, where we know least, and
proceeding from that forward. I should feel so much happier if instead of
proceeding from the unknown toward the known, one could proceed
toward the unknown from the known. And now I really wonder
whether, by taking my three orders of cognition in their reverse order of
time with the protohistoric first and the telehistoric last, one could not in
fact attempt to do that.

To take what one knows from history and protohistory first would
be like using what in the New World would be called the direct historical
method, combined where possible with the use of recorded ethnological
data (which of course are tantamount to history, in their own way). By
this one could establish that in historic or protohistoric time there had
been certain specific movements or diffusions or developments, which account for certain distributions and interrelations of culture within one's
field. One could plot these in time and space as historic or protohistoric
diffusion-spheres. That would be the first step. Then one would take
those as data, preconditional to the next step in the investigation. That
next step would be the plotting of parahistoric diffusion-spheres, to account for as much as possible of one's evidence that the historic and
protohistoric ones would not account for. Next, one would take those in
their turn as data, preconditional to the next step again, which, of course,
would be to do the same thing with telehistoric diffusion-spheres. When

one had exhausted all the possibilities offered by this series of steps, there would be left a residue, which none of them would have accounted for. For this there would remain only the possibility of ante-historic diffusion-spheres, such as those created by the spread of Paleolithic or Mesolithic culture about the world—for example, out of Asia into America. So one would take one's courage in both hands and try what one could do with those.

And then finally, when the whole gamut of the music of these diffusion-spheres had been played through, one would at last be in a position to try assessing the ultimate postulate of the comparative method in anthropology, which of course was the postulate with which the old style researchers began, assuming its validity a priori. That postulate is that the culture of all mankind rests in the last resort on things common to all men as a species, inherent in their culture-capacity from the start. If there are such things, it seems to me, they can in good logic be apprehended only by the abstraction of all those whose comparability is due to subsequent diffusions or developments. Some might argue that when all those had been abstracted one would find the remnant to consist only of truisms, too general to give insight into specific cultures. Or one might find nothing specifically human left at all, because one would be down to the level of the prehuman primates. At all events, I do not see any other way of enabling ourselves to judge, except the method I have suggested which is essentially a historical method. It begins with the historic, and works backward through from that to the ante-historic. It works as one peels onions; and so it reaches the final question, has the onion in fact got a central nucleus at all or is it just all peel?

That, I suggest, is the way in which archeology can create what anthropology cannot escape the intellectual need of, namely, a sound critique of the comparative method in its reasoning. It was the fashion once to contrast the historical, as something merely particular and episodic, with the scientific, as something alone capable of formulation in general laws of what is now called "process." What these laws or "regularities" may be we all want to find out; and I believe that my suggested way of doing this, just because it is essentially historical, is essentially scientific. For logic, which is wisdom, should be justified of all her children.

It will follow that whereas the old style conception of prehistoric archeology regarded it as most fully anthropological where the cultures examined by it were most primitive—that is, in the Paleolithic, as one has it argued in a book like W. J. Sollas's *Ancient Hunters and their Modern Representatives*—we shall regard it as most fully anthropological at precisely its opposite end, the protohistoric and historic one. The making more fully anthropological its other end, if that is feasible, we shall take not as our a priori starting point, but as our goal, or ultimate objective.

What we should do, therefore, is to divide up our Old World research program by historically or protohistorically determined regions, like those in Europe carrying Greek or Italic or Illyric or Slavic or Teutonic or Celtic culture in historic or protohistoric times, and institute a policy of regional research to work through their prehistory backwards. One would then be doing far more than finding out about the Greeks or Celts; one would be contributing directly to the progress of the whole science or study of mankind.

Archeological method must not merely be technically excellent; it must express good archeological theory. Good archeological theory demands a conjunction of methods, conjoined on a rational basis of good logic. History and Science have not to be segregated, but identified together. And that should be archeology's service to anthropology as a whole.

31 Radiocarbon Dating

Willard F. Libby

IN EARLIER SELECTIONS (NOS. 7 AND 8) WE RAPIDLY SURVEYED THE FIELD OF *dating, tending to emphasize the techniques which inform human paleontology. Archaeology, of course, has equal interest in accurate dating. Until fairly recent years, however, the main technique was dependent on stratigraphy, the association of cultural elements with particular layers of earth that could be dated, usually in a relative sense. This means that most archaeological horizons were said to be older than this or younger than that, but in the absence of some fortuitous indicator of an historical kind it was usually impossible to give a reasonably firm absolute date.*

One of the most exciting of the modern absolute dating techniques is that which depends on C_{14}, the radioactive isotope of carbon which is as ubiquitous as life. Unfortunately, the C_{14} method is not infallible nor can it be employed on all archaeological materials from every site. Its use has not displaced traditional methods of dating. Also, as indicated in the Smiley article (No. 7), newer methods have been developed so that archaeologists already have a toolkit of possible dating alternatives from which the most appropriate may be selected an any particular site.

In the first edition of these Readings the editor pointed out that the effective range of the C_{14} technique was about 50,000 years. Coming from a culture that stresses technological optimism, the editor speculated that "figures twice this in magnitude would soon be offered." That

SOURCE: *Endeavour*, Vol. 13 (1954), pp. 5–16. Reprinted by permission of the author and publisher.

The author (b. 1908) is Professor of Chemistry and Director of the Institute of Geophysics and Planetary Physics, University of California at Los Angeles. He was a Commissioner of the United States Atomic Energy Commission, 1954–59 and 1960–62. A pioneer in the field of nuclear dating, he is the author of, among many other things, *Radiocarbon Dating* (1952, 1955).

450

optimism seems now to have been unjustified; the effective span has not increased, and the difficulties of pushing more deeply into time by this method are apparently very great.

Since the pioneering article that appears below was published, much additional work on the C_{14} method of dating has been done. Among the things that have required adjustment is the estimate of the half-life which Libby gave as 5568 ± 30 years; the figure presently used is 5730 years, which gives age estimates that run about 3 percent higher than Libby's.

The bombardment of the Earth by cosmic radiation results in the production of neutrons by the disintegration of nuclei of the air atoms. If Geiger counters are sent aloft in balloons one observes that the neutron intensity rises to a maximum at some 50,000 ft. and then falls abruptly at higher altitudes, as though the neutrons were not present in the incident primary radiation but were produced by collisions of the primary portions and alpha-particles with the air. This supposition is reasonable since the neutron is known to be unstable, decaying with a half-life of about 13 minutes to form a proton, and could hardly live long enough to traverse the great distances of interstellar space, though it could just reach the Earth from the Sun. Careful measurements made with the balloon technique have revealed an average production rate of 2.4 neutrons/cm²/ sec over the Earth's surface, strong variations with latitude being averaged out. As the neutrons produced by cosmic rays never reach the Earth's surface, some absorptive process must occur in the air, and the question arises of what nuclear species neutrons will produce by reaction with air. In the laboratory, oxygen is observed to be almost completely inert to neutrons, but nitrogen, the principal constituent of air, to have a strong interaction (the nuclear cross-section for thermal-energy neutrons is $1:7 \times 10^{-24}$ cm²). This interaction is almost exclusively due to a single reaction:

$$n + N^{14} = H + C^{14}.$$

Various other possibilities exist. One of these is the production of radioactive hydrogen (tritium) at a small fraction of the radiocarbon yield, but the principal product of the cosmic ray bombardment of air, at least that involving neutrons as an intermediary, must be radiocarbon; we can conclude that some 2.4 radiocarbon atoms are produced each second for each square centimetre of the Earth's surface at the present time.

If this rate has obtained in times past, especially during the last several lifetimes of radiocarbon (5568+ 30 years half-life, or 8030 years average life), we can say with complete certainty that a sufficient store of radiocarbon must exist on the Earth for a steady-state balance to be assured; that is, there must be enough radiocarbon for exactly 2.4 radiocarbon atoms to disappear each second per square centimetre, to ensure that the rate of formation is just equal to the rate of disappearance. Therefore we can calculate with equal certainty that there should be some 80 tons of radiocarbon on the Earth. The rates of radioactive disintegrations are immutable, and under no conditions yet obtained in the laboratory have any appreciable alterations of these rates been observed. We therefore can expect with very considerable confidence that the rate at which radiocarbon reverts to N^{14} by beta-decay is independent of whether it is present in a living organism or in limestone rock or as carbon dioxide in the air.

Where should one expect to find this considerable quantity of radiocarbon, and why has it not long ago been observed? Returning to the mechanism of genesis, we observe that the carbon atoms are formed at an altitude of about 6 or 7 miles on the average. It seems reasonable to suppose that the carbon atoms will burn in the air soon after their birth, to form carbon dioxide, so we conclude that the cosmic rays introduce radioactive carbon dioxide into the air, and that this is probably mixed by the winds so that all the atmospheric carbon dioxide is contaminated at the rate of 2.4 atoms of C^{14} per second for each cm^2 of the Earth's surface. However, it is of course well known that atmospheric carbon dioxide is the main source of plant carbon, through photosynthesis. Therefore we conclude that all plant life must contain radiocarbon. It is obvious also that since animal life lives on plant life it too must contain radiocarbon, and in addition the carbonate and bicarbonate and other inorganic carbonaceous materials dissolved in the sea, which are in interchange equilibrium with atmospheric carbon dioxide, must contain radiocarbon. The total diluting reservoir apparently contains about 8.3 g of elementary carbon per cm^2 of the Earth's surface. The bulk of it is the dissolved inorganic material in the sea, which amounts to 7.25 g, and the remainder is 0.12 g of atmospheric carbon dioxide and some 0.9 g of living matter all over the Earth, together with dissolved but dead organic matter in the sea-water. Since the bulk of the reservoir is inorganic matter in the sea, which is particularly easy to determine accurately, we are entitled to assume that the total figure, 8.3, is probably accurate to about 10 per cent, even though the estimation of the total amount of living matter on the Earth is a task of great difficulty. If it be correct that there are 8.3 g of carbon involved or being mixed with the atmospheric carbon dioxide on a time-scale of the order of the 8000-year average life of radiocarbon, we can immediately calculate the specific activity of living matter to be 2.4 divided by 8.3 disintegrations per second (16.1 per minute) per gram of carbon contained. The experimentally observed value is 2.12 divided by 8.3 disintegrations per second per gram, or 15.3 per minute.

This satisfactory agreement leads us to believe that the postulate of the constancy of the cosmic radiation in the last 20,000 years or so, and the implied but not specifically stated postulate that the volume of the reservoir has not changed, are probably both correct. It would seem extremely unlikely that the cosmic ray intensity should be causally related to the volume of the sea, for two less cognate physical quantities could hardly be imagined. Therefore we may take it that, since our determination depends on the ratio, the agreement between the calculated and observed specific activity must mean that both the cosmic rays and the volume of the sea have been relatively constant for the last 10,000 or 20,000 years.

Since the cosmic ray neutron intensity varies considerably with latitude one might expect living matter at the equator to be less radioactive than that in the northern and southern regions, the cosmic ray neutron intensity at 50–60° north geomagnetic latitude being some four times that at the equator. On second thought, however, one realizes that this is not likely to be so, for average radiocarbon atoms live 8000 years and therefore have this great length of time to be evenly distributed by winds and ocean currents. Direct tests have shown that this prediction is correct, and that all over the Earth's surface all forms of living matter possess the same radiocarbon activity per gram of contained carbon to within the error of measurement.

Radiocarbon dating is based on the fact that at the time of death the assimilation of radiocarbon ceases. The radiocarbon present in the body at the time of death then proceeds to disappear at its immutable rate. Therefore, we expect that a 5568-year-old mummy or piece of tree or cloth or flesh will show one-half the specific radioactivity observed in living organic matter at the present day. The radiocarbon content of dead matter accordingly reveals the age of the specimen, the age being taken as time elapsed since death rather than, as in normal usage, time elapsed since birth. The error of measurement is determined by the accuracy with which the specific radioactivity can be measured. Direct comparison with organic matter of known age back to 5000 years, the oldest material of known age available, appears to confirm these postulates and deductions. Utilization of the method in the great periods of prehistory has resulted in a series of dates which display some element of consistency and give reason for belief in the validity of the dating technique.

Methods of Measurement

The radiocarbon content of living matter is so low that its measurement is difficult. The procedures used in the author's laboratory consist in the conversion of the sample to pure carbon and the measurement of the radioactivity of the latter. Pure carbon is used, since any diluent atoms will reduce the measurable effect by absorbing the very soft radiocarbon radiation. The measurement of the pure carbon is accomplished by a Geiger counter in which the sample of carbon lines the cylindrical wall.

This places the sample in a most advantageous position, where the radiations have a high probability of being recorded. The actual probability attained with a 400 cm^2 area of carbon sample weighing 8 g in all is 5.46 per cent. Since, on the average, we find 15.3 disintegrations per minute per gram of carbon in modern organic matter, we can expect $8 \times 15.3 \times 0.0546$, or 6.7, counts per minute for modern material in our special Geiger counter.

A counter of the size used normally has a background of five or six hundred counts per minute, this background being due to laboratory contamination by naturally radioactive materials and to cosmic radiation. It is obviously necessary, therefore, that the background be reduced to a very small fraction of its normal value if we are to hope to measure the radiocarbon content of even modern organic matter. Since the background is due to two different types of radiation, namely, the cosmic rays and the natural radioactivities, we use two types of shielding. For the natural radioactivities a shield of several inches of iron is employed; this will reduce the unshielded background from 600 to 100 counts per minute. This residue of 100 counts per minute is very little reduced by the further addition of iron. As much as 20 ft seems to reduce it by only 20 or 30 per cent. It is clear, therefore, that the cosmic rays cannot be absorbed, and some device for eliminating their effect must be employed. A ring of protecting counters in close contact with one another is placed around the central Geiger counter in which the carbon sample is being measured. They are then wired so that each response in the protecting ring renders the central counter inoperative for a very small fraction of a second. Since the cosmic radiations will penetrate several inches of iron, there is little doubt about their ability to penetrate the fraction of an inch of brass or copper involved in the counter bundle, and any radiation passing through the central counter must necessarily pass through one of the shielding counters, unless it passes directly down the length of the counter. We have not thought it necessary to place curtains of shielding counters at the ends. With this device the background is reduced to 5 counts per minute. One might worry about the loss of efficiency due to the fact that the central counter is turned off by the action of the protecting counters operating in anti-coincidence. The aggregate count-rate of the shielded counters when located inside the 8-in iron shield is only 900 counts per minute, and since each impulse turns off the central counter for only 1 millisecond at most one is certain that not more than one second is lost out of each minute. It is true in principle, however, that this type of shielding-arrangement has limitations if the size of the assembly is increased greatly. The advantage of putting the shielding counters within the iron shield will also be clear. It is well to note that the radiations from the radiocarbon itself will not be cancelled by the shielding counters, for they are not sufficiently penetrating to pass through the walls of the central Geiger counter. An ordinary sheet of parchment paper stops the radiocarbon radiation practically completely.

With material such as wood or peat, conversion of the samples to elementary carbon is accomplished by combustion to carbon dioxide. With inorganic material such as calcium carbonate, acidification is sufficient to liberate carbon dioxide, which is thus produced for all types of samples. The carbon dioxide needs purification from radon, since small amounts of uranium and radium can be expected in most materials, and both the combustion and the acidification operations will carry the radon along with the carbon dioxide. The purification is accomplished by precipitating calcium carbonate and washing and drying it. The purified calcium carbonate is then acidified with hydrochloric acid and carbon dioxide is produced again. This carbon dioxide is dried and stored in bulbs. Reduction to elementary carbon is accomplished by reaction with pure magnesium metal. Magnesium turnings are placed in an ordinary iron tube about 3 ft long and 1 inch in diameter, connected to the vacuum line. The air is removed, some of the carbon dioxide is introduced, and the tube is heated to the melting-point of metallic magnesium, 651° C. At this point the reduction begins vigorously, and care must be exercised to prevent holes from being burned in the iron tube. With reasonable care the fire can be kept going until the storage bulbs are exhausted. Normally, about 1 gram-atom of carbon is involved, i.e. some 22.4 litres of carbon dioxide.

After the reduction is complete, the solid products are removed from the iron tube and extracted with hydrochloric acid, to remove the excess of metallic magnesium and the magnesium oxide produced in the reaction. This extraction takes 24 to 48 hours and produces a carbon black of about 90 per cent. purity, the remaining materials being magnesium oxide—which for some obscure reason is difficult to remove completely by hydrochloric acid extraction—and about 5 per cent. non-carbonaceous but volatile matter which may be absorbed water, or chemisorbed oxygen, or both. The samples are analysed for carbon, and appropriate correction of the observed count-rates is made.

World-wide Distribution of Radiocarbon

E. C. Anderson studied the present distribution of radiocarbon throughout the world. As expected, the strong variation in production-rate with latitude was found to be completely masked by the long life-time of radiocarbon and the consequent opportunity for world-wide mixing. The data given in table 1 show no significant variation from the mean for the woods assayed from widely scattered points on the Earth's surface. In examining this table it is well to remember that, as previously mentioned, the cosmic ray intensity and, therefore, the radio-carbon production-rate are about one-fourth as great at the equator as at the latitude of 50 or 60° geomagnetic north—and, presumably, south also. The further point should be recalled that, the average life of radiocarbon being 8000 years, the radiocarbon atoms now present in living organic matter and in the dissolved carbonaceous material in the sea have been on

ACTIVITY OF TERRESTRIAL BIOSPHERE SAMPLES

Source	Geomagnetic latitude	Absolute specific activity (disintegrations per minute per gram)
White spruce, Yukon	60° N	14.84 ± 0.30
Norwegian spruce, Sweden	55° N	15.37 ± 0.54
Elm wood, Chicago	53° N	14.72 ± 0.54
Fraximus excelsior, Switzerland	49° N	15.16 ± 0.30
Honeysuckle leaves, Oak Ridge, Tennessee	47° N	14.60 ± 0.30
Pine twigs and needles (12,000 ft), Mount Wheeler, New Mexico	44° N	15.82 ± 0.47
North African briar	40° N	14.47 ± 0.44
Oak, Sherafut, Palestine	34° N	15.19 ± 0.40
Unidentified wood, Teheran	28° N	15.57 ± 0.34
Fraxinus mandshurica, Japan	26° N	14.84 ± 0.30
Unidentified wood, Panama	20° N	15.94 ± 0.51
Chlorophora excelsa, Liberia	11° N	15.08 ± 0.34
Sterculia excelsa, Copacabana, Bolivia (9000 ft)	1° N	15.47 ± 0.50
Ironwood, Majuro, Marshall Islands	0°	14.53 ± 0.60
Unidentified wood, Ceylon	2° S	15.29 ± 0.67
Beech wood (*Northofagus*), Tierra del Fuego	45° S	15.37 ± 0.49
Eucalyptus, New South Wales, Australia	45° S	16.31 ± 0.43
Seal oil from seal meat from Antarctic	65° S	15.69 ± 0.30
Average		15.3 ± 0.1 *

* Error of calibration of counter raises error on absolute assay to 0.5.

the Earth for 8000 years on the average, and have therefore had abundant opportunity to circulate throughout the cycle of life and to be moved about in the ocean currents and in the winds of the atmosphere.

The absolute radiocarbon content thus appears to be in reasonably good agreement with the present rate of production of radiocarbon, if we assume that the ocean is mixed with radiocarbon essentially to its full depth. The amount of carbon involved in living forms on land is negligible relative to the inorganic carbon in the sea. In other words the 2.4 atoms being produced per second per cm^2 on the average at the present time, when divided by the 8.3 g of carbon in the ocean and in the life cycle, agree to within 10 per cent. with the observed radiocarbon content at the present time. This plainly indicates that in the course of some 8000 years uniform mixing of the waters of the sea occurs, even at great depths—a point of much interest to oceanographers. It indicates further that the present cosmic ray intensity is not far different from that which obtained 8000 years ago. This latter point is of course vital to the radiocarbon dating method, in that we must assume that the radiocarbon content of living matter at the present time has been its content at all times, and that a piece of wood measured now has the same radiocarbon content as a comparable piece would have had in Egypt 5000 years ago. As we shall see later, there is further confirmatory evidence of this in the apparent agreement found among the radiocarbon contents of carbonaceous samples of historically known age.

Radiocarbon Dating

The possible utilization of natural radiocarbon for dating was one of the principal goals throughout the early stages of our research. These consisted in the discovery of natural radiocarbon in Baltimore sewage methane with A. V. Grosse and his collaborators, the development of the measurement techniques, and a world-wide assay. We then approached the interesting and crucial stage of testing the dating method with considerable care. J. Arnold joined the group as principal collaborator in this phase of the research. The American Anthropological Association and the Geological Society of American appointed a Committee on Carbon-14, consisting of F. Johnson (chairman), D. Collier, F. Rainey, and R. F. Flint, to advise on the selection of samples for measurement and, most important, to organize a comprehensive test of the method. The Wenner-Gren Foundation for Anthropological Research, under its director P. Fejos, gave generous financial support to the research. Part of the development of the low-level counting technique was conducted under contract with the United States Air Force.

The advisory committee decided that it would be possible to test the method against samples of known age back to about 5000 years. This was done, and the results are shown in figure 1. The curve drawn is the exponential decay curve fixed by the laboratory determination of the half-life and the world-wide assay of modern organic matter for radiocarbon (table I). The errors indicated are standard errors as determined solely by the counting-statistics. That is, they are essentially governed by the square root of the total number of counts measured. Experience has indicated that this is the principal source of random error in the measurement, in that repeated measurements on a given sample have shown scatter not inconsistent with this single measure.

It is clear that with one or two exceptions the agreement is satisfactory. These exceptions may be acceptable statistically and we need not

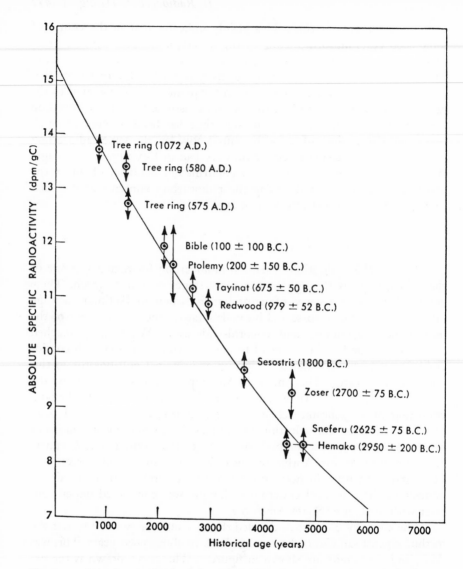

Figure 1   Samples of Known Age. The solid curve is calculated from the assay for modern wood and the laboratory measurement of the half-life of radiocarbon. The individual points are the specific radioactivities of various pieces of organic matter, principally wood, of known age. The errors indicated are the standard deviations (which ensure 2 out of 3 chances), and are calculated solely on the basis of the number of counts taken; they do not include any other errors, such as that arising from contamination.

dwell on them in this short article. One of the most interesting of the 'knowns' is the redwood sample. This giant tree apparently has heartwood still containing the carbon originally deposited there when the wood was formed. This result—very acceptable to most botanists, we understand—seems to be somewhat astonishing chemically. The fine filaments which constitute the cell walls, though made of cellulose molecules which of course are extremely inert, have been bathed for thousands of years with enzymatically active sap.

The radiocarbon deposited at the beginning of history still has more than half the modern assay, so it was obviously necessary to consider how the great periods of prehistory could be used to check the method, and *vice versa*. The committee attacked this problem by setting up a network of projects so designed as to afford the maximum number of internal cross-checks. They arbitrarily excluded certain areas of the world and periods of history in order the more to concentrate, temporally and geographically, on the prehistoric problems being investigated. They then assembled a team of collaborators in geology and archaeology, who proceeded to furnish samples for the study. The results now number nearly 400, including those obtained at other laboratories, though the committee has been advisory to our group alone.

It is somewhat difficult to judge the significance of this group of dates. It seems that one of the principal conclusions is that the ice last covered both North America and Europe some 11,000 years ago. We see this in the Wisconsin Two Creeks Forest results and in the European dates for Germany, and for Ireland, and for England. It would seem that there is some evidence that the northern regions of Europe and of North America were covered simultaneously.

We were afraid that we should find occupation sites older than the last ice age, and had agreed that this would constitute sufficiently conclusive evidence to discredit the whole method; we felt that glaciers sweep very clean and that there should be no evidence of such sites left. So in England, which was completely glaciated, there should be no such evidence older than the time of the last ice sheet. One notes that the Lascaux cave (Dordogne), apparently was occupied, and that its paintings were executed, some 5000 years before the last ice sheet. Other samples not listed have revealed the existence of man around the Mediterranean basin long before the last ice sheet. Such evidence has not appeared in the Americas. This may of course be a fortuitous circumstance, but it does seem significant that abundant evidence of the 10,000-year threshold appears.

The ultimate question of the validity of the absolute dates given by the radiocarbon method is not yet completely answered. The evidence seems to be somewhat favourable, but only the passage of time, with its further accumulation of dates and its further digestion of the results obtained, can furnish us with a final answer.

32 Some New Aspects of Archeological Technology

Froelich Rainey and Elizabeth K. Ralph

IF THE C_{14} METHOD CANNOT BE PUSHED BEYOND 50,000 YEARS, AND IF OTHER *standard methods also have their limitations or drawbacks, hope need not yet be given up. Archaeologists, paleontologists and colleagues in other sciences are generating ideas for new methods of dating at a really remarkable rate. So fast, as a matter of fact, that this volume will probably be considerably behind by the time copies first appear. We are fortunate, therefore, that just before the table of contents was closed, a neat discus-*

SOURCE: "Archeology and its New Technology," *Science*, Vol. 153 (Sept. 23, 1966), pp. 1481–1491. Copyright 1966 by the American Association for the Advancement of Science. Reprinted by permission of the authors and the publisher.

Froelich Rainey (b. 1907) is Professor of Anthropology and Director of the Applied Science Center for Archaeology, University Museum, at the University of Pennsylvania. His major interests are in Arctic archaeology and ethnology. Among his many publications are *Archaeology in Central Alaska* (1939); *The Whale Hunters of Tigara* (1947); and, with Helge Larsen, *Ipiutak and the Arctic Whale Hunting Culture* (1948).

Elizabeth K. Ralph (b. 1921) is an Associate in the Department of Physics and the Associate Director of the Applied Science Center for Archaeology, University Museum, at the University of Pennsylvania. Her association with the museum began with the construction and operation of its radiocarbon laboratory 15 years ago; she is now experimenting with thermoluminescence dating and new instruments for archaeological prospecting.

sion of several of the newest techniques appeared in Science. The authors of the article and the editors of the journal were kind enough to permit the reprinting here of the portions of that discussion that relate to some of the more novel methods of dating, and also a brief word about the new archaeological horizons beneath the seas.

Thermoluminescence Dating

The radiocarbon method for the absolute dating of ancient organic materials has profoundly altered our knowledge of man's past. We now know, for example, that the end of the Ice Age was closer to 10,000 than 20,000 years ago; that food crops were grown in Mexico by 5000 to 6000 B.C., almost as early in the Americas as in the Near East; and that men were building stone-walled towns in Palestine by 7000 B.C. But there has always been one serious drawback to archeological radiocarbon dating— the matter of association of the sample with the event for which a date is wanted. In every case, the archeologist must assess the relationship between the age of the organic material (charcoal, wood, burned bone, shell, and so forth) presumably associated with the artifact, and the artifact itself. Moreover, there is often too little organic material of suitable association to provide an adequate series of samples for reliable radiocarbon dating. There is thus every possibility that many of the published archeological dates may be, to some degree, erroneous.

The new thermoluminescence method of dating pottery avoids these hazards, for it dates the artifact itself rather than presumably associated materials which may or may not be strictly contemporaneous. Moreover, in those sites where pottery is found, it usually appears in abundance, so that samples for analysis are plentiful. Archeological chronologies for human events since Neolithic times are often based on sequences of distinctive pottery types, and many of the dates for these sequences are still more relative than absolute. The thermoluminescence method should provide a means of fixing in time those pottery types which have become horizon-markers of post-Mesolithic prehistory.

Workers in the general field of thermoluminescence studies have made measurements for a variety of purposes, such as those fundamental physical studies by Halperin *et al.*, studies of meteorites by Houtermans *et al.* and age estimation of sediments by Zeller *et al.* But the suggestion that thermoluminescence might provide a means of dating pottery was first published by Daniels *et al.;* and the use of the technique for archeological dating was investigated further by Kennedy and Knopff from 1958 to 1960.

Thermoluminescence in pottery is due to the fact that radiations from traces of radioactive elements within the pottery bombard the other constituents of the clays and raise the electrons to metastable levels.

When the pottery is heated, as in firing, each electron falls back into its stable position, emitting a photon of light. When, much later, the pottery is reheated, the amount of thermoluminescence observed is representative of the accumulated radiation damage, and hence of the time that has elapsed since the original firing of the pottery. For a relatively short time after an object has been heated to a temperature of perhaps 400° to 500°C and its electrons have emitted their thermoluminescence, no further light may be obtained by reheating; consequently, recently fired ceramics or freshly cooled lava, which have all electrons in stable sites, should show no thermoluminescence.

On the assumption that the major portion of this damage is caused by alpha bombardment from traces of uranium and thorium, or is proportional to it, we have constructed low-background zinc sulfide screens and associated components for detection of this low-level alpha bombardment. The samples are counted in "infinitely" thick layers, with the result that only comparative values are obtained. We have found, thus far, that measurement of the alpha component is sufficient, since correction factors for potassium-40 (the other most prevalent radioactive isotope in pottery), obtained from measurements of potassium contents, did not improve the age correspondence.

Our numerous preliminary experiments on the detection of photons emitted upon heating indicated that only very rapid heating and necessarily thin layers of powdered potsherds would permit detection of maximum light output. Rapid heating (now 16°C per second) is essential, or the high sensitivity required to detect the small amount of visible thermoluminescence also permits the detector to pick up the onset of heat radiation from neighboring heated materials. This rapid heating unfortunately prevents discrimination of separate peaks at low, medium, and high temperatures. Sample heating is carried out in a nitrogen atmosphere to prevent possible combustion of organic particles and potential spurious changes in intensity due to the presence of oxygen. The problem, therefore, is quite different from that of detection of thermoluminescence from crystals such as alkali halides, for which experiments are normally carried out between room and liquid-oxygen temperatures.

Very thin uniform layers of pottery are obtained by first grinding the sherds in a ball mill to less than 200 mesh. This powder is then mixed with silicone oil and applied to aluminum foil by means of a silk screen in a "spot" 1.2 centimeters in diameter, so that a thin, uniform, and stable coating of pottery is produced on the foil.

Variations in the susceptibilities of clays to radiation damage demand that some correction factor be applied. To measure the susceptibility of a clay to this damage, a source with much greater intensity than the natural bombardment is used in order to duplicate in a short time the original radiation damage. We have found a moderate x-ray exposure (30 kilovolts, 12.7 megamps, 1 minute) to be sufficient for this bombardment. Even though samples taken from a single piece of pottery have been ground and mixed thoroughly, we have found large variations among them in their susceptibilities. Thus the correction factor obtained through artificial bombardment must be applied to samples from the same piece that is measured for natural thermoluminescence. Fortunately, our silicone mounting oil permits this. Thus when each sample is heated, its natural thermoluminescence measured, and the sample bombarded with x-rays and then reheated, application of the area of the glow curve as a correction factor provides some improvement in the consistency of results.

The glow curves induced by x-ray bombardment exhibit a low-temperature peak, or peaks, which are unstable and decay within 1 to 2 weeks. These unstable low peaks have already disappeared from the natural glow curves as a result of the thermal environment and possible decay. Therefore, after artificial bombardment one must wait for these low peaks to decay in order to obtain a reliable correction factor.

A series of sherds from the Solduz Valley in Iran from 5500 to 900 B.C. (dated through associated charcoal samples in our Radiocarbon Laboratory) have been analyzed, as have samples from the Sybaris region of Italy, and from Pecos pueblo in the southwestern United States (see Fig. 1). The uncertainty of all measurements is still greater than desired, but it is much smaller for the later (300 B.C. and after) sherds from Italy and Pecos than for the earlier ones from Iran. Better results may be expected from pottery of better quality.

The thermoluminescence method is limited in application to the past 8000 or 9000 years (the period since the beginning of pottery manufacture) and, at the present time, the margin of error (at least ±300 years for the older samples) is still too great to satisfy many archeologists. But this is only one of several methods of dating now being developed and, as with all such methods, its accuracy should improve with our increasing development of the technique.

Underwater Archeology

Technology of the postwar years has opened a new world beneath the sea as well as in space, and most of us are only now realizing that the sea holds some of the more promising future discoveries in archeology. Perhaps we failed to see the usefulness of scuba diving equipment in serious archeological research because it was first utilized in underwater exploration as a sport. Today, thanks to the application of many new devices for underwater exploration by such trained archeologists as George Bass of the University Museum, there is a well-defined discipline of underwater acheology which began when archeologists were trained to dive with scuba equipment and to apply the systematic techniques of land archeology to the study of underwater remains. It is now expanding rapidly with the development of equipment that permits more efficient underwater surveys and more effective methods of excavation and recording.

Scuba equipment made possible the systematic excavation of a Bronze Age wreck discovered off Cape Gelydonia by Turkish sponge

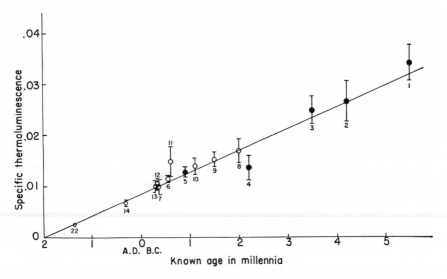

Figure 1 Specific thermoluminescence plotted against known ages for samples from Iran (Nos. 1 to 5 and 8 to 11), Italy (Nos. 6, 7, 12, 13, and 14), and the United States (No. 22). The solid dots represent averages of replicate runs of two or more contemporaneous samples; open circles, one sample only.

divers, the discovery of Maya remains in Lake Amatetlan in Guatemala, the study of many Roman wrecks in the Mediterranean, the exploration of the sunken city of Port Royal in Jamaica, the investigation of the sunken port at Corinth, and the excavation of a Villanovan village at the bottom of Lake Bolsena in Italy. The next step was the development, in investigations of wrecks off Bodrum on the Turkish coast, of stereophotogrammetric mapping, which introduced a new precision and efficiency in underwater work.

Free-swimming archeological exploration, even at shallow depths, is painfully slow. Scuba divers can work for only short periods each day at depths of 45 meters, and work below that depth is unsafe. And it is now clear that more discoveries will be made when better exploration equipment is provided. To that end, the University Museum commissioned the Electric Boat Division of General Dynamics Corporation to build a two-man submarine specifically for underwater archeological surveying. The operators work inside at surface pressures, thereby eliminating many of the physiological hazards of scuba diving. The submarine can cruise at 7.4 kilometers per hour for as much as 8 hours per day, and to depths of at least 90 meters. Viewing ports and outside lights have increased the range and speed of undersea search, and the attachment of the stereophotogrammetric mapping equipment to the submarine has made posssible the accurate mapping of sunken remains in a fraction of the time formerly required by scuba divers.

During the summer of 1965, Bass pioneered still another series of underwater exploration techniques off the coast of Turkey. A steel capsule known as the "Tow-Vane" was used to plane down to 83 meters for observation of the sea bottom. The operator inside the capsule worked at atmospheric pressure, breathing recirculated air to which oxygen was added, and maintained contact with the surface towing vessel by telephone. A closed-circuit televison camera was also towed along the sea bottom by the surface vessel. Natural light was sufficient at 83 meters, and in clouded water the camera could often "see" better than the observer in the capsule. An Elsec proton magnetometer, adapted for undersea use by E. T. Hall of the Oxford Laboratory, was towed along the sea bottom in search of deposits of metal and pottery.

All these instruments functioned as intended and could be used to search the sea bottom for archeological remains. Nevertheless, specific wrecks known to be on the bottom in that area were not found. And from this we reach the conclusions that the sea is large, the wrecks are small, and the scanning range of the instruments is still too limited for rapid and easy exploration. But this sort of search is still in its infancy, and the development of these techniques is proceeding at such a rapid rate as to inspire considerable confidence for the future.

Analytical Techniques

The discovery and development of new tools for the analysis and identification of archeological materials is proceeding in many laboratories throughout the world, and only the barest outline of the work such tools are performing for archeology will be given here. Neutron-activation analysis, based upon nuclear transmutation caused by bombardment in a nuclear reactor, may be used for widely varying analyses—on blood and soil, surveying the Mohole, analyzing the surface of the moon, or for the nondestructive analysis of ancient pottery and metals. The Brookhaven National Laboratory has used neutron-activation analysis to demonstrate, with pottery from Italy and from Central America, that a detailed analysis of elements contained in the clays makes it possible to determine the source of the materials and perhaps the region of manufacture. For example, the fine orange ware found at Piedras Negras in the lowlands of Guatemala has been proved to have been fabricated from deposits located in the highlands.

The Research Laboratory for Archaeology and the History of Art at Oxford has reported on a number of techniques currently under investigation, which, like the neutron-activation method, can be used for both qualitative and quantitative studies of archeological materials directed at tracing the origin of manufacture, trade routes, the understanding of ancient technology, and the detection of fakes. These techniques include x-ray fluorescence, electric-beam x-ray-scanning microanalysis, beta-ray back-scatter meters, and optical-emission spectrometry. The essential point, however, is that these are archeological tools recently derived, for the most part, from postwar atomic-nuclear development. And it is their large number and rapid rate of improvement which indicate the probable future impact upon archeological studies.

HOW OLD IS CULTURE? Whether it is two million years old or only half that, all but the last few thousand years of this period has been devoted exclusively to cultures of the "Old Stone" or Paleolithic Stage. The criteria of a paleolithic culture are two-fold. Most important is the absence of any domesticated source of food whether plant or animal; also important is the inventory of tools, predominantly of rock and fashioned by percussion flaking (early) and pressure flaking (late). Paleolithic cultures were of various types, differing by place and time. Varieties of paleolithic culture are known to have existed on every inhabited continent, though only Africa, Europe and Asia show positive evidence of Lower and Middle Paleolithic cultures. The first non-paleolithic cultures seem to have appeared in the Near East perhaps 12,000 years ago. The advent of domestication did not cause the instantaneous disappearance of all paleolithic cultures, for the spread or independent invention of domestication was slow and hampered by many factors. Some cultures which, by the criteria given above, may be classified as paleolithic persisted almost to the present day.

33 The Prehistoric Origins of African Culture

J. Desmond Clark

HAVING ALREADY SEEN THAT PROFOUND STEPS IN HUMAN EVOLUTION SEEM *to have centered in Africa (nos. 9–14) at the crucial period when our own general type of primate was first appearing, it comes as no surprise to learn that the same area displays a similar precocity with regard to the evidences of culture. The clues to the early evolution of culture are sometimes quite difficult to read, crude tools and weapons with which our ancient ancestors not only made their daily way but unwittingly carved an evolutionary path to dominance among the mammals.*

In his fine summary of the high points of our present knowledge of the early evolution of culture in Africa, Professor Clark skirts a number of exceptionally interesting problems. There is, for example, the lurking question of the association of physical type and culture. There is also the cryptic addendum on the significance of H. habilis.

It is appropriate to call the reader's attention to the fact that the relatively confident grasp of the long period of cultural evolution displayed in this article is itself a most recent matter. Although Clark predicts it will be a decade before we have a really firm chronology, the advance represented by his paper is tangible evidence of the strides which

SOURCE: *Journal of African History,* Vol. 5,2 (1964), pp. 161–182. Reprinted with the permission of the author and publisher.

The author (b. 1916) is Professor of Anthropology at the University of California at Berkeley. He has published widely on the prehistory of Africa, including *The Prehistoric Culture of the Horn of Africa* (1954) and *The Prehistory of Southern Africa* (1959).

are taking place. Small wonder that fields which were once considered musty and dull are now sources of intellectual excitement.

Remarkable and exciting discoveries that have been made in Africa during the last five years suggest that it was here that tool-making first appeared in the geological record, and that it was then carried to other continents by hominid forms, the discovery of which has necessitated completely new thinking about the biological development of Man. In the same way the discovery, undreamed of twenty years ago, of urban centres in the Near East, dating to as early as the eighth millennium B.C., is providing unique details of life in early Neolithic times and is causing prehistorians to look back ever further into the past, almost to the close of the last glacial, for the first signs of the domestication of plants and animals and of settled village life.

Such discoveries are fundamental to the study of the origins and growth of social and economic life, and increasing use is being made of the archaeological record by the cultural anthropologist and ethno-historian, although there is still in places a lingering tendency to consider that prehistory has nothing to offer the student of present-day culture. The success of collaboration between anthropologists, linguists, historians and archaeologists has, however, already been amply demonstrated in several African countries—for example in Uganda and Northern and Southern Rhodesia. Indeed, the archaeologist is now an indispensable part of any co-operative project to reconstruct the history of a pre-literate population.

While, therefore, it is now obvious that archaeology can provide some of the best source material for the reconstruction of cultural antecedents, population movements, and even of the origins of some social and religious practices on a factual basis, it is the new ways in which the archaeologist is using his data that render the results and potential so valuable. Today the archaeologist relies heavily on the help of his colleagues in many disciplines, particularly on those in the natural sciences. This, together with the precision resulting from improved field techniques and more meticulous observation and analysis, is providing an increasing quantity of solid scientific data and permitting radical reassessment in their interpretation. The absolute dating techniques now available have revolutionized chronologies, just as the more accurate knowledge of past environments has imparted new and vital significance to cultural remains, and permitted a deeper appreciation of the importance of the inseparable relationship there has always been between environment, culture and biological adaptation.

In addition to the close collaboration between palaeo-ecologist, physical anthropologist and prehistorian, the cultural anthropologist and ethnographer are drawn upon for help in the interpretation of the cultural

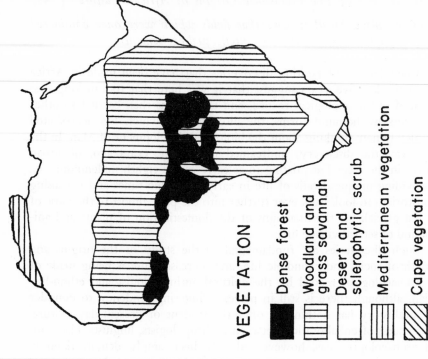

VEGETATION

- ■ Dense forest
- ▥ Woodland and grass savannah
- ☐ Desert and sclerophytic scrub
- ▤ Mediterranean vegetation
- ▨ Cape vegetation

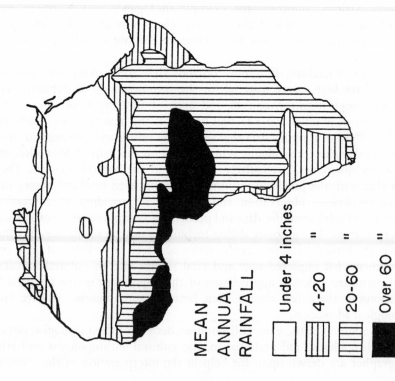

MEAN ANNUAL RAINFALL

- ☐ Under 4 inches
- ▥ 4–20 "
- ▤ 20–60 "
- ■ Over 60 "

Figure 1 Rainfall and vegetation.

evidence. Thus, on the one hand, primate behaviour studies are important as a basis for the reconstruction of life in Australopithecine times; on the other hand, ecological studies of present-day Bantu agriculturalists are a vital necessity for the interpretation of early Iron Age cultures in southern Africa, and it is necessary to study the whole continuous process of culture change in prehistoric times on a continental scale if we are to try to understand it at the regional level.

The earliest evidence of culture in the world occurs at the unique site at the Olduvai Gorge, the discovery of which is due to Dr and Mrs L. S. B. Leakey (as also is so much of our knowledge of the earliest history of man the tool-maker). Olduvai Gorge is situated in northern Tanganyika in the Eastern Rift, and cuts through some 300 feet of old lake sediments of Lower and Middle Pleistocene age. These beds are dated relatively in respect of the fossil faunas and cultural remains they contain, and absolutely by the potassium/argon method. Bed I is between 1½ and 2 million years old, and indisputable evidence of cultural activity has been found from top to bottom within it. The tool-makers camped round the edge of shallow open water near small lakes, and formed temporary camps on the mud flats exposed by seasonal fluctuations of the water level of the kind that can be seen at many of the Rift Valley lakes today. The surfaces on which the artifacts occur appear to have been covered fairly rapidly by falls of volcanic tuffs from the adjacent Ngorongoro crater. The skill and patience with which these occupation areas have been uncovered have permitted the making of floor plans that show beyond any question the artificial nature of the accumulations. On these floors stones and bones are concentrated in quantity, and many of them have been artificially broken. Many stones occur which, though unworked, are not natural in the area and can only have been carried in, while many others have been intentionally flaked, and bashing stones, choppers, cores, flakes and small chunks, some utilized and occasionally retouched, occur inextricably mixed with the smashed bones of a number of different species of animal. Long bones and other bones have been broken to extract the marrow, and some of them show unmistakable marks of having been smashed with a rounded blunt object. The most famous of these floors is that in the upper part of Bed I, on which were lying the remains of the Australopithecine *Zinjanthropus boisei.* Here the Leakeys found a concentration of highly comminuted bone some 15 feet in diameter, with larger bones on the periphery and a mass of worked stone in and among the bone. The remains represented several different antelopes, pig, tortoise, catfish, a snake, and several other small animals. A high proportion of the pig and antelope remains are from immature creatures. The most characteristic forms of tool are a chopper flaked from two directions to form an irregular and usually wide-angled cutting or chopping edge, made on a lava pebble or chunk of quartz, and a sharp flake for cutting.

The other floors are similar, but of especial interest is one only a foot or so above the lava on which the beds rest. Here the stone tools are, on an average, a good deal smaller, but they are associated with various accumulations of natural stones. It is very difficult to see how these could have got to their present position, resting on the clay, except by having been carried there. There is certainly one, and perhaps two, concentrations in rough semicircles, and several stones rest one upon the other as if they had been purposely piled up.

These occupation floors represent the home bases—the living quarters—of early tool-making hominids who were in part carnivorous, obtaining their meat by hunting and scavenging. It is probable, however, on the analogy of modern hunter-gatherers, that quite 75 per cent of their food was vegetable, and, in this connexion, the pebble chopper may have been developed as a tool for sharpening sticks for digging.

Recent geological assessment of the climatic conditions under which Bed I was formed shows that the environment must have been very like that of the Serengeti Plains today, that is to say, semi-arid grass and parkland, with shallow pans and lakes, and forest relicts on the slopes of the adjacent volcanic masses. The relatively sparse scatter of occupation debris suggests that Lower Pleistocene hominids rarely stayed long in one place.

Artifacts of comparable age and form have been found at a few other sites, notably at Ain Hanech in Algeria, at Casablanca in Morocco, in the Albertine Rift, and at Kanam on the Kavirondo Gulf of Lake Victoria (which yielded also an enigmatic hominid jaw fragment), as well as in residual gravels in river and marine high terraces. It would seem that if it is indeed in the Far African tectonic region that tool-making first developed, it was not very long before such a fundamental advance in technology spread widely throughout and beyond the continent (fig. 2).

No hominid more advanced than the Australopithecines is known from any of these Lower Pleistocene sediments. They are well represented by over 300 fossil remains. Two forms are known—a slenderer type *(Australopithecus africanus)*, and a more heavily built type *(A. robustus*, known also as *Paranthropus)*. Their membership of the family of the Hominidae is unquestionable on the evidence of their brains, teeth and jaw patterns, and because of their bipedalism and their possession of hands adapted to tool-using. Lightly built and only some 4 feet 6 inches tall, they were nevertheless able to run fast and had arms adapted to throwing. In the small size of the brain and the massiveness of the face, however, they resembled the apes, with the result that they are sometimes known as the 'Man-Apes'. Napier's study of the hand from the pre-Zinjanthropus horizon at FLK NNI in Bed I at Olduvai shows that though

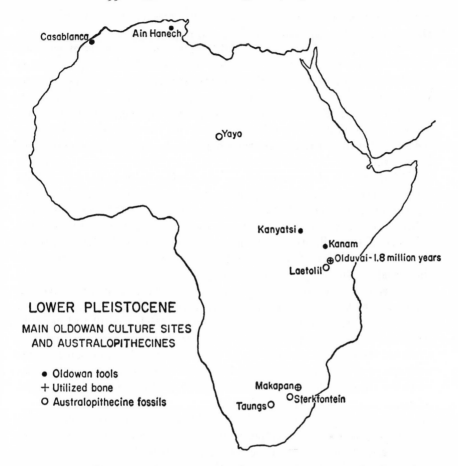

Casablanca

Ain Hanech

OYayo

Kanyatsi ●

●Kanam

⊕Olduvai-1.8 million years

Laetolil O

LOWER PLEISTOCENE

MAIN OLDOWAN CULTURE SITES
AND AUSTRALOPITHECINES

● Oldowan tools
+ Utilized bone
O Australopithecine fossils

Makapan⊕

O Sterkfontein

Taungs O

Figure 2 Distribution of Lower Pleistocene Culture and Australopithecines.

primitive, it is intermediate between the hands of apes and of man, and would have been capable of clumsy tool-making.

The artifacts in the Bed I living-sites show that there can be little doubt that the East African Australopithecines were working stone for use as tools. Indeed, their Pliocene ancestors had been using tools for millions of years. The hand is the best proof of this, though another is the extreme simplicity of the technique involved in making the tools, and we must expect that at the end of the Lower Pleistocene certainly more than one form of hominid was living that was capable of making—and did make—tools.

There is no indication that the Australopithecine tool-makers lived in large groups. The small areas of the living-places rather suggest that there were unlikely to have been more than a dozen or so individuals in the band. While they seem to have been incapable of killing large animals, the concentrations of bones in the Transvaal caves (if they are indeed, as Dart claims, the food debris of the Australopithecines) would argue that they were, none the less, resourceful hunters and scavengers of medium- and small-sized animals. No doubt, also, they made capital of the necessity for the game to seek the only available surface water during the dry season, which was in the deep limestone caves where they were ambushed and slaughtered. For this some co-operation between members of the group must have been essential and, since the young were dependent on the adults for longer than were the young of apes, regular sharing of food is also implicit.

Many find it difficult to accept the wholesale manufacture of bone tools claimed for the Australopithecines by Dart in his 'Osteodontokeratic Culture', and consider that most of this material represents food debris. These caves have, nevertheless, provided fairly good, though rare, evidence of the utilization of bone, as has also one of the Olduvai floors. The most impressive of these bone tools are fragments of long bones that show shallow, highly polished groovings.

Why did stone tool-making first begin in the savannah? The answer is believed to lie in economic and social necessity. The African savannah is an environment with a long dry season in which a small and very defenceless hominid, forced to protect its hunting territory and ill-equipped biologically for digging or meat-eating, had to find some way to supplement the sources of vegetable foods that would dwindle under times of climatic deterioration. It is believed that this was one of the primary reasons why these early hominids turned to meat-eating, just as baboons sometimes do today. The use of some kind of sharp cutting tool to open the skin of an antelope, or of a bashing tool to break open long bones or the shell of a tortoise, or of a sharp tool to point a stick for digging, would have meant a regular and substantial increase in the quantity and variety of food available. The hominids would also have found these tools useful for defence.

Australopithecines have been found in South and East Africa, and now in Chad, as well as in the Far East, so that it is reasonable to suppose that tool-making, this most fundamental of human inventions, spread with remarkable rapidity.

Africa abounds with pebble tools, but the earlier claim that most of these are of Lower Pleistocene age remains as yet largely unsubstantiated, and it is probable that many of these industries belong to the earlier Middle, rather than to the Lower Pleistocene. For knowledge of the cultural pattern of these times we again rely most heavily on Olduvai, for this site preserves a unique evolutionary sequence of developing stages up to the earlier part of the Upper Pleistocene. But there are now several other sites, equally well dated, though without such a long stratigraphy (fig. 3). By the beginning of the second glaciation in the northern hemi-

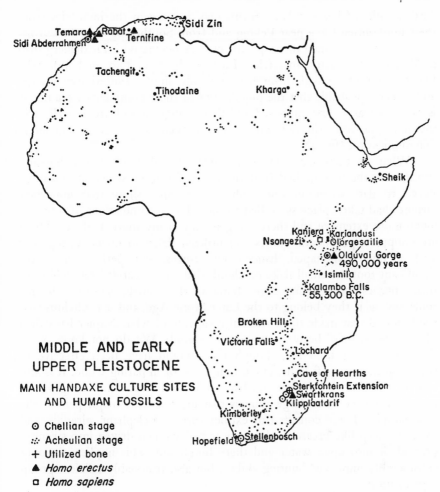

Temara▲▲Rabat•▲
Sidi Abderrahme⊙▲   Ternifine
                    •Sidi Zin

Tachengit•:

•Tihodaine   Kharga•

                              •:•Sheik

                    Kanjera :Kariandusi
         Nsongezi•· □ •Olorgesailie
                    ⊙▲Olduvai Gorge
                      490,000 years
                    •:•Isimila
                    •Kalambo Falls
                     55,300 B.C.

            Broken Hill•:
         •Victoria Falls•
                     •Lochard

MIDDLE AND EARLY
UPPER PLEISTOCENE

MAIN HANDAXE CULTURE SITES
AND HUMAN FOSSILS

⊙ Chellian stage
:•: Acheulian stage
+ Utilized bone
▲ *Homo erectus*
□ *Homo sapiens*

                    •Cave of Hearths
                    •Sterkfontein Extension
                    ⊕▲Swartkrans
                     Klipplaatdrif
         Kimberley•:
Hopefield ⊙Stellenbosch

Figure 3 Distribution of Middle and early Upper Pleistocene Culture (Chellian and Acheulian) and hominids.

sphere, there is substantial evidence that tool-making had spread throughout all the semi-arid regions of the continent and had overflowed into other parts of the Old World. The artifacts are still predominantly choppers, chopping tools and worked flakes, but they are now more shapely, show greater variety, and are generally more skilfully made, though still remaining remarkably crude in appearance. They represent the earliest stages of what is known as the Chelles-Acheul or Handaxe culture, the latter name being derived from the commonest type of tool, roughly the shape of a hand when seen in silhouette, though the earliest examples are very crude and rare.

An evolved pebble culture of this time occurs outside Africa in the

Jordan valley. Closely related forms may be seen in the industries from the Choukoutien Cave near Peking and from South-East Asia. In Europe also it has been claimed that a pebble culture occurs with Heidelberg man at Mauer in Germany. In Africa, Europe, the Near East, and India, the Handaxe culture passed through remarkably similar evolutionary stages, and it seems probable that the populations of those continents were not as isolated as was at first supposed and that changes in culture as well as in the genotype were the outcome of free movement, exchange and inter-communication (fig. 4).

What do these early Handaxe cultures look like? The living-sites stratified at the base of Bed II at the Olduvai Gorge, which are now believed to date to about one million years ago, show that important changes had taken place since Bed I times. The accumulations of tools are much more extensive and there are generally many more artifacts. There are choppers, polyhedral stones and utilized flakes in quantity, together with a few pear-shaped, handaxe-like forms. But perhaps the most significant tool is a small flake or chunk that shows careful retouching to form notches and scraping edges. Some of these small, delicate, informal tools look as if they belong to the Later Stone Age, and it is obvious that the hominid that made them was fully capable of what Napier has called 'the precision grip' between finger and thumb. We do not know what these tools were used for, though they would have been effective in trimming the meat off bone, in cleaning skins or in paring wood. It is also evident that hunting techniques had undergone important changes, and now it was very often large animals that provided the major part of the meat supply. These consisted of extinct forms of elephant, giraffids, and ox- and sheep-like creatures that appear to have ben driven into swampy ground or into open water and there butchered. This implies not only considerably improved hunting ability, but also reasonably efficient group organization.

The only remains of the earliest occupants of Bed II at Olduvai are two teeth, but at Sterkfontein in the Transvaal a similar industry is found in the later, brown breccia. These pebble tools are associated with teeth of *Australopithecus*, but it is suggested that they were really made by an early form of *Homo erectus*. The somewhat later and adjacent site of Swartkrans also contained tools and the large Australopithecine *Paranthropus*, but in addition another hominid is present, previously known as *Telanthropus* and now identified with *Homo erectus*.

About mid-way up in Bed II at Olduvai is a horizon known as 'the Chellean III horizon', the latest potassium/argon date for which is 490,000 years. Handaxes made by a stone technique are now much more common, though the pebble chopper still predominates. All the other types of tool occur, and there are now steep core-scraper forms besides, though full details have not yet been published. Associated with this cultural

DISTRIBUTION OF THE
HANDAXE CULTURE

Figure 4 Distribution of the Handaxe Culture in the world.

stage, Leakey found the greater part of a skull cap which falls within the pattern of the Pithecanthropoids, or *Homo erectus*, as this stock is now called. The Chellean III skull differs, however, in having a larger cranial capacity, and in anticipating in some measure the Rhodesioid type of man. There can be no doubt that the cultural, physical and intellectual developments that had taken place since Australopithecine times are inextricably interconnected, and the rapidity of the biological change could not have occurred without culture.

With this level at Olduvai we can correlate a 'Chellean' (Clacto-Abbevillian) stage from an early marine level at Sidi Abderrahman, near Casablanca, as well as the lakeside site of Ternifine on the Algerian pleateau. Here there is a somewhat more developed stone industry, and the usual bone debris from meals, together with three well-preserved jaws and a parietal bone. Arambourg has described these as belonging to an

African Pithecanthropoid stock which he has named *Atlanthropus*. Thus the African representatives of this 'palaeo-anthropoid' level would be contemporary with those from China and south-east Asia.

The second half of the Handaxe culture—the Acheulian—was a time of population movement into areas where no signs of earlier occupation by man have yet been found, and it was probably a period of population increase also. The extreme richness of Africa in the stone tools of this time points to the very favourable environment in which the Acheulian was practised. It may be inferred, though it has not yet been proved, that with the advances of the polar ice-sheets in the second and third glacials, and during the Great Interglacial, there was a more temperate environment over most of the African continent, so that many areas now desert became favourable for settlement. This was also a time of great proliferation of species among the antelopes, pigs and other African mammals, so that it is to be expected that man was also quick to take advantage of the opportunities now available to him.

The Acheulian populations were, however, still confined to the savannah and, as rainfall and temperature permitted, to the drier parts of the continent. It was only later that the tropical forest zone became permanently occupied. Moreover, man was still virtually confined in his choice of living quarters to waterside sites, probably becasue he had evolved no efficient means of carrying water supplies for any distance. Even more important than the richness of the stone industries of this period is the existence of a number of stratigraphically sealed and dated camping-sites, from which we can gain some idea of the manner of living of the people. Most of these occupation sites belong to later Acheulian times, from perhaps 150–50,000 years ago. There are several sites of this kind: in East Africa, at Olorgesailie, Kariandusi and Isimila; in Rhodesia, at Broken Hill and Kalambo Falls; in South Africa, at Kimberley and the Cave of Hearths; while in North Africa there are caves at Casablanca and Rabat, fossil spring sites in Egypt and the Maghrib, to mention but a few.

Acheulian man still concentrated on killing large animals, and he seems to have been much better equipped to do so than his predecessors. The handaxes are now really fine examples of the stoneworker's craft. They were made by what is known as the cylinder hammer technique, which enabled thinner and flatter flakes to be removed, and the result was most shapely tools with straight cutting edges. Another cutting tool is known as a 'cleaver', and is often U-shaped and axe-like. Balls of stone, different types of steep core-scrapers, and many varieties of small scraping and cutting tools also form an integral part of any Acheulian industry. There was already selection of raw material: the tougher, harder rocks were used for the heavy cutting and chopping tools, while the fine-grained, homogeneous rocks, capable of producing a sharp but relatively brittle edge, were used for the small tools. This must reflect differences in activity.

Some four or five variations in the cultural pattern can now be seen, though as yet no regional specialization is discernible. Sometimes industries consist of high percentages of large cutting tools and low percentages of other forms. Elsewhere the large cutting tools may be completely absent (as at Hope Fountain). At yet other sites there are roughly equal percentages of both large and small tools, or industries occur with high percentages of heavy equipment—choppers, picks, core-scrapers and the like. Finally, there are the mining-sites, where the raw materials were worked up from cobbles, boulders or outcrops. This again shows that Acheulian man engaged in a number of different activities for which he used different stone tools.

Analysis of floor plans and artifact percentages, and the relationships of artifacts to each other and to the other associated material—bones, wood, natural stones that had been carried in, etc.—is helping to distinguish which groups of tools may be associated with butchering, or with hunting, with food getting, with vegetable foods and so on. But it will need a number of careful analyses before we have any data that can be considered reliable.

The sizes of the camp-sites in the open also vary—from a few feet across at Broken Hill to as much as 30 feet or more in diameter at Olorgesailie or Kalambo. In a site of this size, there will often be concentrated a large number of tools of the same kind. If the tools were all made at once, it is difficult to see the reason for such quantities; but if the site were reoccupied seasonally over several years, this profusion presents no particular problem. The same forms and profusion of tools characterize the Acheulian wherever it occurs. There is very little difference between the industries at the Cape, in Rhodesia, East Africa, the Sahara, Egypt or Peninsular India, except in the raw materials used. The reason for this is as yet not fully understood, though it probably results from the Handaxe makers being confined largely to one type of country, namely the savannah, and to the great length of time (about 2 million years) involved. This slow development of technical ability and food-gathering practices is in turn directly related to the evolution of the genotype.

As yet, the physical type of Acheulian man is imperfectly known, whether in Africa or elsewhere, but responses to adaptation and to changes in environment appear to have produced, by genetic modification from a Pithecanthropoid ancestor, several forms. One of these must have approached the massive-browed Rhodesian man of southern Africa, another was an evolved *Atlanthropus* in the Maghrib, and yet a third was a *sapiens*-like stock, such as is represented by the smooth-browed Kanjera crania from Kavirondo.

It was not until the very end of Acheulian times in Africa that man became a regular user of fire. There are some three or four sites where evidence of fire is preserved, and all these probably date to between 50,000 and 60,000 years ago. One such site is at the Kalambo Falls, where charred logs and charcoals occur, and where man used fire to aid in sharpening sticks for digging, to shape clubs, or to make edges on knife-like tools of wood.

Thus fire-making, first known from second glacial times in the Far East, does not appear to have spread universally in Africa before the end of Acheulian times some 50–60,000 years ago, presumably because there was no need for it before. But now the climate became cooler and wetter, bringing about a considerable readjustment in the vegetation patterns and in the distribution of animal and human populations. Under a lowering of temperature of between 4° and 5°C., coinciding with the earlier part of the last glaciation in Europe, higher-living forest species replaced lowland tropical forest down to 600–900 metres below their present altitude range in sub-Saharan Africa, and a Mediterranean flora spread southwards to the southern borders of the Sahara. With the vastly increased potential for food getting, technical development, and living conditions made possible by a regular use of fire, man now spread into country which he had not previously occupied—the now most favourable but formerly forest-covered regions of Equatoria. Here the routes of migration into the Congo basin and the West African rain forest must have lain along the grass-covered interfluves, and man was better able to avail himself of the opportunities offered by, on the one hand, the savannah and, on the other, the forest galleries in the adjacent valleys.

This was a time of considerable population movement and of cultural experiment. It saw the fairly rapid disappearance of the old traditional forms of tool—the handaxe and the cleaver—in the higher rainfall, more heavily tree-covered parts of the continent. Here there developed many heavy chopping tools and smaller denticulated artifacts that are believed to have been associated with woodworking. This complex became dominant throughout the Congo and West Africa, spreading into East Africa west of the Eastern Rift and into south-east Africa down to Natal. It is known as the Sangoan culture. Elsewhere in southern and eastern Africa, in regions favourable for the preservation of the traditional type of habitat, the old handaxe tradition lingered on. This is known as the Fauresmith complex, and it is associated with pans and grasslands and an abundant ungulate and large-animal fauna (fig. 5).

For the first time man now began to occupy caves and rock shelters as regular homes, for, with his control of fire, these provided safe and more comfortable living-quarters. Furthermore, because of the regulation of the seasonal movements of the bands and the use of efficient carrying devices, he could now afford to stay in one place for much longer.

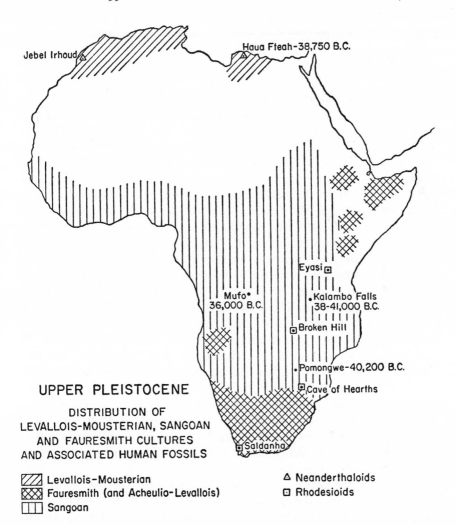

Jebel Irhoud

Haua Fteah-38,750 B.C.

Eyasi

Mufo•
36,000 B.C.

•Kalambo Falls
38-41,000 B.C.

Broken Hill

•Pomongwe-40,200 B.C.

UPPER PLEISTOCENE

DISTRIBUTION OF
LEVALLOIS-MOUSTERIAN, SANGOAN
AND FAURESMITH CULTURES
AND ASSOCIATED HUMAN FOSSILS

Cave of Hearths

Saldanha

Levallois-Mousterian   △ Neanderthaloids
Fauresmith (and Acheulio-Levallois)   □ Rhodesioids
Sangoan

Figure 5 Distribution of early Upper Pleistocene Culture and hominids (Fauresmith, Sangoan, etc.).

Whereas the Australopithecines with their limited technology must very quickly have exhausted the sources of food available to them, the Acheulian and, later, the Sangoan and Fauresmith peoples, who were becoming steadily more proficient and inventive in their methods of food getting, were able to exploit the available resources with ever-increasing efficiency. Increase in the size of the band, more permanent residence, and ability to live in a greater variety of habitats, previously unfavourable, must have been the inevitable concomitant of increasing technical skill and mental ability, and at this time, as the distribution maps show, there were few parts of the continent where man did not penetrate. Figure 6 is an attempt to show the inter-relationship of environment, genotype and culture through time, and their effect on the prehistoric societies of Africa.

After the disappearance of the Acheulian culture from North Africa, which was contemporary with encroaching desertification, there appear, from Cyrenaica to Morocco, flake industries that are closely similar to those from the Levantine coast and the Near East generally. These are known culturally as Levallois-Mousterian and they are associated with a Neanderthal physical type. From the magnificent site of Haua Fteah in Cyrenaica, and from the newly discovered site at Jebel Irhoud in Morocco, we know that the Levallois-Mousterian people were cave dwellers, competent fire-users, and specialized in making light cutting, scraping and piercing tools from fine, thin flakes.

It is an intriguing problem whether these industries and the associated Neanderthal men were the outcome of migration into Africa from the Near East or Europe, or whether they were an autochthonous evolution from the Acheulian. The evidence is equivocal. The Kanjera type of man, if he is accurately dated, could have been ancestral to both the Neanderthal and the *sapiens* forms in Africa and, so far as the industry is concerned, and prepared-core technique is also present in the late Acheulian in North Africa. Any movement could, therefore, equally well have been out of Africa as into it. On the other hand, the closer similarities with the Near East rather than with sub-Saharan Africa, and the appearance of some representatives of the Palaeoarctic fauna in North Africa, suggest that the culture and the human stock could also be intrusive. At present the evidence is, it would seem, if anything weighted in favour of the latter alternative.

Whatever the answer, it is from this time onwards that culture in North Africa becomes differentiated from that south of the Sahara, though influences spread at favourable times in both directions (fig. 7). In the Maghrib the Levallois-Mousterian evolved into a culture—known as the Aterian—specializing in the use of tanged flakes and points, while further east and as far south as the Horn the more generalized Levallois-Mousterian pattern was preserved. The Levallois-Mousterian was largely contemporary with the savannah-living Sangoan and the Fauresmith populations of the grasslands south of the Sahara, thus making the Neanderthalers of the north contemporary with the Rhodesian physical type in the south. This last represents the extreme development of the heavy-browed stock, and it is known from as far apart as Broken Hill and the Cape, where it represents the makers of a late Rhodesian Sangoan (or Proto-Stillbay, since these are now known to be the same thing) and of the Cape Fauresmith.

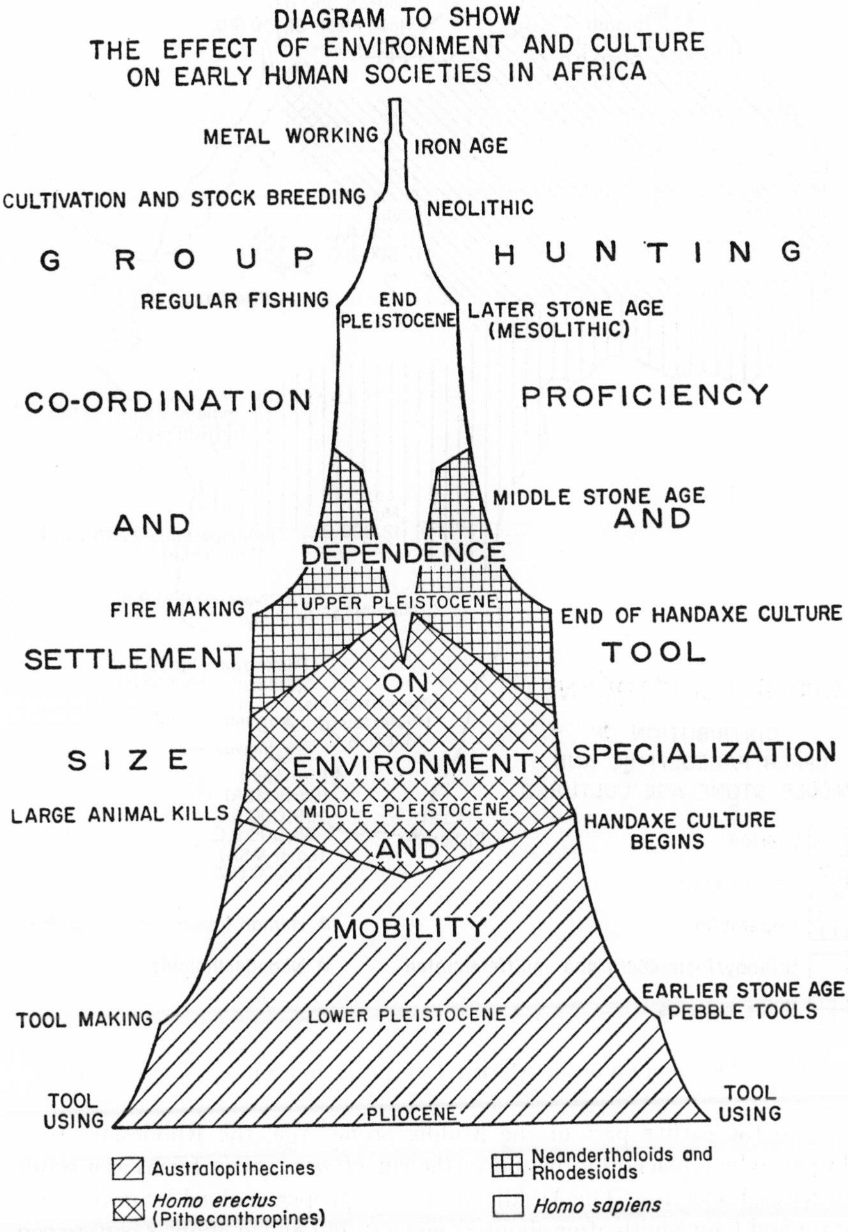

DIAGRAM TO SHOW
THE EFFECT OF ENVIRONMENT AND CULTURE
ON EARLY HUMAN SOCIETIES IN AFRICA

METAL WORKING / IRON AGE

CULTIVATION AND STOCK BREEDING / NEOLITHIC

G R O U P   H U N T I N G

REGULAR FISHING   END PLEISTOCENE   LATER STONE AGE (MESOLITHIC)

CO-ORDINATION   PROFICIENCY

AND   MIDDLE STONE AGE   AND

DEPENDENCE
FIRE MAKING   UPPER PLEISTOCENE   END OF HANDAXE CULTURE

SETTLEMENT   TOOL

SIZE   ON   SPECIALIZATION

ENVIRONMENT
LARGE ANIMAL KILLS   MIDDLE PLEISTOCENE   HANDAXE CULTURE BEGINS

AND

MOBILITY

EARLIER STONE AGE
PEBBLE TOOLS

TOOL MAKING   LOWER PLEISTOCENE

TOOL USING   PLIOCENE   TOOL USING

Australopithecines   Neanderthaloids and Rhodesioids
Homo erectus (Pithecanthropines)   Homo sapiens

Figure 6 Diagramatic presentation of the inter-relationship of environment, genotype and culture through time and their effect on the prehistoric societies of Africa.

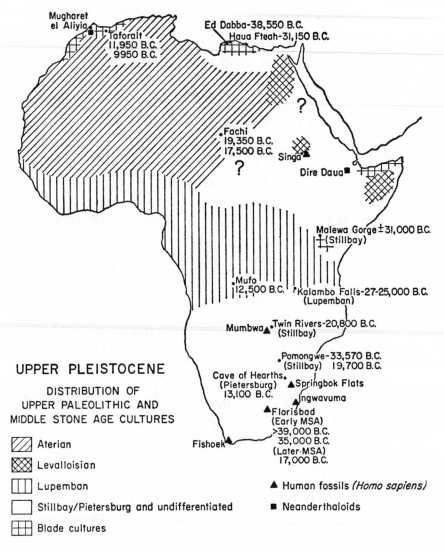

Figure 7 Distribution of the Aterian, Lupemban and Stillbay/Pietersburg.

In the earlier part of the Middle Stone Age, the Rhodesioid type began to be replaced by the more efficient *Homo sapiens* forms as a result of natural selection. The Middle Stone Age proper evolved from the Sangoan and Fauresmith after about 35,000 B.C. and ended about 8,000–10,000 B.C. There has for long been a tendency in Europe to refer to Africa after the end of the Middle Pleistocene as a cultural backwater. This was based initially on the fact that the earliest *sapiens* stock in Europe is associated with what we know as blade and burin, or Upper Palaeolithic, industries, which rather abruptly replaced the Neanderthal populations and the Mousterian culture there about 35,000 B.C. In Africa the prepared-core technique, Mousterian if you like, continued for a further 25,000 years, and by inference drawn from the European associations it was, therefore, considered that in Africa the Middle Stone Age was made by late surviving Neanderthalers. Radiocarbon and later discoveries show that this is not the case, and there is no evidence of any such time lag in the genotype as had been postulated. The reason for the survival of the prepared-core tradition is obviously that it was the most efficient for producing the specialized equipment that was required by a hunting people in tropical and subtropical environments.

These Middle Stone Age cultures, as they are known in sub-Saharan terminology, though based essentially on the prepared core and faceted flake, differ in fact considerably in the nature of their end-products, so that a number of distinct variants can be identified and directly related to environmental specialization. Thus we find the Stillbay and Pietersburg variants in the savannah and grasslands of south and east Africa concentrating on light cutting, piercing and projectile tools of stone, while in the Congo forests, for example, the contemporary form, known as Lupemban, contains many axe and chopping elements and magnificent lanceolate knives or stabbing points. Whereas the tanged point was the speciality of the Aterian population, the foliate form in many varieties was that favoured south of the Sahara.

During the African Middle Stone Age there is the same evidence as in Europe for the appearance of religious beliefs. This is shown by the careful burial of the dead. Simultaneously there appear signs of an aesthetic sense in the use of paint and ornamentation. It would seem, therefore, that it was primarily the contrasting environments of glacial and tropical Africa that were responsible for the basic differences in the stone cultures.

Upper Palaeolithic blade and burin industries are found in two parts of Africa—on the Mediterranean littoral and in the East African Rift. The first appearance of Upper Palaeolithic culture in Cyrenaica has been dated to between 38 and 31,000 B.C. It is considered that this may also be the time of its earliest appearance in East Africa, though most of the evidence there, as also in north-west Africa, belongs to later times. There can be little doubt that these industries are intrusive from the Levant, being introduced presumably by an early *Homo sapiens* stock which must inevitably have hybridized with the existing populations. No human fossils of this culture stage are as yet known, so it is not possible at present to say whether the makers could have been the ancestors of the Erythriote and Mediterranean longheads. There is quite a possibility that this might have been so, for in East Africa, certainly, the later blade and burin industries were the work of populations of this physical type, largely identified today with the Hamites.

The close of the Pleistocene about 8000 B.C. was preceded by a cooler and wetter climate of some 2000 years duration, during which there were two immigrations of Caucasoid stock into North Africa, the one of Cro-magnon type, bringing the Oranian culture to the Maghrib and the other, probably of Mediterranean type, bringing the Et Tera culture to Cyrenaica. At the same time there appears evidence of blade and burin industries in the Horn, while the Aterian populations of the Maghrib were able to move down as far as the southern and eastern Sahara and the Nile. These contacts resulted, for example, in the Congo with the final Middle Stone Age, in the appearance of tanged projectile heads, and in South Africa and Rhodesia in the appearance of new forms of tool made on blades. Similarly, the bifacial foliate points of the later Aterian, the transverse arrowheads and heavy lunate forms of the Mesolithic, and the bifaced axe element of the Neolithic are probably the result of diffusion northwards from the Lupemban and Tshitolian of Equatoria. This was the second major period of cultural readjustment in Africa.

The wet phase known as the Makalian that followed the end of the Pleistocene, which lasted from about 5500 to 2500 B.C., similarly permitted free exchange between Mediterranean and Negroid populations that had both moved into the Sahara with the advance of the Mediterranean flora and the improved water supplies (fig 8). It is from this time that water-side habitats take on new significance. The sea coasts, rivers and lakes were now exploited for their food sources as never before, and it was the permanent food supply provided by the fish, shellfish and other water foods that enabled man to remain permanently in occupation of areas where previously he had been only a seasonal visitor. The wide distribution of, for example, the bone harpoon, the gouge and other traits of a waterside culture throughout the southern Sahara, the Nile and the Central African lakes, shows the rapidity with which the indigenous populations in such favourable localities took the opportunity to improve their economy. It is useful to keep in mind this facility for readjustment when considering the change-over from a stone-using to a metal-working economy.

By the end of the Pleistocene, the Bush physical stock was already present in South Africa and it may be postulated that, similarly, by selective processes, the Negroid and Erythriote types had also made their appearance, though the earliest known fossils representing these types are no older than the Mesolithic or the Later Stone Age. Because of their blood group relationships, the Bushman and the Negro must be derived from the same African ancestral stock. However, only in the case of the Erythriote or Proto-Hamite does there seem to be any close tie between culture and physical stock, and it was not so much race as cultural specialization springing from long adaptation to different habitats that dictated the distribution of culture forms in the post-Pleistocene.

Since the Later Stone Age is also the period of greatest adaptive specialization, a large number of distinctive cultures can be distinguished. In the Congo basin the cultures of the plateaux differ markedly from those of the forests, though both are fairly certain to have been made by an unspecialized Negroid ancestral type. Markedly different again are those in the Albertine Rift or the Kenya Rift. In South Africa the Smithfield of the high veld, using various forms of end-scrapers made from indurated shale, is very different from the crescent-like microliths of the Wilton culture, though both were made by Bushmen and both had a number of traits in common. This specialization of equipment and the greater use that was now made of quite small animals for food is likely to have been

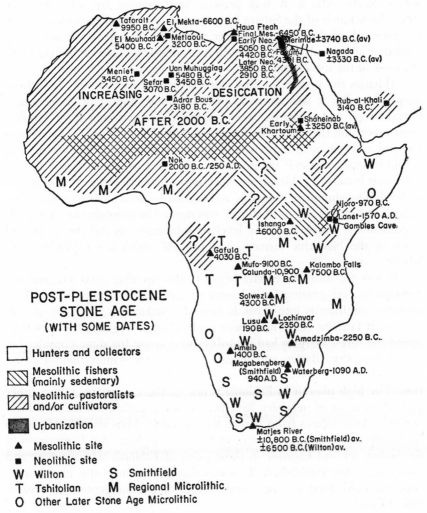

Figure 8 Distribution of Culture in post-Pleistocene times.

stimulated by population increase and a corresponding reduction in the size of the hunting territory of the band. This in turn, however, could only have become possible because of the spread of new technical advances—the bow and arrow, poison, barbed fish-spears and other devices—that raised the yield of the hunting territory.

Food production and domestication first make their appearance in the continent in the later half of the sixth or early fifth millennium B.C. in Egypt. This is, therefore, later than the beginnings of cultivation (of wheat and barley) and of animal domestication in the Near East, and there can be little doubt that in the first instance Africa derived its knowledge of these things from immigrants into the Nile Valley. It took, however, a surprisingly short time for the new economy to spread across North Africa. It was present in Cyrenaica by 5000 B.C. and throughout much of the Sahara by 3500–3000 B.C. Neolithic culture is unknown south of the Sahara, however, until later, and in fact it never succeeded at all in replacing the Mesolithic, collecting, way of life throughout most of the sub-continent.

What is the reason for this cultural lag? In part is must have been geographic. But it was also, and probably more importantly, economic. Cereal crops and domestic stock in the rich environment of tropical Africa were not the necessities for permanent village life that they were in the arid and semi-arid regions in which they were first developed. This would be especially so if the primary importance of livestock was already then, as it is today in Africa, an expression of wealth rather than a source of food. The abundant vegetable and animal resources of the tropical savannah and forests provided all that was needed to maintain the Mesolithic populations at much the same level of subsistence as did the crops and stock of the Neolithic farmers, and probably with less expenditure of labour.

It was not until the Sahara began to dry up after 2500 B.C., and the consequent over-grazing forced some of the Neolithic populations there to move southwards into what is now the Sudan belt, that any serious attempt at farming could have been made, though 'vegecultural' practices round the forest margins had probably been in use for some considerable time before that. Barley and wheat, however, are winter rainfall crops, and can rarely be grown in the tropics successfully except under irrigation. The high plateau in Ethiopia is one of the exceptions, but in other parts there must of necessity have been much experimentation with local potential domesticates from ±2000 B.C. onwards. Thus several indigenous food crops were developed—rice in Guinea, sorghum and *Pennisetum* in the Sudan, tef and *Eleusine* in those parts of Ethiopia where wheat and barley were not established. This experimentation may also have stimulated the cultivation on the forest fringes of the indigenous *Dioscoreas* and of *Ensete*.

We find Neolithic cultivators in northern Nigeria, the makers of the Nok culture, between 2000 B.C. and A.D. 200, when stone began to be replaced by metal for essential tools. Neolithic pastoralists also reached Ethiopia and the Kenya Rift about 2000 B.C., and in the latter region they were not replaced by Bantu immigrants until after the sixteenth century A.D. The only other part where Neolithic industries are known, though they are all believed to be late, is the Congo basin. The whole of the rest of southern Africa remained in the collecting stage. The reason why it did so must be due, as well as to the richness of the wild food resources, to the generally inefficient equipment of Neolithic man for clearing forest and closed woodland and his inability to maintain himself in large enough communities. It was, therefore, not until the population explosion that precipitated the Bantu movements around the beginning of the Christian era that any fundamental change in the economy was feasible. What made this possible, even then, was the development of iron-working—the iron axe and spear—and, no doubt, also the introduction of the Asian food plants.

The many investigations that are going on today are steadily tracing the history of the spread of Negroid and Bantu culture into the subcontinent, and in another decade it is certain that a firm chronology will have become available. We can already trace the spread down the Central African lakes of the earliest Iron Age immigrants, the makers of the Dimple-based and Channelled ware pottery, the earliest date for which is A.D. 100 from Machili in eastern Barotseland. We know that the copper mines of Katanga were being worked and the products traded widely by the eighth century A.D.; that central Angola had been occupied by metal-users a century earlier; that trade was coming up the lower Zambezi at the same time; that by A.D. 300 there were agriculturalists living at Zimbabwe, and that by A.D. 1100 there was a flourishing centre at Mapungubwe (Bambandyanalo) on the Limpopo. At the beginning of the sixteenth century these earlier Iron Age cultivators were joined by other more efficiently organized groups establishing powerful political confederacies, and the process of absorption of the older populations was speeded up.

One point that needs stressing here, however, is that the coming of the Iron Age mixed farmers was not, as is all too often supposed, necessarily coincident with the disappearance of the old hunting-collecting populations. Such apparent anomalies as a Bush-Hottentot physical stock with a Negroid culture, as is found at Mapungubwe or at Inyanga and a number of other places, is surely the result of some of the old hunting populations having changed their economy. In the same way the historic Cape Hottentots were a Stone Age people who had acquired stock and become pastoralists. Moreover, from the skeletal remains from Northern Rhodesia and Nyasaland it can be seen that the Late Stone Age population was already Negroid in a number of its physical characteristics, and in the Bergdama and Hadza we can probably see surviving examples of two of the Later Stone Age populations of Equatoria.

It is, therefore, probably true to say that the origins of the older Bantu populations of these countries are most likely to be found in the Stone Age, though of course the present populations must be the results of subsequent modification by hybridization with small groups of immigrants. The fundamental change is not so much in the population as in the economy, though there is of course ample evidence to prove immigration and replacement in a number of cases. The caves and rock shelters were gradually abandoned as pressures dictated, that is, by all except the unadjustable minority of the hunting populations, and the inhabitants now settled in open villages, planted crops and herded stock. Hybridization completed the transformation that economic expediency had begun.

There is increasing proof to show that this was the pattern in many of the southern and central parts of Africa following the coming of the first groups of iron-using immigrants. The consequence is to emphasize the continuity of African culture, and to show the need to study both the prehistoric populations and their culture, since here lies the clue to the understanding of the present.

Addendum

At the time of correcting the proofs of this paper Dr L. S. B. Leakey has just announced that the Pre-Zinjanthropus fossils from Bed I and new fossils from the lower part of Bed II at the Olduvai Gorge together represent a new species, *Homo habilis* (so called for his toolmaking ability), whose characteristics, it is claimed, fall outside the range of Australopithecine variability. This implies, therefore, that the species *Homo* had become genetically differentiated from the *Australopithecinae* at a time anterior to the deposition of Bed I rather than posterior to this time. If this is so it would also seem unlikely that *Homo erectus* represents a stage of human evolution directly ancestral to modern man. Some lively controversy can be expected when the full details of the new discovery are made available. [Compare the evaluation of Pilbeam and Simons, I:10, pp. 140-46—Ed.]

34 Stone Age Implements

Jacques Bordaz

IF THE AGE OF THE EARTH IS 6,000,000,000 YEARS, AND IF THIS SPAN IS *imagined as one day of twenty-four hours, the total duration of culture is something like 28 seconds. And, except for perhaps the last 5/10ths of a second, this brief span has been squandered in the "stone age," most of it, about 27 seconds worth, in the Paleolithic.*

Now that you are properly impressed we may proceed to the main events of the period when man's technology was significantly based on stone, limited to his own physical energy, and directed toward a world in which only he was domesticated. Of course, stone was not the only substance used for tools or weapons, but like the teeth and bones that are all that usually remain of biological fossils, stone is the perduring material which survives as witness to the skill and intelligence of our remote forebears. In the selection which follows, we not only learn of the major sequential stages of technological evolution, but also some of the means by which archaeologists discriminate culturally altered stones from all other rocks.

It is hard to realize today that only two centuries ago both the origin and nature of the objects to be presented on these pages were totally misunderstood. Mankind's long use of metal had virtually obliterated the

SOURCE: "First Tools of Mankind" and "Stone Age Implements—Part 2: The Mesolithic and Neolithic Periods," *Natural History*, Vol. 68, 1 and 2, pp. 36–51, 92–103. Reprinted with the permission of the author and publisher.

The author (b. 1926) is currently Assistant Professor of Archaeology at New York University and Associate Professor of Archaeology at the Université de Montreal. He is now analyzing results of excavations in Suberde in Turkey, dealing with the circumstances under which food production and a sedentary life were first achieved.

memory of stone as a material for the manufacture of tools and weapons: the hand axes and other surviving implements of the Paleolithic period were then believed, instead, to be works of nature. Over most of the Old World, indeed, they were usually referred to as "thunderstones" or "thunderbolts," in the belief that they represented the end product of a lightning stroke. In certain parts of Scandinavia and France, this belief was still held during the last century, and the *pierres de foudre* were hopefully placed in the walls or under the doorsills of farmhouses in an attempt to deceive lightning, which, as was well known, never struck twice in the same place. Nor was this mere peasant superstition: early scholars called these stones "ceraunias" (from the Greek *keraunos*, thunderbolt) and proposed the most complex explanations as to which proportions of humidity, solar and stellar radiation and lightning had produced the strange objects. Since so many apparently reliable observers had stated for centuries that they had found ceraunias at the very place where lightning had struck, little attention was given to a seventeenth century mineralogist, Boece de Boot, who suggested that—in view of the unique form of the ceraunias—they might have been iron implements which had turned into stone through the ages.

It was not until 1723—as a late-ripening fruit of the Age of Exploration—that the "thunderstone" belief was vanquished by scientific evidence of the true nature of these stone objects. The naturalist Antoine de Jussieu, in a memoir entitled *De l'Origine et Des Usages Des Pierres à Foudre*, pointed out that some stone objects from the West Indies and Canada, which were known to have been manufactured and used by the aborigines of these regions as tools and weapons, were very similar to the European ceraunias, and that it was probable that the early inhabitants of Europe had also manufactured tools and weapons of stone. Still, it required more than another hundred and fifty years—until the end of the nineteenth century—before the period called by prehistorians the "Stone Age" was recognized to represent a vast span of time in man's history: a period now estimated to have lasted perhaps more than a hundred times longer than the five thousand years that have passed since the invention of metallurgy in the Near East.

Of all the activities of man during these distant millennia that are known to us today, the closest to us—that is, the most easily appreciated —are the many cave paintings of the Paleolithic, found in southwestern Europe. Their magnificence, boldness and beauty, the esthetic emotions these works evoke in us, all seem to erase the enormities of intervening time. Prehistoric stone implements also possess a beauty, although their beauty is of another kind. Admirably adapted to their purpose, they cannot but please those able to appreciate the elegance of these tools in their solution of the relationship between form and function. Many of these implements demonstrate form, texture and workmanship that transcend their prosaic uses.

The major concern of scholars specializing in prehistoric stone implements has been with typological studies; that is, the analysis of recurrent forms, which—in conjunction with geochronological evidence leads to temporal and regional classifications of the ancient human societies that produced these tools. In contrast, the purpose of this study is technological, rather than historical: we wish to learn what we can about the uses to which these tools may have been put, and the ways in which they were produced. In consequence, most of our examples have been taken from the area which—at least, today—is richest in this material: western Europe, and France in particular.

By way of preface, some of the terms which prehistorians use should be defined. The division of prehistory into three periods—the Paleolithic ("old stone"), Mesolithic ("middle stone") and Neolithic ("new stone") periods—is essentially a technological one, based on the manner in which stone implements were shaped. Thus, in the Paleolithic, stone was shaped exclusively by *flaking*. In France, the area where all of the implements here illustrated were made, the Paleolithic coincides with the glacial period. The Mesolithic, in this same area, was a transitional era, in immediately postglacial times. During the Neolithic, the most recent period, many stone tools were shaped by *grinding*, in addition to flaking. The final period lasted in Europe until some four thousand years ago, when copper and bronze were introduced.

It is evident that stone was not the *only* material used by man during the "age of stone." In a few early sites, parts of wooden spears have been found; and in rock shelters—where preservation is better than in open sites—a great number of bone and antler objects have been discovered. The fact that stone is practically indestructible (and hence that stone implements constitute the majority of finds) is *not* the primary reason for the use, here, of this prehistoric nomenclature. Rather, it is in recognition of the fact that the stone tools were the most important part of the equipment of early man. For they alone provided him with the working edge and the point he needed for cutting, chopping, scraping, piercing and shaping the now largely vanished materials—such as wood, bone, antler, sinew and skin—which comprised the remainder—and possibly the major part—of his material culture.

For hundreds of thousands of years during glacial and early postglacial times, man successfully survived, first as a hunter and later (from about six thousand years ago in Europe) as a food-producer and husbandman. During all this time stone was his principal means of exploiting nature and man's progress in this exploitation was associated with technological advances in stone implements. These advances show themselves in two main ways. First, there was an evolution in the forms of the imple-ments—which were developing from generalized, all-purpose tools and weapons to more specialized and better-adapted ones. Second, there was an evolution in the mode of their manufacture. Man was learning to make better use of suitable raw material: he not only reduced waste but also developed new techniques which enabled him to utilize a greater variety of materials for the manufacture of his stone weapons and tools.

What were the shapes of the earliest stone implements? It is inevit-able that, endowed with a prehensile hand, the earliest man must have picked up and used ready-made tools, such as sticks, bones and pebbles, which in some cases had naturally broken cutting edges. Smashing stones and selecting those fragments with useful cutting edges would have been a logical first step in tool-making, but we cannot expect to find evidence of this "first" tool manufacture, for such haphazardly flaked stones are indistinguishable from those flaked by nature.

However, archeologists have recovered from sites in East and South Africa—equated with late Villafranchian strata of Europe—collections of flaked stone that must be very close to the beginning of systematic stone-working. Estimated ages of these early finds based on potassium-argon measurements of volcanic minerals associated with the East African sites suggest that tool-making might have started as early as 1.75 million years ago. Many of these early African artifacts demonstrate, in contrast to naturally flaked stone, a certain uniformity of shape and direction of flak-ing, indicating deliberate design.

Flint, when available, has always been a favorite European tool ma-terial, for it has all the necessary qualities found to varying degrees in the other siliceous stones—chert, quartzites and the like. Besides being very hard (it will scratch most steels), flint is also homogeneous. Because flint has no natural planes of cleavage, a force applied at one point on its sur-face radiates symmetrically within the material, and breaks the stone along a plane of segmentation whose position can theoretically be con-trolled, within limits, by manipulative skill alone. For example, both the angle of impact and the degree of force may be varied. The forces radiat-ing from a point of impact at the center of a piece of such homogeneous material will theoretically punch out a cone, leaving a slightly rippled conical scar. If the point of impact is near the edge, a chip will flake off—leaving a rippled half-cone scar similar to those seen on the edge of chipped glass.

How can flint, and allied siliceous rocks, best be worked? There are, essentially, two methods for obtaining implements with a useful working edge by means of flaking. The first is to strike the flint nodule against some projection of a heavy rock—used as an "anvil"—or, alternatively, to use a hard pebble, held in the hand, as a "hammer." The flakes of flint detached in this manner (in most cases referred to as Clactonian, from the name of the English type-site, Clacton-on-Sea), although usable, are generally clumsy and irregularly shaped. Clactonian flakes have a large cone of percussion and a prominent bulb, the latter leaving a deep bulbar depression on the flint's nucleus. These flakes may either be used as tools exactly as they come off the nucleus of flint, or improved by "retouching"—that is, by further flaking. In essence, the end product of this first system is the flake: the remaining nodule is a raw material reserve.

The second method, in contrast, is to remove flakes from the flint nucleus according to a predetermined design, with the aim of shaping the "core" into an implement. Such implements are called core tools, and the knapper—while he will save any usable flakes he produces—is not primarily interested in the flakes. His objective may be a single implement, with its cutting edge formed by the intersection of two opposite series of flaked scars; or the core tool may be formed by flaking part of the edge on one "face" only, leaving the other "face" unflaked. Since core tools tend to be massive, they are better suited to heavy work (such as chopping) than are the thinner, flake tools. Flaking a flint nodule on both faces to obtain a rough point (a form that prehistorians call hand axes, or bifaces) would seem to be an advance that derives naturally from the earliest of these core tools—which were usually flaked, on one or both faces, only along *part* of the edge. This technique of producing bifaces spread early over Africa and into Europe, where it seems to have first been used about two hundred thousand years ago (again, according to the Emiliani "short chronology," used throughout this article).

Bifaces were usually pear-shaped, from five to six inches long, and were flaked over most of their border. They offered a strong picklike point, as well as a cutting edge, the thickness and curvature of which varied around the periphery of the implement, making it useful in a variety of tasks. Exactly how were they used? The evidence is against their being used as missile points: usually they were too bulky and, unless thinned at the base, could not have been securely attached to spears. Some might have been used as daggers, or wedged into the thick part of wooden clubs, but most of them appear to have been all-purpose tools for cutting and chopping. Some were so flaked that the small area which pressed against the palm of the hand was left unchipped: in other cases, the user's palm probably was protected either by a pad of skin, a mass of resin or by bark. In general, we may assume that bifaces were used for all heavy chopping, scraping and cutting that could not have been done with the thinner, flake tools. Bifaces could also have been used for cutting and roughing-out wooden spears.

The stone age technologist progressively improved the effectiveness of the biface. The early types (called Abbevillian, after the type-site in France) had some serious defects due to the primitive technique used to flake them. When a nodule of flint is flaked by direct hammerstone or anvil technique, the resulting flakes are short and massive. Their bulbs of percussion leave deep scars, whose intersections form a wavy, inefficient cutting edge. Moreover, since the scars rarely carry very far across the face of the implement, part of the original surface of the nodule remains in the center of the tool, making the Abbevillian biface clumsy because of its thick section. It is possible, in some cases, to partially straighten the working edge by flaking away the marginal spurs formed by adjacent scars. But this does not give the tool the tapering section necessary for deep chopping or cutting. Modern experiments have shown that if blows are struck nearer to the flint's edge in an effort to extend the scars across the face the edge will frequently be crushed. To sum up, then, the Abbevillian tool-maker doubtless had a mental picture of the tool he wanted, but his technique was too primitive to allow him to control the shape of his implement in any but a general way. New techniques had to be developed: from them came the Acheulian biface—with its straight cutting edge, tapering section and two smooth faces.

The Acheulian knapper seems to have used two new techniques for production of his core tools. The first of these is a method of considerable importance, because it was used extensively—in later times—by more advanced makers of stone tools. It consists of flaking the edge itself, in order to build up preliminary striking platforms set at the correct angle (about perpendicular) to the face to be flaked. The flakes struck from these prepared platforms leave scars carrying back across the face of the implement, resulting in a tool with the desired thinner, more tapered section. Now, the preparation of a striking platform, preliminary to flaking, greatly increased the knapper's degree of control over the shape of his bifaces. But most modern experimenters believe that the very shallow flake scars, with long parallel sides—observed on the finest of Acheulian bifaces—are possible to produce only by means of an additional trick of technique. This is the baton method.

As the name of this second method implies, it involves the use of a hard wood, bone or antler baton, which, because it is of softer material than stone, can be struck directly against the edge of the nodule without crushing it. The flakes resulting from such baton blows have a very diffuse bulb of percussion and are long and thin. The resulting scars are almost flat and form a very straight edge by intersection. It can be inferred, by analysis of such evidence, that the Acheulian bifaces were first roughed out by hammerstone percussion, with or without preliminary platforms, and then finished with a baton. The Acheulian biface clearly reveals the characteristic deep, rippled scar resulting from hammerstone percussion, together with the long, shallow scars characteristic of the baton technique. Some of the later Acheulian bifaces are the most perfect expressions of the core-tool concept. Once the knapper had decided on the shape (usually pointed, ovate or cleaver-like) and size best suiting his purpose, he could, by using the platform and baton technique, produce symmetrically shaped bifaces tapering smoothly toward almost straight edges.

Although such predetermination of shape was not possible in making the *early* flake tools, flakes nonetheless have certain advantages over the bifaces. For one thing, their manufacture is not so wasteful of flint as the shaping of a biface—which requires the removal of a great deal of material from the flint core, with only a few usable flakes resulting. For another, a flake tool's cutting edge is obtained by a single blow on the flint nucleus, while the production of a similar thin, straight edge by alternate flaking of a biface requires a great deal of time and skill. Finally, the cutting edge of the best possible biface is never so sharp and smooth as that of a flake.

An admirable combination of the basic qualities of both core and flake tools was invented—probably by Acheulian biface-makers—in the technique known as the Levalloisian, or "prepared nucleus." This technique, which appeared in Africa and western Europe about one hundred and fifty thousand years ago, consists in preparing the nodule by flaking *before* the removal of a flake tool. By this method, the size and shape of the tool can be predetermined as for the core tools and the knapper has, in addition, the advantages of ease of execution, smooth tapering and the very sharp edge of flake tools.

This Levalloisian technique allows the manufacture of very large flakes. In regions where flint is comparatively abundant, as in the valleys of northwestern France, it is not rare to find Levalloisian points sometimes as long as three to six inches, many of which have been only slightly retouched to smooth an outline or repair a blunted edge. It was relatively easier for these knappers to find fresh flint nodules, prepare them and flake new implements than to retouch old tools.

The situation was quite different in the Dordogne region of France, where few flint beds are available and most of the nodules are of small size. Living a less nomadic life in caves and rock shelters, the Dordogne hunters repeatedly reflaked their nuclei and tools for further use. One of the most efficient methods of preparing a nucleus for such exhaustive flaking is what we know as the Mousterian "discoidal nucleus" technique. As in the Levalloisian technique, the nodule of flint is first trimmed peripherally, but instead of trying to get one, or at best a few flakes of maximum length, the Mousterian knapper tried to get a maximum number of usable flakes. To achieve this, the nucleus was flaked toward the center—from striking platforms all around the periphery—until it was practically exhausted. The flakes obtained were then retouched into specialized tools: such as the Mousterian points and scrapers. Many scraper types were made for the tasks at hand. The basic principle of their manufacture consisted in steeply retouching the edge of the flake to obtain a thick, beveled working edge which does not dull when drawn transversely over a resistant material like wood. These scrapers were made in sizes varying from two to six inches; the most usual shapes included scrapers with straight or convex edges which evidently were used to work wood or to remove fat from hides. Concave scrapers were also made, probably for use as spokeshaves, to work sticks into spears, hafts and the like.

The methodical manufacture of symmetrically shaped flakes greatly increased the efficiency of the stone tool assemblage. To be sure, the edges of the early, crude types of flakes—such as the Clactonian—had frequently been retouched, so that they could be used for tasks for which the biface was unsuited. But these haphazardly shaped tools were inefficient and were henceforth replaced by a variety of symmetrically shaped flake tools of predetermined design, most numerous among them Levalloisian flakes, blades and points and Mousterian points and scrapers. Experimentation has shown, however, that these new flake tools—while extremely efficient for skinning and dismembering game—are not so useful as projectiles. The section of these so-called "points," Levalloisian and Mousterian alike, would have been too thick to penetrate the hide of the animals—such as the woolly rhinoceros, the mammoth and the bear—then hunted.

During the fourth and last glaciation, about 35,000 years ago, the Neanderthals—whose remains are found in association with tools of the Mousterian type—were succeeded by men of the modern sort. We now enter the Upper Paleolithic, the age of the great murals of Lascaux and Altamira. The very existence of these remarkable paintings is evidence of technological advance. While it is true that the environment was then very rich in game, it was the hunters' technology that enabled this society to exploit its environment effectively enough to have leisure for the creation of its art. The animal ossuaries left by these hunters have contained as many as ten thousand horse skeletons (at Solutré, in France) or nearly a thousand mammoths (at Predmost, in Czechoslovakia): mute testimony to the skill of these men and the efficiency of their stone implements.

The most important technological developments during the Upper Paleolithic included an increase in tool types made from bone, as well as stone. While some bone implements have been recovered from Lower and Middle Paleolithic sites, they are confined to a few roughly shaped pieces. Harder than wood, bone (and antler, too) can be sharpened with suitable stone tools to finer and stronger points. Both materials were used extensively during the Upper Paleolithic to make points (with split or beveled bases for hafting), harpoon heads (with single or double rows of barbs), awls and even needles. Bone and antlers also supplied the material from which spear-throwers and other artifacts—often ornamented by carving and grinding—were made.

This rich development of bone and antler tools is paralleled by a multiplication of specialized stone tools. The great majority of the Upper Paleolithic stone implements were obtained by retouching one basic type of flake—a long, thin flake with parallel sides, known as a blade—which was struck from a specially prepared nucleus. The simplest way to prepare such a blade nucleus is first to break a nodule of flint in two and then, using the plane of segmentation as a striking platform, trim the half-nodule into a roughly cylindrical or conical shape. The blades are then detached from the nucleus by a series of blows struck along a spiral line starting at a point near the edge of the striking platform and finishing almost at its center. Ideally, this knapping process resembles the unwinding and sectioning of a rolled sheet of material.

Most Upper Paleolithic blades are thin and flat, with trapezoidal butt and section. They have a diffuse butt indicating the probable use of baton percussion. The larger, thicker blades were probably struck with a hammerstone, while a certain number of blades might have been struck with the "indirect percussion" method used by some modern experimenters. This consists of placing one end of a length of bone or antler at the point on the striking platform where force is to be applied, and striking the other end with a hammerstone. The force being applied to a very restricted point, the butt of such a blade is usually small, often triangular instead of trapezoidal. It also has a more salient bulb of percussion than does a blade struck with a baton.

Professor Leroi-Gourhan, of the Musée de l'Homme, recently calculated that a flint nucleus weighing some two pounds, flaked in this fashion, would yield up to twenty-five yards of working edge, depending on the thickness of the blades struck. By comparison, a Mousterian knapper would have obtained only about two yards from a similar nucleus. A biface would, of course, be even more wasteful of flint. The single Abbevillian biface that could be manufactured from a two-pound nodule might present only about four inches of working edge while the two Acheulian bifaces which could be obtained from the same weight of flint would provide only sixteen inches. In a manner only half-joking, Leroi-Gourhan presents this as mankind's "first economic statistic" for the development of knapping techniques that consumed less flint must have been of great advantage to prehistoric man. A hunting people could have carried only a limited amount of flint: with less wasteful methods the range of hunting and gathering expeditions could be extended farther and for longer periods of time into areas where flint was not locally available.

Not only were these Upper Paleolithic blade tools more economical, they were also remarkably efficient. Experiments have shown, for example, that an animal may be skinned as rapidly with a "backed blade" as with a steel knife. A "backed blade" has one purposely blunted edge, on which direct pressure can be applied by the index finger. But it is likely that "backed blades," as well as other blade tools, were often inserted into split or grooved wood, bone or antler, or set in a mass of resin as is the practice of Australian aborigines at present.

Progress in knapping methods was accompanied by an increase in types of specialized tools. One of the most important of these special tools, produced in great variety during the Upper Paleolithic, is the "burin," a stone chisel which made possible the manufacture of bone and antler implements on a large scale. Now, unretouched blades or flakes are of little value for working hard materials such as bone or antler. Their thin sharp edges, so useful for cutting skin and flesh, blunt quickly. The retouched edges of the scrapers are' stronger, but even these do not possess the proper shape for carving these hard materials. Only the burin, of which many types were made, gave the Upper Paleolithic craftsman the chisel-like cutting edge he required.

Burins were used principally to carve longitudinal grooves in bone and antler, isolating slivers of material that could easily be pried off once the underlying, spongy tissue was reached. These slivers were then finished by carving, scraping and grinding with abrasive stone into projectile points, awls, needles and the like.

The second most common tool in Upper Paleolithic levels is the "end scraper," a blade that has been sharply retouched at one end. It is similar to a stone implement still in use among the Australian aborigines. Set into a hand grip, it can be used as a "composite tool," scraper at one end, knife on both sides. Such composite or multiple-blade tools were common in Upper Paleolithic times: examples include burin-scrapers, double perforators, and end scraper-perforators.

The diminishing size and increasing specialization of the Upper Paleolithic tools was accompanied by still another technical advance: the development of "pressure-flaking." This technique allowed far greater precision in retouching than does percussion-flaking. The implement used for such pressure-flaking could sometimes have been nothing more than a flake with a square edge, or the surface of an anvil stone. More usually, it probably was a wood, bone or antler implement. One end was applied close to the edge of the tool to be retouched and the knapper then pressed sharply, with a forward thrust, detaching a flake.

Possibly the most spectacular tools of all the Paleolithic—the almost unbelievably delicate and handsome Solutrean "laurel leaves"—were produced by means of such pressure-flaking. The longest laurel leaf ever found was part of a cache of fourteen found near Volgu, in southeast France. This magnificent blade measures thirteen and three-quarters inches in length by three and three-quarters inches at its widest and is only slightly more than a quarter of an inch thick! Solutrean laurel leaves were probably first shaped with a baton before being retouched by the pressure technique. It is likely that the admirably controlled flaking exemplified by these implements was made possible by the preparation of carefully set platforms for the necessary percussion and pressure.

The largest Solutrean laurel leaves were certainly not used as lance or javelin points: they could have been too easily broken by lateral stresses and would have shattered had they missed their mark. The obvious fragility of certain very large specimens suggests ritual use. But most of the leaves were probably used as knives—by means of inserting an edge (or one of the ends) in a piece of grooved wood, bone or antler. There is good reason to believe, also, that the smaller, thicker Solutrean leaves, as well as a few other points made at the same time (such as the shouldered point), *were* projectile points.

Manufacture of these elegant stone leaves was not continued in the following period—the Magdalenian—that marks the end of the Upper Paleolithic. The Magdalenians are known to us principally by the beauty of their mural paintings (such as those found at Altamira) and for their bone and antler implements, often beautifully carved and sculptured. Their flint tools generally resemble the earlier types of the Upper Paleolithic. It is notable, however, that late Magdalenian times bring an increasing use of very small blade fragments—retouched into implements of geometric shape, usually less than one inch long, called "microliths." These microliths, which became even more important in a later period called the Mesolithic, mark the culmination of a trend toward smaller flint implements.

The Magdalenian was the last period of the Paleolithic in western Europe, where it coincides with the end of the fourth glaciation. The environment at that time underwent radical changes. Tundra and steppe —with their vast herds of horses and reindeer—gave way to pine and hardwood forest inhabited by elk, aurochs, deer and boar. New types of implements, and new techniques of manufacture, were necessary to deal with these new conditions.

The glaciers receded from most of Europe about ten thousand years ago and the vegetation belts moved northward. Tundras and steppes, with their large herds of reindeer and horses, were replaced by vast coniferous and deciduous forests where elk, deer, aurochs and boar predominated. These early postglacial times are called by prehistorians the Mesolithic period.

The Mesolithic was for prehistoric man a period of drastic adjustment to the new environment. In dense forests, game is neither so plentiful nor so easily found and killed as on open plains. The remains of mesolithic culture reflect this austerity: they are much less spectacular than those left by upper paleolithic hunters, for mesolithic man left us neither cave paintings nor carving in bone or antler. The greater time he needed merely to obtain the basic necessities of survival left mesolithic man less leisure. Nonetheless, excavations of mesolithic living sites have shown that these postglacial inhabitants were most resourceful in adapting to the new environment.

To augment hunting, the men of the Mesolithic increased their use of other sources of food. Some societies left huge accumulations of shellfish debris. Archeologists' recovery of fish spears (single or multipronged), fishhooks, traps and nets (with weights and floats) indicates that mesolithic man was systematically collecting other sources of protein than the wild game of the forests.

There were also important changes in hunting methods. Tracking and bringing down game in the forests was made easier by man's use of the first animal to be domesticated—the dog. The bow and arrow, more accurate than spear-thrower and spear, became the principal weapon.

The most characteristic flint implements of the Mesolithic are the microliths, the very small flints that first made their appearance in Magdalenian levels of the Upper Paleolithic. Varying in size from a half-inch to two inches, they were designed to form the points or cutting edges of a number of wooden or bone implements. Arrows, for example, usually were tipped or barbed with these small flints. Some archeological evidence indicates that microliths were, on occasion, fixed to the sides of arrow shafts with a resin, which would melt in a wound. The microliths, thus loosened, caused more bleeding and further weakened the quarry. A similar device is used by Australian aborigines at the present time.

Microliths were manufactured from very small blade nuclei (see *Natural History*, January, 1959), sometimes no more than an inch high, or by fragmenting larger blades by means of a notching technique. Once flaked or fragmented, the tiny flints were frequently retouched, especially in later mesolithic times, until they assumed standardized forms such as crescents, triangles and trapezes.

Microliths were used by all societies of the Mesolithic period. For some who lived on sandy soils near the sea or in rocky highlands, they were the principal implement. But other groups, established in forested areas of northern Europe, had started to develop types of heavy stone tools for felling and shaping timber. These were the first heavy stone tools to be made since the flaking of bifaces was abandoned at the end of the Middle Paleolithic.

This ancient technological tradition in all probability had been lost: in any case, it was with entirely new types of tools that the men of the Mesolithic period worked wood to make staves for skin-covered boats, paddles, sledges, bows and arrows, other wooden artifacts and the framework of their huts. Among these new tools, the most remarkable were the heavy stone adzes and axes—usually made by inserting flint heads into antler sleeves, which were themselves perforated for the insertion of wooden shafts. For the first time, certain stone implements had edges shaped by grinding, rather than flaking, and some were perforated so that handles could be inserted directly into the stone blade.

The importance of this new stone technology was to increase greatly with the introduction into Europe of food-producing techniques. In the Mesolithic, the felling and shaping of timber had been largely limited to the wood required to make hunting and fishing equipment; and the European forest cover remained almost unchanged until about 6,000 years ago. At that time, groups of immigrants brought to Europe the revolutionary food-producing techniques that had originated in the Middle East: the cultivation of wheat and barley and the breeding of cattle and swine, as well as such new accomplishments as weaving and pottery-making. Europe's hunting and fishing peoples usually had not settled in the most densely forested areas, but, for these immigrant farmers, dense vegetation was an indication of soil fertility; so, it was in precisely such areas that they first settled.

Archeological evidence points to a primitive type of cultivation involving constant clearing of patches of forests by felling and burning. Then, after a few harvests, the superficial layer of the soil became exhausted and the farmers moved on to new ground. The communities of these early cultivators grew rapidly. A typical community probably numbered between two hundred and six hundred members. When its population increased beyond this maximum, a group would branch off and clear a new area of its own. Never staying in the same location more than a few years—during which they enjoyed the initial richness of the newly cleared soil—these groups diffused rapidly over most of Europe, deforesting much of the land.

The shifting type of cultivation practiced by these early settlers did not prevent them from building substantial wooden houses—which were sometimes reinhabited when the soil had lain fallow long enough to regain fertility. Examples of such early neolithic houses, excavated at Köln-Lindenthal, in Germany, were built of timber and measured thirty to a hundred feet long by fifteen to twenty feet in width. These structures, with mud-plastered walls, probably were used as both granaries and living quarters.

Excavations of one middle neolithic village—on the shores of the Federsee in South Württemberg, Germany, uncovered twenty-two rectangular houses, twenty to thirty feet long by about fifteen feet wide. The main features of their floor plans are strikingly like the houses occupied by American farmers on marginal land in the South today. A wide porch, probably covered by an extension of the gabled thatch roof, gave onto an anteroom. This anteroom contained a hearth and a clay oven, and was separated by a partition from a second room. The walls, of split timber, were plastered with mud and the plank floor was covered with a layer of earth.

Both the great importance of forest clearance in this new economy and the extensive use of timber in building made the adze and axe—and such other carpentry tools as chisels and gouges—a most important part of the equipment of these farmers. It will be recalled that some mesolithic "celts" (the term by which prehistorians generally refer to axe and adze blades), although shaped by flaking, had their working edges ground by abrasion. This technique of shaping stone tools became predominant among the agriculturalists. They usually employed grinding to shape the entire implement. It was for this that prehistorians called the new era the age of New [i.e., grinding method] Stone, or Neolithic, in contrast to the age of Old [i.e., flaking method] Stone, or Paleolithic.

The advantage of a polished celt (polishing refers particularly to the last and finest grinding) has been demonstrated experimentally. Wood can be chopped faster with this type of tool: the smooth head penetrates deeper than a flaked axe, and the strong, symmetrical edge withstands the force of the blow much better than a flaked edge, which, because of unequal distribution of stresses, is more likely to break or chip. Indeed, polished axes are remarkably durable and efficient. Modern experimenters felled a fir tree more than two feet in diameter in eighteen minutes with such an axe, while oaks more than a foot in diameter were cut down in half an hour, without any damage to the polished stone blade.

To manufacture a polished stone celt, a nodule was first flaked into a shape approximating that of the desired implement. This "rough blank" was then ground by rubbing on slabs or outcroppings of gritty rock, such as sandstone. The finish, or final polish, was usually obtained by rubbing the implement with a finer-grained stone, using sand as an abrasive. Wetting the sand gave a smoother finish. Portable grinders, presumably used to resharpen the celt's edges when necessary, have been found.

The over-all efficiency of an axe or adze depends in large measure on the way it is mounted on a handle. Most neolithic axe handles were cut from the roots or branches of oak or ash. Generally, the stone tool was then mounted in one of two fashions: either the celt was perforated, permitting the introduction of a handle, or the handle was perforated or morticed, so that the celt could be set into the wooden handle.

The first would seem to be the better method: perforated tool heads are usual with the axes and hammers of today, while some mace heads were mounted in this fashion as long ago as the Mesolithic in northern Europe. However, this method of mounting was rarely used during the Neolithic. One probable reason lies in the effort required to drill through stone without the help of metal tools. Indeed, consider the steps involved in the earliest method: first, sink a lead-hole in the tool's side by means of percussion with a hammerstone. Then, with a round wooden stick and sand, bore the hole deeper. Because most of the abrasion is done by the sides of the revolving stick, and very little by the tip, it is necessary, after a time, to use percussion on the tool again, pounding a new lead in the bottom of the cavity—then, back to drilling. However, after a certain depth is reached, it becomes impossible to use the hammerstone to sink a new lead in the bottom of the cavity without widening the entire hole excessively. The implement is therefore turned over the same procedure repeated until the two holes meet at the center. Even so, the shape of the resulting, biconical perforation resembles an hourglass.

A great improvement over this laborious method was the hollow-boring method. A bone or hollow reed is rotated as a drill, with sand for an abrasive. This cuts a cylindrical core, which falls out when the opposite side of the tool is reached. Thus, a perfect perforation is obtained, with far less work involved than in the earlier, biconical technique. Use of bow drills presumably further reduced the investment in time.

Despite such improved techniques, few perforated stone implements have been recovered from the Neolithic. For, quite aside from the work involved, the shaft hole through the stone weakened the implement excessively. The shock of each blow, combined with the strain caused by wedging of the handle, tended to break the celt in a short time. Hence, the neolithic preference for the second method of hafting—perforating or morticing the handle itself. One means of doing this was to place the celt directly into a perforation or a mortice in the handle.

The disadvantage of this method was that the shocks of use drove the celt into the softer, wooden handle, and eventually split it. But, another means of mounting was used by the neolithic craftsmen to prevent the handle from splitting. It consisted of using an antler socket as an inter-mediate piece. This socket acted as a shock absorber, while a stop ridge, ground around the socket (or sometimes a thick spur) prevented the celt from being driven through the handle by use.

Another particularly efficient means of mounting—especially for adzes—was knee-shaft hafting. For this type of hafting, a short section of a sturdy sapling, with a projecting branch was selected. The trunk portion was then split, to accommodate the celt, while the branch served as a handle. In other cases, the celt was lashed to the side of the trunk portion. While the latter would not seem to be as strong as a split mounting, it has the advantage of allowing the adze blade to strike almost parallel to the surface of the wood being worked.

Knee-shaft hafting was very popular, and not only in neolithic times: in later periods, knee-shaft hafting was used for metal tools in most of northern Europe. Its main advantages lay in simplicity of manufacture, good balance and the fact that the blade did not tend to split the handle (as did the blade set in a perforated handle).

Increasing demands for stone of good quality for heavy, woodwork-ing tools during this period must have depleted a great number of Europe's most accessible sources of flint. Neolithic man began to mine extensively for this material. Shafts as deep as fifty feet—sometimes connected by radial galleries about six feet high—have been found at Spiennes in Belgium. At Grimes Graves, in Norfolk, the mined area covers more than thirty-four acres. Flint of superior flaking quality was mined there, as well as at locations in northern and northwestern Europe and we have reason to believe that the mining was done by local specialists, who preflaked the nodules into rough shapes and traded them in this "blank" form.

The shortage in supplies of flint of good quality, and of other flakable stone, was largely solved by the development of still a third technique of stone-shaping—one which made possible the manufacture of tools from many sorts of common stone. The new development employed a crumbling, battering or pecking method. Mesolithic man had already used this technique to a limited extent, but it is only in the Neolithic that the shaping of stone implements by crumbling found wide use. In combination with grinding, this technique permitted a great number of dense fine-grained stones to be used for implements—material that could not have been satisfactorily shaped by flaking.

This new process consisted of "hammer-dressing" the potential tool's surface; by crumbling it away with repeated light blows of different-sized hammerstones until the "blank" attained the required shape. Hammerstones of flint were especially useful for this repeated pecking. Not only was flint's superior hardness an asset, but the repeated blows against the tool detached minute flakes from the flint hammerstone, leaving hundreds of very sharp edges, which acted like so many tiny chisels on the surface of the stone being shaped. Once pecked to rough shape, the implement was finished by grinding. Still another way to shape implements of non-flakable stone was by sawing—using retouched flint blades or sand as the cutting agent, and wood or bone as the "saw."

These new methods—pecking and grinding tools out of common stone—were, of course, much more time-consuming than the flaking techniques. Contemporary studies of Australian aborigines have allowed us to break down the time required to manufacture a stone axe. For example, a diorite axe about eight inches long, four inches wide and two inches in thickness can—with luck—be roughed out by flaking in a few minutes. Pecking the surface of the axe, to remove the flake scars, takes an additional day or two, and grinding and polishing the axe to final finish, with sand and water on a slab of sandstone, consumes a further two days. The length of times varies, of course, with the fineness of the stone's grain and the size of the implement desired. It is noteworthy that contemporary Australian quarries—like the prehistoric European ones—are littered with unfinished implements, rejected because of a break due to an ill-placed blow, or a flaw in the stone.

The stone equipment of Europe's neolithic farmers consisted mainly of axes, adzes, gouges and chisels, reaping implements, querns and hoe blades. The excavation of these neolithic settlements indicates a peaceful life. But in later times—possibly because the fast-growing population competed for the better agricultural and pasture lands—one finds these villages protected by moats and palisades, while stone weapons appear in large numbers.

One look at the stone axes will suffice to indicate that their conception is totally different from that of the stone implements previously manufactured. For these are careful copies in stone of metal originals— the, as yet, extremely rare and precious copper axes that were so admired and envied by the late neolithic farmers of northern Europe. The splayed edge of one specimen is reminiscent of the splaying of a repeatedly hammered copper blade; the longitudinal ridge simulates the seam of a metal piece that has been cast in a closed mold. And, in both, the shaft holes are features more suited to metal than to stone, for we have seen that celts are excessively weakened by such holes.

The metal originals that inspired these battle-axes (and flint daggers) were first introduced into Europe about 4,000 years ago by itinerant Aegean smiths, who had learned metallurgical techniques originating in the Near East. Early copper and bronze implements were no sharper than flint implements, but they had a number of other important advantages. First, metal is not so brittle as stone: where a celt may break or chip, copper or bronze merely bends. Axes, adzes and saws of metal are more efficient than stone for cutting wood, because they can be made thinner and thus cut deeper. Moreover, by casting, metal can be formed in a wide variety of shapes and worn-out tools may be remelted and cast anew.

In spite of all these advantages, stone was only slowly replaced by metal. At first, use of copper and bronze was restricted to ornaments and weapons. Only later were these metals used for craft tools, such as axe, adze and saw, and the use of metal for domestic and agricultural implements came much later and infrequently. Indeed, it was not until the last centuries before Christ—with the introduction of iron, a more abundant metal—that the tradition of stone implements was abandoned in Europe.

In other parts of the world, stone continued to be used. In the New World, for instance, implements—some as magnificent as the Danish daggers of the Old World—were knapped. Indeed, these New World stone tools and weapons brought about De Jussieu's suggestion, in 1723, that the ceraunias were actually the implements of prehistoric Europeans. At about the same time, the flintlock firearm was invented, and for about a century—until the invention of the percussion cap—this new use for flint brought about a renaissance of the art of knapping. At Meusne in France and at Brandon in England, places where especially good flint was available, millions of gunflints were produced during this period. Indeed, the Brandon knappers are still exporting gunflints to West Africa. .

Today, the half-million-year-old art of knapping flint—and similar silicious rocks—is, in the main, known only to the scholars concerned with prehistory—and to a few hard-working counterfeiters, here and abroad, who find it profitable to make replicas of mankind's earliest implements for the curio trade. Pecking and polishing techniques, in turn, are still used by sculptors, masons and lapidarists. In a few areas of the world, all these ancient techniques—percussion-flaking and pressure-flaking, and pecking and grinding—are still used by a handful of primitive peoples. These people are the last to use stone for tools and weapons—the last heirs to a technological tradition that made it possible for man not only to survive for millennia, but, also, to establish the base for all mankind's further cultural development.

35 Earliest Men in America

Frank H. H. Roberts, Jr.

WE WHO LIVE IN THE AMERICAS ARE ALL IMMIGRANTS OR THE DESCENDANTS *of immigrants. Some of us, born here, have parents who came from Africa, Asia or Europe. Others are descended from ancestors who arrived during the past four centuries. But even the American Indians are descended from immigrants.*

In this article we survey the most ancient remains of man in the Western Hemisphere.

Since the days of Columbus and the beginning of colonization in the Americas there has been an ever growing interest in the aborigines, their place of origin, their physical relationships, and the length of time that they have inhabited the New World.

Throughout the years many theories have been advanced about them and speculations have led from one extreme to another. Some scholars have identified the American Indians with the Lost Tribes of Israel, others have suggested that they were descendants of the Carthaginians, the Phoenecians or other Old World peoples. There is a small minority which argues that there was an independent racial development in the Western Hemisphere, but lack of evidence for human precursors and the

SOURCE: "Earliest Men in America: Their Arrival and Spread in Late Pleistocene and Post-Pleistocene Times." This article was prepared for the International Commission for a History of the Scientific and Cultural Development of Mankind and was originally published in the *Journal of World History*, Vol. I, ii (1953), pp. 255–277. Reprinted by permission of the author and the International Commission for a History of the Scientific and Cultural Development of Mankind.

The author (1897–1966) was Chief of the Bureau of American Ethnology (BAE), Smithsonian Institution, and Director, River Basin Surveys. He specialized in the archeology of the Southwestern U.S. and contributed several monographs to the BAE series.

absence of primitive types of man are opposed to that idea. Even though they appear to comprise several physical types, striking similarities between the New World peoples and eastern Asiatics, as well as certain cultural resemblances and some possible linguistic relationships, are now generally believed to indicate an Old World genesis with subsequent migration. There probably was no single mass movement, rather a continuing series of migrations by small groups over a long period of time, although the spread eventually may have accelerated and larger bodies of people have been involved. Opinions differ with respect to the routes followed. Many have reached the conclusion that the northern ones were the most likely, with the earliest of the movements from north-eastern Asia to Alaska being in the Bering Strait region. The avenues followed, once the people had reached North America, would be governed in no small degree by climatic conditions and the time when the migrations occurred. Data pertaining to the latter are gradually accumulating and at least the broad outlines of the picture are beginning to appear. From early Colonial days to the present occasional finds have been made which tend to indicate a reasonable antiquity. At first there was overemphasis of the significance and age of such discoveries. Later they were greatly underrated and in many cases what undoubtedly was sound evidence was either ignored or thrown away. During the last twenty-five years, however, the study of the subject has progressed satisfactorily and it is now generally accepted by scholars that there were some early Americans, the term "early" being used in the sense of its relation to modern aborigines and not in its Old World meaning. To differentiate the older from the later peoples, the name Paleo-Indian is used for the former. The choice of designation may not have been entirely appropriate but it has served the purpose.

There are several kinds of evidence for an early occupation. Stone implements are found in association with the bones of extinct species of animals and invertebrates, or with species no longer living in that particular region. Artifacts occur in conjunction with pollens and plant remains differing from the existing flora. Tools, hearths, and human skeletons are present in deposits that can be correlated with geologic phenomena, and former habitation areas are located on old terraces and along the shores of lakes that dried up long ago. The materials thus far found can hardly be classed as cultures, although such has been done in a few cases, because they are insufficient for a well-defined picture of the group or groups concerned. In many instances there are no human bones which can be correlated with the other remains. At best they consist of a definite lithic industry or a complex of implements with an indication of a few cultural traits and frequently are recognizable only by the presence of one or two characteristic types of artifacts. However, there appear to have been two basic patterns. One was predominantly a hunting economy with gathering a secondary feature, while the other was primarily gathering with hunting and fishing playing a minor role. This, no doubt, is attributable in some degree to environment but other factors seem to have been involved and just what they were is not clear from present knowledge.

1. Fluted Blade Industry

The best known and most widely distributed of the North American materials attributable to an early horizon are those in which the artifact assemblage contains projectile points or blades which are characterized by facial fluting. Longitudinal channels on each face extend from the base towards the tip and produce lateral ridges paralleling the edge of the blade. The length of the channels varies from face to face and from blade to blade, but the feature is readily recognizable and is one that thus far has been noted only in North America. The first examples of the type found in situ came from a fossil bison quarry near the town of Folsom, New Mexico, and were called by that name. Subsequently all fluted blades were designated Folsom and there was much loose talk and writing about Folsom Man and the Folsom Culture. As more discoveries were made it became apparent that there were regional differences in the forms of the fluted blades and that perhaps some of the variations might have chronological significance. Also, it was observed that the artifact assemblage was not always consistent. This led to the conclusion that there was a basic industry of which fluted blades were the main criterion, but that there were regional centers and local developments which could not be included in a single category. Now, instead of calling all such finds Folsom more specific names are given.

Most of the fluted blades and occasional traces of associated implement assemblages are found in the eastern part of North America, although a few examples are known from Alaska, some have been reported from northern California, southeastern California, southwestern Nevada, and one example was recently reported from the State of Durango, Mexico. The main area of distribution, however, extends from Alberta and Saskatchewan in Canada on the north to southern New Mexico and southeastern Arizona on the south, and from the eastern slopes of the Rocky Mountains on the west to an eastern boundary which cuts across the western portions of the Dakotas, Nebraska, Kansas, Oklahoma, and into Texas where it turns eastward to the Mississippi River and thence northeastward along the Ohio River to western Pennsylvania and north to the southern shores of Lakes Erie and Ontario. The chief concentration of material appears to be in the western plains, although smaller centers are indicated at the junctures of the Missouri and Ohio Rivers with the Mississippi, in Ohio, western Pennsylvania, western New York, Vermont, Virginia, northern North Carolina, Tennessee, and Georgia. The best information about the significance of the fluted blades and associated materials has come from sites in New Mexico, Colorado, and Texas. This is particularly true with respect to their age and the reason for the difference between the two main forms of the blades. One series shows excellent workmanship with fine secondary chipping along the edges, while the other tends to be larger, less carefully made and does not have the peripheral retouch.

The original site near Folsom, New Mexico, was of definite importance because it established beyond question the fact that man-made objects could be found in association with the bones of extinct species of animals and in deposits of some geologic age. It was the first discovery of that nature which was accepted by most scholars as being authentic and paved the way for the investigations of subsequent years. At that location nineteen fluted points, the kind with fine secondary chipping along the edges, were found in association with the bones of about twenty-three large bisons which were identified as being an extinct species and to which the name of *Bison taylori* was given. *Bison taylori* may be a variety of *Bison antiquus* or perhaps actually that species. Folsom clearly was the scene of a kill and there was no question about the contemporaneity of the animals and the men who made the artifacts. The bones and the fluted points were in a stratum of dark clay containing gravel lenses and small concretions of lime. The deposit undoubtedly had been left by an old bog or water hole. Extending above that layer were several feet of sediments consisting of highly restratified earth that some geologists have identified as belonging to the close of the Pleistocene period and others have attributed to the early Recent. There is general agreement, however, that their age closely approximates the transition between the end of the Pleistocene and the beginning of the Recent. There was little to indicate what the tool complex associated with such points might be because the only other artifacts found consisted of a portion of a nondescript flake knife, and one example of a generalized type of scraper. Considerable additional information about that aspect of the problem was obtained subsequently from two other locations where there was a whole series of implements in association with similar points or blades.

At the Lindenmeier site in northern Colorado the same kind of fluted point, now generally called Folsom fluted, with secondary rechipping occurred in an occupation level together with several types of planoconvex end and side scrapers; scrapers with concave edges, often called spokeshave scrapers; a number of different forms of cutting edges; large blades; drills, flakes with small, sharp graver points, frequently more than one on each flake, that may have been used for scratching lines or designs on bone (these are not to be confused with the European burin but are an American form sometimes erroneously classified with the drills); rough choppers; hand hammers; shaftsmoothers and rubbing stones of sandstone; small tabular-shaped pieces of sandstone which were used as palettes for the mixing of paint, nodules of hematite and red and yellow ochers that provided the pigment. There are no polished stone tools. Most of the implements are flake-type, only the large scrapers, choppers, and hammers were made from cores. The flaked artifacts show that either percussion or percussion-and-pressure techniques were used in their manufacture. Bone artifacts in the assemblage consist of awls and punches; pointed fragments that may have served as spearheads; small, slender needle-like specimens with eyes that may actually have functioned in sewing or may have been parts of a necklace, tubular beads with scratched ornamentation, tabular pieces of the game-counter type with simple incised decorations, and ornamented scraps from larger objects of unkown purpose. All of this material was found in association with bones of *Bison taylori* and the large American camel, species long since extinct. Included, however, were bones from deer, pronghorn, wolf, fox, and rabbit, species still living in parts of the area. As there has been little or no change in these mammals from late Pleistocene times to the present, their presence is not significant from the standpoint of age. There was evidence for the mammoth at the Lindenmeier site but not in direct association with implements, although it came from the same horizon as the other assemblages.

The Lindenmeier site is located on the bottom of a vestigial valley that has taken on the appearance of a terrace as the result of the wearing away of the ridges that formerly bordered its southern edge. The bone and implement assemblages occur in the bottom of or just below a dark-soil layer that was formed during a wet cycle. Numerous layers of geologic debris extending above it show that there were several periods of erosion and aggradation, alternating arid and humid eras, between the abandonment of the location by the Paleo-Indians and the present. By determining the relationship between the occupation level and the terraces of the main drainage systems of the region, and by correlating those terraces with traces of glacial stages in the mountains on the west, it was possible to demonstrate that the period of the occupation was in late Wisconsin times, during the closing stages of Wisconsin 3 or the Mankato.

The other location where fluted points with fine secondary rechipping, Folsom fluted, were found with other types of implements is in eastern New Mexico, about 170 miles south of Folsom, between the towns of Clovis and Portales in an area known as the Black-Water Draw. Several sites there produced a variety of scrapers and blades accompanying the points. Again they were in association with bones from the same extinct bison and were in deposits identified as late Pleistocene. The sites in question, however, contain much additional material and are extremely significant in helping to explain the difference between the finely chipped fluted blades and the larger less carefully made ones. In the various Black-

Water Draw locations examples of the latter occur in a stratum below that containing the kind found at Folsom and are in association with mammoth, native horse, and bison bones. Native camel bones are present although there is some question whether that animal was hunted. Several species of turtles are also represented and there are bones from various small mammals. It is obvious from the evidence that the larger points, called Clovis fluted, primarily were intended for killing larger animals and that they probably represent an early stage in the development of the type. This does not necessarily mean, however, that similar specimens found elsewhere under differing conditions are older than the form found at Folsom. The large crude types may have continued to be made for a long time in other parts of the country after the smaller, finer variety was developed. Other finds of similar large points in association with mammoth skeletons have been made at Dent, Colorado; near Miami and Abilene, Texas; and at Naco, Arizona, not far from the Mexican border. One or two other cases have been reported but there is some question as to their authenticity. There have been other discoveries of implements associated with mammoth but the blades were of a totally different type. In addition to the large fluted blades at the Black-Water Draw sites bone artifacts which may have been projectile points, and hammer stones were found in the same level. As a matter-of-fact there is some indication bone points may have preceded those of stone not only in that district but in other parts of North America as well. An upper layer in the sites, overlying those with both types of fluted points, contained several different kinds of blades which have a bearing on a number of implement assemblages or complexes. Since they do not pertain to the present series they will be discussed in a later section of this paper. It is significant, however, that they are stratigraphically the most recent of the Black-Water Draw materials.

Black-Water Draw consists of a series of dry basins. Bluish-gray deposits in their bottoms indicate that they were at one time more or less permanently filled with water. Excavations have shown that the lake beds rest disconformably on caliche, a white and greenish calcareous clay, or its corresponding gravels. Rising above the latter are a layer of speckled white sand, the upper part of which contains some diatoms; a layer of bluish-gray diatomaceous earth, which also contains mollusks; a layer of brown to gray silt and sand; a layer of dark-colored wind-blown sand; and a layer of light-coloured surface wind-blown sand. The speckled sand stratum has been interpreted as recording the transition from a dry era to a relatively moist one as recorded by the diatomaceous earth. The lack of diatoms in the lower part of the speckled sand is believed to show that in the beginning the lake was temporary, later becoming permanent and slightly brackish. There seems to have been some interruption in the growth of the lake because in places there is a disconformity between the speckled sand and the layer above. The bluish-gray silt is clearly a lake deposit, although it is likely that the water occasionally receded from portions of the shore and made it possible for hunters to gather there, build their fires and leave the artifacts and animal bones which are now the concern of archeologists. The brown to gray silt and sand is actually a continuation of the bluish-gray stratum but progressive coarsening of the material and an increase in the percentage of saline diatoms demonstrate a decrease in moisture and that the lakes were drying up. Their final disappearance is shown by the layers of wind-blown sand. The speckled sand stratum is the one which contains the mammoth, camel and horse, and large fluted blades, the bluish-gray one is that of the small fluted blades and *Bison taylori*, while the brown-gray layer is the source of the other types of blades. In general it may be said that the main body of the deposits records the last definitely moist or pluvial age in the region. It undoubtedly was the same pluvial as that which produced the ancient Lake Estancia farther west. The heavier precipitation at that time probably resulted when the Azores high pressure area moved northward with the retreat of the Wisconsin ice sheet. A late Pleistocene age is also indicated by the correlation of the Black-Water Draw lake beds with clay deposits in Texas which have been identified as belonging to Wisconsin glacial times. In that respect there is good agreement with the evidence from the Lindenmeier site.

At two localities in Texas, one near Lubbock and the other near Lipscomb, a considerable number of the Folsom fluted were found in association with bones from *Bison taylori*. At the Lubbock site the situation was quite similar to that in the Black-Water Draw in that the bones and artifacts came from a diatomaceous earth stratum in the bed of a filled lake. The formation has been referred to the same age horizon and is believed to correlate with the same phenomena. There was only the one level at Lubbock but it is significant, so far as the main problem is concerned, in that material from it has been dated by the radiocarbon method. That feature will be considered later, however, in connection with other radiocarbon dates for Paleo-Indian sites. At the Lipscomb site the manifestations were that a herd of large bison had been trapped in a natural depression, perhaps during a heavy snow storm, and that hunters had taken full advantage of the situation to slaughter many of the animals. Others may have perished naturally as a number of the skeletons were complete and showed no traces of butchering. There was nothing from which to judge the geologic age of the site, but the animals were again *Bison taylori*.

Augmenting data were also obtained from two caves. One is located in the Sandia Mountains east of Albuquerque, New Mexico, and the other is in the Guadalupe Mountains in the southeastern corner of the state. At Sandia cave Folsom fluted points were contained in a layer lying beneath a crust of calcium carbonate that entirely covered and sealed in the deposits beneath it. The points were found in a stratum of cave debris which had been consolidated into breccia. There were numerous other artifacts similar to those found at the Lindenmeier and Black-Water Draw sites and a few blades of which the type affiliations are not wholly clear. Associated with the implements were bones from bison, camel, horse, mammoth, ground sloth, and wolf. The bison was a somewhat smaller animal than *Bison taylori* but appears to be an extinct species. The presence of horse, mammoth and ground sloth is of interest because that is the only site thus far reported where those animals apparently belong in a Folsom fluted blade horizon. As previously noted, such an association is not uncommon in strata where Clovis fluted specimens are found but it is not expected at Folsom fluted levels. In Sandia Cave there also was other evidence of an early occupation. It does not pertain to the fluted blade industry, however, and will be considered later. The cave in the Guadalupe Mountains contained relatively late materials belonging to one of the widespread Pre-Columbian southwestern culture patterns. Two and one-half feet below those remains lying close to charcoal and ashes from a fire, were a Clovis fluted point, bones from an extinct species of bison, and from an animal of the musk-ox family which is now found only in much colder climates than that of southern New Mexico. Other faunal material, although not directly associated with the remains of the fire and the Clovis fluted blade also indicates a much cooler climate and adds weight to the late Pleistocene dating of the other assemblages.

In the eastern United States are two sites in which the fluted blade industry is well represented and several others where its former presence is indicated. None has produced any geologic evidence of age but the implement assemblages do suggest relationship to the general widespread pattern. In Dinwiddie County, Virginia, on the Williamson farm about five miles east of Dinwiddie, fluted blades, plano-convex scrapers, rough flake knives, and considerable chipper's debris are scattered along a flat-topped ridge for a distance of about one mile. The area where they occur varies in width from a few hundred feet to about two hundred yards. Nothing has been found in situ thus far and the likelihood of doing so is not promising because the location has been cultivated since earliest Colonial times. There are no animal bones with the lithic specimens and there is nothing to provide a geologic correlation. Consequently there is no clue to the possible age of the site. The general character of the artifacts, however, and the fact that the stone from which they were made, while mainly of local derivations, differs completely from that used by more recent Indians in that area suggests that they may have reasonable antiquity. The artifact assemblage definitely is that of a hunting complex. The points are interesting in that they more closely resemble the Clovis fluted in style and workmanship but are nearer in size to the Folsom fluted. It would seem that they had some relationship with the western forms, possibly were derived from them although some are inclined to believe that such was not the case. They do exhibit certain local characteristics. An analogous situation is to be noted for the Shoop Site northeast of Harrisburg, near Enterline, in southeastern Pennsylvania. At that location fluted blades occur in association with end and side scrapers, flake knives, biface knives, burin-like tools, a few flakes with small graver points similar to those in the western assemblages, and utilized spalls. The number of artifact forms is much smaller than in western sites and in that respect is quite similar to the Williamson site in Virginia. The specimens were all surface collected, test excavations revealed no depth to the deposits, and there is no evidence upon which to base an estimate of age beyond the type of the artifacts and the weathering of the stone from which they were made. It is interesting to note that, as was mentioned for the Williamson site, the implements were not made from stone such as was commonly used by later groups. As a matter-of-fact most of the lithic material from the Shoop site originated elsewhere, the bulk of it probably being from western New York state. In that connection it should be pointed out that at the Williamson site in Virginia there were small quantities of non-local stones, the most abundant being from sources in extreme southeastern Pennsylvania. Farther south on the Yadkin River in North Carolina fluted points and implements similar to those from the Shoop and Williamson sites are reported from a narrow terrace which is the highest habitable spot in that particular district. Most of the artifacts were made from a local stone which did not work well and the fluted blades are rough and atypical. The site has not been thoroughly investigated as yet but there is every indication that it is related to the other two. Furthermore, in the non-local stones is a good representation of the material which predominates at the Williamson site. Because of the similarities and apparent relationships between the three sites and the materials from them, they have been considered as representing a single phase and are designated the Enterline Industry. The matter of the differences in lithic materials is interpreted as showing that peoples moving rapidly southward from the Western New York area took their implements, possibly rough blanks also, with them and did little chipping at the Shoop site. Some of them may have roamed toward the southeast and finding suitable stone there made tools which were carried with them as they swung back in a southwesterly direction and eventually arrived at the Williamson location. There they tarried and finding a good source of local material proceeded to manufacture points and other implements. Subsequently they drifted on into North Carolina carrying some of their implements with them, but after settling on the Yadkin began to use the stone from deposits there. On the basis of typology and certain techniques in the manufacture of the implements the Enterline industry has been suggested as representing the oldest of the fluted blade series. Such a conclusion, however, is open to question and at present many do not agree with it, although they recognize that the Enterline Industry does represent a variant of one of the early horizons in North America. It may not have been an outgrowth of the fluted blade industry as known on the western plains but may have stemmed from the same basic tradition which was carried by a group which crossed Canada and migrated southeastward through Ontario to New York and thence into Pennsylvania, Virginia, and North Carolina.

2. *Other Complexes*

Mention has already been made of additional materials in the Sandia Cave, New Mexico. Besides the stratum containing Folsom fluted blades there was a lower artifact bearing layer separated from that above by a deposit of yellow ocher containing neither artifacts nor animal bones. This ocher rested on a layer of cave breccia similar to that of the Folsom fluted level. From the breccia came a series of stone projectile points, knives, scrapers, fragments from large blades, and a number of grooved stone balls, possibly bolas such as were used in South America in later times. Associated with the implements were bones of the native horse, camel, and extinct bison, mammoth, and mastodon. Some of the bones and artifacts were mixed with ashes and charcoal in hearths on the original floor of the cave. The distinctive implements in the assemblage were the projectile points. They are an easily recognized type because the blades are lanceolate in shape and have one side notch at the base. Such forms are not common in North America and except for those in Sandia Cave have been reported only as scattered and isolated finds, most of them in the southern plains area although one example has been noted from the Columbia River basin in Oregon and one from southern Ontario. The form is suggestive of the well-known points from the Solutrean Industry in the Old World, although it probably was not related to or derived from them. The worksmanship of the Sandia specimens certainly is not comparable to that of the Solutrean. It has not been possible to show any direct physical connection between the deposits in the cave and those of known geologic age outside, but the nature of the breccia in the Folsom fluted and Sandia layers coupled with that of the yellow ocher stratum indicates that all were laid down during a much wetter period than any known for the region in recent times. The faunal material represents that of a cooler climate and as cool moist conditions sufficient to produce comparable phenomena have not occurred in that area since the pluvial following the maximum of the Wisconsin glaciation the occupation of the cave is believed to have been at that time. The chief interest in the older Sandia assemblages, however, is in the evidence for a hunting culture in the region prior to that of the Folsom fluted group. Whether or not the older Sandia level is contemporaneous with or perhaps older than that of the Clovis fluted is still not known.

Mention was made of the fact that an upper layer in the Black-Water Draw sites in New Mexico contained types of blades or projectile points which do not belong in the fluted category. A number of the forms fall into a group which originally was called Yuma from the county in eastern Colorado where the first examples were found. Subsequently it was learned that there were numerous variations in the group and that more specific designations were required. At the Black-Water Draw specimens of the Plainview, Eden Yuma, and Scottsbluff Yuma type points were taken from the stratum overlying the Folsom and Clovis fluted forms. They were associated with large numbers of bison bones and were accompanied by rather nondescript flake scrapers. Thus far the bison has not been identified as to species. The main importance of the evidence there is that it demonstrates that the types are subsequent to the fluted examples. Other sites have indicated that such might have been the case but did not show it as clearly. It is possible that some of the points had a late contemporaneity with Folsom fluted and then continued in use after that form was no longer made. The Plainview points, which resemble Clovis fluted forms but have only basal thinning produced by removing several small short flakes running lengthwise of the blade instead of a pronounced groove, have been found in situ at several locations. The type site is near Plainview in the high plains of northwestern Texas. The remains of approximately one hundred bison much larger than the modern animal and provisionally identified as *Bison taylori* were found there. Associated with the bones were the projectile points, scrapers, and blades which probably were used as knives. The deposits in which they were found tentatively have been assigned to the late Pleistocene but it seems more likely that the age probably is early Post-Pleistocene. At the Red Smoke site on Lime Creek in western Nebraska a Plainview assemblage is present in the upper levels of a terrace which has been correlated with the Mankato substage of the Wisconsin glaciation. This would indicate a late Pleistocene age for that locality and it may well be that the hunters making that type of projectile point were in that portion of the Great Plains for some time before drifting on south to the Texas–New Mexico area. Two of the Plainview points were found at the Lindenmeier site lying on top of the dark soil layer containing the Folsom fluted assemblage and from the geologic dating there late Pleistocene would not appear to be out of order.

The situation with respect to the Eden and Scottsbluff Yuma types is not as satisfactory as that for the Plainview. There are indications that the two forms were partially contemporaneous with the Plainview and that they probably continued to be made for a longer period, in fact outlived it. On the other hand one or two bits of evidence also suggest that the Scottsbluff may have had its beginning prior to the Plainview. The Eden point is long and narrow with horizontal parallel flaking extending across the face of the blade and has a marked median ridge which produces a diamond-shaped cross section. There is a slight stemming at the base and the edges of the stem are smoothed. Examples of this type have been found in situ at the Finley site in the Eden Valley, Wyoming. They were in an assemblage consisting of stone knives, Scottsbluff points and bison bones which have tentatively been referred to *Bison occidentalis* Lucas. The lack of skulls and horn cores makes the identification uncertain. The deposit in which the materials occur has been placed in the period following the maximum of the Mankato, but prior to the onset of the arid and warmer climate of middle Post-Pleistocene times. Hence it would seem that the age probably is early Post-Pleistocene. Eden type points also were found at the Horner site near Cody, Wyoming. The assemblage there was similar to that at the Finley site, except that the Scottsbluff points were missing and that there was a greater variety of knives and scrapers. Geologically the age appears to be approximately the same. The presence of Scottsbluff forms at the Finley site shows that they were, at least in part, contemporaneous with the Eden.

The Scottsbluff type usually has horizontal parallel flaking across the face of the blade, is rather wide in comparison to the length, is relatively flat and without marked median ridges. The stem indentations are rather more marked than in the case of the Eden. The type site for the form is near Scottsbluff, Nebraska, and the assemblage there consisted of points, knife blades, and scrapers in association with fossil bison. The latter has been referred to *Bison occidentalis* Lucas. The deposit in which the materials were found was originally identified as post-Kansan and pre-Wisconsin. There has been considerable scepticism over that dating, however, and it seems more likely that the age should be late Pleistocene, if not actually early Post-Pleistocene. Similar points found at other locations in Nebraska rather clearly indicate the latter. But that the form may be basically old is suggested by a recent discovery in Mexico where a point or blade that could be considered as representing the prototype of the Scottsbluff was in association with remains of Imperial mammoth and other artifacts of a nondescript nature. The mammoth skeleton was partly articulated and the artifacts were among the bones in such a fashion as to warrant the conclusion that hunters had been butchering the animal. The deposits in which the material occurred have been correlated with a post-pluvial beach of ancient Lake Texcoco which is believed to be of late Pleistocene age. That the Scottsbluff form was widely distributed is indicated by specimens found in Alaska, Alberta, Saskatchewan, Montana, various Wyoming and Colorado localities, and Texas. In general, however, it should be said that most stratigraphic evidence has been that it was a later form than the blades of the fluted industry.

In southwestern New Mexico, also recently reported from the Rio Grande drainage in the central part of that state, southeastern Arizona, and extending across the international border into northern Mexico, erosion has exposed concentrations of artifacts, hearths, and other traces of human occupation. These manifestations have been called the Cochise Culture. From geological evidence, the typological characteristics of the artifacts, and the accompanying fossil material the remains have been grouped into three stages or sequent phases. The oldest is found in sand-gravel deposits that also contain bones from the mammoth, native horse, camel, bison, and extinct wolf, pronghorn, and coyote. Hickory charcoal, a form of wood no longer growing in the area is present in the assemblage. The sand-gravel layer is believed to represent flood-plain deposits from a permanent stream and as such a feature would require much moister conditions than now prevail in the region, the same being true for the growth of hickory, the last pluvial seems to be the period indicated. In combination with the extinct animal forms such a condition would imply a terminal Pleistocene or early Post-Pleistocene for the artifacts. The latter are mainly grinding or hammering stones, only a few knives and scrapers have been found and there are no projectile points. The economy appears basically to have been food-gathering rather than hunting. The two later stages fall definitely within Post-Pleistocene times, the second possibly not beginning until the start of the late Post-Pleistocene stage. The second continues the tradition of a predominance of food-grinding implements, although it has a few projectile points which are not considered an integral part of the complex. The third stage is characterized by many projectile points as well as an abundance of grinding stones and bespeaks a combined hunting and food-gathering subsistence. The later stages are of interest because they have cross-ties with other remains.

At Bat Cave in the southwestern end of the Plains of San Augustin in south central New Mexico there are three levels in the deposits. Points similar to those noted in the second stage of the Cochise occur in the upper fourth of the middle and lower half of the upper layer in association with points of a type that is widely distributed over southern New Mexico, Arizona, and northern Mexico. Above them were points similar to those found farther west in Pinto Basin in southeastern California and others like those in the third stage of the Cochise. The grinding tools, rough scrapers, and knives throughout are quite similar to those of the second and third stages of the Cochise and show no changes from top to bottom. The middle layer in the cave deposits is considered as dating from middle Post-Pleistocene times and the first artifacts did not appear until late in the period. The top level is believed to have started with the beginning of late Post-Pleistocene. Strictly speaking Bat Cave does not belong in the Paleo-Indian category but it is important because of the associations of materials belonging to a somewhat later horizon and also because of the light that it throws on the problem of the development of maize or Indian corn. A series of shelled cobs, loose kernels, various fragments of husks, leaf sheaths, and tassels, was recovered from the accumulated refuse constituting the top layer. A distinct evolutionary sequence is shown from the bottom to the top. The bottom level maize is a primitive variety that is both a pod corn and a pop corn, while that at the top was an essentially modern form. Since the primitive maize was not introduced into that area from Mexico until late Post-Pleistocene times, the evolutionary process leading to modern maize apparently required only a few thousand years instead of the many millennia formerly postulated.

Westward from the Cochise area in southern Arizona is Ventana Cave located in the Castle Mountains. It probably is one of the most important archeological sites ever found in the southwestern United States because of the depth of its deposits and the long sequence of cultural materials found there. In the bottom level were stone implements accompanying bones from the extinct horse, ground sloth, tapir, jaguar, and wolf. The artifacts were projectile points, choppers, scrapers, and graver points. The complex was quite similar to that noted for the fluted blade industry but in this case the blades or points were not fluted. The assemblage of artifacts and bones was in a lime-cemented layer of volcanic debris which, with other indications of water action, presents strong evidence for a wet cycle in that part of the arid Southwest. Furthermore, the faunal remains are interpreted as indicating more moisture than at present and that there was a savannah type of habitat, an open grassland crossed by permanent, shaded streams, rather than the characteristic desert with intermittent drainage as known in recent years. The wet period necessary to produce such phenomena is believed to be that coincident with the Wisconsin 3 glaciation. Since the artifacts were found almost in the top of the beds which indicate the humid period they must date after the climax of the period but could still be considered as late Pleistocene. Some think that the pluvial lagged somewhat in areas that far south and for that reason consider the Ventana Complex as falling in the beginning phase of early Post-Pleistocene. On the basis of archeological evidence the Ventana assemblage is believed to be somewhat older than the first stage of the Cochise.

The top of the bed containing the Ventana materials gave evidence of considerable eroison and the overlying deposits which are largely of a midden nature rest disconformably on it. There is nothing to indicate the length of the time interval represented by the break in continuity. The upper midden consisted of two zones. The one resting on top of the Ventana layer was moist, probably the result of seepage from a spring, while the upper one was dry. The deepest part of the moist zone yielded artifacts like those of the second stage of the Cochise and projectile points similar to those found in the Pinto and Mohave basins in California. In the upper part of the moist zone were artifacts correlating with the third stage of the Cochise. The dry zone contained potsherds and other cultural material left by peoples living in the area from about the beginning of the Christian era until as late as A.D. 1400. The faunal remains throughout the two upper zones are all of modern species. The age of the moist zone has been correlated with the beginning of the late Post-Pleistocene stage. The main significance of the materials in the two upper zones is that it shows an almost unbroken sequence of remains during that period and also helps to crossdate the later Cochise stages and the Lower Colorado River Basin and southern California remains farther west.

The Pinto and Mohave basins in the desert area in southeastern California are formations attributed to the pluvial of late Pleistocene times. Assemblages of implements consisting of projectile points, choppers, a large variety of scrapers, flake knives, gravers, drills, leaf-like blades and oval blades are found along their old shore lines, occasionally in association with bones from extinct animals. From this it has been suggested that the implements must have been contemporaneous with the ancient lakes. The material is mainly from the surface, however, and in view of the relationships with Ventana Cave and the Cochise probably should be regarded as Post-Pleistocene. A related complex, called San Dieguito, occurs as far as the west coast in southern California and is thought to be of approximately the same age. Along the lower Colorado River and in neighbouring desert regions are scattered artifacts, primarily simple choppers and flakes, which are said to pre-date the Pinto basin and related forms. The complex has not been clearly defined as yet and is not widely accepted. Recent announcement of the occurrence near La Jolla of artifacts attributable to third interglacial man in southern California is supported by such debatable evidence that it has not been given serious consideration. As a matter-of-fact present concensus is that the oldest traces of man in California date toward the end of the early Post-Pleistocene stage. Associated with the artifacts of the Pinto Basin and San Dieguito complexes are projectile points similar, although somewhat smaller, to those found in Gypsum Cave, Nevada. Like Ventana Cave, Gypsum Cave contained several cultural horizons in its deposits. In upper levels was evidence of occupancy by the modern Paiutes, by earlier Pueblo peoples of pre-Columbian times and below them, separated by a sterile layer of considerable thickness, where deposits in which artifacts were found in association with dung and bones of the giant sloth, bones from three species of extinct camels, an extinct wolf, and the native horse. There has been some question about the contemporaneity of the men who occupied the cave and the horse but the fact that projectile points similar to those collected there, long triangular-shaped blades with square shoulders merging into a stem that tapers into a rounded or pointed base, are also found in open sites in western Nevada in conjunction with horse and camel bones seem to validate the occurrence. The man-made objects and extinct animal remains were found in deposits correlated with the beginning of the period of aridity following the pluvial which was responsible for the last great rise in the level of ancient Lake Lohantan in Nevada. This would place the first occupation of the cave in the early Post-Pleistocene. Other caves in Nevada, particularly in the Humboldt Valley, give evidence of inhabitation in later times than the first at Gypsum Cave. Their age is toward the end of the early Post-Pleistocene. A better understanding of the sequence of developments and relationships in the aboriginal industries of the Great Basin and its southern peripheries will be forthcoming when the material recently obtained from Danger Cave, near Wendover, Utah, has been studied and reported upon. At that location there were midden deposits ranging from 11 to 14 feet in depth resting on an old beach of glacial Lake Stansbury. The strata in the midden record a series of frequently recurring occupations and the artifacts definitely belong in the Pinto Basin–Gypsum Cave–Cochise tradition. The first occupation of Danger Cave was shortly after the water had receded below the level of the cave floor. The beach level is that of the 110 foot level and is considerably later than that of the maximum reached during the Wisconsin glaciation. It apparently dates from about the end of the early Post-Pleistocene and is in agreement with the age noted for some of the other complexes.

In the extreme northern part of the Great Basin in south-central Oregon are a number of sites where traces of the Paleo-Indian have been found. The materials were either beneath layers of pumice from the Mt. Mazama or the later Newberry eruptions, the terminal activity of each of those volcanoes. Extensive studies have shown that the Mt. Mazama eruption, which created Crater Lake, took place late in the early Post-Pleistocene. At the Wickiup Dam site on the Deschutes River, two stone knives were recovered from a stratum of glacial outwash, some distance below the pumice layer, and there is little doubt but that they must have been deposited in terminal Pleistocene or beginning Post-Pleistocene times. In one of the Paisley Caves, No. 3, which actually was a shelter on the high beach level of ancient Lake Summer, fragments of crudely-shaped points and scrapers were present in a stratum separated from the Mt. Mazama pumice by several sterile layers. The artifacts were in an assemblage of bones from aquatic birds, bison, fox, wolf, bear, mountain sheep, camel, and horse. The two latter, of course, being extinct forms. The occupation appears to have been not long after the shrinking lake exposed the shelter floor and has been referred to the latter part of the last pluvial. The Fort Rock Cave contained, in the deposits beneath the pumice layer which is attributed to Mt. Newberry, numerous stone scrapers and points, bone tools, fragments from wooden implements, numerous sandals made from shredded sagebrush bark, and some basketry fragments. The Newberry eruption is considered to have taken place after that of Mt. Mazama but in view of the fact that the artifacts are quite comparable to the Paisley Cave materials they must be of about the same age. As a matter-of-fact they probably are considerably older than the pumice. At Lower Klamath Lake on the Oregon-northeastern California line artifacts have been noted in association with extinct fauna, including the mammoth, in a deposit identified as probably late early Post-Pleistocene. Other sites in the same area show an occupation beginning with the onset of the late Post-Pleistocene period. The latter correlates with the start of the upper zones in Ventana Cave and the second stage of the Cochise. It is significant to note that none of the northern Great Basin materials suggest relationship to the fluted industries of the plains or the various Yuma forms. They unquestionably followed a separate line of development.

3

There are numerous other sites and cultural remains in the United States and Canada which supplement and corroborate the evidence in preceding pages, but space will not permit their consideration. However, a site on Cape Denbigh on the North Bering Sea coast of Alaska should be mentioned. At that location a complex of implements was found in a stratum that stratigraphically is older than previously defined coastal cultures of the area. Deposits containing the latter are separated from the older level by a sterile layer of laminated sandy loam representing an interval of unknown duration. Geologically the bottom level gives evidence of deposition at a time when the climate was colder than that of the present but its age has not been determined. The implement complex shows the closest similarities to Old World industries of any thus far discovered in the Americas. It includes finely rechipped lamellar flakes, tiny blades made from such flakes and the polyhedral cores from which they were removed; burins comparable to the major types of the Aurignacian and the modified forms made throughout the Mesolithic and the sliver-like spalls resulting from the sharpening of the burins; flake knives; keeled scrapers; plano-convex blades, probably end hafted; side scrapers and end scrapers; several variations of Yuma type blades; and one fluted point more suggestive of the Enterline Industry than any of the other fluted blade forms. The small representation of fluted and Yuma specimens suggests that they were not an integral part of the complex. In fact they may well be vestiges of an earlier period. If they are removed from the assemblage and the various burins are disregarded the remaining artifacts constitute a series strikingly similar to that of the third stage in the Gobi Desert Mesolithic described by N. C. Nelson. That there was any close relationship between the Cape Denbigh peoples and the Paleo-Indians of the Plains and Great Basin areas to the south seems unlikely at this time, although future evidence may require some modification of that idea. They did, however, have a bearing on the development of subsequent Eskimo cultures.

Evidence for the Paleo-Indian in Mexico is rather meager because until recently little attention was paid to the older type of remains. Discovery of the mammoth with associated artifacts in the Valley of Mexico has already been mentioned. Other implements are reported from deposits which have been identified as late Pleistocene or have been assigned to early Post-Pleistocene. The much debated Tepexpan man is purported to have come from the same deposits as the mammoth and some of the artifacts and has been regarded as belonging to the late Pleistocene. The largest series of implements antedating the better known ceramic horizons is that of the so-called Chalco Industry which occurs in and above beach gravels and on hill slopes in strata referred to terminal early Post-Pleistocene or beginning middle Post-Pleistocene. At all events it appears that there was a Paleo-Indian in the Valley of Mexico at approximately the same time as in regions farther north. The only suggestion of an early man in Central America is in Nicaragua where barefooted human beings and several kinds of animals left imprints in a layer of volcanic mud which subsequently was covered by other volcanic debris and numerous successive mud flows and soil zones. The mud flows have long since turned to stone and resting on top of these deposits, 10 feet above the tracks, are archeological remains correlated with the earliest ceramic horizon in Guatemala and El Salvador. Hence it seems that the tracks represent considerable antiquity, although their geologic age is still undetermined.

In South America there have been numerous discoveries that have been interpreted as evidence for an early occupation. There is considerable disagreement over their actual significance because of difficulties in identifying and correlating deposits in many portions of the continent, because of the apparent longer survival of animal forms now extinct with a lessening of the significance of faunal associations, and because of a tendency to rely too much on the typology of implements in making age determinations. That many of the finds do have importance, however, is indicated by materials from caves in southern Patagonia where stone and bone implements were found in association with horse and giant sloth bones in deposits correlated with phenomena pertaining to the retreat of the last advance of the Pleistocene ice sheet in that area with attendant land rises, changes in river levels, and lake shrinkages. That people were present there in the early Post-Pleistocene seems unquestionable and to reach Patagonia they must have traversed South America, migration by boat at that time probably not being possible. Consequently it is reasonable to assume a Paleo-Indian population for that continent.

4

Human remains attributable to the Paleo-Indian have not been described. Thus far no skeletons have been found which can be correlated with the better known implement complexes. Burials have come from deposits which have been referred to the late Pleistocene or early Post-Pleistocene in both continents. In no case, however, have the bones been other than *Homo sapiens*. The physical features tend to follow a general pattern in that the oldest are characterized by dolychocephalic crania with no artificial deformation, and are followed by mesocephalic and brachycephalic forms with a progressive increase in the practice of cranial deformation. The brachycephalic group for the most part exhibits more Mongoloid traits than the others. Occasional primitive features may be noted in individual skeletons but they are not sufficient to suggest other than modern man.

Present evidence is that the earliest occupants of the Americas did not antedate the climax of the Wisconsin glaciation, although large portions of North America undoubtedly were still covered by remnants of that Ice sheet when the first immigrants arrived. Little is known about the early peoples beyond the fact that they were hunters and food gatherers, made certain types of bone and stone implements, and hunted some species of animals now extinct. No form of habitation beyond rock shelters or occupied caves has thus far been found which can be attributed to them. The time of their arrival in the New World is uncertain. During the last stage of the Pleistocene the great central plain in Alaska and the lowlands bordering Bering Sea and the Arctic Coast were not glaciated and shortly after the climax of the Wisconsin there was an open corridor along the eastern slopes of the Rocky Mountains leading from Alaska to the northern plains. On various occasions a land bridge connected Alaska with Asia, from time to time there were ice bridges, and there no doubt were periods when the strip of water at Bering Strait was narrower than it has been in recent years. Knowledge of glaciation in Siberia is limited but passage from central Asia would have been possible at the time of the open corridor. Consequently movement from Asia, probably crossing just north of the Strait proper, and eastward to the MacKenzie River were wholly feasible. As a matter-of-fact the migrants could have reached Alaska before the opening of the corridor and as soon as it was available have followed up the MacKenzie and into the northern plains. That they did so is indicated by the fact that the earliest traces of their presence are in late Pleistocene deposits. When they had moved as far south as the

Missouri River in western Montana some of them may well have turned and continued along its valley upstream to the passes leading to the Snake River plain and the northern Great Basin, reaching that area at about the time other groups arrived in Wyoming and the western Dakotas. Subsequently another route opened by way of the upper Yukon and its tributaries and thence down the Liard and Peace River valleys to the plains. Later still another avenue south along the Fraser River, between the Rockies and the Coast Range, leading to the Great Basin became available. There is a possibility that there was some migration along the southern coast of Alaska but it must have been later and the evidence for it is not convincing as yet. That full advantage was taken of the several inland paths is demonstrated by the finding of artifacts, camp sites, and associated bones from extinct species of animals along their courses. Some of the groups from the Great Basin no doubt moved on southward through California and Nevada into northwestern Mexico and along the strip of coast west of the Sierra Madre Occidental. A few apparently turned eastward across southern Arizona and eventually drifted back northward a short distance in the Rio Grande Valley. From the northern plains the diffusion was along the eastern edge of the mountains with some groups spreading out to the more southerly reaches of the Mississippi River and on to the eastern part of the country, while others continued on southward and thence along the plateau between the Sierra Madre Occidental and the Sierra Madre Oriental. Somewhat later others probably passed across southern Canada in moving east. As yet there is no evidence of contact between the peoples going southeast of the mountains and the backwash from the western group in the Rio Grande Valley. Descendants from both groups eventually must have passed through the Central American funnel and into South America where some may have diffused along the Venezuelan Andes to the plains of the Orinoco, while others traveled along the Andes to southern Bolivia where they spread southeastward across the Gran Chaco into Brazil, south of the Amazonian Forest, and on southward into Argentina. Small groups may have crossed the range moving westward into the coastal belt south of the Atacama Desert.

The question of dates for the various occurrences discussed in preceding pages is somewhat difficult to answer. Estimates based on geologic evidence are that the maximum of the final stage of the Wisconsin glaciation was reached about 25,000 years ago, that the final recession of the ice sheets started about 20,000 years ago and that the corridor along the eastern slopes of the Rockies opened between 15,000 and 18,000 years ago. There appears to have been a similar opening 35,000 to 40,000 years ago, but there is nothing thus far to indicate that use was made of it by man. The beginning of Post-Pleistocene times is placed at approximately 9,000 years ago. Using the same criteria the age of the Lindenmeier site was given as 10,000 to 25,000, the Black-Water Draw as 10,000 to 13,000, the oldest Cochise at a little over 10,000, Gypsum Cave is approximately 10,000, the bottom level at Ventana Cave about 10,000, and the fall of the Mt. Mazama pumice between 4,000 and 7,000 years ago.

The recently developed and still debated radiocarbon (C-14) method of age determination has provided a number of dates which are interesting even though they may not be accepted as final. Material suitable for dating by that method is not available from all of the Paleo-Indian sites and many of them still can be placed only in a relative chronology. The Mankato substage of the Wisconsin has consistently shown an average of 11,400 years before the present which is somewhat less than half of the estimated geologic age. The Folsom fluted blade deposit at Lubbock, Texas, is reported as 9,883 ± 350 years before the present which is the only fluted blade industry date available as yet. From stratigraphic evidence the Clovis fluted blade complex obviously is older and the geologic estimate of 10,000 to 13,000 years does not appear too greatly out of line although it is somewhat at odds with the radiocarbon date for the Mankato. Gypsum Cave in Neveda gave dates of 10,455 ± 340 for a level 6 feet 4 inches below the top of the deposits and an average of 8,527 ± 250 for a level 2 feet 6 inches below the top. The latter probably is the date for the oldest cultural material. Sandals from the Fort Rock Cave in Oregon tested 9,053 ± 350 and a piece of wood from a tree killed by the Mt. Mazama eruption tested 6,453 ± 250 years. The first stage of the Cochise yielded dates of 7,756 ± 370 and 6,210 ± 450, the second stage 4,508 ± 680 to 4,006 ± 270, and the third stage 2,463 ± 310. The site in Wyoming which contained both Eden and Scottsbluff Yuma points dated 6,876 ± 250. The oldest date for Bat Cave was 5,931 ± 310 years before present. The Humboldt Valley caves provided specimens which tested 7,038 ± 350, 5,737 ± 250 and 2,482 ± 260 years. California thus far has produced a date of only 4,052 ± 160, but beads made from shells which must have come from the west coast were found at the 7,000 years level in one of the Nevada caves which is good evidence for an earlier occupation in California. The oldest date for archeological material in Alaska thus far is 5,993 ± 280. The Patagonian Cave containing artifacts in association with extinct horse and giant sloth has a radiocarbon age of 8,639 ± 450 years before the present, which is quite in line with those for North America.

In closing it should be pointed out that the early industries in the Americas in the main suggest a late Paleolithic–early Neolithic tradition without marked similarities to Old World forms. The only Mesolithic is found in a limited area in Alaska. There is widely scattered evidence for occupation from late Pleistocene through the early Post-Pleistocene but, with one or two questionable exceptions, there is nothing to show that people were present during the warm-dry middle Post-Pleistocene. From the beginning of the late Post-Pleistocene to the present there is an unbroken record of an aboriginal population. Whether the apparent gap is real or only because archeologists have failed to look for sites falling in that period is still to be determined. An interesting phase of the whole American problem and one which as yet has received virtually no attention is that pertaining to the events in Asia which may have induced or at least stimulated the migrations to the New World.

36 Ancient Alaska
and Paleolithic Europe

John M. Campbell

IF EVEN THE AMERICAN INDIANS ARE DESCENDED FROM IMMIGRANTS TO THE
*New World, where did those ancestors come from and how did they get
here? An archaeologist who has specialized in this question suggests some
of the answers while also showing us once again how wide is the range of
material processed by the modern archaeologist. We also note the ease
with which areal boundaries are surmounted in the quest for more
complete understanding, as John Campbell's quest takes him to Siberia,
further west in Asia and even beyond.*

Various complexes from sites scattered the length of the Americas
contain archaeological traits which unquestionably resemble elements in
the Paleolithic of Europe and in the Paleolithic of Siberia and central Asia.
Are these resemblances fortuitous, or do they stand for a Paleolithic
genetic connection of one kind or another between America and, ultimately, Europe?

William C. Sturtevant has recently summarized (under two categories of criteria, *viz.*, "analogy vs. homology" and "distributions") the
methodological requirements for determining genetic relationships from
trait comparisons. These criteria, most pertinent to the present problem,
are—the traits compared must be of sufficient complexity; they must be
sufficiently similar; the effect of similar natural environments must be

SOURCE: *Anthropological Papers of the University of Alaska*, Vol. 10 (1963), pp. 35–
49. Reprinted with permission of the author and publisher.
    The author (b. 1927) is currently Associate Professor of Archaeology and Chair-
man of the Department of Anthropology at the University of New Mexico. His most
recent publication is *Prehistoric Cultural Relations Between the Arctic and Temperate Zones of North America* (1962).

ruled out as must independent invention and the principle of limited possibilities; they must be shown to actually occur in different places, i.e., their attributed distribution must be shown not to be spurious; and finally, the traits must have a continuous spatial distribution.

Sturtevant's cautionary summary is, of course, necessarily and ultimately important to the present problem, but at the moment it is not possible to strictly measure much of the data reviewed in this paper against most of his criteria. For in the absence of highly detailed comparisons, first, among the American collections and, second, of the American materials with the several Old World complexes, the importance in this instance of, for example, possibly spurious similarities of traits, remains unknown. And much the same can be said regarding the practical applications here of most of the rest of those methodological criteria. The most outstanding exception is the requirement of continuous spatial distribution of traits. In archaeology, obviously, known discontinuous distributions do not always stand for actual discontinuities and I shall note that the geographical gap between Siberian and Alaskan Paleolithic sites does not negate any proposition that the sites are related. The spatial gap between the appropriate North American and South American sites seems more important; not primarily because of the distances involved, which are impressive, but because of the variety of ecological zones which have lain for uncounted millenia between the areas in which the sites occur. But, since those zones were successively transgressed by man, and since it is generally held that South America was largely populated during a relatively few thousand years, even the question of close relationships between early northern North American and southern South American cultures must presently remain in argument.

Thus, on the comparative artifactual evidence any case for Paleolithic cultural relationships between Europe and the Americas must presently be stated something as follows: Resemblances of technique and form between some Paleo-Indian and some Paleolithic European artifact assemblages appear too many, and, in several instances, appear too specific to be dismissed out of hand as fortuitous. Therefore, the artifactual data, inconclusive as they may be, raise the distinct possibility of a genetic connection. ("Genetic" is used broadly here to mean historical contact of one kind or another.) I conceive that one or more of three major genetic mechanisms were involved in any early contacts between Europe and America: (1) the passing of traits across cultural boundaries without, necessarily, accompanying population shifts, (2) emigration, the movement, and permanent resettlement, of a people from one locality to another; emigration is a rapid process and implies, consequently, relatively little time lag between the departure of a population from one locality and its occupancy of another, although sequential emigrations within a single population may extend through several or many generations, (3) population spread of the type discussed by Giddings, which is not precisely emigration (nor is it migration), but is instead the slow colonization of new lands by a population which gradually extends its territorial boundaries in response to changing cultural and/or ecological variables; this process, when it results in the eventual shifting of a population to a region greatly distant from its locality of origin, invariably implies considerable time slope. As I shall further note, if there were early genetic connections between Europe and America, one or both of the latter two processes appears most likely to have been the principal mechanism involved.

In view of the new Brooks Range, Alaska finds, and on the Eurasian record, at least one such possible connection seems reasonable. It is generally agreed that the Paleolithic cultures of Siberia (some of which also appear to have incorporated traits diffused northward from the chopper-chopping tool tradition of south and southeast Asia) derived major elements directly from Europe. From as early as Mousterian times successive European Paleolithic industries contributed traits or constellations of traits to remote north Asian localities. Some of those influences reached eastward at least as far as the Lake Baikal region and the upper Lena River, areas lying considerably closer to Bering Strait than to Europe. A consequential portion of the necessary geographical link between Europe and America is thereby provided by the Siberian Paleolithic.

No absolute dates are available for the early Siberian materials. James B. Griffin's recent interpretation implies that European traits reached the Baikal (Mal'ta site) and Lena localities as early as 10,000 to 15,000 B.C. He also suggests that populations from those regions, in response to environmental change, may have moved northward and eastward across Bering Strait between 13,000 and 8,000 B.C. Griffin's estimates are not presently susceptible to verification, but his dates, in conjuction with the known or postulated ages of the American sites or site components in question, provide a plausible way of explanation for an American-European connection.

The radiocarbon dates of about 8,700 B.C. and 8,000 B.C. for the pertinent levels in Fells Cave and the Texas Levi Rock Shelter, respectively, are the only absolute dates for any of the American assemblages treated here. The presence of "Plano" points in the Ohio McConnell and Alaska Naiyuk complexes does not necessarily mean that they are younger than 8,000 B.C.; but the comparative general technological sophistication of the Naiyuk collection as a whole, implies that the Naiyuk complex, at least, is not as old as the South American, Levi Rock Shelter, Alaska Kogruk and Northern Yukon British Mountain assemblages. The ages of the Kogruk and British Mountain phase are not precisely known, but on the basis of typology and geological associations of artifacts, I have estimated that Kogruk should be no younger than 6,000 to 8,000 B.C.; and

MacNeish for similar reasons, thinks British Mountain dates to perhaps 7,000 B.C. The early, open Patagonian sites also lack absolute dates. However, for typological, and in some instances stratigraphic reasons, artifacts from these several components should be as old, if not older, than remains belonging to the 8,700 B.C. level in Fells Cave (the earliest dated level in the southern South American sequence). Keeping in mind the vagaries of radiocarbon dates, and the weaknesses in the sorts of relative age estimates and postulated cultural relationships offered here, it is perhaps more than coincidental that these several American complexes, which seem to share certain cultural characteristics, also seem to group rather closely in time. Further, if the far northern and far southern American sites are indeed related, and if their estimated and absolute ages are even approximately accurate, then it is axiomatic that their antecedents were in the New World at a time respectably earlier than 8,000 or 9,000 B.C.

Griffin's speculation that there may have been an eastward and northward movement of Siberian populations (possessing European traits) into America as early as 13,000 B.C. (and, I would add, if not earlier) is therefore given support by these New World finds. The presence of constellations of European traits, rather than single elements, in several of the American sites more likely indicates population movements than occasional or limited borrowings across cultural boundaries.

The question of access to America from the interior of Siberia during the appropriate time interval has been adequately settled by Chard's summaries, which note the Bering land bridge, and describe a route of travel along the arctic coast of Siberia from the lower Lena River to Bering Strait, a pass between the mountains and the sea which was probably ice-free during the whole of the Fourth Glacial Stage.

Of more consequence, therefore, than the problem of access itself, is the absence of reported finds of Paleolithic sites, along that route, of the kind which would connect the Baikal and Lena localities to Alaska. That enigmatic gap of more than 2,000 miles presently defies a conclusive explanation. Perhaps, as Chard has suggested, most of the old sites now lie under the sea, but it is also likely that the answer has to do with the practical problems of conducting adequate archaeological surveys in the area.

Thus, to somewhat embellish Griffin's remarks, the present evidence suggests that beginning as early as Middle Paleolithic times, successive populations of European hunters moved eastward over the open lands of northern Asia. By as early as 15,000 to 18,000 B.C. (and perhaps earlier), some of those populations had penetrated east to at least the longitudes of the Baikal region and the upper Lena River. Along the way there was probably some mixing with other populations, but much of the land over which they traveled was very probably previously uninhabited, and for those who traversed the more northern regions it is likely that few, if any, men were there before them. That travel through unoccupied terrain would largely serve to explain the strong persistence in eastern Siberia of sizeable, cohesive, constellations of European traits in spite of the distances and generations involved, and perhaps also implies that European physical traits, in considerable strength, reached far eastward across northern Asia.

By at least as early as 13,000 B.C. cultural descendants of those industries reached North America, where, again, the artifactual data, while not as strongly European as those from the Siberian localities, nevertheless reflect considerable cultural integrity through time and space. (It is perhaps possible to avoid the trap of confusing race and culture, and at the same time to suggest that the material culture elements accompanied some European physical traits.)

What were the subsequent histories of those European trait constellations? The new data imply that they achieved wide spatial distribution in the Americas, which further suggests that they influenced later cultural developments in several New World areas. I have previously noted here J. B. Bird's belief (personal communication) that the old industry from the open, Patagonian sites is related to early South American complexes occurring northward from Patagonia as far as Ecuador. If I understand him correctly, he also holds that the old, wide ranging industry was a part of a South American culture base which contributed heavily to at least some of the later lithic cultures of that continent, including those represented by the El Inga assemblages, and successive periods in Fells Cave.

For North America, there are some intriguing, if puzzling, possibilities. The associations in the pertinent level of the Levi Rock Shelter prompt the speculation that there is a connection between Paleolithic Eurasia and the Fluted Point and Plano traditions. And, while the Levi Rock Shelter level is too young to be antecedent to Clovis Fluted, it nevertheless recalls Byers' remark that an industry "of a general late Levalloiso-Mousterian order" was possibly ancestral to Clovis Fluted and to the American Archaic.

A stronger relationship, of one kind or another, between the Old World and an early American tradition is implied by the presence of both Eurasian and Plano elements in the Naiyuk, and probably also the Mc-Connell, complex. Since, with few exceptions, the numerous Plano sites in North America do not contain the Eurasian traits of Naiyuk and since the maximum possible ages of the earlier Anaktuvuk Pass, Alaska, site are in question, there is no clear evidence for claiming that Naiyuk represents a developmental stage between the Old World industries and the Plano complexes. (The age of the last major glaciation of Anaktuvuk Pass is doubtful, but the most recent local geological investigations indicate the last great glacier may have occupied the Pass until as late as 6,000 B.C. If that date marks the melting of the glacier, and if I am correct in thinking that the Naiyuk complex is younger than the Kogruk complex, Naiyuk is obviously younger than 6,000 B.C.) Nevertheless, the Naiyuk complex quite decidedly appears to stand for a relationship of some kind between the Plano complexes and Eurasian industries. Perhaps Naiyuk testifies to a blending of two traditions, but this does not rule out the possibility that, on earlier levels at least, several American hunting cultures were ultimately rooted to Europe. The postulated dates of arrival in North America of European traits do not have to be pushed backward very far in order to place them in the New World well before Clovis Fluted, for instance. And in view of the predominant artifact types contained in the American fluted and lanceolate point assemblages, types which must speak for flake or blade origins, it seems not unreasonable to derive them from European technologies; particularly in the absence of convincing alternative descriptions of the progenitors of those distinctively American complexes.

This does not mean that the presently assigned dates for the recent American finds discussed here must necessarily be pushed further down the time scale, since, as I said before, there is reason to think that none of them mark the earliest arrival of the European traits in question, and there is no present way of temporally measuring the survival of those traits in the Americas.

With the possible exception of the rude Patagonian assemblages, the British Mountain and Kogruk complexes typologically relate more exclusively to Eurasia than any of the rest. Both the Kogruk and British Mountain sites lie nearly on the edge of an area which was ice-free during the length of the Wisconsin, but which was absolutely isolated by glacial ice from most of the rest of North America for perhaps several thousand years following. That isolation, one might logically suspect, left its mark on early north Alaskan cultures, and British Mountain and Kogruk may well represent relatively late arctic survivals of industries long resident in the Americas. Naiyuk poses a further question. If, as they appear, the Plano complexes originated to the south, the Naiyuk complex possibly expresses far northern survivals of European traits until such times as Plano influences reached northward from the interior of North America; but this speculation is perhaps contradicted by the McConnell complex. I would suggest that accurate definitions of the ages of these two assemblages, and the relationship between them are of major importance to both the central problem of this paper and the problem of the history of the Plano tradition.

A remaining question deserves comment. What is the testimony of the total ecological record, if it be granted, on the artifactual record, that there may have been a Paleolithic connection between Europe and America, and that a European Paleolithic base may have influenced the development of Paleo-Indian hunting cultures? Geographical distances and long existing geographical features, such as mountain masses, are of general consideration. More specifically, in view of the estimated age or ages of the postulated connection, summaries of the intercontinental climatological and paleontological records during the last glacial age are pertinent.

The distance across Asia, between Europe and America, is not of particular consequence one way or the other. Granted that it is about 6,000 air miles between Europe and Bering Strait, and keeping in mind R. S. MacNeish's wise counsel (offered several years ago in a paper read at the annual meeting of the Society for American Archaeology) to the effect that one should never confuse air miles with "walking miles," neither air nor land miles are, in themselves, of great importance; note, again, the colonization of both of the Americas in what is commonly held, if perhaps inaccurately, to have been a relatively few thousand years.

More important, of course, is the lay of the land. On the latitude of the Arctic Circle, the Anadyr Range, which trends from southeast to northwest across the Chukchi Peninsula, contains rough terrain, but that Range is full of low passes, several apparently less than 1500 feet above sea level. Further to the west there are similar, if somewhat higher, passes through the north-south trending Cherskiy and Vekhoyansk ranges, the latter of which bounds the valley of the Lena. (The inhibiting effect of mountains on the movements of food collectors should not be over-emphasized as it commonly is. Because they sometimes separate a productive natural environment from an impoverished one, or because they sometimes conveniently divide two mutually hostile societies, mountains may mark cultural boundaries. But at least among hunters, in the absence of extensive mountain glaciers or ground so steep that it cannot be traveled, excuses are usually found to see what is on the other side. In fact, in some areas, because passes constrict the movements of game herds, mountains become the more favorable places of settlement. In the Brooks Range [as massive and as high as the Anadyr, Cherskiy, and Verkhoyansk mountains] nearly all of the major passes were historically occupied by hunters in order to intercept migrating caribou; the same animal [*Rangifer*], incidentally, which has long been resident in the eastern Siberian ranges. My point here is that while the arctic coastal corridor described by Chard was probably the only route across the top of northeast Siberia which remained open at all times during the last glacial age, it was only one of several practical routes during times of reduced glaciation. And, for the reason noted, it should be remembered that those Siberian mountains may well have encouraged, rather than inhibited, the early exploration and settlement of far northeastern Asia.)

Westward from the Lena valley to Europe, there is relatively little high ground. Directly to the west of the Lena, the Central Siberian Plateau contains few, if any, elevations higher than 1600 feet above sea level. Beyond the Plateau, the Siberian and East European plains, divided by the low, narrow Urals, are lower, most of the land lying less than 700 feet above sea level. Some of the Central Siberian Plateau is hilly, and some of it is broken; the Siberian and East European plains are flat or rolling. That broad reach, from the Lena River to Eastern Europe, contains no large bodies of water, nor other extensive barriers, such as deserts; indeed, historically, it has represented a nearly continuous grassy prairie. Some parts of it consist of extensive areas of tundra marshes, lakes, and streams, which during the warm season variably affect, according to species, the movements of large game, but which greatly restrict human overland travel. That those sorts of wet arctic and subarctic areas provide excellent traveling for man and beast alike during three-fourths of the year, however, is sometimes overlooked. Physiographically then, and in spite of the distances involved, the north Eurasian traverse is not a difficult one at present.

It is not my intention to minimize the physical difficulties of mountain and steppe-tundra travel, not am I unaware of those psychological hazards which persuade man to stay at home, be he primitive or otherwise. Wormington, in reference to the present geographical area of discussion, quotes Rainey's statement that "Northwestern America and northeastern Asia, under present climatic conditions, together form one of the most formidable barriers to human communication one can find anywhere in the world." And she further comments that "to the primitive the unknown and the unseen are strange and terrifying, and primitive man does not willingly depart from known familiar things to face the unknown. Only some strong compulsive force, such as the need for food, will cause him to make a drastic change."

I am willing to accept Wormington's remark, keeping in mind that there have been enough "strong compulsive" forces to cause primitive man to explore practically every nook and cranny of every continent but Antarctica. But Rainey's statement is misleading. As I have noted, for those parts of northeastern Asia treated here there are no mountain, desert, or sea barriers. (The same is true for far northwestern North America.) Rainey refers to the barrier of climate in both northern forest and tundra. But the literature on tundra or steppe-dwelling peoples and my observations in north Alaska, make me think he has taken a far too pessimistic view of the latter ecological zone. As in the instance of mountain ranges, the northern cold season is not in itself a barrier to man, at least not to the more recent species. On the contrary, in much of the arctic, winter is a highly advantageous time of year.

For example, it is about 150 miles via the John River from the summit of Anaktuvuk Pass southward to the Koyukuk River. More than two-thirds of the way the river is bordered by swampy, pond-filled thicket and forest. In winter a man in a reasonable hurry, walking the river ice, can travel from the summit of the Pass to the Koyukuk in four or five days. If he resorts to a dog sled, it will take him 24 to 36 hours. In summer, if he walks, the same journey takes ten days to two or three weeks, depending upon the condition of tributary streams he must ford, and what luck he has eating along the way. One further example: For all practical purposes it is impossible during the warm season for a man afoot to traverse the long and wide Arctic Coastal Plain of north Alaska because of its uncounted thousands of lakes. But from October to June he can go afoot in any direction across it at a rate of 20 to 30 miles a day, and if he can keep a compass heading, he can travel it in a straight line, for there are no terrain features which he must avoid. If primitive man is to live at all in the cold regions, he must learn to live in them the year around, and I suspect that in the open lands of the north, Paleolithic Europeans as well as Nunamiut Eskimos learned to exploit the advantages of winter. (As I shall further remark, the barrier of the subarctic forest, where the hunting is poor and the winter snows lie deep, is far more formidable during the season of cold than the arctic mountains or prairies.)

This does not mean that the northern summer is prohibitively formidable either, although mid-summer for some far northern hunting societies is a time of relative want. But in many far northern regions warm season overland travel is severely inhibited, and I am thereby led to the conclusion that the long winters and short summers, of the arctic and subarctic were nearly essential to the earliest explorations and colonizations of much of northern Asia and northern America.

Returning, momentarily, to present day physiography, and turning to the American side of Bering Strait, low lying prairies stretch with few interruptions from the Chukchi Sea eastward to Hudson Bay. There are few essential physiographic differences between this reach and that across northern Eurasia, and the general physiographic (and total ecological) requirements of living and traveling in both are historically similar.

But at the present time there is no such continuity between far northwestern North America and the more southern interior of the continent; more specifically, there are no good overland approaches between, for instance, northern Alaska and the Great Plains. A possible route from the area of Bering Strait lies north around the eastern end of the Brooks Range; eastward across the top of Alaska to the Mackenzie River (the Arctic Coastal Plain, between the northwest corner of Alaska and the mouth of the Mackenzie, is good walking in winter, but, as noted, literally impassable in summer. The Arctic Slope, which parallels the Arctic Coastal Plain and lies between the Plain and the northern scarp of the Brooks Range, is an open, gentle, east-west highway at all seasons); and thence southward in the Mackenzie valley to the area of Great Slave Lake and drainages which lead on southward toward the Plains. An alternate approach is southward from the northwest Alaskan coast to the

Yukon valley, and thence east and south to the head of the Yukon River (about latitude 59°N.), where passes lead out through the Rockies in the direction of northwest or west-central Alberta.

However, while no "absolute" physiographic barriers occur along either passage, much of both lie through a water-filled boreal forest. This means (according to the testimony of both the ethnographic and ecological records) that in order for human communities to successfully live (and travel) in these immense forest wildernesses they must be highly proficient in the ways of (1) water transportation, and (2) deep snow transportation, and, in addition, they must primarily base their economies on something other than large game mammals. Again, in reference to the relationship between hunting societies and climate, this leads to the conclusion that early explorations and colonizations of some northern hemisphere areas (including, very possibly, the Great Plains of North America) were accelerated by cold intervals (retreating forests), and slowed or prevented by warm intervals (advancing forests). This proposition is hardly new, but it should be kept in mind that it does not contradict the theory that encroaching forests dislocate hunting societies, thereby causing them to seek new hunting territories. It simply means that the greater the open lands, the greater the potential ranges of hunters who occupy them, and, here, it suggests a review of recent interpretations of the last glacial stage with an eye for ways in which glaciations may have encouraged, rather than inhibited or prevented, early discoveries of North America and the subsequent spread of populations on this continent.

In North America, the Wisconsin glacial stage, generally thought to have ended about 8,000 B.C., apparently spanned 50,000 years or more and reached its maximum advance 16,000 to 18,000 B.C. According to the recent classification of Frye and Willman, major preceding events in the life of Wisconsin ice included the Farmdale interval, which perhaps spanned from 20,000 to 25,000 B.C., and the Altonian substage, a long lived advance, which extended from about 25,000 B.C. to the beginning of the Wisconsin.

During the maximum it seems likely that all of North America north of the southern Canadian boundary was ice-covered except for a very large area in the lowland interior of Alaska. Alaskan coastal areas from about Kuskokwim Bay around the top and eastward to the mouth of the Mackenzie River, the Arctic Coastal Plain, and portions of the Arctic Slope. Wisconsin maximum ice completely covered all of New England and also invaded portions of all those states that adjoin the southern Canadian boundary. There is no reason to think that at any other time during the Wisconsin stage glacial ice was as extensive as it was 18,000 or 20,000 years ago, although during the Altonian substage very large areas of northern North America were ice-covered, and, of course, there was much glacial ice in the north for varying periods before and after advances or readvances.

In Siberia, the Zyrianka glacial stage appears to have begun about 63,000 B.C. and to have lasted for 55,000 years. According to recent Russian interpretations it contained three major advances: the early Karaul and the slightly later Nyapan, which together spanned 33,000 years, and the youngest, Sartan, which perhaps reached its maximum at 8,000 B.C. The very short Kargin interval of about 2,000 years duration separated the Nyapan and Sartan advances. There is also at least one interval implicit in the available descriptions of the Karaul-Nyapan advances, but apparently Russian geologists have not defined its length or given it a name.

In general there appear to be good correlations between major Wisconsin and Zyrianka events. It is noteworthy, however, that the maximum extensions of Zyrianka ice occurred during the Karaul advance, early in the Zyrianka glacial stage rather than late, as in the Wisconsin and, while recent Russian work indicates that there was more glacial ice in Siberia during Zyrianka times than was previously believed, Zyrianka maximum ice was never as proportionately extensive as was that of the Wisconsin maximum. During the Zyrianka maximum, ice covered a large land area lying between the Kara and Laptev seas, but it extended southward only to the Arctic Circle. Further east, a large multi-lobed glacier reached from the Lena valley nearly to the Sea of Okhotsk, and southward on the mainland to about the latitude of 60°N. Even during that early, maximum advance, however, there were large ice-free areas in Siberia north of the Arctic Circle; for example, there were tens of thousands of square miles of open ground between the Cherskiy and Anadyr ranges, and with the exception of portions of the previously noted multi-lobed glacier and glaciers on the Kamchatka Peninsula, all of eastern Siberia was ice-free south of the Arctic Circle.

In Europe, except for Alpine ice, the maximum glaciation during Würm times extended south beyond the Scandinavian Peninsula only about as far as present Breslau, Germany. That ice coalesced with a western Siberian glacial sheet which reached eastward to the eastern side of the Taymyr Peninsula. South of the Arctic Circle, however, its easternmost limit lay at about 83°E.

As reviewed by Movius, the Würm glaciation in central and northern Europe spanned from about 68,000 to 8,000 B.C. Major Würm phases included the Early Würm stage, from 68,000 to 40,000 B.C.; the Gottweig interstadial, from 40,000 to 29,000 B.C.; the Middle Würm stage, from 29,000 to 12,000 B.C. (which contained two phases separated, between 25,000 and 23,000 B.C.; by the Paudorf oscillation); and the Late Würm stage, from 12,000 to 8,000 B.C., and I have omitted some subsequent "retreats," "oscillations," and "readvances."

These summaries show that there are good correlations between the beginning and terminal dates of the last major glacial stages in North America, Siberia, and Europe, and that there are also some internal parallels. Of particular consequence here, however, is the discrepancy between the age of the Zyrianka maximum and those of the Würm and Wisconsin, for the early retreat of the Zyrianka maximum appears to have subsequently left the top of Asia ice-free from the Chukchi Sea to the Taymyr Peninsula. Some of that corridor may have been occupied, at one time or another, by sea or lake waters, but the apparent fact of its long existence, together with the known glacial geography of the rest of Siberia, and of Europe and North America suggest that glacial barriers were never great enough to have prevented man from traversing the breadth of Eurasia to Alaska at any time since the beginning of the Third Interglacial. Nor, except at the time of the Wisconsin maximum, did ice barriers completely block the open lands of far northwestern North America from the rest of the continent.

During times of glaciation the wide corridors, of course, changed direction and dimension according to the movements of the glaciers; but that for long periods these routes were variously bounded by ice, raises the question of how generally suitable they were for human settlement and travel, and, more specifically, what subsistence resources they contained. In North America, long, severe winter, and tundra biomes (conditions of glacial climates) unquestionably opened the boreal forest barrier for long intervals before and after the Wisconsin maximum, and, on both continents provided the sorts of terrain necessary to northern hunters. The presence of those biomes also implies the potential presence of certain mammalian food resources.

It is not presently possible to discuss specific Asian or North American faunal assemblages in relationship to specific Fourth Glacial corridors or other ice-free areas within the glaciated regions, nor do the data permit faunal descriptions according to short, in sequence, time intervals. But the literature illuminates two or three noteworthy general characteristics of faunal distributions in the geographical areas under consideration (since economies based on land mammal hunting typically require open lands species which are numerous, large, herbivorous, and gregarious, with few exceptions only forms which most obviously meet those criteria are noted here).

For central unglaciated Alaska, the Wisconsin or late pre-Wisconsin megafauna included, among others, mastodon *(Mammut americanum)*, woolly mammoth *(Mammuthus primigenius)*, probably several horses *(Equus* sp.), at least one camel *(Camelops* sp.), several bison *(Bison* sp.), at least one caribou *(Rangifer* sp.), and more than one muskox including, at least, the genus *Ovibos*. In view of the supposedly preferred habitats of those forms listed above which are now extinct, and on the basis of radiocarbon dates, it is quite certain that many of them survived in the tundra regions of Alaska, and elsewhere in northern North Amerca, until 10,000 to 6,000 B.C.

For northern Eurasia, the summaries of Colbert, Flint, Hay, Loukashin, and Sauer, among others, show that several forms nearly identical to those of North America ranged the width of that continent during Third Interglacial and Fourth Glacial times. Old World elephants and bison spread over northern Eurasia, and early in the Pleistocene had reached North America. American horses and camels colonized northern Eurasia even earlier. The Old World *Rangifer* (reindeer and caribou) has had wide, abundant, inter-continental distribution since at least the beginning of the Fourth Glacial Stage. These data mean that during the last major glacial stage a large, homogeneous fauna occupied the northern regions of North America and Eurasia, and that it persisted essentially intact from long before the beginning of the Fourth Glacial until 8,000 or 10,000 years ago. In other words, during the last glacial stage big game, in abundance, occurred across Eurasia and in the open lands of North America, and, with few exceptions, the same or similar forms occurred everywhere within that range.

This is the gross picture. It is certain that from time to time during the past 60,000 or 70,000 years encroaching glaciers displaced that fauna from large continental areas. Is it likely, also, that during or near times of maximum extensions of glacial advances, when ice-free areas were greatly reduced in size, increasing cold and increasing proximities of glaciers in one way or another drove the game herds from even the remaining northern corridors and other open ground localities? On the basis of some archaeological and ecological observations, I think not.

First, the Kogruk site at Anaktuvuk Pass appears to have been imhabited by hunters during a time when glacial ice may have occupied portions of the Pass floor, and when very little, if any, vegetation existed on the kame terrace upon which the site is situated. It is possible that the Kogruk hunters camped there for purposes other than hunting, but more likely, I think, they were there to intercept large game traveling through the Pass, from one open grazing area to another.

Second, there is a noteworthy characteristic about the ranging habits of the West Greenland caribou which inhabit the area about Søndre Strømfjord, on the Arctic Circle. In summer, I have found herds of them grazing 200 yards from the massive western front of the ice cap, and, while in that region there are thousands of square miles of open ground lying well away from the glacier, many of the caribou prefer to stay relatively close to the ice the year around. In winter, Eskimos from the coast must travel to the head of the fjord and beyond (5 to 20 miles from the glacier front but more than 100 miles from the sea) in order to hunt them. Excavations, in that region, of a far inland Eskimo winter camp show that the caribou have maintained this ranging pattern for several human generations, at least (perhaps several centuries); apparently, therefore, the caribou preference for the pastures lying close to the glacier has nothing to do with recent European or Eskimo activities. These observations are not conclusive, but they do support the contention that a glacial climate or the immediate proximity of glacial ice does not discourage large, cold-adapted mammals. The combined climatological and paleontological evidence may thus be interpreted to mean that at no time during the last glacial stage were there intercontinental environments of the kind which would have excluded man from living in the northern regions.

A final question concerns the water gap presently separating northwestern North America from northeastern Asia. A number of anthropologists have discussed the importance of a former Bering land bridge to early contacts between America and Asia, and Chard has specifically commented on its possible role as a route of access for peoples moving into America from Asian areas lying far south of Bering Strait. It is sufficient here to note that recent geological studies indicate that during the last glacial stage lowering sea levels at least twice created bridges (during the Altonian substage, and again at the Wisconsin maximum); broad, flat valleys which extended generally north and south for probably several hundreds of miles. The Wisconsin maximum bridge, apparently a grassy, tundra plain which remained for some time following the advance, very possibly attracted the herbivores which were followed by the hunters with which this paper is concerned.

In summary, while the question of Paleolithic connections between Europe and the New World is hardly settled, the presently available data suggest the possibility that (1) eastward expansions by European hunters, which began at least as early as Mousterian times, eventually resulted in colonizations of the New World by peoples whose technological inventories contained constellations of European traits, (2) that some subsequent American flake and/or biface industries, including the Fluted Point and Plano traditions, at least in part developed directly from that European Paleolithic base, and (3) that while European populations or cultural influences could have reached America, via northern Asia, at practically any time during the Fourth Glacial Stage, the colonizations in question most likely occurred shortly after the Wisconsin maximum.

NEOLITHIC AND THE RISE
OF CIVILIZATIONS

WITH THE WANING of the last advance of the Fourth or Würm glaciation came changes in the basic conditions of life in several key areas. The changes arrived gradually between twenty-five and twelve thousand years ago but their cumulative impact was to breed a cultural revolution. At the heart of the change was a movement from food gathering to food production through the medium of domestication. Like the retreat of the northern continental ice sheet, the movement from gathering to cultivation was slow and doubtless irregular, with many reversals of direction. Inexorably, however, the greater efficiency of domesticated sources of food, whether vegetable or animal, prevailed and spread.

Where was domestication invented? The answer to this problem is not simple. At the least, there seems to have been independent discovery of the principles of domestication in both the Old and the New World, the latter lagging by several millenniums. In the Old World, the earliest evidence of agriculture and domestic animals comes from the Near East, but there are serious and respected scholars who believe that there may have been two or three independent developments of domestication in the Old World and they mention, as possible loci, Southeast Asia and East Africa. Even within the Near East there is uncertainty as to the priority of sites. The problem is not simply one of location or the rivalry between different investigators, each wanting the earliest site, but the type of environment most likely to have seen the transition to the new means of subsistence.

In the previous edition, much of this exposition was carried in the context of an amiable debate between Kathleen Kenyon and Robert Braidwood. To some extent their clash has been by-passed by subsequent work, and the editor has chosen to permit Braidwood to present a summary view. Additionally, we have a chance to see the growing contribution of ecologically oriented work, both in the old world and the new.

37 Near Eastern
Prehistory

Robert J. Braidwood

IT IS DIFFICULT TO THINK OF "EVENTS" THAT MAY BE COMPARED IN THEIR *consequences to the development of dependence upon domesticated rather than wild sources of food. The taming of fire may be comparable and the Industrial Revolution also comes to mind. The release of nuclear energy through fission and fusion may someday be regarded as just such a watershed, if we do not first destroy ourselves by nuclear war.*

For all its impact on human society and culture, indeed, on the whole planet we inhabit, the development of domestication may well be considered revolutionary. V. Gordon Childe, recognizing this, used the catch phrase Neolithic Revolution. Yet the developments involved in this great transition occurred over a period of centuries, perhaps even two or more millenniums. While this is a fast pace by usual Paleolithic standards, the rate of general cultural change has become much faster. We think of a revolution as temporally compact; if it consumes so much as a generation, it becomes something else, another part of the evolutionary process.

If concern has been voiced about the "revolution" part of the phrase, there has also been an attempt to avoid the word "neolithic." Chief among those who avoid the term is Robert J. Braidwood, who dislikes,

SOURCE: *Science*, Vol. 127 (1958), pp. 1419–1430. Reprinted by permission of the author and publisher.

Robert J. Braidwood (b. 1907) is Professor of Anthropology and a member of the Oriental Institute at the University of Chicago. A specialist in the archeology of the Near East, he has concentrated on the revolutionary transitions between paleolithic cultures and the emergence of civilization. Among his publications are *The Near East and the Foundations for Civilization* (1952), *Prehistoric Men* (revised and enlarged, 1957), and *Archeologists and What They Do* (1960). He also edited *Courses Toward Urban Life* (1962).

among other things, the emphasis this terminology automatically places on certain kinds of stone tools. The "new stone" tools are not the really significant diagnostic of what has been called the Neolithic, nor are such tools invariably associated with it. The crucial thing is the development of domesticated sources of food and the social and demographic consequences of this development.

The first edition of these Readings was enlivened by the presentation of a debate between Robert Braidwood and Kathleen Kenyon, a distinguished English archaeologist who has excavated many levels of culture at Jericho. At the focus of disagreement was Braidwood's contention that the breakthrough from wild foods to domestication occurred somewhere in the hilly regions flanking the Fertile Crescent, perhaps at a site like his own Jarmo in Iraqi Kurdestan. Kenyon countered with an oasis, her own site of Jericho. At the time Kenyon seemed to have the better of the exchange; C_{14} dates were in her favor, although not without some lingering doubts. Braidwood's ideas, however, had great attraction because they fit the origin of domestication and its consequences into a much broader framework. Since the time of their "debate," new discoveries have broadened the stage on which the argument takes place. We are less certain now than then where the breakthrough occurred, and we are inclined, with Braidwood, to see the process as a zonal or interzonal one, rather than as something peculiar to a restricted area much less one or a few localities.

In subsequent selections we will see in some detail the state of current ecological thinking about the emergence of plant and animal domestication in both Old and New Worlds. In the present selection, Braidwood, who pioneered in the interdisciplinary approach to the solution of this problem, offers his own overview of Near Eastern prehistory, supplementing his previous treatment with a postscript written especially for this volume.

The Near East (or Middle East—I have no preference) is traditionally taken to mean the area that stretches from the Libyan flanks of Egypt to include all of southwestern Asia as far as the rim of the Baluchi Hills, which overlook the Indus Valley. The Indus itself, parts of Transcaspian Turkestan and Transcaucasia, and even Greece and the Sudan might also be included, but this is not usual. The geographic core of the area is the drainage basin of the twin rivers, the Euphrates and Tigris, and the highlands and plateaus which immediately flank this drainage basin. In this sense, the Nile and Indus basins lie on the western and eastern boundaries of the core area, as do the Mediterranean, Black, Caspian, and Red seas and the Indian Ocean.

The Area and its General Problems

Since all human prehistory is restricted to the Quaternary period, it is sufficient to say that the Pleistocene physiographic history of the area has been essentially one of superficial erosion and deposition, sometimes on a large scale. The area shows traces of such world-wide climatically determined features as high marine and river terraces and localized glaciation in the higher mountains, but the over-all structural geography and the positions of the major land masses and seas were essentially set in pre-Pleistocene times. It now appears that extreme climatic change during the late glacial to early postglacial range of time was not *the* important factor in the appearance of plant and animal domestication. C. E. P. Brooks' much quoted "propinquity theory," which attempted to explain the appearance of food production through the concentration of men, plants, and animals in oases and river valleys as the Atlantic rain winds withdrew northward at the end of the last glaciation, is no longer tenable.

Unfortunately the geochronological details of Pleistocene events in the Near East may not yet be directly equated with those of western Europe, save in a most general way. This lack of intercontinental geochronological precision allows differences of opinion among prehistorians about how this or that range of Pleistocene artifacts in the Near East may be related to more or less similar types in Europe. Sometimes these disagreements have bearing on the construction of grand syntheses of culture-historical evolution.

For the prehistorian—for any culture-historian for that matter—the area was the scene of three great culture-historical events.

1. The earliest appearance (on present evidence, if we take the more probable geochronological long view) of the blade-tool tradition. This relatively sophisticated set of habits in the preparation of long parallel-sided flint tools seems to have been roughly coincident, in Europe, with the appearance of anatomically modern men, about 40,000 years ago. The Palestinian ("nonclassic" or "sapiensized") Neanderthals may be regarded as ancestral to modern men, and the blade-tools make a tentative appearance in the Syrian and Palestinian stratigraphy even earlier than do these unspecialized physical types. It is not impossible, therefore, that the general Near Eastern area was the focus of differentiation and eventual spread of anatomically modern man and of his earliest characteristic habits in the preparation of flint tools.

2. The earliest appearance of the settled village-farming community, based on small-grain agriculture and animal domestication, about 10,000 years ago. The word *agriculture* is here used in a more restricted sense than that given it by Sauer. This was Childe's "food-producing revolution" par excellence, and its consequences were momentous. It is prob-

ably very difficult for us now to conceptualize fully (or to exaggerate) the consequences of the first appearance of effective food production. The whole range of human existence, from the biological (including diet, demography, disease, and so on) through the cultural (social organization, politics, religion, esthetics, and so forth) bands of the spectrum took on completely new dimensions.

3. The earliest appearance of urban *civilization*, first in alluvial Mesopotamia, about 5500 years ago, and only slightly later in Egypt. This is usually categorized archeologically by certain reclaimable artifactual criteria such as cities, monumentality in art and architecture, public works, and writing, but the general social and cultural implications of the achievement were even broader. In fact, there is no general agreement with Childe in considering this step a further "revolution" on technological-economic grounds alone. Civilization appeared as a special intensification of cultural activity which effective food production made possible, but it was not necessarily the predetermined consequence of food production.

The subject matter of this article does not include the third event, which needs delineation of its own, requiring far more space than is available here. Nor shall I examine here the other experiments in the achievement of effective food production and of civilization which occurred, at slightly later times, in other parts of the world.

It will quickly become apparent that the reclamation and interpretation of the culture-historical evidence for Near Eastern prehistory is only in its infancy. The broad outline and the major problems are beginning to come into focus, and the research tools are being sharpened, but we still have a very long way to go. In the range of time we deal with here, each of the levels of culture involved required a very intimate balance with its environment. Superficially, it does not seem necessary for our own culture to maintain such a balance, due to vastly more sophisticated means of production, transportation, and distribution. But the expert in prehistoric archeology faces the duty of reclamation and interpretation in two realms: culture history and natural history. He will have been trained, more or less well, to cope with and be thoughtful about the evidence for culture history, and this in itself is a full-time job and more. But archeologists' excursions into natural history have usually ended in disaster; evidently competence in the biological and earth sciences also demands a full-time commitment!

During our last (1954–55) field season in Iraqi Kurdistan, for work on the problem of the appearance of the settled village-farming community, we were enabled to take out a skeleton team of natural scientists: a botanist, a geologist, a radiocarbon and ceramic-soils technician, and a zoologist. What we learned together, in daily communication in the area itself, about the reconstruction of an ancient environment doubtless marks a new departure in the study of prehistory. It is probably also worth saying that such teamwork between archeologists and natural scientists is not without contemporary importance. Both the Israeli and Iraqi governments are utilizing such teams in gaining knowledge about how ancient irrigation and land-usage patterns functioned (and eventually failed to function) in making their plans for modern land-reclamation projects. What is important for our present purposes, however, is that the archeologist (both in the range of prehistory and of conventional ancient history, for that matter) is faced with problems which have dimensions that go into sciences far beyond his competence. A joint attack on these problems, with at least some field participation and the establishment of easy communication with interested natural scientists, does pay off handsomely.

Pleistocene Prehistory of the Near East

The basis for subdivision of earlier Pleistocene times is somewhat confused, but a working definition might be that the lower Pleistocene proceeds from the end of the Villafranchian fauna to the end of the Mindel glaciation. The middle Pleistocene runs thence to the end of the Riss glaciation, and the upper Pleistocene runs from the Riss/Würm interglacial to about 10,000 years ago. Fleish assigns a few rolled flint tools to the +45-meter marine terraces near Beyrouth, Lebanon (which some authorities take to be late lower Pleistocene), but a general lower Pleistocene occupation of the Near Eastern area is not yet evidenced. Even middle Pleistocene flint-tool occurrences, again on marine terraces of the east Mediterranean littoral and on the highest Nile terraces yet examined, have only geological (not archeological in the sense of "living site") context at best. There is little question but that men, who prepared their flint tools according to the persisting habits of both the core-biface and flake-tool traditions, had already arrived in the Near East by middle Pleistocene times, but we have, so far, little knowledge of their culture history. Really early traces of Pleistocene men, such as have been found in southern and northwestern Africa, have not yet been noted in the Near East.

In the geochronological long view, the archeological sequences in several caves near the east Mediterranean littoral began to be deposited early in upper Pleistocene times, if not with the recession of the Riss glaciation itself. An excellent sequence from fossil springs in the Kharga Oasis west of the Nile parallels the littoral sequence in its earlier ranges, and the tools from the Nile terrace fit this same picture in a general way. On both sides of Suez there were fluctuations in utilization of various types of tools: coarse flake-tool industries (Tayacian), developed core-bifaces (Acheulean and Micoquian), and developed flake tools (Levalloiso-Mousterian, and so on). Clark Howell's detailed synthesis of these developments will soon be available.

Three remarkable things appear in our present knowledge of the earlier portion of upper Pleistocene times in the Near East. The first is the tentative occurrence of the blade-tool tradition, in the Tabun cave on Mount Carmel, in contexts which include Acheulean core-biface tools; blades also appear in the Yabrud cave near Damascus soon thereafter. The second is the appearance, in the just-subsequent Levalloiso-Mousterian levels on Mount Carmel and in nearby caves, of fossil men who show a trend toward anatomically modern morphology. This third is the apparent long persistence, in Egypt and its environs, of the Levalloiso-Mousterian industries, after—at the end of the earlier subphase of the upper Pleistocene—the blade-tool tradition had taken over in southwestern Asia. If the geochronology is as we expect, the early appearance in southwestern Asia of the blade-tools and of human beings with anatomical tendencies toward modern man (at a time when "classic" Neanderthal man was flourishing in western Europe) makes this area a focus of some interest. There is not, of course, complete agreement that either the blade tools or anatomically modern men did first appear in the area. The long persistence and diminution in size of Levalloiso-Mousterian tools in Egypt remain inexplicable in the light of our knowledge of southwestern Asia, but this trend parallels what happened in the rest of Africa. There is some promise that work in caves in Libya may help elucidate the Egyptian situation, which is still poorly known for later upper Pleistocene times.

Traces of the earlier aspects of the upper Pleistocene are now being recovered in Iran and Turkey and in the Tigris-Euphrates basin. A typologically quite early open site, Barda Balka in Iraqi Kurdistan, worked by the Iraq-Jarmo project staff for the Iraqi Directorate General of Antiquities, yielded tools of the earliest of the standardized traditions—the pebble tools—along with upper Acheulean core-bifaces and a flake-tool facies. Howe compares the industry, on typological grounds, with so-called "lower paleolithic" occurrences in both northwest Africa and in the Punjab, and Wright suggests that its geochronological position is probably contemporaneous with the onset of the Würm glaciation. Core-bifaces and earlier aspects of the Levalloiso-Mousterian flake tools are reasonably common surface finds in the core of southwestern Asia, as they are on its Mediterranean littoral. The cave sequences in the interior, with the exceptions of the core-bifaces at the bottom of Jerf Ajla, near Palmyra, begin with a developed Levalloiso-Mousterian industry. This industry, first discovered by Garrod in Iraqi Kurdistan in 1928, has since been tested in several caves by the Iraq-Jarmo project, and Solecki has recovered the remains of several fossil men in the same horizon at the

Shanidar cave. It appears to at least some human paleontologists that the physical types involved are of the Mount Carmel rather than the European "classic" Neanderthal type.

As time went on in the upper Pleistocene, blade tools began to make a more persistent appearance in the higher levels of the caves along the east Mediterranean littoral. The now developed Levalloiso-Mousterian flake-tool industry began to include blade-tools and a peculiar long, thin flint point, and this horizon is the earliest of a six-phase developmental scheme, proposed by Neuville and followed by Dorothy Garrod, although the latter prefaces the scheme with a "phase O." The details of this "upper paleolithic" sequence are not critical for our present purposes; it is enough to say that the Levalloiso-Mousterian industry is completely superseded by the developing blade-tool industries and that microbladelets (microliths) presently appeared. Garrod believes that the sixth or Kebaran phase was immediately followed by the Natufian; this point is not completely clear from the evidence, but I do feel justified in considering the Natufian post-glacial in time.

The general cultural picture is still not so well known as that for the roughly equivalent range in western Europe. It does, however, suggest the same transition from an earlier, more "natural" food gathering to a more intensified collecting type of activity. Two interesting remarks of Garrod's might summarize this six-phase range; (i) the climate and fauna of the littoral changed very little in latest upper Pleistocene times, and in the immediately succeeding range—which Haas assesses as being essentially modern; and (ii) with the speeding up of change and development, detailed similarities between the blade-tool sequences of western Europe and the Near East need not be expected, as cultural evolution now starts to outstrip diffusion.

Strangely, there is not yet a radiocarbon date for this late glacial range in the littoral.

Even within the interior of southwestern Asia, there were blade-tool industries differing from those of the littoral. In Iraqi Kurdistan the Zarzian "extended Gravettian" industry, with microliths, is known now to be prefaced at Shanidar by the earlier Baradostian industry. The Baradostian has two radiocarbon dates: 29,500 ± 1500 years, and older than 34,000 years. The base of the Zarzian at Shanidar is dated at 12,000 ± 400 years, or about 10,000 B.C. A new date of about 8650 B.C. for the upper part of the Zarzian at Shanidar is now announced. Howe finds it increasingly impressive, as more caves are tested in Kurdistan, that no post-Zarzian materials have appeared in caves (save the oddments left by occasional transients). Evidently the transition to year-around open-settlement living immediately followed the Zarzian range. Reed's preliminary examination of the faunal remains from several Zarzian horizons has convinced him that an essentially modern climate had already been established.

On the eastern flank of the core area, in Afghanistan, the Kara Karmar cave has yielded blade tools and steep scrapers with radiocarbon dates comparable to those of the Baradostian, but a developmental sequence in the area is not yet available. To the west, in the Libyan cave in Haua Fteah, on the other hand, blade tools appear to have arrived late; this seems to be in keeping with the curious flake-tool conservatism noticed earlier for Egypt.

There are doubtless at least several disconformities (for which industries have yet to be discovered and intercalated) in the archeological sequences of the Lebano-Palestinian littoral and of Iraqi Kurdistan. These are, so far, the only areas known in any detail. While there is a gratifying increase in the attention now being given to the climatic and environmental history of the late Pleistocene to early postglacial time range in the area, it appears increasingly certain that much more effort will have to be given to the reconstruction of the natural history of the region. It might be said in this connection that a liberalization—in the interest of prehistory, of the national antiquities laws of some of the countries in the Near East would stimulate more field research. Many of these laws had as their purpose the very justifiable prevention of exploitation, by foreigners, of spectacular sites of the historic range, but the laws have been applied to the detriment of prehistorians and their colleagues in the natural sciences (who need to study materials in their home laboratories). But enough is already known of parts of the area to suggest that, at least in its upper Pleistocene range, it will yet yield answers to many of the more meaningful questions about how man became what he was ten thousand years ago.

Postglacial Prehistory

There is increasing agreement among some geologists that the late glacial to early post-glacial time boundary, in what is now the North Temperate Zone, is to be set at about 10,000 years ago, or 8000 B.C. There is also an increasing number of radioactive carbon dates for sites in the era of the settled village-farming communities in the Near East which show that this era must already have been established by about 9000 years ago, or 7000 B.C. Between the earliest village sites known to us and such terminal Pleistocene industries as the Kebaran and the Zarzian, mentioned above, there are clear hints of a range of materials probably best conceived of as the traces of incipient cultivators. If Solecki's single radiocarbon date for the beginning of the Zarzian is essentially correct (12,000 ± 400 years before the present) and some time is allowed for the flourishing of this industry [as the newly announced date of sample W-667 suggests] and of its possible Kebaran equivalent, then the sites of the incipient cultivators probably were in use about 10,000 years ago, or 8000 B.C.—at the onset of early post-glacial times. Within a thousand years, this experimental cultivation and—in the Kurdish area, at least—year-around life in the open were succeeded by the settled village-farming community.

The chronology suggested in the above sketch—the correctness of which is not yet guaranteed—could not have been given prior to January of 1958 and depends primarily on a new but modest-sized cluster of radiocarbon dates, from samples in northern Iraq and from two sites on the littoral, counted by Meyer Rubin of the U.S. Geological Survey in Washington. Unfortunately, all the problems of the "geobiochemical" contamination of radiocarbon samples, before they reach the counter, beset the use of this and several other series of radiocarbon dates from the Near East. It is clear that at the present moment (and this will be true until many more samples are counted, from many more different sites), the available fabric of radiocarbon dates can give us no more than a *general* indication of the late prehistoric time ranges of the area. This will throw us back primarily upon our old-style typological assessments of the comparative archeological stratigraphy of the various sites in the area. To these assessments we may then add our own judgments of the dating probabilities based on the general pattern of the radiocarbon dating fabric. For the Near East, at least, the cutting edge of radiocarbon dating as a research tool is still blunt because of our difficulties with the "geobiochemical" contamination factor. Understanding of this contamination factor will demand competences in a middle ground lying between archeology and nuclear physics, which badly need to be developed.

The chronological sketch at the beginning of this section was made by selecting a cluster of three radiocarbon dates of about 8500 years ago, or 6500 B.C., as the probable true general date (out of a series of 11) for the early village site of Jarmo in Iraqi Kurdistan. Jarmo was a single-phase manifestation which cannot have had a time duration of more than a few hundred years. The next phase of the early village-farming community era, in terms of comparative archeological stratigraphy, as seen at Matarrah and Hassuna in the upper Tigris piedmont and at Mersin on the Cilician coast of Turkey, seems to cluster at between 500 and 1000 years later, say at about 5750 B.C. Since each of the pertinent phases, on the sites mentioned, will probably have had durations of several hundred years, no essential gap between the Jarmo phase and the Matarrah-Hassuna and Mersin phase need be postulated. The group of five Jarmo dates will not work if the Matarrah, Hassuna, and Mersin dates are correct, since Jarmo clearly precedes the pertinent basal materials of these sites in terms of comparative archeological stratigraphy and has several categories of technological descendants in Matarrah and Hassuna. The two earliest Jarmo dates, of over 11,000 years ago, are simply not conceivable in terms of comparative archeological stratigraphy as we now understand it. Jarmo must lie near, but not at, the very beginning of the era of village-farming communities; in my judgment this beginning should be put at about 7000 B.C.

It should be made clear that Jarmo is *not* conceived of as *the* spot where the village-farming community level of existence came into

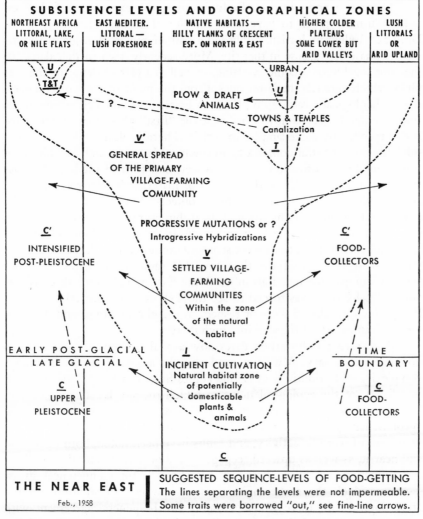

SUBSISTENCE LEVELS AND GEOGRAPHICAL ZONES				
NORTHEAST AFRICA LITTORAL, LAKE, OR NILE FLATS	EAST MEDITER. LITTORAL — LUSH FORESHORE	NATIVE HABITATS — HILLY FLANKS OF CRESCENT ESP. ON NORTH & EAST	HIGHER COLDER PLATEAUS SOME LOWER BUT ARID VALLEYS	LUSH LITTORALS OR ARID UPLAND

U
T&T
PLOW & DRAFT ANIMALS
URBAN
U
TOWNS & TEMPLES
Canalization
?
V'
GENERAL SPREAD OF THE PRIMARY VILLAGE-FARMING COMMUNITY
I
PROGRESSIVE MUTATIONS or ?
Introgressive Hybridizations
C'
INTENSIFIED POST-PLEISTOCENE
V
SETTLED VILLAGE-FARMING COMMUNITIES
Within the zone of the natural habitat
C'
FOOD-COLLECTORS
EARLY POST-GLACIAL
LATE GLACIAL
C
UPPER PLEISTOCENE
I
INCIPIENT CULTIVATION
Natural habitat zone of potentially domesticable plants & animals
TIME
BOUNDARY
C
FOOD-COLLECTORS
C

THE NEAR EAST
Feb., 1958

SUGGESTED SEQUENCE-LEVELS OF FOOD-GETTING
The lines separating the levels were not impermeable.
Some traits were borrowed "out," see fine-line arrows.

Figure 1 C, food-collecting; C′, intensified food-collecting; I, incipient cultivation; V, village-farming communities; V′, intensified village-farming communities; T + T, towns and temples; U, urban communities.

being—we do not even believe that there ever was one single such spot—but only that Jarmo represents the earliest example of settled village life which the accident of its prior discovery has allowed us to use as a basis for description. To my mind, however, it is not an accident that Jarmo was found in the hilly-flanks zone of the "fertile crescent." This zone of upper piedmont and intermontane valleys, stretching at least from Syro-Cilicia into Iran, flanking the Taurus-Zagros arc and still receiving ample rainfall, appears increasingly to have been *the* natural habitat of the potentially domesticable plants and animals.

There is a complication. Early in 1956, the excavators of Tell es-Sultan (usually taken to have been the site of Joshua's Jericho), in the Dead Sea Valley in Jordan, published a pair of radiocarbon dates for the second phase above base in that site. More recently, two further dates for the same level have become available, as well as a pair of dates for the first phase which parallels the latter ones. From the point of view of comparative archeological stratigraphy, the two basal phases of Tell es-Sultan are enigmatic, and there is now word that the "first" phase may in fact have been preceded by some simpler materials. There is clear evidence of considerable architectural complexity in the basal layers, which include thick stone-founded fortifications, with a tower, and formed mud-brick house walls, but the remainder of the catalog of materials is relatively primitive and includes neither pottery nor metal objects. Taking her cue from the relatively large area of the site and its architectural complexity, Kathleen Kenyon used the words *urban* and *civilization* in describing its cultural level, and these implications were strongly contested by Childe and Braidwood. Also, in view of the then available radiocarbon dates for other roughly comparable materials in the Near East, which were all considerably later, Kenyon was forced to see the Tell es-Sultan material as something which developed without respect to the chronological and developmental framework of the area in which it lay.

With earlier radiocarbon dates now available elsewhere, this view is no longer necessary. My own tendency, in assessing the dichotomous complexity and primitiveness of the Tell es-Sultan catalog, along with the peculiarity of the ecological niche in which the site lay (some 900 feet below sea level, in an arid valley), is still to suspect that there is some "geobiochemical" contamination in the radiocarbon samples. The site lies in an area of tectonic activity, and faults have been noted, both in the site and near it, as well as upward seepage of radioactive natural gases. The contamination possibility, however, clearly calls for competences in assessment which the archeologist does not possess. In addition, on the archeological side, there would certainly not be general agreement with Kenyon's reading of the comparative archeological stratigraphy of her site.

The controversy has been of some culture-historical importance for the reason that Kenyon and her colleagues have raised again the old issue of the "propinquity theory" for an oasis origin of agriculture and animal domestication. In spite of its arid, below-sea-level situation, Tell es-Sultan does lie adjacent to an excellent fresh-water spring. But the evidence for the origins of domestication—while still limited and badly in need of further bolstering—has increasingly pointed rather toward the upper piedmont and intermontane valley zone of the "hilly flanks of the crescent." This not only appears to have been the natural habitat for the potentially domesticable wild plants and animals but also seems to have had no important climatic variation since later upper Pleistocene times. While to take this view may be to ignore certain minor depositional features, especially in the first millennium b.c., which may have been climatically determined, one does feel justified in making a general assessment of the environmental situation of some 10,000 years ago in terms of the present situation. In fact, it is not clear that, in the core area of the Near East, the late glacial to early post-glacial time boundary was at all an "event" in climatic or environmental terms. Some allowance must naturally be made for the loss of vegetation through overgrazing and charcoal burning, and for the extinction of certain wild animals (hunting from Ford model T's finished off the onager about 1928!). Our reconstruction here is founded on the proposition that the available evidence does locate the natural habitat in the hilly flanks zone, and that domestication took place within this natural habitat.

There are, of course, more excavated sites upon which to base our reconstruction than those which [have been] indicated. But there are by no means enough. Our knowledge of the potentially rich (from the point of view of natural habitat) districts of Iran, Turkey, and Syria is almost, if not completely, blank, and little has been done in this range of interest in Egypt in some years. This situation reflects in part the prevailing unfavorable circumstances discussed above for making an up-to-date prehistoric excavation and in part the great cost of mounting a well-rounded expedition (with a proper staff complement of natural scientists). Hence the reconstruction may be, to a degree, an artifact that reflects the incompleteness of the record. A fairly recent assessment of much of the area is available, and it will therefore not be necessary to name too many of the sites involved.

Incipient Cultivation

Figure 1 indicates how the principle of sloping horizons for the successive eras must be involved in thinking about the subregions of the Near East. I have suggested above the general picture given by the archeological materials for the range of Pleistocene times in the Near East. The means of obtaining food during the whole range was through gathering or collection; the range is usually referred to as the food-gathering stage. If the stage had substages or eras, the last of these was one of more intensive collection—a more intimate "living into" a given environment. We noted that the Kebaran of Palestine and the Zarzian of Iraqi Kurdistan appear to have terminated this era, sometime after 10,000 B. C. [The newly announced date of the upper part of the Shanidar Zarzian is about 8650 B.C.] The data in Fig. 1 suggest, however, that food collection was continued in areas adjacent to the central core of the Near East, and certain materials in caves on the Caspian and Libyan foreshores suggest even further intensifications in collecting activities. In connection with these peripheral areas, the notion of a "mesolithic" stage has been advanced, as in the case of northwestern Europe, to describe archeological materials showing cultural readaptations—still on a food-collecting level —to the post-glacial environment. The notion will gain validity only if a significant environmental change can be shown to have occurred.

It appears increasingly doubtful, however, whether this or any other meaningful concept of "mesolithic-ness" can be applied to the core area. In Iraqi Kurdistan, the next materials (following the Zarzian), from Karim Shahir and comparable sites, which are simple open-air establishments, suggest an incipience of cultivation. One of these open sites, Solecki's Zawi Chemi, now has a newly announced radiocarbon date of about 8900 B.C. In Palestine, these are paralleled by the Natufian materials, still primarily in caves but perhaps slightly more convincing as evidence of an era of incipient cultivation. An important Natufian open-air site has just been announced for northern Palestine by Jean Perrot. This era prefaces the swing from the food-gathering to the food-producing stage. Its catalog includes some suggestion of animal domestication, some authorities claiming domestication of the dog. There are flint sickles for reaping, crude milling stones for grinding seeds, and celts; the latter may have been used as either hoes or axes, or as both. Further delineation of this era is very badly needed, and since the era was one of transition and, doubtless, of making-do with some old tool types, it will be an exceedingly difficult one to substantiate fully. The era is still characterized by flint blade tools and microliths. The probability is that the natural scientists will do better here than the conventional archeologists.

Village-farming Communities

Next, in the core area, comes the first phase of fully settled village sites, of which Jarmo is simply the earliest example which happens so far to have been found. In the next phase of the village-farming community era, which rather quickly succeeds the Jarmo phase, there are at least five regionally different village assemblages (catalogs of artifactual materials): those of Hassunan type in the upper Tigris piedmont, those of the Amouq

A-Mersin type of Syro-Cilicia, those of the third (?) Tell es-Sultan-Abou Gosh type in inland Palestine, those of the Fayum A type in Egypt, and those of the Sialk I type in northern Iran. Unless the radiocarbon dates on the Fayum A of Egypt are wrong—and more samples should be counted —the principle of the sloping horizon is clearly involved. This, of course, has a bearing on the actual chronological position of the Tell es-Sultan materials.

The earliest of the village-farming communities appear to have clustered still within the natural habit zone of the upper piedmont and intermontane valleys of the "crescent," where the wild wheats, barley, sheep, goats, pigs, cattle, and some kind of equid were all at home in nature. It has been suggested that the development was bound to this zone until permissive mutations, or introgressive hybridization, operated, especially on the plants, to allow the domesticates to be removed from their natural area. The curve in Fig. 1 is inflected to suggest more general spread after this had taken place.

One consequence of this spread was the diffusion of the wheat-barley-sheep-goat-cattle complex, and much of the generalized cultural know-how which had developed with it, to the boundaries of the Near East and far beyond, wherever the environmental situation allowed such spread. We have hints, through radiocarbon dating, that the new way of life had extended well up the Danube Valley by about 4000 B.C. and that by 2500 B.C. it had pretty well covered Europe. It also went eastward; wheat, at least, was being grown in China by at least 1500 B.C., although it does not appear to have been the earliest domesticated plant there. A different consequence of the spread from the hilly-flanks zone of the natural habitat— given the mutations or hybridizations—was the apparent "fingering" movement of early farmers down the mud flats of the Tigris and Euphrates into classic southern Mesopotamia. This probably took place toward the end of the Hassuna phase or early in the succeeding Halaf phase. It is our suggestion that the principles of canalization were learned on these mud flats; canalization made the occupation of classic southern Mesopotamia by farmers feasible. The data in Fig. 1 suggest that a new era arose on this basis in southern Mesopotamia, and one radiocarbon date indicates that this era was well under way by 4000 B.C. This was an era which is archeologically manifested by town-sized settlements, temple structures of some degree of monumentality, metallurgy as a specialized craft, and evidently (since they are already present at the beginning of the next era) the use of draft animals and the plow. Even in the first or Ubaidian phase of this era of towns, the strength of the new cultural potential of southern Mesopotamia is suggested by the *oikoumenê* of the spread of its painted pottery style—from the Mediterranean coast to the rim of the Anatolian plateau to the uplands of Iran.

This is the place to end our survey; the next era is that of the appearance of urban civilization in southern Mesopotamia, about 3500 B.C., followed by the beginning of the Egyptian dynasties around 3000 B.C., and by that time prehistory per se is theoretically ended in the Near East.

Conclusions

In summary, it needs to be repeated once more that what is offered here is only one prehistorian's interpretation of very incomplete evidence. For late upper Pleistocene times especially, much more must be learned of the environments which were available, of the human physical types (only one juvenile example and various fragmentary bits exist), and of the different cultural levels. Only snatches of evidence are now available for the era of incipient cultivation, which prefaced the great swing from the food-gathering to the food-producing stage, and very sophisticated environmental reconstructions will be necessary before the cultural achievements of this era can gain meaning. The same holds particularly for the earlier phases of the era of the settled-village–farming community. In reconstructing the general culture history of the Near East, for late glacial to early postglacial times, the concept of sloping horizons appears to be a useful one. It also appears that the zone of the natural habitat may have been a focus of "nuclearity," and that some eras and phases of cultural development may have been manifested there but not elsewhere.

It must be obvious how much the prehistoric archeologist needs the aid of his interested colleagues in the natural sciences. First and foremost, however, the prehistorian's business is with men—with the anthropology of extinct cultures. He needs to discover all he can about the plants and animals that lived with the men, but the plants and animals did not domesticate themselves. Men domesticated them. The prehistorian is very much aware of the innumerable "how" and "why" questions which still confront him. In the Near East, it is simply a matter of his requiring much more information from the good earth, and some help in interpreting it.

Appendix: July, 1966

The manuscript for the above article was completed almost nine years ago. A very considerable amount of prehistoric archeological and paleoenvironmental research has continued in the Near East since then. This note briefly supplements a slightly more detailed up-dating (drafted in April, 1963) of the article, given in Joseph R. Caldwell's *New Roads to Yesterday*, and concentrates on the central problem of the article—the appearance of a village-farming community way of life.

1. The most important additions to knowledge of the early village sequence along the littoral come from the range of the so-called "Pre-

Pottery Neolithic B" (P.P.N.B. of Tell es-Sultan). Beidha, Munhatta, Ramad and certain sites in the Lebanese Bekaa are to be reckoned with. On the middle Euphrates in Syria, Mureybat and Bouqras *may* fit into the same general picture. The interest here lies in Jean Perrot's recent questioning of the availability of *primary* evidence for effective food-production in at least the Natufian, P.P.N.A. and P.P.N.B. ranges of the littoral. In effect, were village-like settlements of some architectural complexity already established by intensified food collectors? What effect will this have on my heuristic device of a range of incipient cultivation and domestication, when more evidence is in hand? Were we too quick in assuming that "village-ness" necessarily implied food-production?

2. Corollary to the above questions, also, what will be the final interpretation of new evidence on the Sebilian sequence in Egypt, which may have persisted long enough to at least be contemporary with the Natufian of Palestine? I am not yet convinced, however, that Egypt will yield hints of independent beginnings toward effective food-production.

3. Our knowledge of the Zagros flanks has been considerably expanded through the work at such Iranian sites as Asiab, Sarab, Hajji Firuz, Ali Kosh, Guran, and Ganj-i-Dareh. Following suggestions made in *Courses Toward Urban Life* as to the importance of environmental diversity in this region, Kent Flannery [see I:38] has recently and usefully surveyed the evidence available to him. It has been clear to me for over five years that my original conception of the effective limits of the "natural habitat zone" were too restrictive. Ali Kosh, lying at an elevation of ca. 650 ft., and Asiab and Ganj-i-Dareh at ca. 4500 ft., emphasize this. All of the above sites together cover some range of time (perhaps ca. 8500 to 5500 B.C. on present radiocarbon indications) and may be fitted into the rough comparative stratigraphy established earlier in northeastern Iraq by the Soleckis and Braidwood *et al.* With indications of domesticated sheep at Zawi Chemi Shanidar and of both domesticated cereals and animals at Jarmo, it would appear that settled villages, along the Zagros flanks at least, do imply food-production.

4. In its first season at Çayönü, near Diyarbakir, the Joint Istanbul and Chicago Prehistoric Project in 1964 began work on the general problem along the Tauros flanks in southeastern Turkey. The Çayönü village site yielded an inventory somewhat analogous to that of Jarmo, but with links towards the littoral in its flint industry. Radioactive carbon indications suggest that the site was already occupied by about 7000 B.C. Some domesticated animals are tentatively indicated, but it is not yet clear whether the cereal grains were of cultivated varieties. Although the inventory was without pottery, tools of native copper were being worked.

5. Of work so far reported on the Anatolian plateau, only that at Suberde seems to call for addition to basal Hacilar as pertinent to our cen-

tral problem. In my opinion, the bulk of the spectacular yield at Çatal Hüyük was probably contemporary with the late Hassuna or earlier Halaf manifestations further east. In this connection, a word of caution is again necessary regarding radioactive carbon age determinations. Some excavators and some authors of general accounts persist in ignoring international convention and the journal *Radiocarbon's* policy, and list their determinations in terms of the "new" rather than the Libby half-life. This makes their "dates" *appear* to be considerably earlier than determinations given in conventional terms. It may be added, also, that there is now reason to believe that radiocarbon "years" did not always correspond to calendar years—some laboratories are beginning to cite their determinations as "C^{14} years ago," and will *not* attempt to equate these to real B.P. or B.C. "dates." This, of course, also concerns the determinations noted here and in my original article, although all are given in Libby half-life terms.

6. If it were to be rewritten now, the article would surely stress the apparent early spread of food-production to Greece, Crete and the lower Balkans.

In retrospect, I believe the article represented a fair assessment of the evidence as it was available to me in late 1958. But as a synthesis which needed (and has had) further testing, there would now be necessary changes. This does not embarrass me in the least. As Robert M. Adams wrote recently, few scholars but anthropologists ". . . combine a sense of the importance of the pivotal episodes of man's cultural evolution, a necessarily reconstructive or synthetic outlook, and a tolerance for ambiguity." There is still much ambiguity about any synthesis we can yet make concerning Near Eastern prehistory.

38 The Ecology of
Early Food Production
in Mesopotamia

Kent V. Flannery

AS KENT FLANNERY, FOLLOWING LESLIE WHITE, POINTS OUT IN THE ARTICLE
below, mankind probably knew that seeds sprouted "for tens of thou-
sands of years before cultivation of plants began." The important thing
was not this discovery, which must have been made and forgotten many,
many times, but the network of relationships between men, animals and
plants. It is essential, then, if one wishes to understand the origins of the
Neolithic, or of simple food production, if the former term offends you,
to adopt an ecological viewpoint, feeding available archaeological data
into a complex framework of what is known and guessed about the inter-
play of biological, geological, climatological, culturological and other
situations and forces. Obviously, the first casualty of such an approach is
the simplistic explanation. As methods become complex, the content of
knowledge becomes more voluminous. The archaeologist must always use
his spade and his trowel, but these first-stage tools cannot substitute for
finer instruments of analysis. Now the archaeologist must command the
relevant theories of many contingent fields: genetics, agronomy, clima-
tology, comparative mammalian anatomy, to mention only some. The

SOURCE: *Science,* Vol. 147 (March 12, 1965), pp. 1247–1256. Copyright 1965 by the
American Association for the Advancement of Science. Reprinted with the permission of the author and publisher.

The author (b. 1934) is presently Assistant Professor of Anthropology at the
University of Michigan. His central interests in archaeology have been the beginnings
of agriculture and animal domestication in Mesoamerica and the Near East. Among his
recent publications are *Early Cultures and Human Ecology in South Coastal Guatemala* (1966) and *Vertebrate Fauna and Prehistoric Hunting Patterns in the Tehua-
can Valley, Mexico* (in press).

work is hard and some of the allure is lost, but the different picture of origins that emerges is the reward. Where earlier reconstructions were hazy, and sometimes generalized to the point of fantasy, the new interpretations, although still tentative and slated for far-reaching changes, are sharp, clear, and usually logically comprehensible and coherent. It is something like the evolution of hi-fi out of the scratchy and distorting pioneer phonographs; we may still lack "concert-hall realism," which is to say perfectly probable reconstructions, but we begin to hear all the instruments and they sound more and more as they should.

The article that follows should be compared with the similar analysis of Middle American archaeology in which Flannery was joined by Michael Coe (No. I:41). Both articles are marked by interest in the reconstruction of a highly probable sequence of stages of events, are extensively informed in terms of available archaeological data, and reach out into other disciplines in order to achieve their analytical goals.

Greater Mesopotamia—broadly defined here as the whole area drained by the tributaries of the Shatt al-Arab—has long been the scene of popular interest and scholarly research. In recent years attention has been drawn to the fact that this was one of the few areas in the world where agriculture and animal husbandry seem to have arisen autonomously. A number of excellent cultural-historical reconstructions of the way food production began in the Near East are already available, but most of these reconstructions do not deal directly with some of the ecological questions most commonly asked by the interested nonspecialist. This article examines some of those questions.

The Environment

From the standpoint of agriculture and grazing potential, the area under consideration includes four main environmental zones: the alluvial plain of Mesopotamia proper, the steppeland of Assyria, the woodland belt of the Zagros Mountains, and the edge of the high central plateau of Iran (see Figs. 1 and 2). The first three of these zones have already been described by Hatt; I have added the high plateau although it is not actually drained by the Shatt al-Arab system, because its mineral resources figured prominently in the early village period.

1) *The central plateau of Iran.* Central Iran is an interior drainage basin at altitudes of 900 to 1500 meters, with annual rainfall as low as 100 to 230 millimeters. The basin is filled with sierozem and desert soils, overlain in places by shallow brackish lakes surrounded by salt-crusted flatland. Rugged mountains jut unexpectedly from the plain, some of them ore-bearing; there are veins of copper just east of the prehistoric site of Tepe Sialk, and one of the world's major turquoise sources lies in the

northeast corner of the plateau near Meshed. Both turquoise and copper were traded as far away as the Assyrian steppe zone by 6500 B.C.

Herds of gazelle (*Gazella subguturosa*) and wild ass (*Equus hemionus*) would have been available to hunters in the area, but without irrigation the high plateau is very marginal agricultural land; the only source of hope for the early farmer would have been the alluvial aprons of mountain soil produced where streams break through the Zagros to enter the salt lake basins. Despite the uncertain rainfall, some of these "oasis" locations appear to have been permanently settled by 5500 B.C., especially those near copper sources.

2) *The oak-pistachio woodland belt.* The Zagros Mountains break away from the eastern edge of the high plateau and descend in tiers toward the Tigris-Euphrates basin. In places the mountains form parallel ridges which are separated by long, narrow, synclinal or anticlinal valleys, frequently poor in surface water; in other areas there are irregular mountain masses bordering wide flat valleys. Acting as aquifers, these porous mountain masses may trap tremendous quantities of winter snow or rain and release it through springs, which in turn feed permanent poplar-bordered streams. At elevations of 600 to 1350 meters there are alluvial valleys of chernozem, chestnut, brown, or red-dish-brown soils, with alpine meadows scattered through the surrounding peaks. Summers are warm and dry, winters cool and wet; depending on altitude and topography, the annual rainfall varies from 250 to 1000 millimeters, and hillsides have varying densities of oak, maple, juniper, hawthorn, pistachio, and wild pear. On well-watered slopes grow hard-grained annual grasses like wild emmer wheat (*Triticum dicocoides*), barley (*Hordeum spontaneum*), and oats (*Avena fatua*).

Much of the area is too rugged for large-scale agriculture, but even the narrower and drier valleys have been used for sheep or goat grazing since at least 8500 B.C.; broad valleys with annual rainfall in excess of 300 millimeters have been farmed for at least the same length of time.

3) *The Assyrian steppe.* The Zagros Mountains fall away through a series of foothills and eventually level off onto a steppe region of great natural winter grassland at elevations of 150 to 300 meters; these plains have reddish-brown or brown prairie soils of high fertility. Here the mountain streams have collected into larger rivers like the Tigris, Karkheh, Diz, and Karun, which flow into the area through erosional valleys and have wide, farmable floodplains. Hot and dry in the summer, the Assyrian steppe is transformed by 250 to 380 millimeters of winter rain into meadows of Bermuda grass, canary grass, and wild narcissus. Herds of gazelle, wild ass, and wild cattle once roamed the plain, and the rivers had carp and catfish. The Assyrian steppe is oil country, and one of its most widely traded commodities in prehistoric time was bitumen or natural asphalt, used for cementing flint tools into their handles.

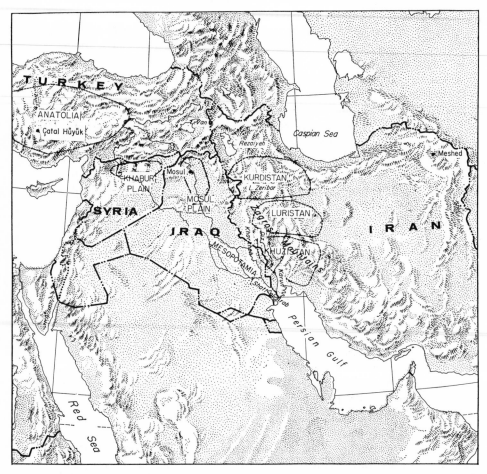

Figure 1   Map of Greater Mesopotamia and adjacent areas today.

Some parts of the steppe, too salty for effective agriculture, are used for winter grazing. Other areas are real breadbaskets for winter wheat (like the upper Khabur plain; the area near Mosul, Iraq; or the Khuzistan plain of southwest Iran), and the density of prehistoric villages in these regions is staggering. Adams' comments on northern Khuzistan—that the adequate rainfall, underlying gravels, and consequent good drainage in this zone facilitated the crucial transition from dry farming to irrigation —may apply to other favored parts of the steppes.

4) *Southern Mesopotamia.* Below 150 meters the Assyrian steppe gives way to the lower drainage of the Tigris, Euphrates, and Karun, as they flow together and empty into the Persian Gulf. Here the annual rainfall is under 250 millimeters (an amount usually inadequate for dry

farming) and the grassland is replaced by two kinds of biotopes: alluvial desert and blowing sand dunes on higher ground, and reed-bordered swamps in the low-lying areas. The delta area is a subsiding geosyncline, slowly settling and filling with river alluvium, across which the big rivers run between their own natural levees, flooding and changing courses periodically. Contrary to what was once believed, the area has never been under the waters of the Persian Gulf (at least not since the Pliocene), and in prehistoric times it must have looked much as it does today. It was in this environmental zone that urban life, civilization, and writing began, about 3000 B.C. When permanent settlement began here is undetermined, but villages dating back to 5500 B.C. are known even in the bleak area west of the Euphrates. Surely these villages must have followed the old swamps and water-courses, beyond which agriculture would have been impossible and grazing difficult.

The Local Climatic Sequence

The possibility that the environment in the Near East might have been different during the beginnings of agriculture has intrigued archeologists for generations. The few prehistoric pollen sequences we have suggest that, although some climatic fluctuations did occur, they were not on a scale capable of creating or destroying the complex of plants and animals that were eventually domesticated. The facts we have are too few to permit us to say dogmatically that climatic change played *no* role, but it appears that the problem is cultural rather than climatic; the inescapable conclusion is that agriculture began in an area where, then as now, only about 10 percent of the land surface is suitable for dry farming.

One pollen sequence comes from Lake Zeribar in the wooded mountains of western Iran, at an altitude of about 1200 meters. Studies by van Zeist and Wright show that during the late Pleistocene the area was steppe, characterized by the sagebrush-like *Artemisia*, which implies a cool dry climate. About 11,000 B.C., at the end of the Pleistocene, the area became warmer and the vegetation made the transition to savanna, with scattered oaks and pistachios. The savanna thickened to oak forest about 3500 B.C., either through increased precipitation or through lowered temperature. Cereal-type pollen (possibly wild wheat and barley?) is present throughout the entire sequence, so climatic fluctuation would seem not to have been a determining factor in the beginning of agriculture there.

Six hundred meters lower, in the Zagros Mountains of Iraq, a slightly conflicting pollen story is available from human occupational debris in Shanidar Cave. More striking climatic fluctuations are implied, one of which Solecki interprets as the "shock stimulus" which triggered the beginnings of food production. Actually, however, the late-Pleistocene to

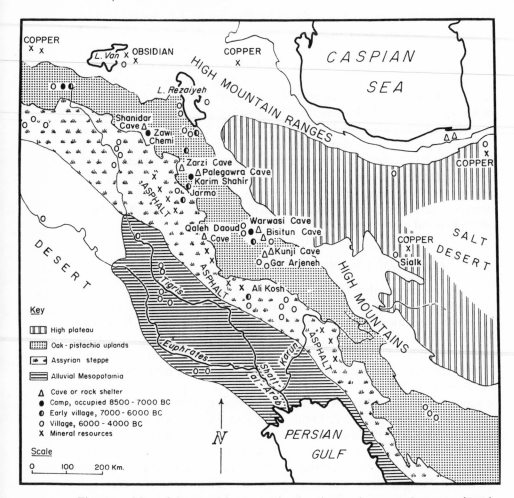

Figure 2 Map of Greater Mesopotamia, showing environmental zones, mineral resources, and archeological sites. Only sites mentioned in the text are labeled.

early-Recent pollen sequence from Shanidar is not in much conflict with that from Lake Zeribar: at about 10,000 B.C. a "relatively cool climate" changed to "a warmer one similar to the present climate." Cereal pollen is known at least as early as 14,000 B.C., and potential animal domesticates (sheep and goat) are present in the cave debris even at 40,000 B.C.

Neither of these pollen sequences supports the age-old myth that the Near East was once lush and well watered, then suffered from desiccation. Nor do any of the inferred climatic fluctuations imply the sudden, overnight appearance of wheat, barley, sheep, or goats. I do not feel qualified to evaluate the "shock stimulus" theory, but I suspect that, although drastic climatic change explains why certain plants and animals become extinct, it does not explain how or why cultures change.

Pre-Agricultural Subsistence Pattern

Scattered caves, rock shelters, and open-air sites have given us only hints of how man lived in this part of the world before domestication of plants and animals. All appearances are that his way of life conformed to a flexible, "broad-spectrum" collecting pattern, keyed to the seasonal aspects of the wild resources of each environmental zone, with perhaps a certain amount of seasonal migration from zone to zone. The less mobile members of society appear to have collected such resources as snails, turtles, fresh-water clams and crabs, and the seeds of wild annuals and perennials, while more mobile members pursued wild ungulates by special techniques, according to the species involved. Although cave remains include fish, birds, and small mammals, the bulk of the meat diet—often more than 90 percent—came from ungulates, like the wild sheep, goat, ox, pig, wild ass, gazelle, and deer. Note that the first four were early domesticates.

Hunting patterns were influenced by the topography of the region. In the Shanidar Cave, wild goat (*Capra hircus*) was the animal most frequently taken. The goat, a resident of the limestone crags, is difficult to hunt by means of drives; it is best pursued by small groups of agile men who know their country well and are equipped with light projectiles. Rock-shelters or caves overlooking broad, flat valleys are usually rich in the bones of the wild ass, a plains-dwelling animal which could best have been hunted by drives or surrounds, then dispatched with a larger weapon, like a thrusting spear. Gazelles and hares are also creatures of the flat valley, while the wild sheep of the Near East (*Ovis orientalis*) frequent rolling, round-top hills and are hunted today by ambush in the brushy stream-canyons where they hide during the noon hours. Some of the smaller rock-shelters excavated in the Zagros Mountains seem to have been stations or overlooks used mainly for hunting or butchering a single species of ungulate, or two species at most.

In recent years the oak-pistachio uplands, in the 400 to 1000-millimeter rainfall belt at altitudes of 450 to 900 meters, have been singled out as an "optimum" zone which includes all the potential domesticates. Actually, topography is a much more important ecological factor for wild sheep and goats than either altitude or rainfall; sheep range down to sea level along the Caspian Sea, and up to 2700 meters in the Zagros Mountains, if rolling mountain meadows are available. Goats reach sea level on the foothills flanking the Persian Gulf, and are as much at home on the last rugged sandstone hills separating southwest Iran from southern

Mesopotamia (180 meters above sea level) as they are on the 3000-meter crags of the northern Zagros. Pigs range over a wide area, from sea level to timberline, and if we knew more about the ecological requirements of wild cattle we might find their range equally broad. The crucial factor for hunters of wild ungulates, or early herders of semiwild ungulates, would have been the ability to move from upland to lowland as seasonal pasture was available, a pattern known as "transhumance."

Let me give one example. Khuzistan, the Iranian arm of the Assyrian steppe, is lush winter grassland from December to April while many of the mountains to the east are covered with snow. Through late spring and summer the steppe becomes blisteringly hot and dry, while the melting snow on the mountains gives rise to good spring and summer grassland. The Persian herder classifies the steppe as *quishlaq* (winter pasture) and the mountains as *yehlaq* (summer pasture), and he moves his herd from one to the other as the season demands. Prehistoric hunters may have followed game over the same route and as for prehistoric herders, Adams reminds us: "It is, in fact, erroneous to consider the upper plains as a zone of occupance distinct from the surrounding uplands. Both together constitute a single natural ecosystem, whose seasonal alternation of resources provides as strong an inducement to migratory stockbreeding as to intensive, settled agriculture."

The wild plants of southwestern Asia have much the same seasonal aspect. MacNeish's work in the New World has shown that a long period of intensive plant collecting preceded agriculture there; archeologists have long assumed that this was the case in the Near East, but preserved plant remains were not available to tell us which specific plants were used in the pre-agricultural era. New light was thrown on the problem in 1963 by a collection of some 10,000 carbonized seeds from basal levels at the site of Ali Kosh in lowland southwestern Iran. The area, a part of the Assyrian steppe, lies outside the range of wild wheat and barley, but locally available plants were intensively collected; the most common were wild alfalfa (*Medicago*) and the tiny-seeded wild legumes *Astragalus* and *Trigonella*, as well as fruits like the wild caper (*Capparis*), used today mainly as a condiment. These data indicate that intensive plant collecting may have been the pattern everywhere in southwest Asia, not merely at the altitude where wild wheat grows best. Moreover, the fact that *Astragalus* and *Trigonella* occur in the mountains as well as the lowlands suggests that prehistoric collectors could have harvested one crop on the Assyrian steppe in March, moved up to 600 meters for a harvest in April or May, and arrived at 1500 meters for another harvest in June or July. Somewhere between 600 and 1200 meters these migrant collectors could have harvested the seeds of the annual grasses ancestral to domestic wheat, barley, and oats. These cereals, which are dependent on annual rainfall of

400 to 750 millimeters, do not range down to the Assyrian steppe today, although they are available over a surprisingly wide area; according to Helbaek, wild barley "grows in the mountain forest, on the coastal plain, in the shade of rock outcrops in semidesert areas, and as a weed in the fields of every conceivable cultivated crop" from Morocco to Turkestan.

Other plants useful to the collector—and eventually, in some cases, to the primitive cultivator—were ryegrass (*Lolium*), *Aegilops* grass, wild flax (*Linum bienne*), and large-seeded wild legumes like lentil, vetch, vetchling, chick pea, and *Prosopis* (a relative of mesquite). The lowlands had dates; the foothills had acorns, almonds, and pistachios; and the northern mountains had grapes, apples, and pears.

Most of the important species occurred in more than one zone, and their months of availability were slightly different at different altitudes —key factors from the standpoint of human ecology. An incredibly varied fare was available to the hunter-collector who knew which plants and animals were available in each season in each environmental zone; which niche or "microenvironment" the species was concentrated in, such as hillside, cliff, or stream plain; which species could be stored best, and which it was most practical to hunt or collect. From 40,000 to 10,000 B.C., man worked out a pattern for exploiting the natural resources of this part of the world, and I suspect that this pre-agricultural pattern had more to do with the beginnings of food production than any climatic "shock stimulus."

Beginnings of Food Production

Leslie White reminds us that "we are not to think of the origin of agriculture as due to the chance discovery that seeds thrown away from a meal subsequently sprouted. Mankind knew all this and more for tens of thousands of years before cultivation of plants began." The cultivation of plants required no new facts or knowledge, but was simply a new kind of relationship between man and the plants with which he was most familiar.

One striking aspect of the late pre-agricultural pattern in the Greater Mesopotamian area was the trading of obsidian from its source in central and eastern Turkey to cave sites in the central Zagros, such as Zarzi and Shanidar. Natural asphalt was traded in the opposite direction, up from the tar pits of the Assyrian steppe to campsites in the mountains, wherever flints had to be hafted. By 7000 B.C., handfuls of emmer wheat from the oak-pistachio belt had reached the lowland steppe of Khuzistan. Typical of the prehistoric Near Easterner was this penchant for moving commodities from niche to niche within environmental zones, and even from zone to zone.

It has been argued that the last millennia of the pre-agricultural era were a time of "settling in" to one's area, of increasing intensification and regionalization of the exploitation of natural resources. This is indeed reflected in the flint tools, but such "regional specialization" may not be the essential trend which led to food production. From the standpoint of human ecology, the single most important factor may have been the establishment of the above-mentioned pattern of interchange of resources between groups exploiting contrasting environmental situations—a kind of primitive redistribution system. It was this pattern that set the stage for the removal of certain key species of edible grasses from the niches in which they were indigenous, and their transferral to niches to which they were foreign.

With the wisdom of hindsight we can see that, when the first seeds had been planted, the trend from "food collecting" to "food producing" was under way. But from an ecological standpoint the important point is not that man *planted* wheat but that he (i) moved it to niches to which it was not adapted, (ii) removed certain pressures of natural selection, which allowed more deviants from the normal phenotype to survive, and (iii) eventually selected for characters not beneficial under conditions of natural selection.

All that the "settling in" process did for the prehistoric collector was to teach him that wild wheat grew from seeds that fell to the ground in July, sprouted on the mountain talus in February, and would be available to him in usable form if he arrived for a harvest in May. His access to those mature seeds put him in a good position to bargain with the goat-hunters in the mountain meadow above him. He may have viewed the first planting of seeds merely as the transfer of a useful wild grass from a niche that was hard to reach—like the talus below a limestone cliff—to an accessible niche, like the disturbed soil around his camp on a nearby stream terrace. Happily for man, wild wheat and barley both grow well on disturbed soils; they will sprout on the back-dirt pile of an archeological excavation, and they probably did equally well on the midden outside a prehistoric camp. It is obvious from the rapid spread of agriculture in the Mesopotamian area that they grew as readily on the midden outside the forager's winter camp at 180 meters as they did in his summer camp at 900 meters, in the "optimum" zone.

Viewed in these terms the advent of cultivation may have been a rather undramatic event, and the concept of "incipient cultivation" becomes rather hard to define. Was it a fumbling attempt at cultivation, or only the intensification of an already existent system of interregional exchange?

Biological Obstacles to Early Food Production

The transfer of species from habitat to habitat made the products of all zones available to all people; but it was a process not without difficulty, since some of the plant and animal species involved had not yet developed the most tractable or productive phenotypes, from man's point of view.

Some of the biological obstacles faced by early agriculturalists were as follows.

1) The difficulty of harvesting wild, brittle-rachis grains. One adaptive mechanism for seed dispersal in wild wheat and barley is a brittle rachis or axis which holds the seeds together in the mature head of grain. When a dry, ripe head of wild barley is struck by a twig or a gust of wind, the rachis disintegrates and the seeds are spread far and wide. The disadvantages of this mechanism for the prehistoric collector are obvious: the slightest tug on the stem of the plant or the slightest blow with a flint sickle might send the seeds scattering in every direction.

2) The difficulty of removing the grain from its husk. Even after a successful harvest, the prehistoric collector's troubles were not over. Primitive grains like emmer or einkorn wheat have a tough husk, or glume, which holds each kernel in a stubborn grip long after the brittle rachis has disintegrated. Even vigorous threshing will usually not release these primitive grains from the glume so that they can be eaten.

3) The difficulty of farming in the niche to which the grain was adapted. Both wild wheat and barley are grasses of hillsides and slopes, and they usually do not occur on the flat stream floodplains, where it would have been most convenient for prehistoric man to farm. The deep alluvial soils in the valley centers, prime areas from an agricultural standpoint, were already occupied by competing grasses and wild legumes.

Research on archeological grain remains by Danish botanist Hans Helbaek has shown us some of the ways in which early farmers either consciously or unconsciously overcame these three obstacles.

1) Selection for tough-rachis grains. Within the gene pool of wild wheat and barley were variants whose rachis was tough enough so that it did not shatter on contact. Normally these variants would have left few descendents, because of the inadequacy of their seed-dispersal mechanism. When man harvested with sickles or flails, however, he automatically selected *for* the tough-rachis grains because their heads stayed intact despite the rough treatment of the harvest. When seeds from the harvest were planted, the next generation of plants contained an abnormally high proportion of tough-rachis individuals, and each successive generation reinforced the trend.

2) The development of techniques for removing the seeds from their glumes. Sometime before 7000 B.C. man discovered that by roasting

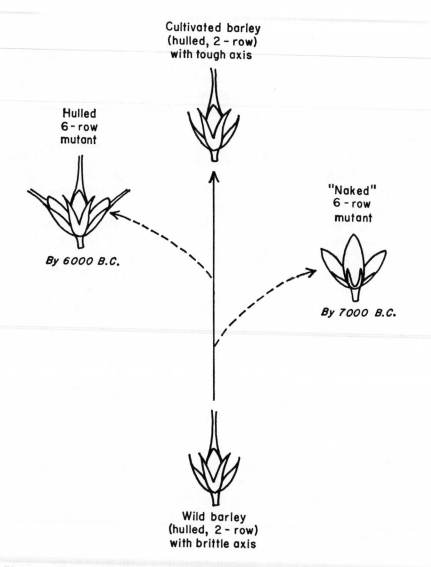

Cultivated barley
(hulled, 2 – row)
with tough axis

Hulled
6 – row
mutant

By 6000 B.C.

"Naked"
6 – row
mutant

By 7000 B.C.

Wild barley
(hulled, 2 – row)
with brittle axis

Figure 3 Simplified diagrams of barley spikelets, showing some of the changes which took place after domestication. Data courtesy of Helbaek (see text).

the grain he had collected he could render the glumes so dry and brittle that they could be crushed by abrasion; roasting, moreover, killed the wheat or barley germ so that it would not sprout, and the grain could be stored even through the winter rainy season. Many of the preceramic villages excavated throughout the Near East contain clay ovens appropriate for roasting grain in this manner, and nearly all seem to have stone grinding slabs of one kind or another on which the dry grain could be abraded out of its glume. Further grinding resulted in "groats," or coarse grits of grain which could be cooked up into a mush or gruel. (By and large, the tough-glumed primitive grains were unsuitable for bread-making.)

3) Actual genetic change in the grain species themselves, resulting in new strains. Because early cultivated grain was somewhat shielded by man from the natural selection pressures to which uncultivated grain was subjected, the chance that random mutants would survive was much greater. One of the first mutations that occurred, apparently, was a change from the standard adhering-glume kernel to a "naked" kernel which could be easily freed by threshing. According to Stubbe, a single gene controls the difference between "hulled" and "naked" barley, and when a mutation took place at that locus, sometime before 7000 B.C., free-threshing barley was born. A second genetic change was that which transformed standard wild barley (*Hordeum spontaneum*), which has only two fertile kernel rows, into mutant barley with six fertile rows (*Hordeum hexastichum*). Helbaek, who has actually produced the six-row mutant in his laboratory by subjecting wild two-row barley to x-rays, feels that ecological factors probably determined the early distribution of these two strains: two-row barley is adapted to the fairly late (April and May) rainfall of the cool Zagros Mountain uplands, while mutant six-row barley may be more successfully adapted to much drier spring weather and the irrigation farming of the Mesopotamian plain. Archeological remains tend to support this. The two-row form seems to be the only one known so far from the highlands before 5000 B.C., while six-row barley is known from lowland Khuzistan by 6000 B.C.; the two-row strain does not seem to have caught on in the lowlands, possibly because it was poorly adapted to the climate there. Present data, in fact, suggest that although the cool uplands probably contributed the original ancestor (two-row hulled barley) it may have been the lowland ecology which stabilized the important "naked" and "six-row" strains (see Fig. 3).

Another important early genetic change was polyploidy, an actual increase in the chromosome number, which produced new strains of wheat. Wild emmer wheat (*Triticum dicoccoides*) is tetraploid—that is, it contains 4×7 chromosomes and has tough glumes enclosing the kernels. A native annual grass of well-watered mountains, it prefers the 400- to 750-millimeter rainfall zone, from Palestine and Syria to the Zagros Mountains of Iran and Iraq. By 6000 B.C., however, on the Anatolian plateau of central Turkey, a mutant had been produced which was free-threshing: this was hexaploid wheat (*Triticum aestivum*), with 6×7 chromosomes. Such polyploid strains, together with irrigation, were instrumental in the spread of free-threshing wheat throughout southwest Asia.

Mutations and changes in gene frequency also played a role in the establishment of races of domestic animals, and once again there were biological obstacles to be overcome by early herders. Some of the adaptive and nonadaptive changes which took place were as follows.

1) A change in the sex and age ratios within the captive population. If early herds of domesticated sheep or goats were small, as we assume they were, how did the animals avoid being eaten during the winter and survive until the spring lambing season? Work by Charles A. Reed and Dexter Perkins on archeological bones from early villages in Kurdistan suggests that some kind of conservation may have been practiced. Perkins notes that the proportion of immature sheep relative to adult sheep at

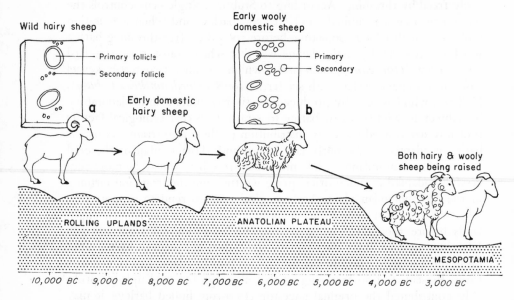

Figure 4 Simplified diagram showing some of the steps in the evolution of domestic sheep. (a) Section, as seen through a microscope, of skin of wild sheep, showing the arrangement of primary (hair) and secondary (wool) follicles; (b) section, similarly enlarged, of skin of domestic sheep, showing the changed relationship and the change in the size of follicles that accompanied the development of wool.

Zawi Chemi, Iraq, was far higher than that in any normal wild herd, an observation from which he infers domestication. Evidently the young animals were eaten, while the older breeding stock was saved. The practice was much the same at the village of Jarmo, where Reed noted a high proportion of butchered young males, as if the females were being held back for breeding. Such practices would have resulted in an abnormally high proportion of adult females in the herd, and consequently in milk surpluses in late winter and early spring. Although wild sheep and goats produce very little milk in comparison to today's domestic breeds, such seasonal surpluses may eventually have been exploited by early herders. Today, milk, yogurt, and cheese are part of the whole trading complex of southwest Asian pastoralists.

2) Changes leading to wool production. Wild sheep (*Ovis orientalis*) have a coat like a deer or gazelle, and are no woolier than the latter. Microscopic examination of their skin reveals two kinds of follicles: "primaries," or hair follicles which produce the visible coat, and "secondaries," which produce the hidden, wooly underfur. In the skin of wild *Ovis* the secondary follicles lie intermingled with the primaries in groups of three to five. After domestication, genetic changes moved the secondaries out to the side, away from the primaries, and greatly increased their numbers; while wild strains of sheep or goat may have a ratio of only two to four secondaries for each primary, the ratio may be as high as seven to one in fine Merino sheep. The wool of the domestic sheep grows from these dense clusters of secondary follicles. Wool may already have been spun as early as 6000 B.C. at Catal Hüyük in Anatolia. Both "hairy" and "wooly" sheep were known by 3000 B.C. in Mesopotamia, and the now-famous Dead Sea Scrolls, dating to the time of Christ, have been shown by Ryder to have been written on parchment made both from hairy and from wooly sheep (see Fig. 4).

3) Nonadaptive genetic changes, such as the twisted horns of domestic goats. One of the most interesting (if poorly understood) changes which followed domestication was one affecting the horns of the goat (*Capra hircus*). The wild goat of the Near East has scimitar-shaped horns whose bony cores are quadrangular or diamond-shaped in cross section near the skull. Sites dating from 8500 to 7000 B.C. are known where goat domestication is inferred from the ratio of immature animals to adult animals, but no changes in the cross section of the horn during this period are noted. By 6500 B.C., from the Jordan Valley to the Zagros Mountains, there are scattered occurrences of goats whose horn cores show a flattening of the medial surface, and thus a triangular or almond-shaped cross section. By 6000 B.C. in the Mesopotamian area, from the Assyrian steppe to the oak-pistachio woodlands, a new type of horn core makes its appearance: the core is medially flattened in section, and it also shows signs of a corkscrew twist like that of the modern domestic goat in southwest Asia. The irregular geographic distribution of the trait suggests that it was strongest in the Iran-Iraq area, occurring only sporadically elsewhere before 4500 B.C.; even at 3500 B.C. not all sites in the Palestinian area show goats of a uniformly "twisted horn" type. Possibly its rapid spread in the Zagros was due to transhumant herding (see Fig. 5).

4) The problem of pig domestication. One of the questions most frequently asked is why the pig was domesticated at 6000 B.C. in some parts of the Near East, like the Zagros Mountain valleys, but was apparently never domesticated in prehistoric time in other areas, such as the

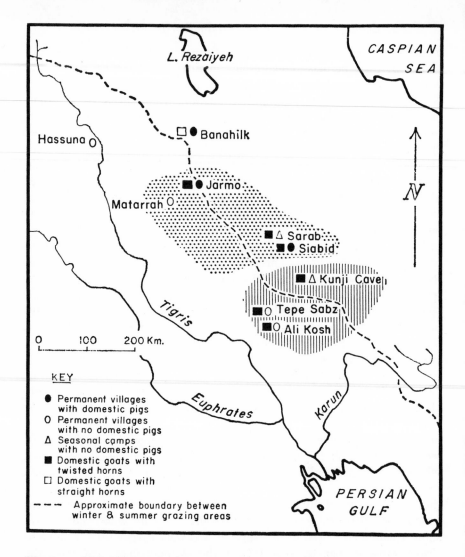

Figure 5 Map of Greater Mesopotamia, showing areas where transhumance is believed to have been of importance in prehistoric times. Ceramic objects from sites in the stippled area (Jarmo, Sarab, Matarrah) all have one set of traits; those from sites in the hachured area (Kunji, Ali Kosh, Tepe Sabz) all have another set. The rapid spread of the twisted-horn goat in both areas suggests that flocks may have been moved from one elevation to another seasonally; so does the almost complete absence of the domestic pig, an animal unsuitable for transhumant herding. In the summer grazing area (northeast of the dashed line), many sites appear to be seasonal shepherds' camps in caves or on valley floors. These camps seem to have stronger ties, from the standpoint of traits of ceramic objects, with sites in the adjacent winter grazing area (southwest of the dashed line) than with other sites in their own environmental zone (see text).

Khuzistan steppe. The most common answer is that this was the result of religious or dietary laws; but in fact, the reasons may be ecological. According to Krader, "the disappearance of the pig from Central Asia is not the clear-cut case of religious determination that might be supposed. The pig is not a species suitable to pastoral nomadism . . . it is nomadism with its mastery of the steppe ecology and movements of herds and herdsmen which is the decisive factor in the disappearance of pigs from this part of the world." Figure 5 shows the sites where domestic pigs are known either to have been, or not to have been, present in the Mesopotamian area between 6000 and 5000 B.C. Since pigs seem to be incompatible with transhumant herding, the areas where they do *not* occur may be those where there was greatest reliance on seasonal movement of flocks.

Effects on Human Life and Cultural Ecology

In the past it has been customary to treat each of the Mesopotamian environmental zones as if it were a "cultural and natural area"—a region characterized by a certain flora and fauna and exploited by a certain group of inhabitants who knew it particularly well. There are hints that such a situation obtained in Palestine, for there Perrot has distinguished two archeological traditions, one adapted to the moist Mediterranean side of the mountains, the other adapted to the arid eastern foothills.

In 1956 Fredrik Barth pointed out that the "cultural and natural area" concept did not fit northern Pakistan, and there are a considerable number of data to suggest that it does not fit the Mesopotamian area at 6000 B.C. either. Barth showed that a single valley system might be occupied by three distinct ethnic groups, each of which occupied only a portion of the total resources, leaving the rest open for other groups to exploit. The first group consists of sedentary agriculturalists who practice intensive irrigation agriculture on the river floodplain, growing two crops a year and never moving to a higher elevation. A second group raises one crop a year in this same floodplain area, but its members also migrate annually with their flocks up through five seasonal campsites to high mountain meadows. Still a third group is made up of pastoral nomads who are assimilated into the society of the intensive agriculturalists as a special "herder caste," contributing milk and meat in exchange for grain; they are permitted to use prime grazing land not needed by the sedentary farmers.

At 6000 B.C. there are striking contrasts between archeological sites in the oak-pistachio belt and the Assyrian steppe of the Greater Mesopotamian area which suggest Barth's model. Jarmo, at an elevation of 750 meters in the oak woodlands, was a village of permanent, mud-walled houses with courtyards and ovens; Tepe Sarab, at an elevation of 1260 meters, has no obvious houses, and only the kind of ashy refuse beds that might occur around a tent camp. The pottery objects at the two sites are nearly identical, but Jarmo has goats, sheep, and even domestic pigs, along with two strains of wheat and one of barley, whereas Tepe Sarab has only goats and sheep, and no grinding stones suggestive of local agriculture. The ages of the domestic goats show that Tepe Sarab was occupied in late winter or early spring. In this case we suspect that the camp at 1260 meters may have been occupied by seasonal herders who obtained their grain from more permanent farming villages at 750 meters.

From the Assyrian steppe of Khuzistan, southwestern Iran, come further data of the same type. From 7000 to 6500 B.C. at the site of Ali Kosh, goat grazing and tiny amounts of agriculture supplemented the collection of wild legumes; from 6500 to 6000 B.C. the growing of wheat and barley greatly increased at the expense of wild plants. At 6000 B.C. a striking expansion of sheep and goat grazing occurred, and amounts of wild wheat and wild barley lessened, while the pod-bearing perennial *Prosopis* came to the fore. We doubt that this was a simple case of abandonment of agriculture; *Prosopis*, Helbaek reminds us, is intimately associated with herding peoples in southwest Asia, and the increase in domestic sheep and goats suggests that this was a time when, in conformity with Barth's ecological model, Ali Kosh became primarily a "herding village" coexisting in a symbiotic framework with "farming villages" in adjacent areas.

Finally, we have the occurrences of typical Khuzistan pottery at a shepherds' camp in Kunji Cave, 1200 meters up, in the mountains of western Iran. This part of Luristan seems to have stronger cultural ties with lowland Khuzistan than with other mountain areas in the same environmental zone, suggesting that at 6000 B.C. some valleys in Luristan were summer grazing land for herds that wintered in Khuzistan.

Summary and Speculation

The food-producing revolution in southwestern Asia is here viewed not as the brilliant invention of one group or the product of a single environmental zone, but as the result of a long process of changing ecological relationships between groups of men (living at varying altitudes and in different environmental settings) and the locally available plants and animals which they had been exploiting on a shifting, seasonal basis. In the course of making available to all groups the natural resources of every environmental zone, man had to remove from their natural contexts a number of hard-grained grasses and several species of ungulates. These species, as well as obsidian and native copper, were transported far from the biotopes or "niches" in which they had been at home. Shielded from natural selection by man, these small breeding populations underwent genetic change in the environment to which they had been transplanted, and favorable changes were emphasized by the practices of the early planter or herder.

Successful cultivation seems to have intensified exchanges of natural resources and cultivars between groups, and there are hints that the diversity of environments made village specialization in certain commodities the best means of adapting to the area. We have suggestive evidence that by 4000 B.C. the redistributive economy had produced regional temple-and-market towns which regulated the produce of a symbiotic network of agriculturists engaged in intensive irrigation, transhumant herders, and perhaps even traders who dealt in obsidian, copper, salt, asphalt, fish, and regional fruits.

39 The Prehistoric Civilizations of Nuclear America

Gordon R. Willey

TECHNICAL HALLMARKS OF CIVILIZATION—METALLURGY, TOWNS, FORMAL *government and other criteria of cultural complexity—occur in the New World as well as the Old. Though Mexico and Peru were conquered by a mere handful of Spanish soldiers, the victors were amazed and even awed by some of the achievements of the empires they reduced. Oddly, of two inventions which underlie the great Near Eastern civilizations, one, the art of writing, appears in the high cultures of Yucatan and Mexico but is absent in pre-conquest Peru. The other, the wheel, was absent throughout the New World except on children's toys in Mexico.*

In the absence of extensive historical documents, other than the chronicles of sixteenth century Spaniards, the recreation of the great cultures of Meso-America is primarily the task of archeologists. Here a specialist summarizes what we know of these cultures and their interrelations with a postcript written especially for this volume to bring us up to date. The reader, who is likely to be buffeted by the intensity of detail in this article, is counselled to concentrate on the appearance of those criteria which Childe (No. I:42) utilizes to distinguish civilization in the Old World. The reader may also note the existence in the New

SOURCE: *American Anthropologist*, Vol. 57 (1955), pp. 571–589. Reprinted by permission of the author and publisher.

The author (b. 1913) is Bowditch Professor of Archeology at Harvard University. An expert on Peru, he has also worked elsewhere in the Americas. Included in his publications are *Prehistoric Settlement Patterns of the New World* (1956) and, with Philip Phillips, *Method and Theory in American Archeology* (1958). His most recent book is *An Introduction to American Archeology* (1966).

World of a problem similar to that posed by the relation between Meso-
potamia and Egypt in the Old World—namely, the question of priority
between Mexico and Peru and the interaction between these two pivotal
areas (see Steward, No. I:43).

Introduction

The native agricultural civilizations of the New World had their
beginnings and their highest development in those areas that have been
subsumed under the term "Nuclear America." The designation has both a
geographical and a cultural connotation. The areas involved embrace central and southern Mexico, Central America, the north Andes, and Peru.
This is the axis of aboriginal high culture in the Americas and, as such,
the major center of prehistoric diffusion for the western hemisphere. To
the best of our knowledge, it stands clearly apart and essentially independent from the comparable culture core of the Old World.

Kroeber has suggested the analogy between the American civilizational nucleus of Mexico-Peru and the "Oikoumene" of the Old World.
Readapting the old Greek concept of the "inhabited" or civilized world,
he has defined the Oikoumene for purposes of culture-historical analysis
as ". . . . the millennially interrelated higher civilizations in the connected mainland masses of the Eastern hemisphere," and "as a great web
of culture growth, areally extensive and rich in content." It is, in effect, a
vast diffusion sphere interlinked across continents by common cultural
content. The comparison with Nuclear America seems particularly apt.
In both cases the great historic nexuses have considerable time depth at
their centers, and in both they have influenced those cultures marginal to
them at relatively later points on the time scale. Further, as Kroeber has
also pointed out, the essential and underlying bonds in each are those of
content as distinguished from style or value. Within each, diverse civilizations (or styles) have sprung up as unique reworkings of a common
cultural content held within the "Oikoumene." The differences in
configuration between the Oikoumene of the Old World and what might
be considered the New World "Oikoumene" appear to be functions of
time. The much greater age of civilization in the eastern hemisphere
seems to have allowed for a more complete dispersal of cultural content
throughout the Old World Oikoumene. As Kroeber has stated: ". . . inventions or new cultural materials have tended to be transmitted, sooner
or later, from end to end." Within the Americas these processes of dissemination were well under way, spreading fanwise from the Middle
American and Peruvian nuclei, but they were terminated by the European conquests before much of the content of the New World "Oikoumene" had reached its outermost marches in the northern and southern
continents. Similarly, certain styles, specific civilizations and their value

systems spread throughout large parts of the Old World Oikoumene—
their propagation and acceptance undoubtedly facilitated by the ancient
base of mutually held cultural content upon which they rode; and these
knit together more tightly the grand diffusion sphere of Eurasia-Africa.
In America these epiphenomena of the "Oecumenical" base were in their
infancy, yet the Inca style and civilization and its diffusion throughout
much of Andean South America may be prototypical of events which,
with opportunity, might have transpired on a wider scale.

This analogy between the Oikoumene of the ancient world and
Nuclear America provides a basis of understanding for the following discussions of New World prehistory. We are considering the cultures of
Mexico-Peru (and intervening areas) as a great historical unit or diffusion
sphere which, in spite of important regional stylistic differences possesses
a certain common culture content. In the succeeding pages I propose to
examine this content, to offer hypotheses as to its origins and dissemination, and to further treat the similarities and differences of the course of
civilization in the two principal sub-centers of Nuclear America—Middle
America and Peru. Before setting out on this task it seems advisable to
review, briefly, a concept which is closely related to the Oikoumene
analogy and which is fundamental to all our ensuing discussions. This is
the idea of an "Archaic" or "Formative" type of culture (or cultures) as
underlying, and basic to, the later American high civilizations.

The theory of an "Archaic" cultural substratum, characterized by
sedentary village life, agriculture, pottery making, and other "neolithic"
arts, as being basic to the later New World civilizations was first advanced by Spinden. He concluded that these ideas of the old substratum
were diffused north and south from Middle America to provide the basis
for much of aboriginal culture in the New World. At the time Spinden
proposed this, many of the earlier culture phases of Middle America and
Peruvian prehistory, which have since been revealed, were unknown;
hence he lacked data to support his hypothesis. Certain particulars of the
scheme—such as the specific center of "Archaic" origins being attributed
to the Valley of Mexico and the selection of pottery figurine types as
inevitable hallmarks of an American "Archaic"—remain unproved or
highly unlikely. Nevertheless, the central theoretical theme stands. Continued archeological research has shown that the Middle American and
Peruvian civilizations are preceded by less complex cultures of a village
agricultural type, that these earlier cultures have a generally similar
content, and that significant portions of this content were diffused widely
beyond the geographical boundaries of the later civilizations. Recent
recognition of New World "Formative" cultures is based upon these
stratigraphic facts and their interpretation. The "Formative" concept, as
it has been used in Peru, Middle America, and for interareal comparisons,
is a reformulation of the Spinden "Archaic" hypothesis. The Formative

cultures are, in the sense of our foregoing analogy, the foundation layer of the New World "Oikoumene."

The Rise of the American Civilizations: A Synopsis

Middle America The prehistory of Middle America (central and southern Mexico and the Mayan regions of upper Central America) is usually generalized under three main chronological subdivisions for which various terms have been used. Alternatives are included in parentheses:

1. Formative (Archaic, Developmental, Pre-Classic)
2. Classic (Florescent)
3. Postclassic (Militaristic, Expansionistic, Historic).

All these subdivisions refer to agricultural-sedentary patterns. Cultural remains preceding the Formative have been found, and some of these appear to be of remote age and to represent early hunting groups. Others, such as the Tamaulipas cave finds on the northeastern periphery of the Middle American area, are somewhat later, dating at about 2500 B.C. The Tamaulipas caves reveal a primitive type of maize but no pottery, and the total artifact assemblages indicate hunting and collecting economies in spite of the presence of maize.

The earliest Formative culture phases, according to radiocarbon dating, are in the Valley of Mexico. Here, the Early Zacatenco level dates from the middle of the second millennium B.C. Early Zacatenco is represented by a large village site of deep living refuse. Corn-grinding metate and mano implements are numerous; the ceramic art is revealed in competently made incised and simply painted vessels; and handmade figurines of human form are abundant. A number of successive culture phases of the Formative follow the Early Zacatenco. There is substantial cultural continuity from one phase to the next, but the sequence also registers strong outside influences at various times. Toward the close of the Formative stage flat-topped or platform mounds appear, and these constructions seem to mark ceremonial sites. These are the first evidences in the Valley of Mexico of large-scale architectural works.

Elsewhere in Middle America the Formative pattern is repeated. This is not to say that culture is uniform throughout the area on the early time levels. There are some close cross-ties, such as the ones between the Formative phases of the Valley of Mexico and Michoacan or between the earliest periods of the Huasteca and Peten Maya chronologies; but there are few widespread stylistic linkages at this time. The widely held similarities tend to be of a general technical sort—the predominance of plain and incised wares, hand-made figurines, and the absence of well-developed architectural features—indicating a gradual diffusion of certain technologies rather than rapid dissemination of more specialized traits. Apparently, the mound building-ceremonial center complex is a late Formative concept, belonging to such phases as the Peten Chicanel (but not the earlier Mamon), the Cuicuilco (but not Early Zacatenco or other pre-Cuicuilco manifestations), and the Monte Alban I. Yet it should be pointed out that the case for a "village farmer" preceding a "village farmer-plus-ceremonial center" complex is not a clear-cut one. In the long Formative sequence in the Guatemalan highlands at Kaminaljuyu platform mounds are placed in the next-to-earliest Arevalo phase and may even be part of the still earlier Las Charcas phase. In Yucatan there is also evidence that mounds belong to the earlier part of the Formative. The difficulties in resolving this problem are those of cross-dating. For example, we cannot be certain just where the Guatemalan highland Arevalo phase equates with the Peten or Valley of Mexico Formative chronologies. Until this is established, the earliest appearances of a trait like temple mound construction and its diffusion cannot be pinned down and plotted.

In brief, the Formative cultures of Middle America come upon the scene as fully integrated sedentary agricultural, pottery making complexes. Formative pottery, though usually not elaborately decorated, was by no means crude or experimental. The total impression is that the Formative cultures have behind them a considerable period of growth and development. Evidences of this have not yet been found. The Tamaulipas cave cultures, such as the La Perra phase, may show the ancient beginnings of agriculture; but the intermediate periods, if such do exist, are still lacking. In the latter part of the Formative, ceremonial center construction began, and many of the mounds built at this time are of impressive size. Radiocarbon dates from the late Formative cluster between about 600 B.C. and 200 B.C., suggesting a closing date for the Formative cultures at just before the beginning of the Christian Era.

The beginnings of Middle American Classic cultures coincide with the first Initial Series stelae of the Maya calendar in the Peten, with the Teotihuacan II (or Miccaotli) phase of the Valley of Mexico, with Monte Alban IIIa in Oaxaca, and the Aurora-Esperanza phases of Kaminaljuyu. It is believed that these events are more or less contemporaneous. It is possible that the opening of the Teotihuacan II phase antedates the earliest Uaxactun stela by three hundred to four hundred years; however, if the 12.9.0.0.0 (Spinden) correlation of the Maya long count is followed rather than the 11.16.0.0.0 correlation (Goodman-Thompson), lowland Maya early Classic (Tzakol phase) beginnings would be about coeval with the advent of Teotihuacan II. The demographic trends between Middle American Formative and Classic are not clear. In some localities, such as the Valley of Mexico, the settlement indications imply population increase and population concentration; in others, as is the case in the Guatemalan highlands, overall population size appears to be as great in the Formative phases as in the Classic, and concentration of population seems to be even greater in the earlier periods. A number of Classic trends are, however, definite and distinguish the stage quantitatively and qualitatively from the Formative. Ceremonial architecture is more elaborate, architectural devices such as apron moldings and plinths are widely used, and the ceremonial units themselves— the mounds, plazas, temples, and palaces—are more numerous and more carefully planned than in the late Formative. There is a general tendency toward the production of more finely decorated pottery with the use of polychrome painting and ornate modeling. Similarly, other craft products enjoy an aesthetic refinement.

There is observable continuity of early Classic out of late Formative cultures in most regions. In the Valley of Mexico the strong figurine tradition of the Formative is maintained in the Classic phases, but with the technical innovation of the mold. At Monte Alban the Classic anthropomorphic modeled urns have Formative prototypes in the same site zone, and the development of the Classic Zapotecan glyphs can be traced back to the Pre-Classic inscriptions. In the lowland Maya regions there are a number of carry-overs in ceramic shapes and technical features from the late Formative Chicanel phase into early Classic Tzakol, but a host of new Maya traits—the stelae, sculpture, the corbelled vault, writing, and the calendar—appear with dramatic suddenness. Thus, in addition to local growth, the early Classic was a period of new ideas. Some of these ideas, like the basal-flanged bowl of Maya or the tripod fresco jar of Teotihuacan II–III, can be traced approximately as to original source and distribution; others are more difficult to plot as to origins and routes of dispersal. To generalize, the trait diffusions of the Classic, particularly the early Classic, must have resulted from rapid processes of dissemination of ideas and products (trade), whereas the Formative diffusions seem to have been much more gradual.

The end of Classic Teotihuacan is marked by the catastrophic destruction of that great site and by the appearances of new styles and, perhaps, peoples. In the south, the Maya Classic centers of the Peten, the Usumacinta, and the Motagua-Chamelecon were all abandoned shortly after the beginning of the tenth cycle of the long count. How closely coordinate in time these events were is debatable. If Teotihuacan was destroyed by A.D. 700, the collapse of the "Old Empire" Maya centers would be approximately coeval if the terminal date for the Maya lowland Classic is interpreted in the 12.9.0.0.0 correlation. Recent radiocarbon dates from the late Classic period at Tikal support this correlation. On the other hand, the 11.16.0.0.0 correlation places the end of Maya lowland

Classic at about A.D. 900. In general, the archeological sequences of Middle America as a whole seem to accord more closely with the 11.16.0.0.0 correlation than with the 12.9.0.0.

Causes of the decline and fall of the Middle American Classic cultures have been the subject of a good deal of speculation. In the Valley of Mexico there seems little doubt but what the immediate cause was military disaster, probably resulting from the pressure of new population groups entering the orbit of Mexican high civilization from the northern frontiers. Such happenings may also have had indirect effects upon the southern centers; the Tula-Toltec influences into Yucatan after the close of the Maya Classic certainly suggest this. There are, in addition, other possibilities as to causes which may have contributed to the Maya Classic decline.

The Postclassic stage of Middle American prehistory, which dates in the last eight hundred to five hundred years preceding the Spanish conquest, has been characterized as militaristic, expansionistic, secularized, and urbanized. There are evidences for these trends, but they are not manifested in all Middle American regions. An increase in warfare is reflected in the appearance of fortifications and fortified sites in many regions. This trend is paralleled by what were probably larger political domains than existed earlier, the Aztec state of the late Postclassic being the outstanding example. There is also considerable evidence of "expansionism" in the archeological and legendary-historical records. Toltec-style Chichen Itza in the heart of Yucatan, in the early Postclassic, and Nahua towns deep into Central America, in the late Postclassic, are examples. Secularism must be judged relatively. Religion seems always to have been a powerful force in Middle American civilizations. There is, it is true, something of a decline in the size, amount, and fineness of religious architecture in the Postclassic as opposed to the Classic. There are, however, exceptions to this; and, also, it must be questioned just how sure and sensitive a guide architecture is for the interpretation of cultural values. Urbanism, in the sense of population size and density, is easier to measure than the attribute of secularism, at least from the archeological standpoint; but, unfortunately, there has been little field research along these lines. In the Valley of Mexico there are some indications that Teotihuacan had, in effect, become an urban zone, in addition to the ceremonial precincts, before the close of the Classic stage. Certainly Postclassic Tenochtitlan, with its estimated 60,000 inhabitants, appears to have had urban qualifications. In Yucatan, Mayapan, with its some four thousand houses within the enclosure wall, suggests the urban trend, but we know too little of the preceding Classic Maya settlement patterns to be able to judge its full significance. In highland Guatemala the Postclassic sites, although frequently fortified, are not especially large.

There are a number of horizontal traits which characterize the

Middle American Postclassic, such as the widespread appearances of Plumbate and Fine Orange wares in the early part of the stage and the popularity of Mixteca-Puebla polychrome pottery and related styles in the later periods. Metals come into use in the Postclassic, particularly in southwestern Mexico, and there is some evidence to suggest that irrigation now became important in western Mexico and in the Valley of Mexico.

Finally, and somewhat impressionistically, most Middle American prehistorians agree that there is a tendency for aesthetic decline in the Postclassic. This is difficult to measure, and it may be that, rather than decline, a plateau of achievement was attained in the Classic which was not, subsequently, surpassed in the Postclassic cultures. In some places, as in the Mayan regions, this putative decline does seem to have been accompanied by a lessening of intellectual and scientific accomplishments, as revealed in the calendar, astronomy, and writing.

Peru The natural environment of the Peruvian area, by contrast with the varied regional settings which compose Middle America, has an impressive uniformity. There are essentially two types of country for human occupation: the small oases valleys of the desert coast and the highland basins. These two types are in juxtaposition to one another. Many of the coastal streams head up into the highlands in such a way as to offer reasonably easy means of contact between sierra and coast. The archeology of Peru, or Peru-Bolivia, seems to reflect this environmental homogeneity. Regional styles develop, but they are, again and again, interpenetrated by styles which have an area-wide or broad horizontal significance. This complex interlacing of small regional cultures, over long periods of time, has given rise to the "co-tradition" or culture-area-in-time-depth concept. Regional independence should not be minimized, but it is important to note that Peruvian prehistoric cultures, *in toto,* form a somewhat tighter diffusion sphere than do those of Middle America.

Peruvian archeology has been divided into major chronological segments in much the same fashion as Middle America. These divisions have varied in name, number, and, to some extent, in attributed content, but in essentials they are similar. All classifiers agree upon a Formative (Evolutive, Cultist-Experimenter) stage or epoch as marking the beginnings of maize agriculture and developed pottery. This is followed by a Classic (Regional Classic, Florescent, Mastercraftsman) stage of artistic climax and architectural achievement. The final stage, or stages, which we will refer to here as Postclassic, have been designated variously as Fusional-Imperialist, City Builder-Imperialist, Expansionist, and Militarist.

As with Middle America, this classification refers to the fully agricultural patterns. The projectile points and other flint tools of early hunting groups have been found in both Peruvian highlands and coast, but these remains appear to long antedate the Peruvian Formative. On the north Peruvian coast, immediately precedent to the Formative phases of that region, there is evidence of a long occupation of agricultural-collecting peoples which ranges from about 2500 B.C. up to the advent of the Formative Cupisnique and Middle Guañape phases at approximately 1000 B.C. This agricultural-collecting period is without maize and lacks pottery except for its final three or four centuries when a plain ware of simple vessel forms makes its appearance. There is, however, a continuity, or near-continuity, of occupation and culture between the premaize period and the subsequent Cupisnique phase of the early Formative.

The early Formative cultures of the Peruvian coast have as their basis the small agricultural village. It is doubtful if the canal irrigation, which was to make possible the dense populations of the later periods, had yet appeared. Sites are relatively few in number. Platform mounds, which almost certainly represent religious, or politicoreligious, centers, were constructed. Cerro Blanco and Pungurí in the Nepeña Valley are the best known coastal examples, and others have been reported from the Chicama Valley. These early-period phases of Peru are linked by a developed and sophisticated art style, the Chavín. The Chavín style, with its specialized feline-condor iconography, covered all north and central Peru on this early horizon, varying in its expression from the monumental stone carving of highland Chavín de Huantar to the incised pottery decoration of the coastal valleys.

Most of our knowledge of the development of the Peruvian Formative cultures comes from the north coast, so it is from this region that the trends or changes which are here briefly reviewed have been observed. Between early and late Formative there was a great population upswing, and this increase in numbers of people in each valley almost certainly is related to the appearance of canal irrigation. Village communities remained small, but there are numerous evidences of multivillage activity in addition to the canal systems. Large hilltop fortifications and platform mounds are the principal examples. At the very close of the late Formative, or the beginning of the Classic phases (depending upon where the classifier draws the line), canal systems are so complex that it is obvious that there were sociopolitical means of close co-operation within each coastal valley. The degree of centralization and authoritarianism can only be speculated upon, however. In general, the late Formative was a time of technical advance or èxperimentation. Metallurgical techniques, as applied to ornaments, were diffused. Ceramics lacked the distinctive Chavín-style incised decorations, and a variety of simple painting techniques (white-on-red, two-color negative) were substituted; but new firing methods, vessel forms, and life modeling came to the fore.

Regionalism and regional traditions in prehistoric Peru must not be lost sight of in the above generalizations, which, as stated, apply to the north coast. It is probable that population increase characterized most of Peru during the Formative, but this is not certainly known. Some strong regional tendencies are, undoubtedly, tied to environmental differences between coast and highland. Adobe architecture as opposed to stone, or the emphasis upon canal irrigation versus terracing, is self-evident. Other regional differences cannot be explained so readily. On the south coast and in the south highlands Formative pottery is often multicolored, whereas in the north painting always took a secondary role to incising and modeling. It is noteworthy, too, that Chavín stylistic influence was never strong in the south and that the art of the south, while showing some element similarities to the central and northern Peruvian regions, followed traditions of its own.

Peruvian Classic cultures, such as Mochica, Early Lima (or Maranga), Nazca, Classic Tiahuanaco, and Recuay, apparently date from about the beginning of the Christian Era. This is in accordance with radiocarbon datings. Guess estimates have been somewhat later. Judging from the settlement studies in a single north coast valley, there was little population increase between late Formative and early Classic. However, larger site concentrations are reported, as well as more impressive mound and ceremonial constructions. This increase in site size, particularly of ceremonial or politicoreligious centers, seems to hold for the north and central coasts and, probably, for the south coast. In the highlands this trend is not definite. Classic Tiahuanaco and Pucara of the south highlands, both large and elaborate architectural complexes, would seem to be consistent with it; but Chavín de Huantar, the Formative stage center, is probably larger than later shrines or centers in the north highlands. On the north coast the fortified strong points of the late Formative developed into specialized military centers, and Mochica representative art is a testimonial to warfare. Large buildings with big rooms and corridors are also constructed in conjunction with great platform mound sites. Presumably these had palace or administrative functions.

The art of the Peruvian Classic is regionally specialized and technically and aesthetically climactic. Old regional continuities can be detected in all the great styles. Mochica sculptured and moldmade pottery derives from the sculptural and modeling tendencies of the earlier north-coast Cupisnique, Salinar, and Gallinazo phases. In the same manner the polychrome features of the south-coast Paracas phase are retained and elaborated in the subsequent Nazca styles. Trade and exchange among regional centers appear to have been going on at this time, particularly between coast and highland, but these contacts do not seem to have been sufficient to have deflected or modified well-organized regional styles.

The Tiahuanaco horizon style has been used by archeologists to mark the termination of the Classic cultures. However this style and its near pan-Peruvian diffusion are interpreted, there can be no doubt that it was concomitant with significant social and political changes. New settlement and architectural types appear on the central and north coasts at this time. These new types and changes include the planned rectangular inclosure site; a multiroomed dwelling unit of symmetrical plan ranging from small to great size; large, apparently empty, garrison-like enclosures; the widespread use of massive tapia, rather than small brick, adobe; and a definite decline in platform mound construction. Stylistic changes vary in kind and intensity during the Tiahuanaco horizon. On the south coast the changes are definite, but there is a tendency for a blending of old Nazca vessel shapes, designs, and colors with the Tiahuanaco iconography. On the central coast the Tiahuanaco artistic impact is somewhat starker, while north coast Mochica styles are virtually obliterated by the new influences. The origins of the Tiahuanaco influences are still a puzzle. Wari, a great ceremonial and dwelling site in the central highlands, may be the most important source of the art style and, perhaps, some of the forces behind the diffusion of the style. The actual iconography of the pottery paintings and textiles which are found so widespread over coast and highland may have an earlier and Classic-level origin at the Tiahuanaco site proper in highland Bolivia. Rowe, by historical reckoning, has placed the onslaught of the Tiahuanaco stylistic wave at A.D. 1000. If this is correct, and if radiocarbon dates are also correct, the Classic civilizations of Peru had a time range of a millennium or more.

The latter part of the Peruvian Postclassic stage is the period of the large local kingdoms of the coast, such as the Chimu and the Chincha, and of the various states of the highlands which were, subsequently, overrun by the Inca empire. On the coast the Postclassic sites—Chan Chan, Pacatnamu, and Cajamarquilla, to name a few—represent the largest population concentrations of Peruvian, and perhaps New World, prehistory. The planned rectangular inclosure community, noted in early Postclassic times, is the dominant architectural motif of these late coastal cities. Some of these aggregates and complexes of inclosures with their numerous rooms and courtyards also contained units which appear to be palaces or temples. These have been referred to as "urban elite" centers; other massed clusters of houses and rooms without the more elaborate specialized buildings are designated as "urban lay" centers. The various late Postclassic states are characterized by distinct new styles, but styles of a quality inferior to those of the Classic cultures. The Chimu pottery and metalwork show an interesting blend of old Classic Mochica concepts, Tiahuanacoid infusions, and other less readily identifiable elements. Similar fusions of local and Tiahuanacoid traditions are seen elsewhere. Throughout Peru, at this time, metalcraft was widely known. Ornaments of gold, copper, silver, and alloys were manufactured and widely traded, and in some regions weapons and tools were made of copper or bronze.

The Inca expansion from a small national hearth around Cuzco, in the south highlands, to a domain reaching over the entire Peruvian area and far beyond was a series of events that can be telescoped into the last century before the arrival of the Spanish in 1532. In general technology and culture the Inca participated in the common Peruvian co-tradition. Their empire thus appears to be an achievement of social and political organization. That there was precedent or tradition for empire building in pre-Incaic Peru is probable in the light of such a phenomenon as the Tiahuanaco stylistic diffusion.

Chronological Correlation of Middle American and Peruvian Sequences

The above synopses are attempts to present the salient facts—plus some integrative interpretation—of the prehistory of native Middle America and Peru. These are the peaks of New World civilization, the contours, so to speak, of the American "Oikoumene." What is their inter-relationship? What archeological traces of historical contact can be identified between these two centers? That some relationship existed is evident. Maize and a variety of other cultivated plants are shared by the two areas. So are numerous culture elements. To deal with these problems most effectively it is necessary to turn to chronologies—absolute and relative—and to see if we can co-ordinate in time, in any manner whatsoever, the sequences of events in prehistoric Peru and Middle America.

The greatest difficulty in effecting chronological correlations between Middle America and Peru is the lack of adequate archeological sequence data in the intervening regions of lower Central America, Columbia, and Ecuador. Middle American relative chronologies have been pushed southward only to the Ulua-Comayagua drainages in Honduras, and reliable Peruvian archeological sequences have been established only as far north as the Chicama Valley and the Callejon de Huaylas. For the vast area between, there is a substantial amount of survey information, but, except for an occasional, isolated stratigraphic datum, there is little in the way of time ordering of prehistoric cultures. A long sequence in northeastern Colombia which as yet has only local significance, the beginnings of chronology in Panama, and some partly established, partly inferential, chronological arrangements in Ecuador are among these few exceptions. It is, of course, possible to trace various traits through these intervening areas, between Middle America and Peru, without reference to the time factor; but in the absence of relative chronological alignments such trait distributions are not convincing as proof of historical interrelationships. In attempting cultural and chronological correlations between Peru and Middle America we must, then, rely chiefly upon sequences within these two areas and upon means of supplying absolute dates for these sequences. Where possible we shall utilize such chronological information as is available from the intervening regions.

In recent papers I have reviewed the subject of Middle American-Peruvian interrelationships from an archeological point of view, discussing certain conditions and limiting circumstances which surround the problem. In the first place, the nature of the evidence linking the two major American civilizational areas is that of culture content, not style. Second, certain myths and nonmaterial traits recorded from the ethnohistoric periods, while strong arguments for ancient contacts, are not, in most cases, identifiable in the archeological and relative chronological records. Third, the data of physical anthropology are not yet complete enough, or are not sufficiently specific, to be of much help on this problem. A possible exception is the cultural-physical trait of cranial deformation. The case for contact, then, is essentially an archeological one.

Prior to about 1000 B.C. there are no good evidences of diffusion between the Middle American and Peruvian centers of Nuclear America. That New World migrations and diffusions of a general north-to-south direction took place long before this date is attested by the presence of man in the Valley of Mexico and at the Straits of Magellan as early as 9000 and 6000 B.C. A few thousand years later it is likely that techniques of grinding and polishing stone and certain stone forms, such as the Californian "charm-stone," were diffused from North to South America. But such contacts antedate the rise of American maize agriculture and have no immediate bearing upon the growth and historical interrelatedness of the New World "Oikoumene." Maize agriculture, it will be remembered, is at least as early as 2500 B.C. in northeastern Mexico, and a similar primitive strain of corn was present in preceramic cultures in New Mexico as early or earlier. A local agricultural complex of the Peruvian coast is approximately contemporaneous with these dates, but this complex is without maize. The first substantial evidence of interrelationship between Middle America and Peru comes several hundred years later with the appearance of more fully developed maize and the Cupisnique culture of North Peru. The most reliable radiocarbon dating association with Cupisnique culture is the mean date of 715 B.C.

Historical connections between Middle American cultures of about 700 B.C. and Peruvian Cupisnique are suggested by much more than the common possession of developed maize. As Porter has shown, there are a number of fairly complex items which are shared by Cupisnique and the Valley of Mexico Tlatilco phase. Tlatilco appears to date somewhere in the middle Formative sequence of Mexico. Such a placement would be approximately midway between the Early Zacatenco and Cuicuilco phases whose previously cited dates are *circa* 1350 and 400 B.C., respectively. Such a time position is reasonably consistent with the Cupisnique radiocarbon dates, and this chronological alignment enhances the possibilities of Middle American–Peruvian diffusions of Tlatilco-Cupisnique culture elements. One of the trait elements which Cupisnique and Tlatilco share is rocker-stamped pottery. In general, rocker-stamped ware has a consistent middle to late Formative time position wherever it is found in Middle America. Between Honduras and Peru the rocker-stamped technique has been found in only one locality. This is on the lower Magdalena River in northern Colombia where Reichel-Dolmatoff places it at the bottom of a sequence of polychrome wares and postulates a respectable antiquity for it. In Peru, rocker-stamped pottery is known only from Cupisnique and other Chavín horizon phases. Traits besides the one of rocker-stamped decoration of pottery which link Tlatilco and Cupisnique include stirrup-spouted vessels, combined incised and painted pottery, predominance of polished black-brown wares, whistling jars, the jaguar motif, and pottery stamps. All these traits are found in one or another region of the interlying Ecuadorian-Colombian-Central American areas, but they are not found as a complex nor can their earliest occurrences be defined as to sequence position.

Another important trait which is first known from Peru on the Chavín horizon is the platform mound used as a base for presumed religious or politico-religious buildings. In coastal Peru these are constructed largely of adobe; in Middle America they consist, variously, of adobe, rubble, and stone masonry. In Middle America, as we have noted before, the platform mound is a late Formative trait in most regions although it appears to be somewhat earlier in the Guatemalan highlands. Thus, although platform mounds are not associated with the Tlatilco phase in the Valley of Mexico middle Formative, they are widespread throughout Middle America at a slightly later time and, in Guatemala, seem to be as early as, or earlier than, Tlatilco. It is suggested that the idea of the platform mound diffused from Middle America to Peru between 1000 and 500 B.C. and that it was a part of the same general diffusion that introduced developed maize and rocker-stamped pottery. This is, in effect, a restatement of Spinden's "Archaic" hypothesis. At the present time it cannot be proved, but the typological, stratigraphic, and radiocarbon dating evidences so far assembled favor the interpretation. Temple or platform mounds are found in Nicaragua and Costa Rica, and a few small ones have been reported from Panama. Large mounds are known from parts of the Ecuadorian coast, but in Colombia mound building seems to have been restricted mainly to burial tumuli. Nowhere in these geographically intervening areas can the earliest appearances of platform mounds be dated securely or with reference to Middle American sequences. The distributional data, thus, do little to support the hypothesis of the diffusion of the platform mound from Middle America to Peru, but, at the same time, they do not rule it out.

Historical contact between Middle America and Peru seems to have continued, following these earliest evidences for diffusion. Resist-dye painting of pottery, which in Peru is just post-Chavín horizon, has its first Valley of Mexico occurrences as a minority type in Tlatilco and as a more important type in the late Formative Ticoman phase. This is, for the most part, the chronological position of negative painted ware in other Middle American regions. An exception is Usulatan ware which, in the Guatemalan highlands, is as early as the Las Charcas phase. There is, however, some doubt whether Usulatan is a resist-dye technique. Considering the popularity of negative painted ware in intervening Ecuador, Colombia, and much of lower Central America, it is reasonable to suspect that it diffused between Peru and Middle America. Inasmuch as chronological priority cannot be established for either the Middle American or the Peruvian negative painting occurrences, the point of origin of the technique is obscure. Its greatest frequency would appear to be in the north Peruvian and Ecuadorian highlands.

Another technical trait, the figurine mold, has a later inception than negative painting or any of the traits yet discussed. It first occurs in the Valley of Mexico in the early Classic Teotihuacan III (Xolalpan) phase, where moldmade figurines are common. In the Maya region the date for the figurine mold seems to be a few centuries later, coincident with the late Classic Tepeu phase. In Peru, the first moldmade figurines date from the Mochica culture of the north coast. The Teotihuacan III (or Xolalpan) phase of the Valley of Mexico, as placed on the early Classic horizon, would date from about A.D. 300–600 if we follow the 11.16.0.0.0 correlation as it applies to the cross-datable Tzakol phase of lowland Maya. Following the 12.9.0.0.0 correlation, these dates for Teotihuacan III might be pushed back to about A.D. 0–300. Radiocarbon is of little or no help in dating Teotihuacan III. In Peru, the Mochica date which seems most consistent with other dates and with the stratigraphic record is A.D. 112 ± 190. From this, about all we can conclude is that the use of the mold appeared in the early centuries of the Christian Era in the Valley of Mexico and in north Peru. No continuity of distribution by land from Mexico to Peru can be demonstrated, but the argument for diffusion is strengthened by the occurrences of moldmade figurines on the north and central coasts of Ecuador. In the Guayas region of Ecuador, moldmade figurines first date from the middle periods of the prehistoric sequences —a position which can be reconciled, in a general way, with their Classic-stage chronological appearance in Peru and Mexico. Added to this, there are a number of rather specific resemblances between figurines of various Mexican regions and those of the Ecuadorian coast. There is in all this a strong suggestion of contacts by sea between Middle America and Ecuador-Peru which were responsible for the diffusion of the figurine mold as early as the first centuries of the first millennium A.D. The center of origin of the figurine mold in the Americas is uncertain, but the ancient and well-established tradition of handmade figurines in the Formative phases of Mexico offers a logical situation for the development of the mold device.

Metallurgy, in the sense of technical processes such as casting, gilding, annealing, soldering, and alloying, appears to have its earliest American centers in Peru. On the north coast metalwork goes back to the Chavín horizon, and by the Gallinazo phases of the late Formative–early Classic it was well developed. Gold and copper and alloys of these were the principal metals of the Formative and Classic; silver and bronze came into common use in the Postclassic. Both ornaments and utilitarian artifacts were fashioned. The age of metallurgy in Ecuador and Colombia is unknown, but it seems likely that the Guangala-phase occurrences of copper tools and ornaments are contemporaneous with the Peru Classic periods. Colombian metallurgical centers, such as the Quimbaya, may have arisen as the result of Ecuadorian and Peruvian stimuli. Certainly the Panamanian, Costa Rican, and Nicaraguan prehistoric metalcraft is closely allied to Colombia both in technology and in style, and all these lower Central American metallurgical developments appear to be relatively late (within the last five hundred years preceding the Spanish conquests). Although some metal trade objects undoubtedly reached Middle America from lower Central America, it is likely that the most important Mexican metallurgical centers resulted from direct sea trade with Peru or Ecuador. The abundance and variety of metals in southwest and west Mexico substantiate this. Middle American metals are generally thought of as being entirely Postclassic, but occasional copper and gold finds come from contexts which are Classic and, perhaps, even earlier. Continued research in west Mexico may reveal a deeper tradition of metallurgy than has heretofore been admitted for Middle America.

There are other traits which strongly indicate the possibility of at least an occasional coastwise sea trade between Middle America and Peru-Ecuador on a relatively late time horizon. Pottery, reminiscent of Postclassic Peru in shape and design, has been found in Pacific Guatemala. A pottery seal from the Ecuadorian coast has a design which incorporates the Middle American concept of the speech scroll. These and other items suggest a pattern of random acceptance, and rejection, in the diffusion between the two areas—a pattern consistent with intermittent and casual contacts.

In summation, the archeological records in the Middle American and Peruvian centers support the hypothesis of an early and significant contact between the two areas. Maize agriculture, temple platform mounds, and several ceramic traits may have been diffused at a time between 1000 and 500 B.C. As there is a still earlier record of agricultural-sedentary, pottery-making civilization in Middle America, it is further suggested that this primary diffusion moved from Middle America to Peru. For later times, these evidences of contact continue to appear in both the Middle American and Peruvian sequences. The direction of diffusion can only be postulated, but there is a suggestion that it was, first, from north-to-south and, later, from south-to-north.

So far this discussion has not taken into account the question of contacts between Old and New World. Nuclear America has been treated as an entity, separate in its history, from the Old World Oikoumene. This may have been the case, but we are, as yet, unable to rule out all possibilities of trans-Pacific diffusion. There are a number of writings on this theme, and they cannot be dealt with, or even summarized, here. I am unconvinced of the linkages of style, in art and architecture, which have been advanced. On the other hand, certain technical inventions, modes, or complex features do argue for pre-Columbian contact. Some of these traits, like the well-known patolli game, may be of trans-Pacific derivation, or, possibly, the results of ancient migrations and diffusions across the Bering Straits and down through the Americas. One such trait is the rocker-stamped technique of pottery decoration which we have pointed to as a Middle American–Peruvian connective. Rocker-stamped ware dates back to 2000 B.C. in Mongolia-Manchuria. I am inclined to believe that it has a common world-wide history. The rocker-stamped technique may have been diffused into the New World from across the Pacific. From an original American focus in Middle America it may have spread to Peru (as we have argued), and it may also have spread into the Mississippi and Ohio valleys. We should not, however, overlook the other possibility—that the diffusion of the trait was from north Asia into North America and, thence, from Mississippian and Ohio centers into the pottery complexes of Middle America. Radiocarbon dates on the rocker-stamped technique in the Ohio-Illinois regions range from about 300 B.C. to A.D. 200, seemingly a bit too late to have antedated the Middle American occurrences; but the data and radiocarbon dates are still few, and the question must be kept open.

It is, then, possible that technical and other traits and elements of the New World civilizations are Old World inventions and that they have, by one route or another, moved into Middle America or Peru. I do not feel, however, that these possibilities invalidate the arguments for diffusion within the Nuclear American orbit. It is a possibility, but in my opinion a very remote one, that trans-Pacific diffusions introduced the same trait onto the shores of both Middle America and Peru, thereby complicating the timing and tracing of diffusion between these two areas.

Configurational Correlation of Middle American and Peruvian Sequences

In the preceding section an attempt was made to align Peruvian and Middle American archeological sequences with absolute time and, thereby, with each other. In so doing, certain culture elements in the two sequences have been brought into approximate chronological juxtaposition, and this has served to suggest diffusion and a degree of historical unity between the two areas. It is not, however, these occasional similarities of element content (of which there are many more than the few just described) which provide the most spectacular resemblances between the high civilizations of pre-Columbian Middle America and Peru but the striking likenesses in total cultural configuration.

These configurational parallels in the rise of Middle American and Peruvian civilizations are evident in the synopses which have been presented in this paper. They may be summarized here.

On the Formative stage, Middle America and Peru are similar in that the agricultural village is the basic community. Significant cultural content, as well as treatment of content, is shared by the two areas. Arts and crafts show competence but lack the aesthetic brilliance of the later Classic stages. Special structures, probably of a religious nature, were built on flat-topped pyramidal mounds. Throughout, the Formative population seems to have increased. Differences are seen in the presence of a "Village Formative," or early Formative, period in Middle America, where religious or central structures are lacking, and in the absence of a comparable "Village Formative" in Peru. The Peruvian Formative, at least on the north coast, begins with temple mound structures. In other words, the Peruvian Formative has a closer configurational resemblance to Middle American late Formative. There is also, in the beginning of the Peruvian Formative, the Chavín art style and its remarkable distribution. A partial parallel to this is the Middle American late-Formative Olmec style, although the intensity and wide geographical spread of Olmec is not as great as that of Chavín. Military architecture characterizes the Peruvian Formative in Post-Chavín times; it was unknown in the Middle American Formative.

Classic-stage configurations in Middle America resemble those of Peru in the achievement of a climax in pyramid mound and temple construction. In both areas this was foreshadowed in the Formative. During the Classic there was a mutual trend in the construction of what appear to be "palaces" (elaborate multiroomed buildings) in connection with ceremonial centers. Arts and crafts were brought to a peak of refinement and elaboration. Regionalism in style was marked—more so than in the preceding Formative or the succeeding Postclassic. Differences at this time are striking. Although we are speaking mainly of configuration, there are sharp distinctions in cultural content and in emphasis of content that deserve to be mentioned. Metallurgy and the working of gold, copper, and alloys was common to most of Peru but rare or absent in Middle America. The precious material of the latter area was jade rather than gold. Irrigation and terracing begun in the Peruvian Formative was perfected in the Classic. The evidence for Classic-period appearances of these traits in Middle America is uncertain. Writing and the calendar were carried to great heights in some parts of Middle America on the Classic level and were possessed in all parts. Comparable developments are lacking in Peru. Organized warfare and conquest states are very much a part of the Peruvian Classic, at least as far as the north coast is concerned. Although organized fighting and conflict were not completely absent from Middle America at this time, there is much less evidence for them in the archeological record than there is in the central Andes.

Middle American–Peruvian resemblances on the Postclassic stage include the phenomenon of cultural fusion over multiple regions and the apparent large-scale movements of peoples. Probably related to this is the tendency for increased military activities and empire building. In Peru there were Classic forerunners of these trends, but in Middle America the change seems to have been a sharper one. In certain regions of both areas there are evidences of urban concentrations of populations during the Postclassic. In Peru this trend can be traced from the Classic; in Middle America there are some evidences of earlier urbanism but the record for the Postclassic is more convincing. In both areas there are indications of the growing power of secular authority in the Postclassic. There are significant differences between the Peruvian and Middle American civilizations on this late stage, and knowledge of some of these comes from ethnohistoric accounts in addition to the archeological record. Although the two areas share the pattern of cultural fusion of their component regions at this time, it is interesting that horizon style phenomena are Peruvian but not Middle American. In the latter area certain traits like Fine Orange ware or the basal-flanged bowl are widely distributed at specific periods; but Middle American styles, in a sense of a complex iconography, do not have the same far-flung distributions and pervasive qualities that characterize Peruvian Chavín, Tiahuanaco, or Inca. In Peru the Inca state was all powerful and extended well into the adjoining northern and southern Andes. Effective systems of political and social incorporation had been developed. In Mexico, the Aztec domain was much smaller and less systematically administered. Under the Inca the Peruvian became a government worker or bureaucrat whose duty it was to produce and to distribute the productions; in Middle America strong and independent artisan and merchant classes were important parts of the Aztec nation.

The meaning of these configurational parallels between the Peruvian and the Mexican–Central American cultures has been the source of speculation as to causality. The differences and divergences have also given rise to speculation. I do not believe that we can arrive at satisfactory solutions to the problems posed at the present state of Americanist knowledge. We have reviewed the case, or part of the case, for element diffusion between Middle America and Peru, and it is a relatively strong one. The nature of the evidence implies both gradual indirect and rapid direct transferences. In following out the arguments for diffusions it was noted that the major chronological divisions of Middle American and Peruvian archeology have a rough time coincidence. That is, assuming the correctness of a majority of the radiocarbon dates, the Formative stage in the two areas is largely restricted to the millennium preceding the Christian Era, while the Classic stage appears to begin early in the first millennium A.D. and is estimated to continue until approximately A.D. 1000. Postclassic cultures are, then, confined to the last five hundred years preceding the arrival of the Europeans. Thus, the two configurations of culture growth are not only similar but *synchronous*. This synchroneity —of over two thousand years duration—is a powerful argument for historical interrelatedness. Yet, in spite of this evidence and the acceptance of the historical relationship between these two areas of Nuclear America, the story is obviously not one of diffusion alone. Styles and other complex patterns of Middle America and Peru are quite distinct, and this suggests a considerable independence in cultural creativeness.

Summary

The New World has an orbit of prehistoric and native agriculture which covers perhaps two-thirds of the South American continent and nearly half of North America. The generative center for this diffusion sphere lies in the central areas of Middle America, Peru, and the lands which lie between them. This center is Nuclear America—a sort of American "Oikoumene" comparable to the heartland of civilization of the Old World. The available data of archeology indicate that sedentary village life, based upon this agriculture, was fully developed by 1500 B.C. and that the actual domestication of the maize plant was at least one thousand years earlier. The evidence also indicates that this kind of culture was widely diffused at a relatively early date. In Middle America and in Peru these sedentary agricultural beginnings of the later American civilizations have been designated as the Formative. Radiocarbon dates suggest that the Middle American Formative cultures had an earlier inception than those of Peru, and a case can be argued for the diffusion of significant Formative elements from Middle America to Peru at a time between 1000 and 500 B.C. The close of the Formative stages and the opening of the Classic stages appear to be roughly synchronous in both major areas—a date of approximately A.D. I. Throughout the Classic and Postclassic stages there was continued diffusion, direct and indirect, between Peru and Middle America. Traces of some of these Middle American–Peruvian contacts are seen in the intervening regions of lower Central America, Colombia, and Ecuador, but lack of sufficient archeological sequence information from this geographical intermediate area makes synchronization difficult.

It should be emphasized that the evidences of diffusion between Middle America and Peru are those of culture elements and culture content. In style and patterning the arts and institutions of the two areas are quite distinct. This distinctiveness is more pronounced in the Classic and Postclassic cultures than in those of the Formative. There is little question but what styles and patterns resulted from local creativeness and inventiveness in each area and within smaller local regions of each area.

On a grander scale than either cultural content or cultural patterning are the similarities in over-all configurations of culture growth in Middle America and Peru. We do not yet know how to account for these parallels—of trends and emphasis—through time. Perhaps they were conditioned, directed, and given momentum by the intermittent but continued diffusions between the two areas. Perhaps they were largely the result of similar human and social responses to similar situations. And in attempting to appraise the parallels we should not overlook the divergences in cultural configuration. They are of equal interest in the prehistory of Nuclear America and of equal importance in the study of this prehistory for the elucidation of cultural process.

Reconsiderations: 1966

In the little more than 10 years since this article was written there have been several archeological discoveries that provide new insights into, and prompt new interpretations of, Nuclear American culture history. Following the outline of the original article, some of the most important of these discoveries and changes of interpretation are summarized.

Middle America Formation cultures have now been found to date back to 2000 B.C. In the highlands of Puebla, in southern Mexico, they developed gradually from antecedent hunting and plant collecting ones. This development is traced through several millennia of "incipient cultivation." A primitive maize was domesticated by 4000 B.C.; a vastly improved and hybridized maize plant was available by 2000 B.C. These events took place in a context of gradual transition from seasonally shifting camp sites to permanent villages. The earliest known Mesoamerican pottery dates from 2000 B.C. or a little before. The Early Formative Period (2000–1000 B.C.) was, apparently, a "Village Formative" period; major ceremonial constructions and urban concentrations have not been associated with it. It is probable that the northern part of Mesoamerica lagged somewhat in attaining the sedentary agricultural condition that is considered the "threshold" of the Formative Period, and some archaeologists do not accept an Early Formative dating of the Early Zacatenco phase in the Valley of Mexico but place it, instead, after 1000 B.C.

Radiocarbon dates indicate that the elaborate and sophisticated Olmec art style flourished in the Middle Formative Period (1000–300 B.C.), rather than later as was formerly believed. Elements of the style are found throughout southern Mesoamerica, as well as in the Valley of Mexico. Its place of origin is not known: but the site of La Venta, Tabasco, which may be the earliest great ceremonial center of Mesoamerica, was an important Olmec base.

Radiocarbon dates now clearly favor the 11.16.0.0.0 correlation of the Maya calendar which means that the Classic Period is bracketed between A.D. 300–900. The Classic Period was preceded by Late Formative (300 B.C.–0) and Protoclassic (0–A.D. 300) Periods, and it was during these six centuries that art, architecture, writing, calendrics, ceremonial center construction, and a tradition of urban settlement were rapidly developed. The urban center—and the large political state—were probably among the latest of these phenomena, but by the beginnings of the Classic Period they are very clearly in evidence. Recent surveys show that Teotihuacan, in the Valley of Mexico, had an urban zone some 9 square miles in extent. The influences of Teotihuacan are found throughout Mesoamerica on an Early Classic Period (A.D. 300–600) level, and it is likely that the city was the capital of the first Mesoamerican empire. Its fall and destruction (ca. A.D. 700) marks the end of an era, and in the Valley of Mexico and northern Mesoamerica the event may be said to usher in the Postclassic Period.

Peru Along the Peruvian coast there is now a fairly continuous record of occupation from about 9000 B.C. to historic times. Until about 4000 B.C. the inhabitants were land hunters. After that, some groups began to divide their time seasonally between hunting in the fog-shrouded coastal foothills of the Andes and fishing along the shore. Between 4000 and 2500 B.C. marine subsistence of the littoral villages was supplemented by the cultivation of squash and lima beans. Settled, year-round life became the pattern after 2500 B.C.; and toward the close of this period large coastal towns and huge ceremonial constructions appeared. Nevertheless, subsistence continued to be primarily the harvest of the sea. Between 1800 and 1000 B.C. maize was introduced—probably from Mesoamerica—and pottery appeared. Large urban communities and ceremonial construction continued. At some time after 1000 B.C. there was a probable religious unification of Peru as attested by the Chavín stylistic horizon. The point in time, in all this, at which Peruvian coastal societies could be said to have become primarily agricultural is a matter of debate. Some authorities place such an "agricultural threshold" at 1800 B.C., others at 1000 B.C., and still others at 200 B.C. or thereabouts.

The early cultures of the Peruvian highlands are not as well known as those of the coast although excavations at Kotosh, near Huanuco, have revealed pre-Chavín pottery and temple structures dating as early as 1800 B.C. Here, in this environment, it seems almost certain that subsistence was agricultural—possibly the potato, possibly maize.

Radiocarbon dates have given archeologists a better "fix" on the close of the Peruvian Classic cultures and the inception of the Tiahuanaco horizon. This occurred at about A.D. 600, rather than 1000. That the spread of Tiahuanaco art styles was a manifestation of political and military force is generally accepted although it now appears that two "empires" may have been involved, one with a capital at Tiahuanaco proper, which dominated the south highlands, and the other with a capital at Wari, which controlled the rest of the country.

Chronological Correlation of Middle American and Peruvian Sequences Archaeological progress has been great in Ecuador, Colombia, and Lower Central America in the last 10 years, but it is still not feasible to extend a series of cross-datings from northern Peru to southern Mesoamerica. An interesting discovery of the last decade is that the earliest American pottery seems to be in Ecuador and Colombia, where it dates at about 3000 B.C., a millennium earlier than elsewhere. It is possible that the idea of pottery spread from this "Intermediate area" northward and southward, to Mesoamerica and Peru; however, if such diffusions did occur they cannot yet be pinned down for cross-dating purposes. The first good evidence of Mesoamerican-Ecuadorian ties comes at about 1500–1000 B.C. and involves ceramic complexes of Pacific Guatemala and coastal Ecuador. There are also a number of striking ceramic parallels between the Mexican Tlatilco (Olmec-influenced) complex and Peruvian Chavín. In both of these cases most archeologists have thought of the diffusion running from north to south; but there is a minority opinion that would hold for Peruvian and Ecuadorian origins with subsequent spreads to Mesoamerica. The case for maize passing from Mesoamerica to Peru is a strong one, bolstered by plant genetics as well as by archeology and radiocarbon dates; still, there are some who would argue for maize being an independent domesticate (from a local wild form) in Peru. As noted above, there are dates for Peruvian maize at the beginning of the second millennium B.C. For the later Precolumbian centuries there are various clues to contacts between Mesoamerica and Peru. Comment and modifications could be offered on many of the statements about these in the original article, but space precludes this. In general, chronological correlation between Mesoamerican and Peruvian sequences is most easily achieved through a comparison of radiocarbon dates.

Configurational Correlation of Middle American and Peruvian Sequences Recent findings bring out important differences between the Preclassic or Formative cultures of Mesoamerica and those of Peru. In Mesoamerica, the Formative threshold is defined as sedentary agricultural subsistence. This condition evolved from a long period of "incipient cultivation," with the changeover occurring at about 2000 B.C. Urban life and large ceremonial architecture did not follow for another 1000 years or so. On the Peruvian coast marine subsistence made possible sedentary life and large, permanent communities much earlier than in Mesoamerica. Sizable religious structures were also associated with these early Peruvian fishing towns. These date from 2500 to 1800 B.C. In brief, agriculture was, at first, a side-line in Peru, a modest supplement to fishing activities. Later, perhaps as late as 1000 B.C., or even after that, farming became the primary basis of subsistence. The Formative cultures of the two areas are similar, however, in that in the course of the development of each a highly sophisticated art style appears. I am inclined to think that these styles (Olmec and Chavín) are functionally comparable, that in each area they attest to a religious unification and system of communication among many regional communities. Some archeologists have claimed an historical connection between the two styles although this is uncertain.

For later periods, there is a similarity of configuration between Peru and Middle America in that ceremonial architecture increases in size and elaboration from Late Formative to Early Classic times. This parallelism was noted in the original article except that then it was not realized that great ceremonial construction had quite so early an inception in either area. The parallel of an esthetic florescence in the Classic Period of each area still holds although now we are aware of two such peaks in each sequence, an earlier in the first millennium B.C. (Olmec and Chavín) and a later at ca. A.D. 300–600.

The militaristic trends formerly noted as characterizing the Postclassic Periods are confirmed by all that we have learned in the last 10 years. For urbanism the record is less clear. In Mesoamerica, the urban form of settlement became more frequent in Postclassic times although there is no Postclassic site that compares with Teotihuacan in sheer size. In Peru, there is a trend toward the "planned city" in some regions in the Postclassic; however, this does not seem to be area-wide.

I am still of the opinion that contacts between the two areas were instrumental in determining some of the developmental similarity that we see between Mesoamerica and Peru; however, I also continue to be convinced that the developmental parallelisms are primarily the result of independent responses to natural environmental, demographic, and social factors. I believe that this comes through even more clearly than it did 10 years ago. In the light of what was known then, I appraised the parallelisms in the two sequences as being more fully uniform than they have turned out to be. That the transition from semi-nomadism to permanent sedentary communities has been revealed to be quite different in the two areas makes the subsequent similarities of developmental pattern even more impressive.

40 Ancient
Mesoamerican
Civilization

Richard S. MacNeish

"HOW AND WHY DO CIVILIZATIONS ARISE?" THIS QUESTION MOTIVATES MORE
than one selection in these Readings, *but most of them tend to generalize
well beyond the conditions that generated a particular civilization. In this
article, and in the one by Coe and Flannery that follows, generalizations
are tied to a specific set of archaeological facts and enhanced by carefully
selected additions from geology, biology and other contingent sciences.
Despite this concentration on one case (any single case is always a special
case), this ecological approach to the rise of civilization in one New-
World focus throws light on comparable processes elsewhere.*

*In this selection, then, Richard MacNeish, in advance of a major
team publication, surveys the major stages in the development of a civilization in the Tehuacán Valley of central Mexico. A closer view of the
ecological context in which this civilization arose will follow.*

A problem that has long interested the layman, the scientist, and the
philosopher has to do with how and why civilizations arose. Any

SOURCE: *Science*, Vol. 143 (February 7, 1964), pp. 531–537. Copyright 1964 by the
American Association for the Advancement of Science. Reprinted with the permission of the author and publisher.

The author is the Head of the Department of Archaeology at the University of
Calgary, Calgary, Alberta, Canada, and Director of the Tehuacán Archaeological-
Botanical Project for the Robert S. Peabody Foundation for Archaeology, Andover,
Massachusetts. Dr. MacNeish has written *An Introduction to the Archaeology of
Southeastern Manitoba* (1958) and *Investigations in the Southwest Yukon: Archaeo-
logical Excavations, Comparisons and Speculations* (1964), as well as articles based
on his Tehuacán Valley data.

hypothesis or generalization about this social phenomenon must be based on broad comparative historical data. Specifically, one must compare long archeological sequences, from savagery to civilization, which have been uncovered in relatively independent areas. The ancient high cultures of Mexico and Central America (termed Mesoamerica) have always represented an interesting facet of this problem, for here were prehistoric civilizations which apparently arose independently of any of those in the Old World.

It is generally accepted that the development of agriculture is basic to the rise of village and urban life. And so, in our work in Mesoamerica, it was assumed that if we could but find the origins of agriculture—and in the New World this meant maize or corn—then we would be well on the way to finding out where and how civilization evolved in America.

After a number of years of investigation, it became apparent that the desert valley of Tehuacán (about 150 miles south of Mexico City) was the region in which evidence could most likely be uncovered about the beginnings of the domestication of corn. Precisely why we decided on this area is explained in an article by Mangelsdorf and others in [*Science*, Vol. 143 (February 7, 1967), pp. 538–545], so I confine my discussion to the archeological researches recently undertaken in this southern Puebla valley.

In attacking such an all-inclusive problem, the project was most fortunate in having the cooperation of a number of scientists from a wide variety of fields. Obviously, I am extremely grateful to these various specialists, but I must confess that I say this with a sigh of relief, for at the beginning of the first field season we were far from convinced that the much-vaunted interdisciplinary approach was practicable. We know now that it can and does work, and thanks to our experts' endeavors we have gathered and interrelated specialized studies in botany, corn, beans, squash, human feces, pollen, zoology, geology, geography, physical anthropology, prehistoric textiles, ethnohistory, and ethnography.[1] These

---

[1] Drs. P. C. Mangelsdorf and W. C. Galinat of the Harvard Botanical Museum and E. J. Wellhausen and R. Hathaway of the Rockefeller Foundation studied the corn remains: Drs. T. Whitaker, senior geneticist of the U.S. Department of Agriculture, and H. Cutler, executive director of the Missouri Botanical Gardens, investigated the prehistoric cucurbits, and Dr. L. Kaplan of Roosevelt University studied the prehistoric beans. Dr. C. E. Smith of the U.S. Department of Agriculture made botanical studies in the Tehuacán Valley; Dr. R. Drake, at the University of British Columbia, identified the shells; and Dr. Eric C. Callen, of McDonald College of McGill University, analyzed the human feces found in the caves. Miss Monica Bopp, and later Dr. James Shoenwetter of the University of Southern Illinois, studied various pollen profiles in the valley to determine ancient changes in climate and vegetation. Dr. Carmen Cook De Leonard of the Centro de Investigaciones Antropologicas of Mexico aided us with her knowledge of the ethnohistory and ethnobotany of the Tehuacán Valley, and Mrs. I. Johnson of the National Museum of Mexico examined the textiles we found in the excavations. Kent Flannery, a student at the University of Chicago,

investigations, of course, were in addition to the usual archeological re-searches carried out so ably by my field staff.[2]

Before discussing what our diverse group accomplished in the Tehuacán Valley, let me briefly describe the valley itself. It is located in the southern part of the state of Puebla, and in the northernmost section of the state of Oaxaca, in the central highlands of Mexico. Efforts were concentrated in a relatively small area, about 70 miles long and 20 miles wide. Although the valley is considerably longer than it is wide, it has a basin-like appearance, for it is ringed by high mountains. The Sierra Madre Oriental is to the south and east, while to the north and west are the Mixteca Hills. Both rise considerably above the Tehuacán Valley floor, which is 1500 meters above sea level. Because of these precipitous mountains the valley is in a rain shadow and extremely dry. Most parts of the valley floor receive less than 600 millimeters of rainfall a year, and some parts receive less than 500 millimeters. Moreover, most of this rain falls during a 2-month period. Needless to say, the resultant vegetation is xerophytic. Thus, the Tehuacán Valley has all the characteristics of a desert.

Intensive archeological investigation in this region has now been under way for 3 consecutive years; in addition, I spent a brief 10 weeks in the area in 1960. Archeological reconnaissance has resulted in the dis-covery of 392 new sites or prehistoric habitations. These range from small temporary camps to large ruins of cities. At about 30 of these sites test trenches were dug. These were superficial, but even so, one sounding yielded stratified remains with five occupational floors, one above the other. Twelve test trenches in other sites revealed deep stratified remains. Excavations in these particular sites were expanded into major digs and became the basis for establishing a long prehistoric sequence of culture.

In these 12 sites of major excavation (selected from the original 392 sample sites), 140 stratified floors and occupational zones were unearthed. Five of these were open sites or middens, while seven were caves or rock shelters, or both.

---

identified the 12,000 archeological bones we uncovered; Dr. J. L. Lorenzo, chief of the Prehistoric Section of the Instituto de Antropologia of Mexico, and Dr. J. Moser of the Federal Department of Geology of Mexico surveyed the geology, and Dr. R. Woodbury of the U.S. National Museum, Dr. J. Anderson of the University of Buffalo, and D. Byers of the R. S. Peabody Foundation investigated, respectively, the ancient irrigation systems, the human skeletal remains, and the geography of the Valley. F. Johnson, also of the R. S. Peabody Foundation, carried out a program of dating the archeological remains by the carbon-14 method.

[2] The Tehuacán field staff included Mr. Peterson, assistant director; Dr. M. Fowler of the University of Southern Illinois; F. Johnson of the R. S. Peabody Foundation; K. Flannery of the University of Chicago; R. L. Chadwick of Mexico City College; Angel Garcia Cook and A. Arbide of the School of Anthropology of Mexico; and Miss A. Nelken, a student of the Sorbonne in Paris, and her two "Tehuacanero" assistants in the laboratory, N. Tejeda and F. Molina.

Because of the extreme dryness of the area, in over 55 of the floors in the five caves everything had been preserved: foodstuffs, feces, and other normally perishable human remains and artifacts. This type of refuse not only allows one to make an unusually complete reconstruction of the way of life of the ancient inhabitants, but gives considerable information about subsistence, food habits, diet, climatic changes, and, in many cases, even indicates which months of the year the floors were occupied.

Although our studies are a long way from completion (it has taken much time to even count and catalog the 750,000 specimens so far uncovered), preliminary results have been most encouraging. Some of these I summarize briefly in the following paragraphs.

Ajuereado Phase

The earliest assemblage of artifacts is called the Ajuereado phase.[3] In the caves, we uncovered evidence of seven different occupations, while surface collections have yielded four more sites of this cultural complex. As yet we have only three dates, obtained by the carbon-14 technique, on the final stages of this phase, but another five are being processed. The phase seems to have ended by at least 7200 B.C., and it may have come into being 3 or 4 millennia earlier. Examination of these floors indicates that in this period the inhabitants were grouped together into small, nomadic families or microbands who changed their camps three or four times a year with the seasons. As means of subsistence they collected wild plants and they hunted and trapped. Although they hunted such animals as horses and antelope of now-extinct species during the earliest part of the phase, even then most of their meat came from smaller game, such as jack rabbits, gophers, rats, turtles, birds, and other small mammals. In the later part of the phase they trapped only species that exist today. These people, in the so-called "big game hunting stage" or "mammoth-hunting period," were far from being the great hunters they are supposed to have been. As one of my colleagues said: "They probably found one mammoth in a lifetime and never got over talking about it."

Preliminary studies of the pollen and animal bones seem to show that, in this region, the climate of the terminal Pleistocene was only very slightly cooler and wetter than the climate today. The vegetation was probably xerophytic, but not like the present-day desert vegetation in the Tehuacán Valley—it probably was more like the mesquite grasslands of western Texas.

The manufactured tools of this group were not numerous, and all were made by chipping flint. They include a series of bifacially leaf-shaped knives and projectile points, keeled and ovoid end scrapers, flake

[3] The names of the various phases were taken from the name of the site or cave where these cultural complexes were first unearthed.

and bifacial choppers, side scrapers, gravers, and crude prismatic blades struck from even cruder polyhedral cores. No ground stone was utilized, and the floors held few perishable remains, hence we know nothing about the weaving industry or the traps and perishable tools of these peoples. No burials have been found, though there is one fragment of a charred human bone.

This complex (represented by many more artifacts than have been previously found for this time period) seems to be related to the earliest remains found elsewhere in Central America. It must be noted, however, that even at the earliest stage these peoples were not primarily dependent upon hunting and should be called plant and animal collectors rather than hunters. Further, the material culture of the Ajuereado phase continued unchanged even though the Pleistocene fauna became extinct and gave way to modern fauna.

El Riego Phase

Gradually the Ajuereado phase developed into one which we call the El Riego cultural phase. This is extremely well known, for we have dug up 24 floors and have found 14 open camp sites. Ten dates, obtained by the carbon-14 method, allow us to estimate the time of this cultural phase fairly accurately. It seems to fall between 7200 and 5200 B.C. These peoples were seasonally nomadic like their predecessors, but there had been a definite increase in population and some changes in the settlement pattern seem to have taken place. The sites are almost equally divided between very small camps, which obviously represent the family groups or microbands of the dry seasons, and much larger sites, representing camps of related families or macrobands which gathered together in the spring and wet seasons. The means of subsistence was basically plant and animal collecting, supplemented by some hunting—not very different from the previous period, although these peoples seem to have hunted deer instead of horse and antelope, and the cottontail rabbit instead of the jack rabbit.

As for their hunting and trapping activities, there were no fundamental changes; nor do they seem to have been "forced by the changing climatic conditions that followed the end of the Wisconsin Glaciation to make readjustments." The preserved plant remains, however, seem to show that plant collecting was even more important than it had been in the previous culture. Nevertheless, it was only a seasonal affair. During the dry season, apparently, people still hunted and trapped in small groups and probably nearly starved, but when the spring came, and later the rains, a number of microbands seem to have gathered together in larger groups to live off the lusher vegetation. There is evidence that they were collecting a large variety of plants, and I would guess that this was the period when they finally conceived the idea that if you drop a seed in the ground a plant comes up. This concept is, of course, basic to any beginnings of agriculture. Further, these people were eating some plants which later became domesticated. These included one variety of squash (*Cucurbita mixta*), chili, and avocados. It is also possible that they were gathering and consuming wild corn as well as utilizing cotton.

The development of such a subsistence and settlement pattern undoubtedly caused some changes in their social organization. From comparative ethnological data one might guess that these groups were patrilineal bands with some sort of weak temporary leadership in the hands of a male, and perhaps some sort of concept of territoriality. Further, there apparently were shamans, or witch doctors, who had considerable power in both the medicinal and the ceremonial fields. These, of course, would not have been full-time specialists.

The tools we dug up gave considerable evidence about the industrial activities of these peoples. For example, they manufactured a number of varieties of contracting-stemmed and concave-based projectile points which were very neatly chipped and were probably used to tip atlatl darts used in the chase. The most prevalent artifacts were, however, the large plano-convex scrapers and choppers chipped from pebbles or nodules of flint. These could have been used for preparing skins, but it seems more probable that they were used for pulping various plant remains. Some blades, burins, and end scrapers of types found in the previous horizon were still made and utilized. The most noticeable change in the material culture was the use of ground-stone and pecked-stone implements. Mortars and pestles were particularly numerous, and there were many milling stones and pebble manos. Tools of both types were probably used to grind up plant and animal remains into some sort of palatable (or unpalatable) stew.

In addition, it is in this period that we found the first evidence of weaving and woodworking—knotted nets, a few small fragments of twined blankets and coiled baskets, fragments of dart shafts, and pieces of traps.

To me, one of the most surprising findings for the El Riego cultural phase was evidence of relatively elaborate burials, which indicate the possibility of complex beliefs and ceremonies. We uncovered two groups of multiple burials. In the first were the skeletons of two children; one child had been ceremonially cremated. The head of the other child had been severed and roasted, the brains had been removed, and the head had been placed in a basket on the child's chest. The other multiple burial included an elderly man, an adolescent woman, and a child of less than 1 year. There was evidence that the elderly man had been intentionally burned, and the heads of both the woman and the child had been smashed, perhaps intentionally. These findings could certainly be interpreted as some sort of human sacrifice, but the correctness of such an interpretation is difficult to prove. In both these burials the bodies were wrapped in blankets and nets and were richly furnished with basketry. Is it not possible that the ceremonialism that is so characteristic of the later Mexican periods began at this time?

In terms of wider implications, the El Riego phase seems to be related to early cultures occurring in Northern Mexico, the U.S. Southwest, and the Great Basin areas which have been classified as being of the "Desert Culture Tradition." The later preceramic phases that follow the El Riego phase in the Tehuacán Valley are difficult to classify in this tradition because they have incipient agriculture and the numerous large choppers, scrapers, and milling stones decrease in importance. In addition, these Mesoamerican cultures developed their own distinctive types of grinding tools, baskets, nets, projectile points, blades, and other implements—all unlike artifacts found in the Desert Cultural manifestations.

Coxcatlan Phase

The phase developing out of the El Riego phase was termed Coxcatlan. About 12 radiocarbon determinations indicate that it existed from 5200 to 3400 B.C. Twelve components of this phase were uncovered in cave excavations, and four open camps were also found. Although fewer occupations were found than in the El Riego phase, most of them were larger. However, the way of life may have been much the same, with nomadic microbands in the dry season and macrobands in the wet season. The macrobands seem to have been larger than those of the earlier phase, and they seem to have stayed in one place for longer periods. Perhaps this was due to their rather different subsistence pattern.

While the Coxcatlan people were still basically plant collectors who did a little animal trapping and hunting, all through this period they acquired more and more domesticated plants. Early in the period they began using wild corn, chili, avocados, and gourds. By the middle of the phase they had acquired amaranth, tepary beans, yellow zapotes, and squash (*Cucurbita moschata*), and by the end of the phase perhaps they had black and white zapotes. It seems that microbands still came together at some favorite collecting spot in the spring, and it may be that while they were there they planted some of their domesticates. This would have given them food to continue living at that camp after they had consumed their wild foods. As the numbers of domesticates increased, the group could, of course, have stayed together as a macroband for longer and longer periods. But with the onset of the dry season and the depletion of their agricultural "surpluses" they would have broken up again into nomadic microbands.

The changing subsistence and settlement pattern may have been connected with changes in social organization. The bands may still have been patrilineal. But one wonders whether the use of gardens and the more sedentary way of life might not have resulted in bands having definite collecting territories and ideas about property "garden rights." Moreover, a greater dependence upon agriculture (and rainfall) may have made the shaman even more powerful, not only in medicine and in birth and death ceremonies but also in regard to rituals connected with plantings and harvestings. In addition, the more sedentary life involving larger numbers of people may have resulted in some kind of macroband leadership, more stable than just that vested in the oldest or most powerful male in a family.

The industrial activities of the group were not vastly different from those of their predecessors, although different types of tanged projectile points were manufactured. Blades were more delicately made, scrapers and choppers were of new types, and true metates, with manos, were replacing the mortars, pestles, and milling stones. Some minor improvements were also made in the manufacture of nets, coiled baskets, bags, and blankets.

The most distinctive aspect of the Coxcatlan phase is its incipient agriculture. However, I do not want to give the impression that Tehuacán was the only early center of plant domestication or agriculture. In fact, our accruing archeological data having to do with the beginning of New World plant domestication seem to indicate that there was no single center, but, instead, that domesticates had multiple origins over a wide area of Nuclear America and the southern United States. For example, while tepary beans and corn may have been first domesticated near or in the Tehuacán Valley, pumpkins seem to have been domesticated in northeastern Mexico, sunflowers in the southwestern United States, potatoes and lima beans in the highlands of South America, common beans in still another region, and so on.

Abejas Phase

The Abejas phase follows the Coxcatlan phase, and we estimate, on the basis of eight carbon-14 determinations, that it existed from 3400 to 2300 B.C. Thirteen occupations have now been uncovered, and eight sites were found in reconnaissance. We are now making plans to excavate what seems to be a pit-house village of the Abejas phase.

The settlement pattern seems to have changed significantly during this period. Ten of the cave occupations were hunting (dry-season) camps of macrobands, while eight of the macroband settlements were on river terraces in the Valley. The latter appear to have been larger settlements (of five to ten pit houses), and some of them may have been occupied all year round. This even more sedentary way of life was made possible by more efficient food production. This was accomplished with plants already known and, in addition, with domesticated canavalia and perhaps pumpkins (pepo) and common beans, as well as some varieties of hybrid corn with teosinte introgression. The people also used cotton and had dogs. However, even with this increase in domesticates, botanical studies and studies of feces reveal that more than 70 percent of their foods still came from wild plants and animals.

Again, many of the older techniques of artifact manufacture continued, though the types are a little different. Some of the types which carry over into much later times originated during this period. These include: split-stitch basketry and the manufacture of stone bowls and ollas, oval metates and large plano-convex manos, obsidian blades made from long cylindrical cores, and other objects.

If this phase provides evidence of a Marxian "Neolithic revolution," the revolution came long after the first plant domestications; the population showed no sudden increase in size, and the artifacts were little better than those of the preceding phase.

Purron Phase

The next phase, Purron, is dated by six carbon-14 determinations which place it between 2300 and 1500 B.C. It is the least clearly understood phase in the sequence and was represented by only two floors in excavation. The excavated materials include a few plant remains, early tripsacoid corn cobs, manos, metates, scrapers, fine obsidian blades, and a number of very crude, crumbly pieces of broken pottery. The pottery, the earliest so far found in Mesoamerica, has the same vessel forms as the stone bowls and ollas of the previous period. This pottery may not be the first modeled in Mexico but only an imitation of still earlier pottery (as yet unfound) in some other area. One might surmise that the subsistence and settlement pattern and social organization of the Purron phase was much the same as that of the Abejas phase.

Ajalpan Phase

The following phase, Ajalpan, dated by 18 carbon-14 determinations, is much better understood. It is placed between 1500 and 900 B.C. Seventeen floors were found in the diggings, and two open sites were found during survey. These Ajalpan people were full-time agriculturists; they planted early hybrid corn, mixta, moschata and pepo squashes, gourds, amaranths, beans, chili, avocado, zapotes, and cotton. They seem to have lived in small wattle-and-daub villages of from 100 to 300 inhabitants. Whether they built religious structures is not yet known, but their figurines, mainly female, attest to a complex religious life. Male priests and chiefs certainly must have had considerable power, although the rich female burials and the figurines hint that kinship and property ownership may have had a matrilineal emphasis.

Many stone tools of the older types were still made, but one of the more notable industries of this period was pottery making. The pottery, though well made, is usually unpainted, although a few examples of monochrome specular-hemitite red ware are found. A limited number of forms were modeled; the tecomate, or small-mouthed seed jar, is the dominant type of receptacle.

In terms of cultural relationships, the pottery, large figurines, and rocker-dentate stamp decoration are like those found in the earliest cultural manifestations in lowland Mesoamerica—that is, Veracruz, Chiapas, Pacific-lowland Guatemala, and the Pacific coast of Oaxaca. This does not, however, mean there was a migration, diffusion, or relationship only from the coast to the highlands, for remains from periods of comparable age have not yet been found in highland Mexico. In fact, Ajalpan could well be but a local manifestation of an early widespread horizon in Mesoamerica. Spinden, many years ago, concluded that such a horizon existed, and he called it the Archaic. More and more evidence confirming his original hypothesis is being accumulated.

Santa Maria Phase

In the subsequent Santa Maria period the pottery still shows resemblances to pottery of the Veracruz coast. But in addition to these resemblances it shows resemblances to the earliest pottery remains in Monte Alban, the Valley of Mexico, and other highland regions.

Thus, we have good evidence for correlating a number of sequences from a number of areas, not only with Santa Maria but also with each other. Twenty-three carbon-14 determinations indicated that the Santa Maria period lasted from just before 900 to about 200 B.C. The culture is well known, for we have excavated 38 components and have found about 15 surface sites. The settlement pattern reveals that the people lived in small wattle-and-daub houses in villages which were oriented around a single, larger village having ceremonial structures.

These people were full-time farmers, using all of the plants previously known, although many of these plants had been developed into much more productive hybrids. This may be the period in which irrigation was first used.

Although a few new types of chipped stone tools, woven cotton fabrics, and new kinds of ground-stone tools appear, the great majority of the materials we uncovered consisted of pieces of broken pottery. These vessels were well made. They were mainly monochrome (white or grey), though there were a few bichromes. About half of all the vessels found were flat-bottomed bowls; the rest were ollas, water-bottles, composite silhouette bowls, and other forms. Decoration was usually achieved by incising on the interior bottoms of bowls or on the rims or lips, but a few of the vessels have plain rocker stamping, negative painting, and engraving.

Perhaps it was during this period that Mesoamerica became divided into two units, each with a distinctive cultural development. One development, in the lowlands, may have been based on milpa (slash-and-burn) agriculture and have culminated in the development of ceremonial centers, run by a priestly hierarchy. The other development may have been based on irrigation agriculture and have culminated in the rise of secular cities. The Tehuacán sequence would be an example of this second type.

Palo Blanco Phase

This Santa Maria phase developed into the Palo Blanco period, dated between 200 B.C. and A.D. 700 by eight radiocarbon determinations. On the basis of information and materials from 17 excavated components and from about 150 sites found in survey, we are able to make the following reconstruction about the way of life of the people of this phase. They, too, were full-time agriculturists, and they systematically used irrigation. Besides the previously known domesticates, they had acquired tomatoes, peanuts, lima beans, guavas, and turkeys. They lived in wattle-and-daub villages or hamlets either oriented toward or adjacent to large hilltop ceremonial centers having elaborate stone pyramids, plazas, ball courts, and other structures. Some of these ruins covered whole mountain tops and, in terms of population, might be considered cities, albeit sacred cities. Perhaps these centers were under the authority of priest-kings; if so, the priest-kings certainly must have been assisted by full-time specialists and a hierarchy of bureaucrats, at least to run the irrigation works.

The manufactured products were varied and more elaborate than those of previous phases. The fine grey and orange pottery, the obsidian working, the bark cloth, and the elaborately woven cotton fabrics are particularly distinctive.

In terms of relationships, Palo Blanco seems to be an extension of the Monte Alban III (and IV?) cultures of Central Oaxaca and shows similarities to cultures in the so-called "Classic Period" of Mesoamerica. Why this period in the highlands is considered more "classic" than the later periods has never been satisfactorily explained.

Venta Salada Phase

The final period, Venta Salada, is placed, on the basis of five carbon-14 determinations, between A.D. 700 and 1540. Study of the records of early Spanish conquerors of the Tehuacán Valley should shed further light on this phase. Studies made so far reveal that these people were full-time agriculturists who had irrigation. Further, their economy was greatly supplemented by commerce with other regions. Local salt-making and cotton-processing industries made products for exportation. Politically, the Valley seems to have been divided up into a series of little kingdoms each of which had urban centers with surrounding hamlets. Among the manufactured articles were such distinctive artifacts as polychrome pottery, a wide variety of cotton fabrics, bark cloth, chipped stone tools, and arrow points. Since we have excavated over 15 occupations of this final phase and have found about 200 sites in surface surveys, and also have excellent ethnohistorical records available, it will eventually be possible to reconstruct a fairly clear picture of the culture of the final preconquest phase. So far this has not been done.

Conclusion

Obviously, our studies are far from complete, even though some tentative conclusions have been expressed in this article. As more of our data are analyzed and the results are correlated, the total history of the Tehuacán Valley will become better understood. At present, some 30 authors, including myself, are in the process of getting six volumes about our work in Tehuacán ready for publication.[4] Certainly these final volumes will contain information which will permit more perceptive and specific comparisons to be made with other prehistoric cultural developments in Mexico and South America, as well as with sequences in the Old World. Such analysis should lead to more cogent and better documented generalizations about the how's and why's of the rise of civilization than have been expressed heretofore.

[4] The actual investigations were organized under the auspices of the Robert S. Peabody Foundation for Archaeology, Andover, Mass., and were financially supported by generous grants-in-aid from the National Science Foundation and the Rockefeller Foundation. The Tehuacán Project also received support and assistance from the Instituto de Antropologia e Historia of the Government of Mexico.

41 Microenvironments and Mesoamerican Prehistory

Michael D. Coe and Kent V. Flannery

THE ARTICLE BELOW WAS ORIGINALLY PUBLISHED ONLY ONE WEEK AFTER *the article by MacNeish, which precedes it (No. I:40). In some respects, we might have reversed the order. Although one reads this selection with much more understanding if one has previously read the MacNeish article, Coe and Flannery are less concerned with the development of civilization as such, than with the process of cultural evolution in the Tehuacán Valley. Since their article dwells on the emergence of food production and its consequences, it should be compared with Flannery's analysis of similar developments in the Near East (see No. I:38).*

If this article makes us look back to review earlier series of events that played a major role in the emergence of civilization, it also makes us look forward, in a methodological sense, to the main substance of the next volume of these Readings. *That is manifested in the reliance which is placed on contemporary or near-contemporary ethnographic observation to obtain working understandings of the actual nature of the man/culture/environment interactions which underlay ecological analysis.*

SOURCE: *Science*, Vol. 143 (February 14, 1964), pp. 650–654. Copyright 1964 by the American Association for the Advancement of Science. Reprinted with the permission of the author and publisher.

Michael D. Coe (b. 1929) is Associate Professor of Anthropology at Yale University. His predominant interest is the archaeology and ethnology of Middle America. Besides reports on Guatemalan archaeological sites, Professor Coe has written *Mexico* (1962) and *The Jaguar's Children: Preclassic Central Mexico* (1965), the latter based on material gathered for an exhibition of early Mexican art. For biographical data on Kent V. Flannery, see I:38.

A crucial period in the story of the pre-Columbian cultures of the New World is the transition from a hunting-and-collecting way of life to effective village farming. We are now fairly certain that Mesoamerica [1] is the area in which this took place, and that the time span involved is from approximately 6500 to 1000 B.C., a period during which a kind of "incipient cultivation" based on a few domesticated plants, mainly maize, gradually supplemented and eventually replaced wild foods. Beginning probably about 1500 B.C., and definitely by 1000 B.C., villages with all of the signs of the settled arts, such as pottery and loom-weaving, appear throughout Mesoamerica, and the foundations of pre-Columbian civilization may be said to have been established.

Much has been written about food-producing "revolutions" in both hemispheres. There is now good evidence both in the Near East and in Mesoamerica that food production was part of a relatively slow *evolution*, but there still remain several problems related to the process of settling down. For the New World, there are three questions which we would like to answer.

1) What factors favored the early development of food production in Mesoamerica as compared with other regions of this hemisphere?

2) What was the mode of life of the earlier hunting-and-collecting peoples in Mesoamerica, and in exactly what ways was it changed by the addition of cultivated plants?

3) When, where, and how did food production make it possible for the first truly sedentary villages to be established in Mesoamerica?

The first of these questions cannot be answered until botanists determine the habits and preferred habitats of the wild ancestors of maize, beans, and the various cucurbits which were domesticated. To answer the other questions, we must reconstruct the human-ecological situations which prevailed.

Some remarkably sophisticated, multidisciplinary projects have been and still are being carried out elsewhere in the world, aimed at reconstructing prehistoric human ecology. However, for the most part they have been concerned with the adaptations of past human communities to large-scale changes in the environment over very long periods—that is, to alterations in the *macroenvironment*, generally caused by climatic fluctuations. Such alterations include the shift from tundra to boreal conditions in northern Europe. Nevertheless, there has been a growing suspicion among prehistorians that macroenvironmental changes are insufficient as an explanation of the possible causes of food production and its effects, regardless of what has been written to the contrary.

---

[1] Mesoamerica is the name given to that part of Mexico and Central America which was civilized in pre-Columbian times.

Ethnography and Microenvironments

We have been impressed, in reading anthropologists' accounts of simple societies, with the fact that human communities, while in some senses limited by the macroenvironment—for instance, by deserts or by tropical forests—usually exploit several or even a whole series of well-defined *microenvironments* in their quest for food. These micro-environments might be defined as smaller subdivisions of large ecological zones; examples are the immediate surroundings of the ancient archeological site itself, the bank of a nearby stream, or a distant patch of forest.

An interesting case is provided by the Shoshonean bands which, until the mid-19th century, occupied territories within the Great Basin of the American West. These extremely primitive peoples had a mode of life quite similar to that of the peoples of Mesoamerica of the 5th millennium B.C., who were the first to domesticate maize. The broadly limiting effects of the Great Basin (which, generally speaking, is a desert) and the lack of knowledge of irrigation precluded any effective form of agriculture, even though some bands actually sowed wild grasses and one group tried an ineffective watering of wild crops. Consequently, the Great Basin aborigines remained on a hunting and plant-collecting level, with extremely low population densities and a very simple social organization. However, Steward's study shows that each band was not inhabiting a mere desert but moved on a strictly followed seasonal round among a vertically and horizontally differentiated set of microenvironments, from the lowest salt flats up to piñon forest, which were "niches" in a human-ecological sense.

The Great Basin environment supplied the potential for cultural development or lack of it, but the men who lived there selected this or that microenvironment. Steward clearly shows that *how* and *to what* they adapted influenced many other aspects of their culture, from their technology to their settlement pattern, which was necessarily one of restricted wandering from one seasonally occupied camp to another.

Seasonal wandering would appear to be about the only possible response of a people without animal or plant husbandry to the problem of getting enough food throughout the year. Even the relatively rich salmon-fishing cultures of the Northwest Coast (British Columbia and southern Alaska) were without permanently occupied villages. Contrariwise, it has seemed to us that only a drastic reduction of the number of niches to be exploited, and a concentration of these in space, would have permitted the establishment of full-time village life. The ethnographic data suggest that an analysis of microenvironments or niches would throw much light on the processes by which the Mesoamerican peoples settled down.

Methodology

If the environment in which an ancient people lived was radically different from any known today, and especially if it included animal and plant species which are now extinct and whose behavior is consequently unknown, then any reconstruction of the subsistence activities of the people is going to be difficult. All one could hope for would be a more-or-less sound reconstruction of general ecological conditions, while a breakdown of the environment into smaller ecological niches would be impossible. However, much if not most archeological research concerns periods so recent in comparison with the million or so years of human prehistory that in most instances local conditions have not changed greatly in the interval between the periods investigated and the present.

If we assume that there is a continuity between the ancient and the modern macroenvironment in the area of interest, there are three steps which we must take in tracing the role of microenvironments.

1) Analysis of the present-day microecology (from the human point of view) of the archeological zone. Archeological research is often carried out in remote and little known parts of the earth, which have not been studied from the point of view of natural history. Hence, the active participation of botanists, zoologists, and other natural scientists is highly recommended.

The modern ethnology of the region should never be neglected, for all kinds of highly relevant data on the use of surrounding niches by local people often lie immediately at hand. We have found in Mesoamerica that the workmen on the "dig" are a mine of such information. There may be little need to thumb through weighty reports on the Australian aborigines or South African Bushmen when the analogous custom can be found right under one's nose. The end result of the analysis should be a map of the microenvironments defined (here aerial photographs are of great use), with detailed data on the seasonal possibilities each offers human communities on certain technological levels of development.

2) Quantitative analysis of food remains in the archeological sites, and of the technical equipment (arrow or spear points, grinding stones for seeds, baskets and other containers and so on) related to food-getting. It is a rare site report that treats of bones and plant remains in any but the most perfunctory way. It might seem a simple thing to ship animal bones from a site to a specialist for identification, but most archeologists know that many zoologists consider identification of recent faunal remains a waste of time. Because of this, and because many museum collections do not include postcranial skeletons that could be used for identification, the archeologist must arrange to secure his own comparative collection. If this collection is assembled by a zoologist on the project, a by-product of

the investigation would be a faunal study of microenvironments. Similarly, identification of floral and other specimens from the site would lead to other specialized studies.

3) Correlation of the archeological with the microenvironmental study in an overall analysis of the ancient human ecology.

The Tehuacán Valley

An archeological project undertaken by R. S. MacNeish, with such a strategy in mind, has been located since 1961 in the dry Tehuacán Valley of southern Puebla, Mexico. The valley is fringed with bone-dry caves in which the food remains of early peoples have been preserved to a remarkable degree in stratified deposits. For a number of reasons, including the results of his past archeological work in Mesoamerica, MacNeish believed that he would find here the origins of maize agriculture in the New World, and he has been proved right. It now seems certain that the wild ancestor of maize was domesticated in the Tehuacán area some time around the beginning of the 5th millennium B.C.

While the Tehuacán environment is in general a desert, the natural scientists of the project have defined within it four microenvironments (Fig. 1).

1) *Alluvial valley floor*, a level plain sparsely covered with mesquite, grasses, and cacti, offering fairly good possibilities, especially along the Río Salado, for primitive maize agriculture dependent on rainfall.

2) *Travertine slopes*, on the west side of the valley. This would have been a niche useful for growing maize and tomatoes and for trapping cottontail rabbits.

3) *Coxcatlán thorn forest*, with abundant seasonal crops of wild fruits, such as various species of *Opuntia*, pitahaya, and so on. There is also a seasonal abundance of whitetail deer, cottontail rabbits, and skunks, and there are some peccaries.

4) *Eroded canyons*, unsuitable for exploitation except for limited hunting of deer and as routes up to maguey fields for those peoples who chewed the leaves of that plant.

The correlation of this study with the analysis, by specialists, of the plant and animal remains (these include bones, maize cobs, chewed quids, and even feces) found in cave deposits has shown that the way of life of the New World's first farmers was not very different from that of the Great Basin aborigines in the 19th century. Even the earliest inhabitants of the valley, prior to 6500 B.C., were more collectors of seasonally gathered wild plant foods than they were "big game hunters," and they traveled in microbands in an annual, wet-season-dry-season cycle. While slightly more sedentary macrobands appeared with the adoption of simple maize cultivation after 5000 B.C., these people nevertheless still

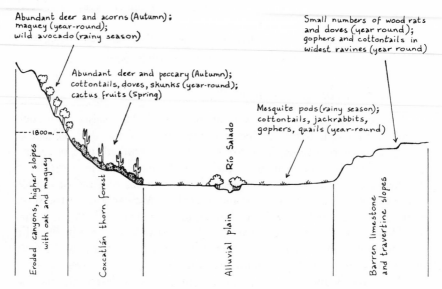

Abundant deer and acorns (Autumn);
maguey (year-round);
wild avocado (rainy season)

Small numbers of wood rats
and doves (year round);
gophers and cottontails in
widest ravines (year round)

Abundant deer and peccary (Autumn);
cottontails, doves, skunks (year-round);
cactus fruits (Spring)

Mesquite pods (rainy season);
cottontails, jackrabbits,
gophers, quails (year-round)

----1800m.----

Río Salado

Eroded canyons, higher slopes
with oak and maguey

Coxcatlán thorn forest

Alluvial plain

Barren limestone
and travertine slopes

Figure 1 An idealized east-west transection of the central part of the Tehua-cán Valley, Puebla, Mexico, showing microenvironments and the seasons in which the food resources are exploited. East is to left. The length of the area represented is about 20 kilometers.

followed the old pattern of moving from microenvironment to micro-environment, separating into microbands during the dry season.

The invention and gradual improvement of agriculture seem to have made few profound alterations in the settlement pattern of the valley for many millennia. Significantly, by the Formative period (from about 1500 B.C. to A.D. 200), when agriculture based on a hybridized maize was far more important than it had been in earlier periods as a source of food energy, the pattern was still one of part-time nomadism.[2] In this part of the dry Mexican highlands, until the Classic period (about A.D. 200 to 900), when irrigation appears to have been introduced into Tehuacán, food production had still to be supplemented with extensive plant collect-ing and hunting.

Most of the peoples of the Formative period apparently lived in large villages on the alluvial valley floor during the wet season, from May through October of each year, for planting had to be done in May and June, and harvesting, in September and October. In the dry season, from

[2] The research discussed in this and the following paragraph was carried out by Flannery as staff zoologist for the Tehuacán project during the field seasons of 1962 and 1963.

November through February, when the trees and bushes had lost their leaves and the deer were easy to see and track, some of the population must have moved to hunting camps, principally in the Coxcatlán thorn forest. By February, hunting had become less rewarding as the now-wary deer moved as far as possible from human habitation; however, in April and May the thorn forest was still ripe for exploitation, as many kinds of wild fruit matured. In May it was again time to return to the villages on the valley floor for spring planting.

Now, in some other regions of Mesoamerica there were already, during the Formative period, fully sedentary village cultures in existence. It is clear that while the Tehuacán valley was the locus of the first domestication of maize, the origns of full-blown village life lie elsewhere. Because of the constraining effects of the macroenvironment, the Tehuacán people were exploiting, until relatively late in Mesoamerican prehistory, as widely spaced and as large a number of microenvironments as the Great Basin aborigines were exploiting in the 19th century.

Coastal Guatemala

Near the modern fishing port of Ocós, only a few kilometers from the Mexican border on the alluvial plain of the Pacific coast of Guatemala, we have found evidence for some of the oldest permanently occupied villages in Mesoamerica. We have also made an extensive study of the ecology and ethnology of the Ocós area.

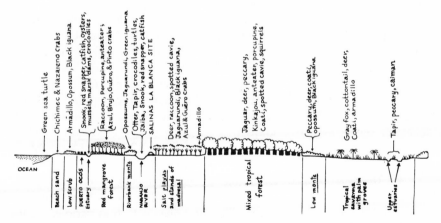

Figure 2 Northeast-southwest transection of the Ocós area of coastal Guatemala, showing microenvironments in relation to the site of Salinas La Blanca. Northeast is to the right. The length of the area represented is about 15 kilometers.

From this study [3] we have defined no less than eight distinct micro-environments (Fig. 2) within an area of only about 90 square kilometers. These are as follows:

1) *Beach sand and low scrub.* A narrow, infertile strip from which the present-day villagers collect occasional mollusks, a beach crab called *chichimeco* and one known as *nazareño*, and the sea turtle and its eggs.

2) *The marine estuary-and-lagoon system*, in places extending considerably inland and ultimately connecting with streams or rivers coming down from the Sierra Madre. The estuaries, with their mangrove-lined banks, make up the microenvironment richest in wild foods in the entire area. The brackish waters abound in catfish (*Arius* sp. and *Galeichthys* sp.), red snapper (*Lutjanus colorado*), several species of snook (*Centropomus* sp.), and many other kinds of fish. Within living memory, crocodiles (*Crocodylus astututs*) were common, but they have by now been hunted almost to extinction. The muddy banks of the estuaries are the habitat of many kinds of molusks, including marsh clams (*Polymesoda radiata*), mussels (*Mytella falcata*), and oysters (*Ostrea columbiensis*), and they also support an extensive population of fiddler and mud crabs.

3) *Mangrove forest*, consisting mainly of stilt-rooted red mangrove, which slowly gives way to white mangrove as one moves away from the estuary. We noted high populations of collared anteater (*Tamandua tetradactyla*) and arboreal porcupine (*Coendu mexicanus*). A large number of crabs (we did not determine the species) inhabit this microenvironment; these include, especially, one known locally as the *azul* (blue) crab, on which a large population of raccoons feeds.

4) *Riverine*, comprising the channels and banks of the sluggish Suchiate and Naranjo rivers, which connect with the lagoon-estuary system not far from their mouths. Freshwater turtles, catfish, snook, red snapper, and mojarra (*Cichlasoma* sp.) are found in these waters; the most common animal along the banks is the green iguana (*Iguana iguana*).

5) *Salt playas*, the dried remnants of ancient lagoon-and-estuary systems which are still subject to inundation during the wet season, with localized stands of a tree known as *madresal* ("mother of salt"). Here there is an abundance of game, including whitetail deer and the black iguana (*Ctenosaura similis*), as well as a rich supply of salt.

6) *Mixed tropical forest*, found a few kilometers inland, in slightly higher and better drained situations than the salt *playas*. This forest includes mostly tropical evergreens like the ceiba, as well as various zapote and fan palms, on the fruit of which a great variety of mammals thrive —the kinkajou, the spotted cavy, the coatimundi, the raccoon, and even the gray fox. The soils here are highly suitable for maize agriculture.

---

[3] The study was carried out largely by Flannery.

7) *Tropical savannah*, occupying poorly drained patches along the upper stream and estuary systems of the area. This is the major habitat in the area for cottontail rabbits and gray foxes. Other common mammals are the coatimundi and armadillo.

8) *Cleared fields and second growth*, habitats which have been created by agriculturists, and which are generally confined to areas that were formerly mixed tropical forest.

Among the earliest Formative cultures known thus far for the Ocós area is the Cuadros phase, dated by radiocarbon analysis at about 1000 to 850 B.C. and well represented in the site of Salinas La Blanca, which we excavated in 1962.[4] The site is on the banks of the Naranjo River among a variety of microenvironments; it consists of two flattish mounds built up from deeply stratified refuse layers representing house foundations of a succession of hamlets or small villages.

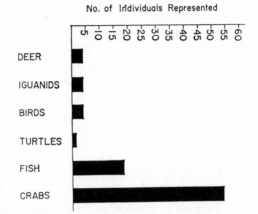

Figure 3 Animal remains, exclusive of mollusks, found in Cuadros phase levels at Salinas la Blanca.

From our analysis of this refuse we have a good idea of the way in which the Cuadros people lived. Much of the refuse consists of potsherds from large, neckless jars, but very few of the clay figurines that abound in other Formative cultures of Mesoamerica were found. We discovered many plant remains; luckily these had been preserved or "fossilized" through replacement of the tissues by carbonates. From these we know that the people grew and ate a nonhybridized maize considerably more advanced than the maize which was then being grown in Tehuacán.[5] The

[4] The final report on Salinas La Blanca by Coe and Flannery is in preparation. The research was supported by the National Science Foundation under a grant to the Institute of Andean Research, as part of the program "Interrelationships of New World Cultures." The oldest culture in the area is the Ocós phase, which has complex ceramics and figurines; the paleoecology of Ocós is less well known than that of Cuadros, which directly follows it in time.

[5] P. C. Mangelsdorf, who has very kindly examined these maize specimens, informs us that they are uncontaminated with *Tripsacum*, and that probably all belong to the primitive lowland race, Nal-Tel.

many impressions of leaves in clay floors in the site will, we hope, eventually make it possible to reconstruct the flora that immediately surrounded the village.

The identification of animal remains (Fig. 3), together with our ecological study and with the knowledge that the people had a well-developed maize agriculture, gives a great deal of information on the subsistence activities of these early coastal villagers. First of all, we believe they had no interest whatever in hunting, a conclusion reinforced by our failure to find a single projectile point in the site. The few deer bones that have been recovered are all from immature individuals that could have been encountered by chance and clubbed to death. Most of the other remains are of animals that could have been collected in the environs of the village, specifically in the lagoon-estuary system and the flanking mangrove forest, where the people fished, dug for marsh clams, and, above all, caught crabs (primarily the *azul* crab, which is trapped at night). Entirely missing are many edible species found in other microenvironments, such as raccoon, cottontail rabbit, peccary, spotted cavy, and nine-banded armadillo.

There is no evidence at all that occupation of Salinas La Blanca was seasonal. A effective food production carried out on the rich, deep soils of the mixed tropical forest zone, together with the food resources of the lagoon-estuary system, made a permanently settled life possible. Looked at another way, developed maize agriculture had so reduced the number and spacing of the niches which had to be exploited that villages could be occupied the year round.[6]

Conditions similar to those of the Ocós area are found all along the Pacific Coast of Guatemala and along the Gulf Coast of southern Veracruz and Tabasco in Mexico, and we suggest that the real transition to village life took place there and not in the dry Mexican highlands, where maize was domesticated initially.[7]

Conclusion

The interpretation of archeological remains through a fine-scale analysis of small ecological zones throws new light on the move toward

[6] To paraphrase the concept of "primary forest efficiency," developed by J. R. Caldwell, we might think of the Cuadros phase as leaning to a "primary lagoon-estuary efficiency." We might think the same of the Ocós phase of the same region, which may date back to 1500 B.C.

[7] An additional factor which may in part account for the priority of coastal Guatemala over Tehuacán in the achievement of a sedentary mode of life is the presence of an extensive system of waterways in the former region, which might have made it less necessary for local communities to move to productive sources of food. By means of canoes, a few persons could have brought the products of other niches to the village. However, our evidence indicates that the Cuadros people largely ignored the possibilities of exploiting distant niches.

sedentary life in Mesoamerican prehistory. In our terms, the basic difference between peoples who subsist on wild foods and those who dwell in permanent villages is that the former must exploit a wide variety of small ecological niches in a seasonal pattern—niches which are usually scattered over a wide range of territory—while the latter may, because of an effective food production, concentrate on one or on only a few microenvironments which lie relatively close at hand.

Fine-scale ecological analysis indicates that there never was any such thing as an "agricultural revolution" in Mesoamerica, suddenly and almost miraculously resulting in village life. The gradual additon of domesticates such as maize, beans, and squash to the diet of wild plant and animal foods hardly changed the way of life of the Tehuacán people for many thousands of years, owing to a general paucity of the environment, and seasonal nomadism persisted until the introduction of irrigation. It probably was not until maize was taken to the alluvial, lowland littoral of Mesoamerica, perhaps around 1500 B.C., that permanently occupied villages became possible, through reduction of the number of microenvironments to which men had to adapt themselves.

42 The Birth of Civilization

V. Gordon Childe

NOW THAT WE HAVE SEEN SOME OF THE DATA AND READ ABOUT THE EVENTS *in the emergence of specific civilizations in the Old World and the New (Nos. I:37–41), we are ready for some of the grand attempts at synthesis and broad generalization. Even though the materials from which he worked have been greatly expanded in the few years since he was writing, one of the most graphic and stimulating accounts of the great transitions of antiquity is that of Childe. It was he, for example, who coined the phrases "Neolithic Revolution" and "Urban Revolution" which, though controversial, attract attention to some of the most vital aspects of the phenomena we are studying. It was in response to attacks on his concept of the "Urban Revolution" that Childe wrote the synopsis of his views which follows.*

Approximately five thousand years ago occurred an event as unique in the Earth's history as the Alpine folding—the "birth of civilization in the Near East." We could translate the last phrase in Toynbee's metaphor and say "the emergence of a new species of society" or, more precisely but still metaphorically, the creation of a new kind of culture. In any case, it can be called an "event" only in the same sense as the Alpine folding or the establishment of a new species by mutation and selection of mutants;

SOURCE: *Past and Present*, No. 2 (1952), pp. 1–10. Reprinted by permission of the publisher.

The author (1892–1957) was Professor of Prehistoric European Archaeology and Director of Archaeology at the University of London. Described by Robert Braidwood as "one of archaeology's very few great synthesizers," Childe is known for his interpretations rather than recovery of original data. Among his many books are two which are available at almost any bookstand in America, *Man Makes Himself* (1936) and *What Happened in History* (1942).

for it was a long process, though the culmination, the critical point in the transformation of quantity into quality, can be defined rather more precisely: in archæological terms, this was reached during Dynasties 0–1 in Egypt and during the Protoliterate a-b (Uruk) period in lower Mesopotamia. It was unique in that what happened altered the whole human situation; other civilizations were indeed subsequently "born," but all can be regarded as more or less descended from those of Egypt and Sumer—confidently in the case of India, the Mediterranean and China, plausibly even in the case of Central America and Peru.

No one has stated this uniqueness more eloquently or documented it more cogently than Professor Henri Frankfort in his recent book, "The Birth of Civilization in the Near East." But in the sequel, he goes on to insist on the individuality of each of the resultant civilizations, Egyptian and Sumerian respectively, and to emphasise the contrasts between them till the legitimacy of his—and my—title seems questionable. Can we, in fact, speak of "an event" which happened, albeit, simultaneously, in two distinct areas of space, the Nile Valley and Tigris-Euphrates delta? In what does the "sameness" of two spatially distinct events consist? We can consider only the six most striking innovations common to both areas.

1. We have firstly a transformation in the scale of human co-operation—both an unprecedented absolute increase in the total population and an equally unprecedented growth in the size of the local unit. Total population for areas like Egypt or Mesopotamia can hardly be guessed, the absolute size of cities can be measured and compared with that of the only units of settlement that had existed previously. We actually know the area of some neolithic villages or the number of graves in the cemeteries belonging to such and can compare these figures with those of the oldest known cities. Thus Jarmo on the edge of the Mesopotamian plain had covered 2½ acres, Merimde on the western margin of the Nile delta about 6 acres; neolithic villages in Palestine and in Europe fall within the same sort of range of size. But after 3000 B.C., Ur of Chaldees covered 111 acres, Khafaje nearly 100. In Egypt no town site of the Old Kingdom has been surveyed and contemporary cemeteries have not been examined so completely as prehistoric ones, but some striking figures are available. A predynastic cemetery, in continuous use for probably 500 years comprises normally some 500 graves, very exceptionally 2,000. The household of a single pharaoh (Zer) of Dynasty I comprised 595 adults who were buried at the time of the royal funeral! In either case the size of the unit would seem to have grown about ten times since the "Birth of Civilization." It is in that sense and in that sense only that I have called this event the Urban Revolution on the analogy of a comparison between rural England before and urbanized England after the Industrial Revolution.

2. The change in scale could equally be illustrated by the measurements of the buildings men co-operated to erect. In Mesopotamia the

most substantial buildings were in both phases houses for gods. At Eridu the prehistoric temple had grown by successive reconstructions from an overall area of 3 m. by 3 m. to one of 23.5 m. by 12.5 m. In Protoliterate times it has out-grown the space available for excavation so that the areas could only be guessed, but at Erech the Protoliterate temple measured over all 76 m. by 30 m.; incidentally it was built not wholly of mud brick, but on foundations of limestone blocks, divided into a series of halls and internally and externally presented an ornate façade. On the Nile in early historical as in prehistoric times, tombs were more substantial and durable than dwellings, even those of gods. Early prehistoric tombs were of course not buildings at all, but just holes large enough to contain a corpse, doubled up and accompanied by a stock of jars; even in late predynastic times the shaft measures only 3.0 m. by 2.4 m. By contrast the second pharaoh (or perhaps just his prime minister) reposed in a shaft 20 m. long by 4 m. wide and 2 m. deep roofed with beams of imported timber and surmounted by an imposing superstructure or *mastaba*—a rectangular structure of mud brick, measuring over all 42 m. by 16.5 m. and enclosed by stout mud-brick walls 2 to 5 m. thick and probably 10 m. high. Its exterior presented a "crenellated" façade of alternating stepped buttresses and recesses just like that of the Erech temple mentioned above.

3. But not only did population increase; its composition changed too. Of course before, as well as after, the revolution the vast majority of the inhabitants of Sumer and Egypt, whether they lived in cities or villages, were peasants, actively engaged in procuring their own food by tillage, herding, fishing, or fowling. Both the number and variety of products of specialized craftsmanship increased enormously, but it cannot be assumed that all the experts concerned were full-time specialists (i.e. lived by exchanging their products or their skills for food produced by others). Among the earliest decipherable Sumerian documents (the texts of the Protoliterate period cannot yet be read) are lists specifying the persons receiving wages or rations from the granaries of a temple at Lagash and mentioning copper-smiths, silver-smiths, carpenters, cabinet-makers, sculptors, engravers, tanners, potters, wool-scourers, spinners, merchants, clerks, butchers, bakers, brewers, cooks, barbers, butlers, doorkeepers and so on. But most of these including the smith, the merchant and the overseer (*nubanda*) not only received wages in kind, but also held lots in the temple lands. Presumably they worked these themselves. Yet the *nubanda* who held 120 acres, thirteen times the normal lot, must have employed "hired labour" (small-holders more probably than slaves) and so perhaps did smiths and clerks. With a First Dynasty monarch were buried carpenters, sculptors, painters, leather-workers, cooks and clerks. To this list of craftsmen attached to a court or a temple must of course be added in Egypt the royal family (polygamy being admitted), high

officers of state and provincial governors; in Sumer, the higher clergy and later kings and their masters; and, in both regions, clerks.

No doubt full-time specialists had existed before the critical point was reached. Still, it should be remembered that among modern barbarians like the Maori of New Zealand or the Kayan of Borneo even chiefs worked on their lands, and crafts were practised by peasants who earned prestige and some material rewards for the exercise of their mysterious skills in their spare time when not engaged in their primary occupation of growing or catching their food. The craftsmen in an early Sumerian temple who received plots of land as well as wages in kind occupy a position between the part-time specialists of barbarism and the full-time specialists of mature urban civilization.

4. Obviously, this social division of labour was at least a step on the road from what Durkheim calls "mechanical solidarity" in which the group coheres like a pack of wolves because all its members are doing much the same thing and therefore feeling alike, towards his "organic solidarity" in which diverse activities supplement each other to the advantage of all actors. No less obviously this result had been achieved by a division of society into economic classes. The social surplus, the food above domestic requirements, produced by Sumerian peasants was concentrated in the temple granaries and then doled out to support the professionals specified in our lists. No doubt the recipient and disburser was a god, the symbol of the community itself; in theory both the "rent" of a third or a sixth for the use of plots in the divine estate (*kur* and *uru-lal* lands) and the proceeds of the exploitation of the god's own *ningenna* land by wage-labourers was collected in the storehouses in his temple. In practice the god's self-appointed servants, the clerks in holy orders, who actually collected the "rents" and paid out the "wages," must have possessed economic power over against other tenants and employees. Already in the oldest decipherable texts we find a few of these holding lots twenty times as big as those of ordinary peasants or manual workers. In Egypt the surplus of the fellahin was quite frankly collected in royal granaries and redistributed by the pharaohs through their officials and nobles.

It was not however the concentration, but the quantity concentrated that was decisive. A Polynesian chief is able to concentrate a certain surplus, and it enables him to feast the peasants who assemble to build a canoe or a meeting house; it is not sufficient for the gigantic work of building civilization. In Sumer, where the alluvial land is so fertile that a plot of 7/8 of an acre under irrigation would support a family of five, accumulation presumably began in the remote prehistoric temples, and increased with the expansion of population and the improvement of techniques until the critical point was reached. This should be definable numerically in tons of grain and gallons of milk, though the prospects of such definition seem very remote. In Egypt, on the contrary, the requisite quantity seems to have been reached almost catastrophically by a series of campaigns extending over at most three reigns which made the warchief of the Falcon clan in Upper Egypt master of the whole Nile valley, entitled to receive all the surplus produce of its peasantry.

5. L. H. Morgan was well advised when he took writing as the criterion of civilization. In fact, the oldest written documents in the world are wooden labels and stone carvings bearing the names of the first pharaoh, Narmer, and his two immediate predecessors and clay tablets of the Late Uruk (Protoliterate b-c) period. The first Egyptian writings are indeed little more than the names of "Ka" and "Narmer" expressed in pictorial signs that are invested with a purely conventional meaning and numerals denoted by symbols that are again pictorial but exhibit a regular periodicity. The tablets found at Erech in a temple that replaced the Limestone one mentioned above are obviously accounts; for they contain signs for units, tens, and sixties or hundreds, but the characters, though some are recognizable pictograms, are all highly conventionalized. Thus both sets of documents present a genuine script and numeral notation—a system of conventional symbols. And writing abolishes the spatial and temporal limitations on communication, while a numeral notation is the necessary precondition of all mathematics and hence of exact sciences.

6. Both in Egypt and Mesopotamia the Urban Revolution coincided with an artistic revolution. The oldest representations of the human form that we can recognize as intended for portraits of persons are bas-reliefs of Narmer and his immediate predecessor "King Scorpion," and a limestone statuette and a basalt stele from Protoliterate levels at Erech. Palæolithic hunters and some modern savages could indeed depict animals in a manner which we can recognize as true to life and naturalistic. Early peasant societies never depicted even animals in a way that we should regard as realistic; they seem to have aimed at symbolism rather than naturalism, as does peasant art today. On the carvings of protopharaonic Egypt and on seals of the Uruk period we know at once what beast the artist means to depict and can admire the verisimilitude of his delineation. But in depicting the human form neither the palæolithic hunter-artist nor his neolithic peasant successor ever achieved what we could regard as a likeness; indeed the rare human figures in palæolithic and neolithic art seem to us grotesque. Even today a human representation among barbarians, a Maori ancestor-figure for example, is meant to be a symbol, not a likeness. King Scorpion, pharaoh Narmer, the Lionhunters and the "goddess" from Erech are just as obviously portraits, full of life and personality.

It is these six agreements that constitute the sameness of the Urban

Revolution in Egypt and Mesopotamia. Admittedly they are very abstract.

1. In Egypt the increase of population took place within a political unit; the critical point coincided with the incorporation of the whole Nile valley below the first cataract in a single State. Sumer, on the contrary, was divided up among a number of city states which by the time of the earliest deciphered writings were often engaged in mutual wars. In Sumer, the city as a physical and political entity is conspicuous both in the archæological record and in written documents. No city in Early Pharaonic or Old Kingdom Egypt has been excavated or even surveyed, and cities are scarcely mentioned in the earlier texts, which speak rather of countries (*nomes*). Professor Frankfort has indeed denied altogether the existence of cities in early Egypt; the peasantry would have continued to live in villages as before the revolution while the specialist craftsmen who are attested would have been attached to the pharaoh's court or the manor houses and mortuary estates of high functionaries and nobles. The court itself would have had no fixed capital but would have moved each reign to the site of the new king's tomb. In fact, however, all kings of Dynasties I and II had tombs at Abydos and probably also at Saqqara, the necropolis of Memphis founded by the first pharaoh. So, on Frankfort's own showing, there would have been one or two capitals occupied by the court for a couple of centuries. The lack of archæological and textual evidence for other cities is explicable by the location of ancient centres of population under modern ones, by the prejudices of excavators who are mostly out for loot rather than information and find graves more profitable than domestic sites, and by the peculiarities of the early written documents—largely sepulchral inscriptions. Yet it remains true that in historical times the city was not important as a political unit in Egypt, while it always was in Mesopotamia.

2. The most imposing and durable structures in Egypt were the tombs of pharaohs and high officials; till 2000 B.C. the temples of the gods were relatively insignificant. In Mesopotamia exactly the reverse was the case.

3. Though on the whole the same crafts were practised in both countries, the instruments and products of the craftsmen—axes, adzes, chisels, saws, knives, vases, spears, personal ornaments—were as different as common use allowed them to be. Again in Egypt clerks were normally laymen; in Sumer generally clerks in holy orders.

4. In Egypt the social surplus was concentrated by a human monarch who received it as tribute, apparently by right of conquest. No doubt his title was sanctified by his identification with the falcon god, Horus. But Horus, it seems, began life as the totem or patron of a single Upper Egyptian group and became a national deity only by virtue of the mili-

tary exploits of his votaries. In Sumer, it was rather gods who accumulated the surplus as creators and owners of the city lands; some of these were cultivated for the god by wage-labourers or serfs so that the whole produce went into the temple stores while the rest was let to citizens in return for a sixth to a third of the yield—and generally labour services too. The god was represented on earth by a corporation of priests. A secular ruler is not recognizable during the Protoliterate period but may be deduced from the royal tombs and palaces of the succeeding Early Dynastic period, and is known in the texts as *lugal, sangu* or *ensi.*

5. The numerals and characters of the script are quite distinct. In particular the earliest Egyptian hieroglyphs include pictures of distinctively Nilotic plants, animals and tools while the Sumerian pictograms, though much more conventional, depict some peculiarly Mesopotamian types.

6. The style and composition of Egyptian art contrasts with the Sumerian just as do the favourite media of artistic expression. The Narmer palette is already unmistakably Egyptian, the Uruk seals peculiarly Sumerian.

Recognition of these and other contrasts emphasizes the high abstraction of the "event" from which we started. We are a long way from that individual character of any one civilization that Frankfort thinks the historian must grasp if he is to understand its dynamics—its birth and subsequent development. To discuss the theory of history implicit in this objection would be beyond the scope of a single article. Suffice it here to note that "any one civilization," say Egyptian civilization or Sumerian civilization, is in its turn an abstraction. When an anthropologist or sociologist says that the Kamilaroi—or the people of Middletown—do this or believe that, he means that from observations of a number of Kamilaroi or Middletowners faced with a specific situation on numerous occasions, he finds that most of them generally do this. He knows there are some deviants, but considers the probability of similar behaviour on a repetition of the situation high enough for practical purposes. The archæologist, unaided by written documents,—and even in the Early Pharaonic and Protoliterate periods such are rare and far from informative, —cannot even recognize deviations at all. The "Uruk style" in Sumerian art, for instance, which Frankfort himself has so ably delineated, is just the style illustrated by numerous seals and other figured documents found in Uruk strata. Any sea, diverging from the canons thus exemplified, is regarded either as an import, i.e., attributed to a foreigner, or as out of place where found, i.e., assigned to an earlier or later period. Our inevitably fragmentary picture of Sumerian civilization at the Uruk period is the whole of such actual uniformities stripped of equally actual, but unrecognizable, deviations.

On the other hand, the contrasts do serve to eliminate in advance one explanation for the agreements with which we started. Civilization was not brought ready made from Sumer and imposed on Egypt as de Rougé and Morgan once suggested, nor was it transplanted from the Nile to the Tigris as W. J. Perry thought.

Are the agreements then due merely to parallelism in social evolution in similar environments and is their coincidence in time just a coincidence? It is not difficult to show logical grounds why an accumulation of wealth such as is illustrated in Sumerian temples and the pharaohs' tombs should have evoked systems of bookkeeping—writing and numeral notation. Again irrigation-agriculture in the sub-tropical valleys of the Nile and the Tigris-Euphrates would easily yield exceptional harvests. Since population tends to keep pace with or even outrun the food supply, the observed densities are what would be expected on general demographic theory. Finally, since the effective exploitation of the riverine environment demands rigorous, co-ordinated and disciplined co-operation, centralized direction was inevitable and concentration of wealth would be expected. In other words, the observed agreements 1, 2 and 3 can be expressed as general rules from which other agreements, e.g. 5, could be deduced. Of course the formulae for 1, 2 and 3 are not *a priori* laws, but have themselves been formulated by induction from empirical observation. No one has in fact deduced agreement 6 from them and the deduction of 5 only followed its empirical "verification."

But is this the whole story? In addition to the abstract agreements between Egypt and Sumer already discussed, Frankfort himself was the first to remark a whole series of concrete and specific agreements between the nascent civilizations of Egypt and Sumer:—(1) crenellation decorating the façades of brick buildings, (2) the use of cylinders instead of stamps for sealing, (3) a distinctive type of boat, (4) several art motives such as the antithetical group (particularly "a hero dominating two lions"), composite animals, and animals with intertwined necks. It is hard to imagine how such peculiar devices should have arisen independently about the same time in Egypt and Sumer, especially as some of them (1, 2 and 4) were given up in Egypt after Dynasty II. I might add that the representation of a Lion Hunt on a monumental Egyptian palette typologically immediately preceding that of pharaoh Narmer and on a Protoliterate stele from Erech look like local versions of a common myth.

Some sort of contact between the two areas would seem the only reasonable deduction from such arbitrary agreements. Indeed one of the earlier Egyptian cylinders resembles so closely a Sumerian group that it is thought to be an actual import from Mesopotamia or at least a local copy of such. Luckily more substantial evidence for contact is available. Lapis lazuli was extensively used both in protopharaonic Egypt and protoliterate Sumer. Now lapis was almost certainly brought from Badakshan in north eastern Afghanistan both in Egypt and Mesopotamia and must have crossed the Tigris and Euphrates to reach the Nile. This archæologically attested transfer of a material substance by human agency—"trade" —marks a channel by which ideas too could be transmitted. Intercourse between the two cradles of civilization about the time of "the birth" is proved as well as archæological methods allow. It will perhaps account for the "Mesopotamian influence in pre- and protodynastic Egypt" detected by Frankfort.

This is no revival of de Rougé's thesis of "l'origine asiatique de la civilisation pharaonique" reducing to one two spatially distinct revolutions. It is not demonstrable that the critical point was passed earlier on the Tigris than on the Nile; in neither area is chronology precise enough to decide that issue. The specific agreements enumerated must indeed be regarded as derived from Asia. It does not follow that they were derived from Sumer. Some common devices might have reached Egypt and Sumer from some intermediate centre; that is quite likely in the case of the cylinder seal and certain items of costume figured on the ivory knife-handle from Gebel el-Arak and the Lion Hunt stele from Erech. In any case, the Asiatic devices do not all appear on the Nile at precisely the same point in the archæological record. On the other hand, there is not a scrap of evidence for postulating a third centre from which civilization, fully formed, could have been transplanted both to the Nile valley and lower Mesopotamia.

Moreover, influences were not all one way. The manufacture of fayence, characteristic of both civilizations, was most probably invented in Egypt, where the natural supplies of alkali in the Wadi Natrun offered an unique opportunity for the discovery. Hence the birth of civilization on the Nile and on the Tigris-Euphrates must be regarded as distinct but not independent events. Cross-fertilization between two progressive so-cieties each following their own proper line of development in similar, but not identical, environments was an essential moment in the process, the unique factor that justifies our title. Having to this extent refuted Prof. Frankfort's criticism of my account of the Urban Revolution, it would not be inappropriate to deal with another misapprehension. To say that Sumerian deities or temple administrators, the pharaohs, and their officials, were supported by rents or taxes and labour owed by the farmers is not to impeach them as parasites or exploiters. That charge would be as irrelevant as Rostovtsev's that the cities of the Roman Em-pire were parasites upon the countryside. Every full-time specialist who neither farms nor fishes lives on the grain, milk and fish produced by the peasantry. If the peasantry is not adequately repaid by the wise govern-ment of Hor-aha, the wise books of Prof. Childe and the technical skill of tractor-mechanic Smith, the latter each and all are parasites and ex-ploiters, but only then. To defend the townsmen of Mesopotamia against this charge of parasitism, Frankfort finds it necessary to deny that they were in fact full-time specialists; every Sumerian citizen, he argues, was a practical farmer, and at seed time and harvest, priests and smiths were busy on the farms. Such a defence is irrelevant, even if the undocumented statement be correct—and there are grounds for doubting this. It is rather the fact and the adequacy of the repayment that should be established.

Without an inconclusive debate on the value of imponderables, such as security against real or imaginary dangers, that issue can be discussed only in the economic sphere. In this domain, the primary producers were undoubtedly repaid; the "Urban Revolution," which is the economic aspect of the "Birth of Civilization," did release new productive forces— irrigation works, metal tools and the instruments which such alone could produce, and so on. And for this release, concentration of the social surplus was indispensable. In so far as the pharaohs used the manpower and resources they controlled for digging irrigation canals and thus extending the cultivable area—such use was attributed to the first pharaoh by tradition and is suggested in the case of the yet earlier king Scorpion by the scene carved on his votive mace-head—they were augmenting the productive forces. And so too with the similar employment of "the god's people" in the Sumerian city. The rapid expansion of population and wealth illustrated by Egyptian cemeteries under Dynasty I and by Protoliterate-Early Dynastic I buildings and graves in Sumer is positive evidence that the mode of production did in fact further the development of productive forces.

But was this repayment "adequate"? Did the primary producers, the vast majority of the population of Egypt and Mesopotamia, benefit from—i.e. consume—the growing output of the newly liberated forces? If their consuming power were not adequate, production itself would cease to expand. This is precisely what happened. The collection of the surplus produce from the peasantry was in practice applied so strictly that they could not benefit from the rising standard of living in Egypt. By the time of Dynasty III it became necessary to return some of it to the peasantry through "relief works"—for that is what pyramid-building amounted to in fact, though neither architects nor workers were conscious of it—to keep them going at all! At Lagash in Sumer, high temple officers managed to secure lots in the temple lands that they could not possibly work themselves and exceeded the average holdings ten or twenty times, till at last the State, personified in the *ensi*, Urukagina, had to intervene to check their exactions and protect the poor and weak. After Dynasty I in Egypt and the Protoliterate period in Mesopotamia, few if any new inventions to increase the productive forces were adopted in either civilization, and this observation shows that the mode of production had become a fetter. It is not the historians' business to try to imagine a mode of production that would have achieved civilization without involving this contradiction. Civilization was in fact born, and the birth justified its midwife.

their objective impossible, but because the data were inadequate and insufficient, the methodology weak, and the application of the schemes too broad.

In spite of a half century of skepticism concerning the possibility of formulating cultural regularities, the conviction is widely held that the discovery of cultural laws is an ultimate goal of anthropology to be attained when fact-collecting and detailed analyses of particular cultures and sequences are sufficiently advanced. White has already offered some general formulations concerning the relationship of energy to cultural development, and he has argued for the importance of formulations of all kinds. Even some members of the so-called "Boas" school expressly advocate a search for regularities. Lowie, for example, remarks that cultural phenomena "do point toward certain regularities, and these it is certainly our duty to ascertain as rigorously as possible." Lesser cites several trial formulations of regularities, which have been made by various persons, including Boas, and calls for more explicit statement of the regularities which, in the course of his work and thinking, every social scientist assumes to exist. The author has attempted to formulate regularities pertaining to the occurrence of patrilineal bands among hunting and gathering tribes and has suggested others that may occur in the origin and development of clans. In reality, hundreds of formulations appear in the literature—for example, correlations of kinship terminologies with forms of social organization—and the possibility of recognizing the general in the particular is implicit in the very terminology of anthropology. The routine use of such concepts, or typological categories, as "clans," "castes," "classes," "priests," "shamans," "men's tribal societies," "cities," and the like are tacit recognition that these and scores of other features are common to a large number of cultures, despite the peculiarities of their local patterning.

The present need is not to achieve a world scheme of culture development or a set of universally valid laws, though no doubt many such laws can even now be postulated, but to establish a genuine interest in the specific objective and a clear conceptualization of what is meant by regularities. It does not matter whether the formulations are sequential (diachronic) or functional (synchronic), on a large scale or a small scale. It is more important that comparative cultural studies should interest themselves in recurrent phenomena as well as in unique phenomena, and that anthropology explicitly recognizes that a legitimate and ultimate objective is to see through the differences of cultures to the similarities, to ascertain processes that are duplicated independently in cultural sequences, and to recognize cause and effect in both temporal and functional relationships. Such scientific endeavor need not be ridden by the requirement that cultural laws or regularities be formulated in terms comparable to those of the biological or physical sciences, that they be absolutes and universals, or that they provide ultimate explanations. Any formulations of cultural data are valid provided the procedure is empirical, hypotheses arising from interpretations of fact and being revised as new facts become available.

Three requirements for formulating cultural regularities may be stated in a rough and preliminary way as follows:

1. *There must be a typology of cultures, patterns, and institutions.* Types represent abstractions, which disregard peculiarities while isolating and comparing similarities. To use Tylor's classic example, the mother-in-law taboo and matrilocal residence, though in each case unique in their local setting, are recurrent types, the cause and effect relationships of which may be compared and formulated. Anthropological terminology demonstrates that hundreds of types of culture elements, patterns, and total configurations are recognized, despite the peculiarities attaching to each in its local occurrence.

2. *Causal interrelationship of types must be established in sequential or synchronic terms, or both.* Any reconstruction of the history of a particular culture implies, though it may not explicitly state, that certain causes produced certain effects. Insights into causes are deeper when the interrelationships of historical phenomena are analyzed functionally. Functional analysis of archaeological data has not been lacking, though archaeology has used an atomistic and taxonomic approach far more than has conventional history. Gordon Childe is exceptional in his effort to treat archaeological materials functionally. Wittfogel has been outstanding in his use of historical data to make functional-historical analyses of the socioeconomic structure of early civilizations.

Where historical data are not available, only the synchronic approach to cause and effect is possible. Radcliffe-Brown, Redfield, and Malinowski, despite important differences in their thinking, are distinctive for their functional analyses.

3. *The formulation of the independent recurrence of synchronic and/or sequential interrelationships of cultural phenomena is a scientific statement of cause and effect, regularities, or laws.* The particularists, though conceding that such formulations are theoretically possible and even desirable, are inclined to hold that in practice it is virtually impossible to isolate identifiable cause-and-effect relationships that operate in independent cases. Similarities between cultures are interpreted as the result of a single origin and diffusion, provided the obstacles to diffusion do not seem too great. If the obstacles are very great, differences are emphasized. Thus, most American anthropologists explain similarities between the early civilizations of the New World as a case of single origin and diffusion, but, impressed by the obstacles to transoceanic culture contacts, they stress the dissimilarities between the civilizations of the Old and New Worlds. Some writers, however, like Elliot-Smith,

Perry, and Gladwin recognize the similarities between the two hemispheres and, unimpressed by barriers to diffusion, use the similarities as proof of a single world origin.

The use of diffusion to avoid coming to grips with problems of cause and effect not only fails to provide a consistent approach to culture history, but it gives an explanation of cultural origins that really explains nothing. Diffusion becomes a mechanical and unintelligible, though universal, cause, and it is employed, as if in contrast to other kinds of causes, to account for about 90 percent of the world's culture. One may fairly ask whether each time a society accepts diffused culture, it is not an independent recurrence of cause and effect. Malinowski states: "Diffusion . . . is not an act, but a process closely akin in its working to the evolutionary process. For evolution deals above all with the influence of any type of 'origins'; and origins do not differ fundamentally whether they occur by invention or by diffusion." For example, the civilizations of the Andes and Mexico were based on dense, sedentary populations, which in turn were supported by intensive irrigation farming. In both cases, the early societies were integrated by a theocratic hierarchy, which controlled communal endeavor and enlisted labor for the construction of religious centers. It is not sufficient to say that the agricultural, social, and religious institutions merely diffused as a unit, for that would be merely stating distributions in historical terms but failing to explain process. Incipient farming appeared first, and it diffused before the other complexes developed. The latter have a functional dependence on intensive farming. They could not have been accepted anywhere until it developed, and in the course of its development similar patterns would undoubtedly have emerged, whether or not they were diffused. The increasing population and the growing need for political integration very probably would have created small states in each area, and these states would almost certainly have been strongly theocratic, because the supernatural aspects of farming—for example, fertility concepts, the need to reckon seasons and to forecast the rise and fall of rivers, and the like—would have placed power in the hands of religious leaders. Diffusion may have hastened the development of theocratic states, but in each case the new developments were within determinable limits, and independently involved the same functional or cause-and-effect relationships.

It is true, of course, that many peculiar features common to New World civilizations do not represent a logical outgrowth of basic patterns and that they can be disposed of with the superficial explanation that they diffused. Thus, the wide distribution of such concepts as the plumed serpent or the jaguar god, or of such constructions as terraced pyramids, may be explained in this manner, though deeper analysis might reveal the reasons for their wide acceptance. In general, it is the rather arbitrary, specific, or stylized features, that is, those features which have the least functional dependence on the basic patterns, that provide the greatest evidence of diffusion. These, in other words, are the particulars, which distinguish tribes or areas and obscure regularities.

Another means of denying the possibility of isolating cultural regularities is to stress that the complexity or multiplicity of the antecedents or functional correlates of any institution makes it virtually impossible to isolate the true causes of the institution; convergent evolution rather than parallel evolution is generally used to explain similarities that seem not to be the result of diffusion. The answer to this is simply that in dealing with cultural phenomena, as in dealing with all the complex phenomena of nature, regularities can be found only by looking for them, and they will be valid only if a rigorous methodology underlies the framing of hypotheses.

It is not necessary that any formulation of cultural regularities provide an ultimate explanation of culture change. In the physical and biological sciences, formulations are merely approximations of observed regularities, and they are valid as working hypotheses despite their failure to deal with ultimate realities. So long as a cultural law formulates recurrences of similar interrelationships of phenomena, it expresses cause and effect in the same way that the law of gravity formulates but does not ultimately explain the attraction between masses of matter. Moreover, like the law of gravity, which has been greatly modified by the theory of relativity, any formulation of cultural data may be useful as a working hypothesis, even though further research requires that it be qualified or reformulated.

Cultural regularities may be formulated on different levels, each in its own terms. At present, the most promising possibilities lie largely in the cultural or superorganic level, for anthropology's traditional primary concern with culture has provided far more data of this kind. Moreover, the greater part of culture history is susceptible to treatment in cultural terms. Both sequential or diachronic formulations and synchronic formulations are superorganic, and they may be functional to the extent that the data permit. Redfield's tentative formulation that urban culture contrasts with folk culture in being more individualized, secularized, heterogeneous, and disorganized is synchronic, superorganic, and functional. Morgan's evolutionary schemes and White's formulations concerning the relationship of energy to cultural development are sequential and somewhat functional. Neither type, however, is wholly one or the other. A time-dimension is implied in Redfield's formulation, and synchronic, functional relationships are implied in White's.

Cultural formulations do not, of course, provide the deeper insights concerning human behavior that may come from a psychological level or a biological level. Research on these latter levels may profitably run concurrently with the other, but for the present their formulations will be more applicable to synchronic, functional studies than to sequential ones. Thus, to advocate search for regularities in cultural terms is not at all in conflict with those who state that "culture does not exist apart from the individual, its human carrier." The latter represents a different problem and level of discourse. Basic and ultimate explanations of behavior that will interrelate cultural, psychological, neurological, physiological, and even physical phenomena would require very different formulation. In view of anthropology's traditional and primary concern with culture, it is both admissible and necessary to deal in restricted terms.

The present statement of scientific purpose and methodology rests on a conception of culture that needs clarification. *If the more important institutions of culture can be isolated from their unique setting so as to be typed, classified, and related to recurring antecedents or functional correlates, it follows that it is possible to consider the institutions in question as the basic or constant ones, whereas the features that lend uniqueness are the secondary or variable ones.* For example, the American high civilizations had agriculture, social classes, and a priest-temple-idol cult. As types, these institutions are abstractions of what was actually present in each area, and they do not take into account the particular crops grown, the precise patterning of the social classes, or the conceptualization of deities, details of ritual, and other religious features of each culture center. The latter are secondary and variable so far as the institutions in question are concerned. In a more comprehensive analysis, however, they would serve to distinguish subtypes, which would require more specific formulations.

This conception of culture is in conflict with an extreme organic view, which regards culture as a closed system in which all parts are of equal importance and are equally fixed. It holds that some features of culture are more basic and more fixed than others and that the problem is to ascertain those which are primary and basic and to explain their origin and development. It assumes that although the secondary features must be consistent and functionally integrated with the primary ones, it is these latter that are more susceptible to fortuitous influences from inside or outside the culture, that change most readily, and that require such a variety of aspects that they give the impression that history never repeats itself.

For the present, it is not necessary to state criteria for ascertaining the primary features. In general, they are the ones which individual scientists are most interested in studying and which the anthropological record shows to have recurred again and again in independent situations. A procedure which attempts to give equal weight to all features of culture amounts to a negation of typing and of making formulations, for it must include all the unique features, which obscure similarities between cultures.

Eras in the Development of Early Civilizations

The present section deals with the development of early agricultural civilizations in Northern Peru (the sequences are longest and best known in this part of Peru, thanks to the Viru Valley project of the Institute of Andean Research), Meso-America (Mexico and the Maya area), Mesopotamia, Egypt, and China. These areas were chosen because they were the cradles of civilization and because their exploitation by a pre-iron technology seems to have entailed similar solutions to similar problems and consequently to have caused similar developmental sequences. The environments are arid or semiarid, which, contrary to a common belief, did not impose great difficulties and thereby stimulate cultural development. Instead, they facilitated culture growth because they were easily tilled by digging-stick and irrigation farming. The tropical rain forests, the northern hardwood forests, and the sodded plains areas, on the other hand, were exploited only with the greatest difficulty by people who lacked iron tools.

The procedure to be followed is first to establish a tentative developmental typology or sequence in which the smaller periods are grouped into major eras, which have similar diagnostic features in each area. This requires considerable revision of current terminology, for no two authors use quite the same criteria for major stages of development. Americanists, who have discussed some of these problems together, are now using such terms as Formative, Developmental, Classical, Florescent, and Empire and Conquest, and they are attempting to reach an understanding about the cultural typology implied by these terms. Old World writers still cling largely to such entrenched terms as Mesolithic, Neolithic, Chalcolithic, Ceramolithic, Bronze, and Dynastic, thereby emphasizing technological features of minor developmental significance. Gordon Childe's use of Neolithic Barbarism, Higher Barbarism of the Copper Age, Urban Revolution, and Early Bronze Age, which incorporate some terms from L. H. Morgan, indicates that his thinking is somewhat closer to that of the Americanists, but his terminology and his period markers still fail to be very comparable to those of the latter. Braidwood has developed a somewhat different terminology for grouping periods of the Near East, but his interest in process is very similar to that of Americanists. His three major divisions are Food-Gathering (Hunting and Gathering), Food-Producing (farming), and Civilization. Whereas the present chapter utilizes the emergence of new levels of organization as the criterion of eras (farm villages or Incipient Agriculture, amalgamation of villages into small States or Formative, the state being achieved by the end of the era, Regional Florescent States, and multi-state Empires based on conquest), Braidwood is more interested in the peasant-urban contrast. This view is not in conflict with that presented here; indeed, it offers supplementary criteria which, in a more detailed comparison of the irrigation areas, could well serve to reveal new interrelationships of phenomena and to distinguish smaller periods. For Iraq, Braidwood's sequence runs from Food-Gathering through Incipient Agriculture to an "era of primary peasant efficiency" under Food-Production, with permanent villages, pottery, metal, and weaving. This is followed by "established peasant efficiency" with market-towns and temples, which grades into "incipient urbanization." These eras are grouped in the present scheme under the Formative and Regional Florescent Eras, because they represent the establishment of basic technologies and the gradual formation of local states, which achieved some esthetic excellence in production. Braidwood's final era of Civilization, with a formal state, cities, laws, social classes, writing, and other features corresponds to our eras of Empire, Dark Ages, and Cyclical Imperial Conquests.

It will be noted that the present taxonomy of developmental periods makes little use of technological features. Diffusion might carry many features from one area to another, but our criterion of their importance is their functional effect upon the society. Since our interest is primarily in sociocultural systems, specific techniques are significant only if they affected the nature of cultural ecological adaptations in an area. Thus, the absence of bronze in Meso-America and the presence of iron in China have minor importance. The methods of irrigation agriculture had little use for metals. The possession of iron could not convert peasant-like folk communities in China into larger systems. Only improved farming and population growth could accomplish this.

The second step in the procedure is to suggest cause-and-effect relationships between the cultural phenomena of the successive eras and to formulate as basic regularities those relationships which are common to all areas. These formulations are offered primarily as an illustration of the generalizing approach to cultural data. Tentative and preliminary, they will be revised again and again as long as research continues and as long as scholars probe for a deeper understanding of the basic processes of cultural development. Even if these formulations were entirely scrapped, they would have served their purpose if they stimulated students of culture development to interest themselves in the same problems, to use comparable methods, and to present their findings in comparable terms—in short, to talk one another's language.

Table 1 groups the periods of each center into eras that have the same general features. Periods in the same relative position, consequently, were similar but were not contemporaneous. Table 2 places the eras of each center on an absolute time-scale, which is fairly precise for the periods of written history but much less accurate for the early periods.

The margin of error in dating these early periods does not, however, greatly affect the functional analysis of cultural development.

In the following characterization of eras it must be stressed that the diagnostic features appeared by the end of each era, not in the beginning. An interpretation similar to ours might appear very different if the classification of periods were such that each era began when the key traits appeared.

PRE-AGRICULTURAL ERA

This era includes all the Old World paleolithic and mesolithic periods, which lacked farming, and the New World pre-agricultural periods. To judge by the simple remains of these periods as well as by the recent hunting and gathering cultures, the technologies were devoted principally to satisfying biological needs for food, clothing, and shelter. Pottery, basketry, loom-weaving, metallurgy, permanent houses, and boat and animal transportation were probably absent until they were borrowed to a limited degree from higher centers. Social patterns were based on kinship, age, and sex, but they varied greatly as they became adapted to local conditions. Warfare was restricted to blood feuds, revenge for witchcraft, and perhaps in some areas retaliation against trespass.

INCIPIENT AGRICULTURE

This era cannot be dated exactly, and it is known through very few finds. It must have been very long, passing through several stages, which began when the first cultivation of plant domesticates supplemented hunting and gathering, and ended when plant and animal breeding was able to support permanent communities. To judge by what are the earliest-known evidences of domestication in Mesopotamia and Peru, technologies made little advance over those of the previous era until settled village life was fully achieved.

Peru   Cerro Prieto.

Culture: Farming based on Canavalia beans, calabash, and cotton; twined weaving; ceramics absent; semisubterranean houses.

Meso-America   As the earliest-known agricultural periods of Meso-America appear to have had technologies and temple mounds, which elsewhere characterized the Formative Era, it is generally believed (Morley excepted) that the cultures of these periods were introduced full-blown from elsewhere. Theoretically, however, it would seem that remains of simpler agricultural peoples should antedate the fairly developed theocratic communities in Meso-America.

Mesopotamia   Karim Shahir?

Culture: Probably domesticated wheat, barley, peas, sheep, goat, pig,

Table 1. ARCHEOLOGICAL AND HISTORICAL PERIODS GROUPED IN MAJOR ERAS

Eras	Mesopotamia, Syria, Assyria	Egypt	China	Meso-America		Northern Peru
				Mexico	Maya Area	
Industrial Revolution	Euro-American 19th and 20th century economic and political empires					
Iron Age Culture	Influences from Greece, Rome; later from north and central Europe. In New World Spanish conquest destroys native empires.					
Cyclical Imperial Conquests	Kassites Hammurabi Dynastic Accad	Hyksos New Empire	Ming Sui, T'ang, Ch'in, Han			Inca
Dark Ages	Invasions	First Intermediate	Warring states			Local states
Initial Empire	Royal tombs Ur Early Dynastic Sumer	Pyramid Age Early Dynastic	Chou	Aztec Toltec Chichimec?	Mexican "Absorption"	Tiahuanaco
Regional Florescent States	Jedmet Nasr Warkan-Tepe Gawram Ubaid	Gerzian Amratian Badarian	Shang "Hsia"	Teotihuacán	"Initial Series" Glyphs or Classical	Mochica Gallinazo
Formative (Peasant communities to states)	Halafian Hassunan-Matarrah Jarmo	Merimdean Fayumian	Yang Shao Pre-Yang Shao	Archaic or Middle Periods (Zacatenco)	Formative or Old Empire Mamóm	Salinar Chavín-Cupisnique
Incipient Agriculture	Karim Shahir?		Plain Pottery?	?	?	Cerro Prieto
Hunting and Gathering	Natufian				Pre-Agriculture	
	Paleolithic and "Terminal Food-Gathering"					

Table 2. ABSOLUTE CHRONOLOGY OF MAJOR AREAS [a]

	Mesopotamia	Egypt	N. China	N. Peru	Meso-America
2000 A.D.					Cyclical Conquests
1000 A.D.	Cyclical Conquests	Cyclical Conquests	Cyclical Conquests	Cyclical Conquests	
A.D. / B.C.					Regional Florescent
1000 B.C.	Dark Ages	Dark Ages	Dark Ages	Regional Florescent	Formative
2000	Initial Empire	Initial Empire	Initial Empire	Formative	Incipient Agriculture?
3000	Regional Florescent	Regional Florescent	Regional Florescent	Incipient Agriculture	Hunting and Gathering
4000	Formative	Formative	Formative	Hunting and Gathering	
5000	Incipient Agriculture	Incipient Agriculture	Incipient Agriculture		
6000	Hunting and Gathering	Hunting and Gathering	Hunting and Gathering		
7000					
8000					
9000					

[a] These dates have been revised on the basis of Braidwood's estimates for the Near East (*The Near East and the Foundations for Civilization*, Eugene, Oregon, 1952) and of radiocarbon dates for the Near East and America. These new dates place the origin of agriculture about 2,000 years more recent than was formerly believed in the Near East and about 2,000 years earlier in the Andes. Period dates for India and China are revised to fit the Near East dates, but still presumably show a time lag. (New World dates are taken from *Radiocarbon Dating* (Assembled by Frederick Johnson), Memoir of the Society for American Archaeology, *American Antiquity*, Vol. XVII, No. 1, 1951).

ox; adobe houses; ceramics (late); mortars; ground stone axes; unbaked clay figurines. Villages on the "hilly flanks."

Egypt
Culture: Possibly domesticated plants. Pottery present.

China Period of Plain Pottery. This period is considered to be the first phase of neolithic China, though the presence of domesticated plants or animals is doubtful.

FORMATIVE ERA OF BASIC TECHNOLOGIES AND FOLK CULTURE

The Formative Era is so named because the principal technologies— basketry, pottery, weaving, metallurgy, and construction—appeared and the patterns of community culture took form at this time. It was an era of population growth, area expansion of cultures and peoples, comparative peace, and wide diffusion of culture between centers of civilization.

The principal domesticated plants were by now brought under intensive cultivation, and irrigation was begun on a community scale. In the Old World, the more important domesticated animals, except the horse, were present from early in the era. In the New World, the absence of suitable wild species for domestication limited such animals to the dog, and, in the Andes, to the llama and alpaca.

Food production was on a subsistence basis, except as a share was provided for the ruling class. Increasingly efficient farming released considerable labor for the satisfaction of socially derived needs; that is, craft production of finer goods and construction of religious edifices for the theocracy made rapid progress during each period.

The sociopolitical unit seems to have been the small local community, but by the end of the era local, multicommunity states appeared. The clustering of rooms in house units suggests that lineages or kingroups were the basis of society. One to several such units were associated with a ceremonial center, which served as the nucleus and integrating factor of a dispersed community. Control of irrigation, which was on a local scale, was one of the more important practical functions of the religious leaders. Warfare was probably limited to raids and contributed little either to social structure or to expansion of the state.

Peru Chavín-Cupisnique, Salinar.
Technologies: Domesticated maize, manioc, beans, gourds, peanuts; small-scale irrigation; llamas. Pottery; metallurgy in gold, copper (?); loom-weaving in cotton; twined baskets, surface adobe houses; balsa (reed bundle) boats.

Social features: Dispersed communities, evidently centering in religious mounds and temples. Feline, condor, and serpent deities. Theocratic control of society; rulers accorded status burial.

Meso-America Armillas' and Kidder's Formative; in Mexico, Vaillant's Middle Periods; in Yucatan, Thompson's Formative and Morley's

Pre-Maya. These include Zacatenco and Ticomán in highland Mexico, Lower Tres Zapotes on the east coast, Mamóm and Chicanel in lowland Guatemala, Miraflores in highland Guatemala, and Playa de los Muertos in Honduras.

Technologies: Probably domesticated maize, manioc, and other plants; local irrigation. Pottery; loom-weaving, probably in cotton; basketry (?); no metallurgy. Wattle-and-daub houses in Guatemala.

Social features: Small, scattered settlements. Female figurines suggest a fertility cult. Temple mounds; funerary architecture; and beginnings of intellectual development, as evidenced by calendrical stelae of the Maya area, which appeared at the end of the era.

Mesopotamia Childe's Higher Barbarism of the Copper Age and beginnings of his Urban Revolution; beginnings of Albright's Chalcolithic; Braidwood's "era of primary peasant efficiency." In Mesopotamia: Jarmo Sialk I, Hassunan, Samarran, and Halafian.

Technologies: Domesticated plants, probably wheat, barley, millet, and others; cattle, sheep, goats, pigs; some irrigation. Pottery; loom-weaving, probably in flax; basketry; metallurgy in gold and copper; possibly the wheel. Rectangular, adobe houses.

Social features: Villages have local shrines. Religion involves female and animal figurines; male and female gods are represented.

Egypt Fayumian, Merimdean.

Technologies: Wheat, barley; cattle, pigs, sheep, goats. Pottery; metallurgy in gold and copper; loom-weaving in linen; coiled basketry. Semisubterranean, circular houses. Balsa (papyrus bundle) boats.

Social features: Clans or kin groups (?); captive slaves (?); female and animal figurines in religion; dog-sacrifice in burials.

China Neolithic (Pre-Yang Shao, Yang Shao).

Technologies: Millet, sorghum (?), rice, wheat; pigs; probably well-and-ditch irrigation. Pottery; loom-weaving in hemp (?); basketry; metallurgy in copper.

Social features: Small, semipermanent settlements of circular pit-houses, possibly based on matrilineal lineages. Religion evidenced by pottery phalli; possibly human sacrifice and cannibalism.

ERA OF REGIONAL DEVELOPMENT AND FLORESCENCE

This era was marked by the emergence and florescence of regionally distinctive cultures. No new basic technologies were invented, but irrigation works were enlarged, thus releasing a larger portion of the population to develop arts and crafts and to further intellectual interests. Multicommunity states arose.

States were still strongly theocratic, but interstate competition and state expansion seem to have entailed some militarism. A class-structured society, which was foreshadowed in the previous era, now became fully established. The ruling class appears to have been predominantly theo-cratic, but it was likely that some status was accorded successful warriors. The priesthood now had sufficient leisure to develop astronomy, mathe-matics, and writing (these were little developed in Peru). The largest religious edifices were built, and the finest art and manufactures of any era were produced toward the end of this era, each region producing distinctive styles. These products were made by special artisans and were dedicated principally to the upper classes and to the temples. Trade at-tained important proportions, and improved transportational devices were introduced.

Peru Willey's Regional Classical; Strong's Late Formative and Florescent; Bennett's late Early Periods. Gallinazo and Mochica (Nazca in south Peru).

Technologies: Maize, manioc, potatoes, sweet potatoes, calabashes, pumpkins, peanuts; llamas, alpacas. Inter-valley irrigation.

Social features: Large communities; population maximum; largest mounds, temples; fanged deity, and gods of agriculture, fishing, celestial phenomena, and places. Ruler was warrior-god. Hilltop forts were built. Regional states (entire valley or several valleys?). War captives, human sacrifice, human trophies. Status burial for the upper class. Trade.

Transportation: Roads; probably llama-packing; ocean-going balsa boats with sails (?).

Intellectual and esthetic traits: Ideographic writing on beans (?); quipus. Finest art of all eras.

Meso-America Armillas' Florescent; Kidder's Classical; Thompson's Initial Series; Morley's Old Empire. These include: Middle and Upper Tres Zapotes on the east coast; Teotihuacán and Monte Albán II and III in Mexico; Esperanza in highland Guatemala; and Tsakol and Tepeu in lowland Guatemala.

Technology: Local irrigation, chinampas, and terracing in agricul-ture.

Social features: Dispersed settlements; local theocratic states that controlled all settlements of a valley or other natural regions. Population maximum (?). Largest mounds and temples. Priestly hierarchy. Gods of rain, water, jaguar, serpent, quetzal. Child sacrifice (?); possibly ancestor worship (as evidenced by figurine portraits in Mexico, status burial in Guatemala). Militarism evidently restricted to raids, with some captive-taking.

Transportation: Roads and causeways; widespread trade; (toy wheel).

Intellectual and esthetic traits: Phonetic writing, mathematics, as-tronomy. Finest art of all eras.

Mesopotamia Latter part of Albright's Chalcolithic; Childe's Urban

Revolution and Early Bronze; Braidwood's "era of established peasant efficiency" and "Proto-Literate phase." These include: Obeidian (Al'-Ubaid), Warkan-Tepe Gawra, and Jedmet Nasr.

Technologies: Wheat, barley, millet, date palm, figs, grapes, sesame, onions, garlic, lettuce, melons, chick peas, horse beans; drained fields, large-scale irrigation. Wheel-made ceramics.

Social features: Urbanization began with riverine settlements. Multi-community states, which were essentially theocratic, though rulers had also war power. Large palace-temples. Gods of agriculture. Some pressures of infiltration by foot-nomads. Widespread trade.

Transportation: Horse (?), chariot and four-wheeled wagon; balsa (reed bundle) boats.

Intellectual traits: Pictographic writing, mathematical systems, astronomy.

Egypt Badarian, Amratian, Gerzian.

Technologies: Farming as in Formative Era, though probably increased irrigation. Rectangular, above-ground, adobe houses.

Social features: Tendency to urbanization; multicommunity states, each with an associated animal god and under the rule of heads of principal lineages (?). Some warfare implements expansion of state. Status burial shows a cult of the dead. Considerable trade.

Transportation: Sailing vessels; ass.

Intellectual traits: Beginnings of writing; calendrical and numerical systems.

Possibly the Semainian period and the beginnings of the Early Dynastic periods should be included in the Era of Regional Florescence in Egypt, for the temple cult appeared, class differentiation became definite, and phonetic writing, a calendrical system, and mathematics were developed. These features, however, continued to develop with little interruption into the era of Conquest and Empire.

China "Hsia" (Black Pottery period) and Shang Dynasty.

Technologies: Wheat, millet, rice, pig, cattle, sheep, in north; buffalo and chicken in south. Beginnings of public works in form of dikes; otherwise, local well-and-ditch irrigation were practiced. Bronze manufactures. Horse and chariot. Weaving in silk.

Social features: Local state, Wittfogel's "Feudal" types, under which serfs cultivated the local ruler's land. Divine monarch; status burial in deep grave. Use of oracle bones to forecast rain and for other divination; dragon deity; human and animal sacrifice. Warfare arising from conflict over grazing lands and from pressure of herding nomads.

Intellectual and esthetic traits: Picture and ideographic writing. Finest esthetic expressions, especially in bronzes.

CYCLICAL CONQUESTS

The diagnostic features of this era are the emergence of large-scale militarism, the extension of political and economic domination over large areas or empires, a strong tendency toward urbanization, and the construction of fortifications. In the social structure, priest-warriors constituted the ruling groups, usually under a divine monarch, whose importance is revealed in elaborate status burial. Social classes now tended to become frozen into hereditary classes, in contrast to society of the previous era, which probably permitted individuals some upward mobility through personal achievements. Gods of war became prominent in the pantheon of deities.

There were no important technological changes. Bronze appeared in Peru, Mesopotamia, and Egypt, and was used for weapons and ornaments, but it contributed little to the production of food or other goods. Iron, though not an iron-age culture, appeared in China. The principal change in manufactures was a strong trend toward standardization and mass production, with a concomitant sacrifice of esthetic freedom and variety. Large-scale trade within the empires, and even beyond, brought the beginnings of a special commercial class, but coinage and an efficient monetary system were not yet developed.

Peru Willey's Expansion and Conquest; Strong's Fusion and Imperial periods; Bennett's Tiahuanaco, Late Periods, and Inca.

Technologies: As before, except that bronze was used for ornaments, weapons, and a few tools. By the Inca period, there was standardized, mass production.

Social features: Planned urban centers were constructed, and they drew off much population from the local communities. Under the Inca, social classes were finally frozen in a caste system, headed by the divine royal family. A priesthood and bureaucracy ruled the state and placed levies on the commoners, but the local folk culture persisted. An ancestor cult occurred along with agricultural, place, and animal gods. The state was enlarged by wars of conquest, which perhaps started in the previous era and originated from population pressures. Populations were moved from place to place by imperial command.

Meso-America Armillas' Militaristic Period (in Mexico, Toltec, Aztec, Monte Alban V, Tzintzuntzan Tarascan; and, in Yucatan, Mexican Absorption). Thompson's Mexican Period and Morley's New Empire in Yucatan. Kidder's Amatle and Pamplona in highland Guatemala.

Technologies: As before, except that metallurgy in copper and gold appeared, being used mainly for ornaments. There was extensive trade, and money, in the form of cacao beans, was used during the Aztec period.

Social features: The population was increasingly concentrated in defensible sites, and special forts were constructed. Larger and larger areas were drawn into empires, and wealth was concentrated through tribute in the hands of the ruling classes. The king-priest had great military power. There were military classes, warrior societies, and slaves. Great population movements are evident in the inroads of Chichimecs into the Valley of Mexico, the Nahuatl migrations to Central America, and the Mexican invasion of Yucatan. Warfare was intensified, gods of war entered the pantheon, and human sacrifice became a major feature of religion.

Mesopotamia Early Dynastic Sumerians to Dynasty of Accad. Braidwood's "Civilization."

Technologies: Bronze was used for weapons, ornaments, and a few tools. There was standardized mass production, especially of goods used by commoners, and widespread trade, mainly for luxury items.

Social features: Urban communities attained great size and served as military, political, religious, and commercial centers. The king combined religious and military leadership and controlled multi-community states. Statuses were strongly differentiated: the king, representing the god (sometimes a war god), was supreme; priests and nobles tended to have hereditary status; farmers, artisans, and wage-earners were either attached to the temple or else worked on privately-owned lands; captives became slaves. Soldiers sometimes gained status. Gods included agricultural and local deities; the cult of the dead attained some importance, as shown in status burials.

Egypt Early Dynasties, I–IV.

Technologies: Bronze was used for weapons and ornaments, and there was evidence of mass production and extensive trade.

Social features: Planned cities were built. The god-king became the military and political head of large states, which were expanded through warfare, and he eclipsed the power of the priesthood. Social structure became rigid, hereditary nobles controlling great wealth. Warfare, probably originating in population pressures and dislocations throughout the Near East, was waged to create empires and to ward off invasions.

Theology was based on a pantheon of general gods, such as the Sun, on local animal gods, and on a cult of the dead. The last, combined somewhat with the first two, became predominant, as evidenced by the divine power of the king and by his status burial in pyramids.

China The Chou through Ming Dynasties. The culture center shifts south from the Yellow River to the Yangtze River, while conquests, starting with the Chou Dynasty, culminate in Wittfogel's type of oriental absolute state by the T'ang Dynasty.

Technologies: Irrigation and water works develop under state control and become large-scale under the Warring States; plow and fertilizer. Iron, glass, and other technologies diffuse from the west.

Social features: The Chou Dynasty initiates the era of conquests. A divine ruler and bureaucracy control a state which is stratified into hereditary nobles with military and economic power, merchants, serfs, and some slaves. Cities develop as administrative, religious, and commercial centers.

Trial Formulation of Developmental Regularities of Early Civilizations

At the present time the difficulties in making any formulation of the development of early civilizations in the five principal centers of the world are obviously very great. Data on early periods are incomplete, not only because research has been limited but also because it has been directed toward special and restricted problems. Archaeology has, until recently, paid comparatively little attention to settlement patterns, demographic trends, and sociological implications of its materials. Historians on the whole are more interested in the fate of particular societies than in culture and its development, and anthropologists have made comparatively little use of the data of written history. These difficulties mean primarily that any present formulation must be highly tentative.

The successive eras in each of the five principal centers of early civilizations appear to have had similar diagnostic features which, arranged chronologically, might be considered as a superficial formulation of regularities. Such a formulation, however, would fail to provide a satisfactory and generally valid functional explanation of cause-and-effect relationships between phenomena. To provide deeper explanations, it is necessary to make cause-and-effect relationships as explicit as possible and to test the explanations offered for the sequence in each center by the data of other centers. This purpose is consistent with the comparative approach of anthropology, and it is far more important to find a common problem than to construct enduring formulations.

The formulation here offered excludes all areas except the arid and semiarid centers of ancient civilizations. In the irrigation areas, environment, production, and social patterns had similar functional and developmental interrelationships. The productivity of farming was limited only by the amount of water that could be used in irrigation. Metal tools and animal-drawn plows, though essential to maximum efficiency of farming in forest or grassland areas, could not increase the yield of irrigation areas beyond the limits imposed by water supply.

Early civilizations occurred also in such tropical rain-forest areas as southern Asia and Yucatan. Yucatan appears to fit the formulation made for the more arid areas to the extent that its sequences were very similar to those of Meso-America generally. Farming in Yucatan, however, required slash-and-burn rather than irrigation techniques, and the rural population must have been very scattered. It is possible, therefore, that the Maya were able to develop a high civilization only because they enjoyed an unusually long period of peace; for their settlement pattern would seem to have been too vulnerable to warfare. Yucatan, consequently, should perhaps be excluded from the present formulation. In southeastern Asia, the environment is extremely humid, presenting the difficulties of rain forests and also requiring large drainage projects. And in both areas, the civilizations appear to have been later than, and in part derived from, those of the irrigation areas.

The era of Incipient Agriculture in the irrigation centers is very little known, but evidence from Peru and Mesopotamia suggests that it lasted a much shorter time than had once been supposed. Farming was at first supplementary to hunting and gathering, and the social groups were consequently small and probably seminomadic. Technologies differed little from those of the earlier hunting and gathering periods. By the end of this era, farming supported permanent communities, and new technologies began to appear.

A local community, "folk" or "peasant," culture took form during the next era. Nearly all the principal crops and animals were by now brought under domestication, but irrigation was undertaken only on a small, local scale. In subsequent eras, agricultural production increased as irrigation works were developed, the only limit being available land and water, especially the latter. The animal-drawn plow, which appeared in the Old World much later, during the era of Cyclical Conquests, and which was unknown in prehistoric America, no doubt released a certain portion of the population from farm work, but neither it nor iron tools, which appeared still later, could increase production beyond the limits of water supply. Population consequently increased as irrigation works were developed to their maximum. For this reason, the Old World possession of draft animals and the plow does not affect the present formulation.

During the Formative Era, all centers of civilization developed ceramics, loom-weaving, basketry, metallurgy (except Meso-America), and the construction of houses and religious edifices. These technologies soon came to be used for two kinds of goods: first, objects that served the simple, domestic—that is, essentially biological—needs of the common folk; second, highly elaborate, stylized goods that served the socially derived needs as well as the more basic needs of the theocratic class. In simple form, some of these technologies spread beyond the areas of irrigation.

Subsequent to the Formative Era, no very important technological advances were made until the Iron Age. Metallurgy ran through similar sequences everywhere (except in Meso-America), starting with work in copper and gold and finally achieving bronze. Copper and tin were so rare that the use of bronze was largely limited to ornaments and weapons, while tools of stone, bone, wood, and shell were used for daily chores. Improvement in the other technologies consisted of embellishments and refinements that enhanced their esthetic qualities and produced varied products; but there were no important new inventions.

Transportation improved in successive eras. Domesticated animals were first probably used for packing in all centers except in Meso-America, which lacked species suitable for domestication. Wheeled vehicles appeared in the Old World during the era of Regional Florescence. The wheel was evidently used on toys during the same era in Meso-America, but its failure to be used in transportation perhaps may be explained by the absence of draft animals. The importance of transportation increased as states grew larger and as trade expanded. Although draft animals and wheels, which were used on war chariots before they were used on carts and wagons, gave the Old World some technical advantage, every New World center developed roads, boats, and canals to a degree of efficiency which enabled them to achieve states as large as those of the Old World.

The general sequence of social, religious, and military patterns ran a similar course in each center of civilization, and a generally valid formulation is possible. Certain problems which cannot yet be answered will be stated subsequently.

In the era of Incipient Agriculture it is reasonable to suppose that sociopolitical groups were as varied in nature as they are today among the hunting and gathering peoples of arid areas.

At the beginning of the Formative Era, the sociopolitical unit was a small house cluster, which probably consisted of a kin group or lineage. As population increased, new clusters evidently budded off and established themselves in unsettled lands. In Mesopotamia, the Formative Era villages were on what Braidwood calls the "hilly flanks," where rainfall permitted farming, rather than along the river. This raises the question of whether the riverine flood plains were the principal habitat in any of the areas at this time. In the course of time, as flood plains became densely settled and as need arose to divert water through canals to drier land, collaboration on irrigation projects under some co-ordinating authority became necessary. That the need was met by the rise to power of a theocratic class is shown by the appearance toward the end of the Formative Era of evidence of religious domination of society, for example, ceremonial centers, such as mounds and temples, and a large number of religious objects. Farming required careful reckoning of the seasons, considerable ritual, and worship of agricultural gods, tasks which necessitated a special priesthood. During the Formative Era, a small number of house clusters were dispersed around a ceremonial center and were ruled by a priesthood. The priesthood provided centralized control of irrigation and new patterns of group religion. Society became differentiated into theocratic and common classes. Thus, society became organized on a higher level than that of the localized lineage.

In the Formative Era, state warfare was probably of minor importance. There is little archaeological evidence of militarism, and it is likely that warfare was limited to raids. As long as there was ample land for the expanding population, competition for terrain cannot have been important. Because pastoral nomads during this era were unmounted and probably had not become very numerous, they cannot have been a great threat. In the Near East, they probably had asses, cattle, sheep, and goats, but did not ride horses and camels until the Iron Age, and horse riding did not appear in China until the era of Dark Ages or Warring States.

The precise patterning, content, and history of religion, which supplied the socially integrating factor, varied with each center of civilization. In some centers, such as Egypt, China, Peru, and Guatemala, elaborate burials for certain individuals suggest a cult of the dead or ancestor worship, which elevated these persons to the status of god-priests while living and to the status of gods after death. Other kinds of gods are represented by animal, place, and fertility deities. In some instances, the priesthood may have developed from an earlier class of shamans.

The particular religious patterns of each center arose from complex factors of local development and diffusion, and they gave local distinctiveness to the cultures. In terms of the present formulation, however, these differences are secondary in importance to the fact that in all cases a national religion and a priestly class developed because increasing populations, larger irrigation works, and greater need for social co-ordination called upon religion to supply the integrating factor. The very great importance of religion at the end of the Formative Era is proved by the effort devoted to the construction of temple mounds, temples, palaces, and tombs, and to the special production of religious ornaments, sculpture, and various material appurtenances of the priesthood and temples. It was the priesthood which, devoting full time to religious matters, now laid the foundations of astronomy, writing, and mathematics in all centers.

The era of Regional Florescence fulfilled the potentialities of the Formative Era. Communities were welded into small states, which, however, continued to be essentially theocratic, for archaeological remains of this era are predominantly of a religious nature. The largest mounds, temples, and tombs (mortuary pyramids and burial mounds) of any eras were constructed. Intellectual trends were fulfilled in the development of phonetic writing, numerical systems, and accurate calendars. Even Peru, which never developed phonetic writing, may have used an ideographic system at this time. Ceramics, metallurgy, weaving, work in precious stones, and sculpture attained their highest peak of esthetic expression and their most distinctive local stylization.

The relation of militarism to the enlargement of irrigation works and the expansion of states during the era of Regional Florescence is not clear. Population, irrigation works, and states all increased in size until the end of the era. In Meso-America, it is generally believed that the states were peaceful and theocratic, and Cook believes that population reached its maximum at this time, decreasing in the subsequent era. In this case, a priesthood without the backing of armed force was able to create multi-community states, though the extent of irrigation works at this time is not well known. In other areas, it appears that some militarism was present in the era of Regional Florescence, and that without warfare the rulers could not have increased the size of states and thereby of irrigation works. In northern Peru, warfare was definitely present in the era of Regional Florescence, and in China, warfare arising from conflicts over grazing lands enabled local rulers to extend their authority over subject states, perhaps facilitating the enlargement of irrigation works. Irrigation, however, did not attain maximum size in China until true empires appeared in the following era of Cyclical Conquests. Thus, in China the population maximum came only when militarism achieved empire-wide irrigation projects. In Mesopotamia and Egypt, warfare also appeared during the era of Regional Florescence, and it was no doubt instrumental in enlarging states, but true kingdoms or empires did not appear until the following era. The relation of irrigation and population to warfare and state size in Egypt is not clear, but if Childe is correct in believing that warfare resulted from competition for lands as well as from the pressures of nomads, it would seem that population limits may have been reached.

This seeming contradiction cannot be resolved at present, but it may be suspected either that Meso-America had unusually powerful priests or else that the population maximum was not really reached until after the era of Regional Florescence, when militarism increased the size of states and consequently of irrigation works. In all centers, a temporary decrease of population probably followed the initiation of large-scale warfare.

Social structure seems to have been very similar in all centers of civilization. The local community retained its folk culture, that is, its social structure, local shrines, agricultural practices, and the like, and its members constituted the commoners. Rulers were predominantly priests, though they began to acquire some military functions. It is possible that war achievements gave status to special individuals and that war captives formed a slave class, but as the existence of true economic slavery in native America is in doubt, the social role of captives and the problem of the origin and nature of slavery are open to problems which are excluded from consideration here.

The era of Cyclical Conquests was one of comparatively few culture changes, except those produced by warfare. It initiated a succession of empires and then local states or dark ages that alternated in a fairly stereotyped pattern until the Iron Age and Industrial Era brought cultural influences from other areas. In each center, large-scale warfare, which probably originated from internal population pressures, from competition for resources, and from the pressures of outside nomads, was an instrument in creating true empires and starting dynasties. As the empires grew, irrigation works were increased to the limits of water supply and population also increased. After reaching a peak, marked by a temporary florescence of culture, population pressure and abuse of the common people brought rebellion, which destroyed the empires and returned society to local states and a period of dark ages. Irrigation works were neglected and population decreased. New conquests initiated another cycle.

The cyclical phenomena are strikingly illustrated in China where, during 1,500 years of the era of Cyclical Conquests, each of the four major peaks of empires and dynasties coincided with a population peak. These were separated by periods of internal strife and local autonomy. The series of empires in the Near East, which began in Mesopotamia with the early Dynasty of Sumer and in Egypt with the Dynastic period, ran through cycles generally comparable with those of China and lasted until the northern Mediterranean states of the Iron Age brought portions of the Near East under periodic conquests. In Peru, the widespread Tiahuanaco culture and the later Inca Empire probably represent two cycles of empire growth, while in Mexico, the first cycle, that of the Aztec conquests, had not run its course when the Spaniards conquered America.

In the era of Conquest, militarism produced several important social changes. Braidwood and Childe properly stress urbanization as a characteristic of this era. It should be noted, however, first that cities are but one aspect of state and imperial levels of sociocultural integration and second that the nature of cities changed in each era. Towns, which previously had been ceremonial, administrative, production and trading centers, now became large walled cities, and special forts were built to afford refuge to the dispersed farm settlements. A true military class appeared in the social hierarchy, and warrior-priests ruled the states and empires. War gods became prominent in the pantheons of state deities.

In this era, all aspects of culture were increasingly regimented at the expense of creative effort. There were sharpened differences in social classes, such as nobles, priests, warriors, commoners, slaves, and stronger differentiation of occupational groups. Laws were codified, learning was systematized (astronomy, theology, mathematics, medicine, writing), art became standardized, and goods were mass-produced by specialists.

Specialized production of commodities and widespread trade laid a basis for commercialism, but a free commercial class, factory production, and wage labor could not emerge until economy achieved a strong monetary basis, private property, and specialized cash crops, and until trade was disengaged from the system of state tribute and freed from state control. Though foreshadowed everywhere, this did not occur in the Near East until the Iron Age. In China, the development of private property in land and a system of money and taxation was not sufficient to free economy from the control of powerful states, which existed by virtue of grain taxes which their water works made possible. In the New World, this era was not reached until the Spanish conquest.

The developments of the Iron Age and the Industrial Era are beyond the scope of the present inquiry. Iron appeared in China in the era of Cyclical Conquests, but it did not revolutionize the patterns of basic production and social structure as it did in the forested areas of the northern Mediterranean.

Summary and Conclusions

The above analysis may be briefly summarized.

In arid and semiarid regions, agriculture may be carried on by means of flood-plain and irrigation farming, which do not require metal tools. In Mesopotamia, farming began in the higher altitudes with rainfall some distance from the rivers. Whether or not this was true everywhere, there is no question that maximum production in these areas of critical and minimal precipitation required irrigation, and that in proportion as irrigation works develop, population will increase until the limits of water are reached. Social or political controls become necessary to manage irrigation and other communal projects. As early societies were strongly religious, individuals with supernatural powers—lineage heads, shamans, or special priests—formed a theocratic ruling class, which first governed multihouse-cluster communities of Formative Era "peasants" and later multicommunity states.

The increasing productivity of farming released considerable labor from subsistence activities, and new technologies were developed—basketry, loom-weaving, pottery, metallurgy, domestic and religious construction, and transportational facilities. Products made for home use were simple and utilitarian; those made for the theocratic class and for religious purposes became increasingly rich and varied, and they required an increasing proportion of total productive efforts.

When these societies reached the limits of agricultural productivity set by their water supply, population pressures developed within each state and states began to compete with one another for resources and products. At first, interstate conflict was probably instigated by the ruling groups; for it seems that once a trend toward concentration of wealth and power in any society is initiated it continues under its own momentum. Empire-building meant, therefore, that any local state which was intent on conquest and wished to exact goods and services from other states had to subordinate the rulers of those states.

But empire-building also affected the basic population, the peasant communities, of the states; for they were subjected to increased tribute in goods or services while their per capita productive capacity decreased. In each area, therefore, there came a critical point at which the relationship of population to food and goods fell below the biological or culturally conceived optimum—when the standard of living decreased and the death rate increased to the point that local populations were willing to support revolutions against imperial authority. The crumbling of empires was probably accompanied by deterioration of irrigation works, decrease of food production, decline of population, return of local states to power, and loss of certain cultural achievements. After a "Dark Age" the process of empire-building was begun anew either by a local state or a predatory nomadic group.

The culture of the empires differed from that of the Regional Florescent states in several respects. Extreme militarism brought about the formation of armies, the installation of warrior-leaders, and in some cases the development of classes of warriors. Social life was regimented by strong political controls backed by legal systems and sanctioned by state religion. Few intellectual or technological innovations were made, but goods were produced in quantity and in standard forms.

The Iron Age gave the Old World a revolutionary technology, but as iron tools cannot increase water supply, the irrigation areas were little affected, except as they fell under the empires of the north Mediterranean. Iron Age cultures developed in the forested areas of Europe, which had been exploited only with difficulty under the old technology. The New World never reached an Iron Age in pre-Columbian times. The Spanish conquest brought it an Iron Age culture from the Old World, and native culture development was abruptly ended just after it had entered the era of Cyclical Conquests.

Table 2 showing the absolute chronology of the developmental eras in each center of civilization has been revised for this collection of essays on the basis of recent dates, especially radiocarbon or carbon 14 dates. While these are still subject to revision and while the place of certain prehistoric periods in major eras is by no means clear, an interesting feature has emerged from this revised chart. Previously, it was supposed that culture developed in a rather smooth and ever-rising curve. Incipient farming was thought to have lasted many thousands of years, while the Formative Era and subsequent periods became shorter and shorter. This seems not to have been the case. Apparently, the potentialities of a revolutionary technology such as "food production" or agriculture were quickly realized. In both hemispheres, irrigation-based empires, which we assumed to have represented the sociocultural limits under the given technology, developed within about three thousand years. After this, they endured for an equal or even longer period until the areas were brought under the influence of European sociopolitical systems. In America, the duration of empires was briefer since they were cut short by the Spanish conquest.

The above formulation is rough, cursory, and tentative. It applies only to the early centers of world civilization. The eras are not "stages," which in a world evolutionary scheme would apply equally to desert, arctic, grassland, and woodland areas. In these other kinds of areas, the functional interrelationship of subsistence patterns, population, settlements, social structure, co-operative work, warfare, and religion had distinctive forms and requires special formulations.

The principal grounds for questioning the present formulation will, I suspect, be that diffusion between the centers of civilization in each hemisphere can be demonstrated. The relative chronology of the eras (Table 2) fits a diffusionist explanation perfectly. The essential question, however, is just what diffusion amounts to as an explanation. There is no doubt about the spread of domesticated plants and animals and little doubt about the diffusion of many technologies, art styles, and details of both material and nonmaterial culture. Proof of diffusion, however, lies in the unique qualities of secondary features, not in the basic types of social, economic, and religious patterns—the features of the cultural core. These features could be attributed to diffusion only by postulating mass migration or far-flung conquests.

If people borrow domesticated plants and agricultural patterns, it is evident that population will increase in favorable areas. How shall dense, stable populations organize their sociopolitical relations? Obviously, they will not remain inchoate mobs until diffused patterns have taught them how to live together. (And even diffused patterns had to originate somewhere for good and sufficient reasons.) In densely settled areas, internal needs will produce an orderly interrelationship of environment, subsistence patterns, social groupings, occupational specialization, and over-all political, religious, and perhaps military integrating factors. These interrelated institutions do not have unlimited variability, for they must be adapted to the requirements of subsistence patterns established in particular environments; they involve a cultural ecology. Traits whose uniqueness is proof of their diffusion are acceptable if they are congruent with the basic socioeconomic institutions. They give uniqueness and local color, and they may help crystallize local patterns in distinctive ways, but they cannot per se produce the underlying conditions of, or the need for, greater social and political organization. It is therefore possible to concede wide diffusion of particulars within the hemispheres and even between the hemispheres without having to rely upon diffusion as the principal explanation of cultural development.

We have attempted here to present a conception of culture and a methodology for formulating the regularities of cultural data which are consistent with scientific purpose. The data are those painstakingly gathered and arranged spacially and temporally by culture history. Thorough attention to cultural differences and particulars is necessary if typology is to be adequate and valid, but historical reconstructions need not be the sole objective of anthropology. Strong observed that "the time is coming when the rich ethnological and archeological record of the New World can be compared in full detail and time perspective with similar records from Europe, Egypt, Mesopotamia, India, China, and Siberia. When such comparative data are in hand the generalizations that will emerge may well revolutionize our concept of culture history and culture process over the millennia." Any generalizations or formulations must be subject to frequent revision by new data, for, as Kroeber remarks, "Detailed case-by-case analyses are . . . called for if interpretations are not to become vitiated over-generalizations which more and more approach formulas." At the same time, it is obvious that the minutiae of culture history will never be completely known and that there is no need to defer formulations until all archaeologists have laid down their shovels and all ethnologists have put away their notebooks. Unless anthropology is to interest itself mainly in the unique, exotic, and nonrecurrent particulars, it is necessary that formulations be attempted no matter how tentative they may be. It is formulations that will enable us to state new kinds of problems and to direct attention to new kinds of data which have been slighted in the past. Fact-collecting of itself is insufficient scientific procedure; facts exist only as they are related to theories, and theories are not destroyed by facts—they are replaced by new theories which better explain the facts. Therefore, criticisms of this paper which concern facts alone and which fail to offer better formulations are of no interest.

Correlation of This Book
with Representative Texts

BEALS, RALPH L. AND HARRY HOIJER, *An Introduction to Anthropology*, 3rd ed., Macmillan, 1965

Chapter Nos.	Related selections in *Readings in Anthropology*, 2d ed.	Chapter Nos.	Related selections in *Readings in Anthropology*, 2d ed.
1	I:1–3	15	II:17, 21, 23–25
2	I:6–10, 20; II:16	16	II:18
3	I:9, 34; II:2–4	17	II:26–28
4	I:9, 11, 12–14	18	II:37–41
5	I:4, 5, 22	19	I:23–29
6–8	I:15–19, 21	20	II:42–46
9	II:1, 5–9	21	II:47–49
10–13	I:34, 38, 41; II:10	22–23	II:29–36, 50
14	II:13, 15		

HOEBEL, E. ADAMSON, *Anthropology, The Study of Man*, 3rd ed., McGraw-Hill, 1966

Chapter Nos.	Related selections in *Readings in Anthropology*, 2d ed.	Chapter Nos.	Related selections in *Readings in Anthropology*, 2d ed.
1	I:1–3	19	II:42–46
2	II:1	20	II:22
3	I:23–28	21	II:47–49
4	II:47–49	22–23	II:17–18
5	II:3, 4	24	II:23–25
6	I:29–43	25	II:19–21
7	I:6	26	. .
8	I:9	27	II:28
9	I:10–11	28–29	II:11, 13–15
10	I:12, 24, 33–34	30	II:27
11	I:13, 14, 35, 36	31	II:12, 26
12	I:37–42	32–34	II:37–41
13–14	I:15–19	35	II:5–9, 34, 36, 50
15–18	. .	36	II:35

TITIEV, MISCHA, *The Science of Man*, Holt, Rinehart, Winston, 1963

Chapter Nos.	Related selections in *Readings in Anthropology*, 2d ed.	Chapter Nos.	Related selections in *Readings in Anthropology*, 2d ed.
1	I:1–3	18	I:39–41
2–3	I:4–7	19	I:43
4	I:9	20	II:1–7
5	I:10, 20	21–22	II:10–15
6	I:11–13	23	II:17–21
7	I:15–19	24	II:22–28
8	I:21	25	II:47–49
9	I:22, 24	26–27	II:37–41
10	I:30–32	28	I:23, 25, 28, 29
11–12	I:33–34	29	II:42–46
13–14	I:37–38	30	II:8–9
15–16	I:42	31	II:29–35
17	I:35–36	32	II:36, 50

BOHANNON, PAUL, *Social Anthropology*, Holt, Rinehart, Winston, 1963

Chapter Nos.	Related selections in *Readings in Anthropology*, 2d ed.	Chapter Nos.	Related selections in *Readings in Anthropology*, 2d ed.
1	I:1–3	12	I:15–19
2	II:47–49	13	II:10
3	II:1, 23–29, 42–46	14–15	II:11, 13–15
4	II:19–20	16	II:26
5–8	II:17–18	17	II:27
9	II:23–25	18–20	II:37–41
10	II:21, 22	21	I:43; II:34, 36
11	II:28	22	II:35, 50

BEATTIE, JOHN, *Other Cultures*, Free Press, 1964

Chapter Nos.	Related selections in *Readings in Anthropology*, 2d ed.	Chapter Nos.	Related selections in *Readings in Anthropology*, 2d ed.
1	I:1	8	II:16–18
2	I:3; II:1	9–10	II:26–28
3	I:2; II:10, 36	11	II:13–15
4	II:2, 3, 4	12–13	II:37–41
5	I:23, 28; II:5–7	14	II:30, 31, 34, 35
6	II:8, 9	15	II:50
7	II:19–21, 24, 25		

HOLMES, LOWELL D., *Anthropology: An Introduction*, Ronald, 1965

Chapter Nos.	Related selections in *Readings in Anthropology*, 2d ed.	Chapter Nos.	Related selections in *Readings in Anthropology*, 2d ed.
1	I:1	10	II:17–21
2	I:2	11	II:26–28
3	I:3	12	II:37–41
4	I:4	13	II:42–47
5	I:23–29; II:1–4	14	II:34, 36
6		15	II:47–49
7	II:32	16	II:5–9, 50
8	I:34	17	II:35
9	II:13–15		

SCHUSKY, ERNEST L. AND T. PATRICK CULBERT, *Introducing Culture*, Prentice-Hall, 1967

Chapter Nos.	Related selections in *Readings in Anthropology*, 2d ed.	Chapter Nos.	Related selections in *Readings in Anthropology*, 2d ed.
1	I:1–3; II:1–4	6	II:10–15
2	I:4–14, 20, 21	7	II:16–28
3	I:30–43	8	II:37–41
4	I:15–20, 22	9	II:50
5	I:23–29; II:5–9, 29, 34–36		